HAZARD SIGNS USED IN THIS BOOK

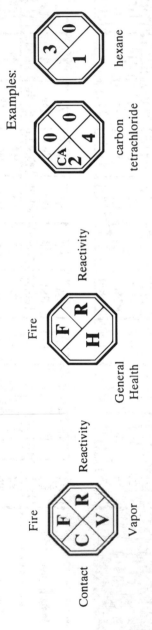

Contact Fire Reactivity
C F R V
Vapor Reactivity

Fire
F R
H
General
Health

Examples:

CA 2 0
4
carbon
tetrachloride

3 0
1
hexane

Meanings of numbers and letters on hazard symbols

Symbol	Health (Contact or Vapor)	Fire	Reactivity
0	No known hazard	Will not burn	Stable
1	May cause irritation if not treated	Ignites after strong preheating	Unstable only at high temperature and pressure
2	May cause injury; requires treatment	Ignites after moderate heating	Unstable, but won't detonate
3	May cause serious injury despite treatment	Ignites at normal temperatures	Detonates or explodes with difficulty
4	May cause death or major injury despite treatment	Very flammable	Readily detonates or explodes
CA	Carcinogen (cancer-causing agent)		
OX			Strong oxidant; may react violently with combustible material
P			Polymerizes readily
W			Reacts violently with water

Periodic Table of the Elements

Main-group elements | Transition elements | Main-group elements

Period	1A (1)	2A (2)	3B (3)	4B (4)	5B (5)	6B (6)	7B (7)	8B (8)	8B (9)	8B (10)	1B (11)	2B (12)	3A (13)	4A (14)	5A (15)	6A (16)	7A (17)	8A (18)
1	1 **H** 1.00794																	2 **He** 4.00260
2	3 **Li** 6.941	4 **Be** 9.01218											5 **B** 10.811	6 **C** 12.011	7 **N** 14.0067	8 **O** 15.9994	9 **F** 18.9984	10 **Ne** 20.1797
3	11 **Na** 22.9898	12 **Mg** 24.3050											13 **Al** 26.9815	14 **Si** 28.0855	15 **P** 30.9738	16 **S** 32.066	17 **Cl** 35.4527	18 **Ar** 39.948
4	19 **K** 39.0983	20 **Ca** 40.078	21 **Sc** 44.9559	22 **Ti** 47.88	23 **V** 50.9415	24 **Cr** 51.9961	25 **Mn** 54.9381	26 **Fe** 55.847	27 **Co** 58.9332	28 **Ni** 58.693	29 **Cu** 63.546	30 **Zn** 65.39	31 **Ga** 69.723	32 **Ge** 72.61	33 **As** 74.9216	34 **Se** 78.96	35 **Br** 79.904	36 **Kr** 83.80
5	37 **Rb** 85.4678	38 **Sr** 87.62	39 **Y** 88.9059	40 **Zr** 91.224	41 **Nb** 92.9064	42 **Mo** 95.94	43 **Tc** (98)	44 **Ru** 101.07	45 **Rh** 102.906	46 **Pd** 106.42	47 **Ag** 107.868	48 **Cd** 112.411	49 **In** 114.818	50 **Sn** 118.710	51 **Sb** 121.76	52 **Te** 127.60	53 **I** 126.904	54 **Xe** 131.29
6	55 **Cs** 132.905	56 **Ba** 137.327	57 *****La** 138.906	72 **Hf** 178.49	73 **Ta** 180.948	74 **W** 183.84	75 **Re** 186.207	76 **Os** 190.23	77 **Ir** 192.22	78 **Pt** 195.08	79 **Au** 196.967	80 **Hg** 200.59	81 **Tl** 204.383	82 **Pb** 207.2	83 **Bi** 208.980	84 **Po** (209)	85 **At** (210)	86 **Rn** (222)
7	87 **Fr** (223)	88 **Ra** 226.025	89 ‡**Ac** 227.028	104 **Rf** (261)	105 **Db** (262)	106 **Sg** (266)	107 **Bh** (264)	108 **Hs** (270)	109 **Mt** (266)	110 **Ds** (271)	111 **Rg** (272)	112 ** (285)	113 ** (284)	114 ** (289)	115 ** (288)	116 ** (292)		118 ** (294)

*Lanthanide series

58 **Ce** 140.115	59 **Pr** 140.908	60 **Nd** 144.24	61 **Pm** (145)	62 **Sm** 150.36	63 **Eu** 151.965	64 **Gd** 157.25	65 **Tb** 158.925	66 **Dy** 162.50	67 **Ho** 164.930	68 **Er** 167.26	69 **Tm** 168.934	70 **Yb** 173.04	71 **Lu** 174.967

‡Actinide series

90 **Th** 232.038	91 **Pa** 231.036	92 **U** 238.029	93 **Np** 237.048	94 **Pu** (244)	95 **Am** (243)	96 **Cm** (247)	97 **Bk** (247)	98 **Cf** (251)	99 **Es** (252)	100 **Fm** (257)	101 **Md** (258)	102 **No** (259)	103 **Lr** (260)

** Not yet named

Multiscale Operational Organic Chemistry

A Problem-Solving Approach to the Laboratory Course

Second Edition

Multiscale Operational Organic Chemistry

A Problem-Solving Approach to the Laboratory Course

Second Edition

John W. Lehman

Professor Emeritus
Lake Superior State University

Pearson Education International

Associate Editor: *Jennifer Hart*
Senior Editor: *Andrew Gilfillan*
Editor in Chief, Science: *Nicole Folchetti*
Marketing Manager: *Elizabeth Averback*
Assistant Managing Editor: *Gina M. Cheselka*
In-house Production Liaison: *Shari Toron*

Cover Designer: *Jodi Notowitz*
Director of Operations: *Barbara Kittle*
Senior Operations Supervisor: *Alan Fischer*
AV Production Liaison: *Connie Long*
Art Studio: *Production Solutions*
Production Supervision/Composition: *Jill Traut, ICC Macmillan Inc.*

© 2010, 2002 by Pearson Education, Inc.
Pearson Prentice Hall
Pearson Education, Inc.
Upper Saddle River, New Jersey 07458

The spectra in this book were reproduced from *The Aldrich Library of FT-IR Spectra,* 2nd ed., and *The Aldrich Library of* ^{13}C *and* ^{1}H *FT-NMR Spectra* with the permission of the Aldrich Chemical Company.

Referenced trademarks:
6-12, Advil, Alconox, Aliquat, Anacin, Bakelite, Bausch & Lomb, BENGAY, Carbowax, Chromosorb, Clorox, Crisco, Deet, Drierite, Drummond Microcaps, Equal, Excedrin, Fluorlube, Freon, Jamaica Hell Fire, Javex, Kimax, Kool-Aid, Lucite, Luer–Lok, Mel-Temp, Mini-Press, Neosporin, Nochromix, No-Doz, Norit, NutraSweet, Parafilm, Perclene, Perkin-Elmer, Plexiglas, Pyrex, Robitussin Scoopula, Spectronic, Splenda, Styrofoam, Sudafed, Tabasco Sauce, Teflon, Thermowell, Tylenol, Whatman.

Printed in the United States of America

10 9 8 7 6 5 4 3 2 1

ISBN 13: 978-0-13-702840-5
ISBN 10: 0-13-702840-7

Pearson Education LTD., London
Pearson Education Australia PTY, Limited
Pearson Education Singapore, Pte. Ltd
Pearson Education North Asia Ltd
Pearson Education Canada, Inc.
Pearson Educación de Mexico, S.A. de C.V.
Pearson Education -- Japan
Pearson Education Malaysia, Pte. Ltd
Pearson Education, Upper Saddle River, New Jersey

This edition of Multiscale Operational Organic Chemistry is dedicated to the many students whose achievements and misadventures in my organic chemistry laboratory provided the substance and inspiration for the book.

About the Author

John W. Lehman received his Ph.D. in chemistry from the University of Colorado in Boulder. He has taught chemistry for 35 years at Lake Superior State University, a small university in Michigan's scenic Upper Peninsula. In recognition of his teaching skills, he received the State of Michigan's Teaching Excellence Award in 1990. In 2001 he funded a chemistry scholarship to help bring outstanding students into the chemistry program at Lake Superior State University. His groundbreaking lab text, *Operational Organic Chemistry,* was first published in 1981, and he has written three additional books for the organic chemistry laboratory.

Contents

Part III Minilabs 515

Part IV Qualitative Organic Analysis   571

Part V Laboratory Operations   619

Appendixes and Bibliography   907

Preface to the Second Edition

To the Instructor

During some 35 years of teaching chemistry, I've witnessed nearly everything that can go wrong in an organic chemistry lab. Having experienced more than one misadventure as a student, I have some sympathy for the hapless students who, like Willy Hackett in Experiment 45, can't seem to do anything right. To give them the benefit of my experience, I've added new "troubleshooting" sections, entitled "When Things Go Wrong," to most of the operations in this new edition of *Multiscale Operational Organic Chemistry*. If a student combines the wrong layers during an extraction, obtains no product upon cooling a recrystallization solution, or records an infrared spectrum with no absorption bands, referring to the troubleshooting section should lead the student to a solution, or at least to an understanding of what went wrong.

The serious damage that can be produced by the release of hazardous chemicals into the environment and the unsustainable rate at which we consume chemical and energy resources have convinced me that chemistry students should learn how to work with chemicals in an environmentally responsible way. This edition therefore contains a new introductory section entitled "Chemistry and the Environment," which includes a discussion of the principals of green chemistry. Several green experiments have been added, and some experiments from the first edition have been revised to make them greener. Information on the environmental impact of various chemicals and exercises on environmental topics have been added to nearly all of the experiments.

Each category of operations in the book now begins with a brief summary of the operations and their uses. Some operations have been reorganized, and a new one on excluding air from reaction mixtures has been added. I have added new information about some instrumental techniques, such as the use of attenuated total reflectance devices (ATRs) and disposable cards in infrared spectrometry, and made substantive revisions of many operations, such as the one on flash chromatography.

This edition of *Multiscale Operational Organic Chemistry* also differs from the first edition in the following respects:

- Sections on personal protective equipment and on finding and using chemical safety information have been added under the "Laboratory Safety" heading.
- Six new experiments have been added (Experiments 22, 24, 31, 35, 40, and 41), replacing three experiments that were in the first edition.
- A new minilab replaces the previous Minilab 7.
- Calculations for solution preparation have been added to Appendix IV.
- The Bibliography has been updated to include more current literature sources, necessitating a revision of Appendix VII, "The Chemical Literature."
- Minor corrections and revisions have been made to all sections of the book.

Every experiment and minilab in this book can be performed by students using either standard scale glassware, such as that available in an organic chemistry lab kit with 19/22 standard-taper joints, or microscale glassware, such as that in a Mayo–Pike-style microscale lab kit with 14/10 standard-taper joints and threaded connectors. Most of the microscale experiments could also be performed successfully with alternative microscale glassware, such as that provided in a Williamson lab kit (described in *Microscale and Macroscale Organic Experiments,* D.C. Heath and Co.). However, some might need to be scaled down further, and the instructor would have to provide additional instructions regarding the use of the glassware. Some organic chemists regard a "microscale" experiment as one involving approximately 0.1 g of the limiting reactant. Dealing with such small quantities can be discouraging to students with standard scale fingers, who are apt to end up with a drop or a few grains of product, if any. Therefore, I have adopted a working definition of a microscale experiment as one that can be performed using the glassware available in a typical microscale lab kit, along with appropriate locker supplies as recommended in the *Instructor's Manual*.

In writing this and other versions of *Operational Organic Chemistry,* I have been guided by my convictions that students (1) perform better in the organic laboratory course if they master the major lab operations early and apply them throughout the course, (2) learn organic chemistry better if they keep their minds engaged by approaching each experiment as a problem-solving exercise, and (3) perform any task better if they are sufficiently motivated.

Part I is devoted to experiments designed to teach the basic laboratory operations, where an *operation,* as used here, is a process that utilizes one or more basic lab techniques, such as heating, cooling, and vacuum filtration, to accomplish some end, such as the purification of a solid. Once students have mastered the major operations by completing the appropriate experiments in Part I, they should be ready to apply those operations in Part II, which contains a large selection of experiments that are correlated with topics found in most organic chemistry lecture textbooks. This operational approach helps students understand that an organic synthesis, for example, is not a unique process that can be carried out only by mechanically following a detailed "recipe." Rather, it is the outcome of a logical sequence of interrelated operations adapted to the requirements of the synthesis.

In addition to teaching lab skills, the experiments in this book are designed to help students develop the observational and critical thinking skills that are essential prerequisites for a successful career in science and in virtually every other professional field. Each experiment requires the student to solve a specific scientific problem through the application of sound scientific methodology. To apply this approach effectively, the instructor should require each student to define the problem posed by an experiment based on information provided in a hypothetical Scenario. After a preliminary reading of the experiment, the student should be able to develop a working hypothesis regarding its outcome. During the experiment, each student should gather and evaluate evidence bearing on the problem and, as necessary, reevaluate and revise the hypothesis based on experimental observations and data. Finally, the student tests the hypothesis by obtaining a melting point, a spectrum, a gas chromatogram, or by some other means, and arrives at a conclusion. Because of the level at which most undergraduate organic chemistry courses are taught, the problems must, of necessity, be kept relatively simple and (with a few exceptions) should not be compared to "real" research problems tackled by professional chemists. It is not the intent of this book to make every student a research chemist; most students who take an organic chemistry course have no intention of going into the field. But the critical thinking and methodological skills required to solve the problems are comparable to those applied by research scientists, and applying those skills should give the student a better understanding of the nature and practice of science.

As a motivational device and to provide a frame of reference for the problems, students are asked to regard themselves as "consulting chemists" working for an institute operated by their college or university. Various individuals and organizations come to the institute with their scientific problems, and the problems are relayed to the "project group" comprising each lab section, to be solved individually or (sometimes) through collaboration. Although some of the Scenarios are admittedly a bit contrived, most of them describe tasks similar to those a practicing chemist might be called upon to perform.

To implement this problem-solving approach in the organic chemistry lab, each experiment includes a section, "Applying Scientific Methodology," intended to help the student understand the problem, formulate a meaningful hypothesis, and solve the problem. The Introduction and Experiment 1 describe in some detail how the student can apply scientific methodology to the solution of a problem, so students should read at least the section "Problem Solving in the Organic Chemistry Lab" in the Introduction, and should be asked to read the scenario and "Applying Scientific Methodology" sections of Experiment 1, even if you choose not to assign that experiment. Because each experiment is designed as a problem for the student to solve, the outcome is not explicitly stated in the experiment itself. In a few experiments, such as Experiments 32 and 38, the identity of the starting material is unknown as well. For these and other reasons, *it is essential that the instructor or laboratory coordinator obtain a copy of the* Instructor's Manual, *which is provided free of charge by Prentice Hall to adopters of this book.*

Part III contains a number of minilabs to provide additional flexibility. These short experiments can be used to fill in those gaps in a lab course when, for example, the students finish a two-period experiment during the first hour or so of the second period. They can also be used to teach techniques (such as paper chromatography in Minilab 9) that are not used in the major experiments or to introduce additional theoretical topics, such as photochemistry (Minilab 24). Part IV is a self-contained introduction to qualitative organic analysis, which is also incorporated into some of the Part II experiments, particularly Experiments 39 and 50. Part V contains detailed descriptions of the laboratory operations, which are flagged in the experiments by operation numbers in brackets, such as [OP-30].

Acknowledgments

Although I have personally lab-tested all of the experiments in this book, many students and faculty members have been involved in their development and testing as well. The procedures have also been class-tested by undergraduate organic chemistry students at Lake Superior State University and elsewhere. I am especially grateful to the students who occasionally suffered through the earlier versions of some experiments. I learned from their misadventures and improved the procedures to smooth the path of future students using this book. I owe a debt of gratitude to the late Miles Pickering, whose articles in the *Journal of Chemical Education* stimulated me to develop the problem-solving approach used in this book. I also wish to express my appreciation to James G. Vogel and Roger Kugel, from whom I got the idea for the Consulting Chemists Institute, and to Anthony Winston, John Penn, and the other organizers of West Virginia University's microscale chemistry workshop, which helped me apply microscale techniques in my own organic chemistry lab. For this edition of *Multiscale Operational Organic Chemistry,* I would like to acknowledge the contributions of Austin Johnson, who lab-tested some of the new procedures, and Lake Superior State University professors Marshall Werner and Judy Westrick, who supervised the class testing of various procedures. I am indebted to my editors at Prentice Hall, Nicole Folchetti, Andrew Gilfillan, and Jennifer Hart, who provided encouragement and assistance throughout the project, to Jill Traut of Macmillan Publishing Solutions, who managed the production of the book, and to Dr. Maria Vogt, professor of chemistry at Bloomfield College, who checked the manuscript pages for accuracy. Most of the spectra in this book and in the *Instructor's Manual* are reproduced from the spectral libraries of the Aldrich Chemical Company, whose generosity is gratefully acknowledged.

All textbooks can benefit from comments and criticism by their readers, so I welcome correspondence to point out errors or to suggest improvements in the book.

John W. Lehman
jlehman@lssu.edu

Introduction

Problem Solving in the Organic Chemistry Laboratory

Organic chemistry isn't most people's idea of a "fun" course, but that is no reason not to enjoy your organic chemistry lab experience. Many experiences can be enjoyable if they give you the opportunity to use your imagination and to test your mental and manual skills. During this lab course, you will play the role of a consultant in a Consulting Chemists Institute operated by your college or university. When D. K. Little wants to know what happens to his company's food preservative in stomach acid, when Rusty Tappet accidentally pours diesel fuel into a barrel of racing fuel, when Gilda Lilly wants to know the color of a synthetic dye, or when the Olfactory Factory needs a way to convert an oversupply of anisole to a perfume ingredient, you and the other members of your "project group" (lab section) will be called upon to solve their problems.

To solve such a problem, you must *think* before you *act*. In other words, you will need to read the experiment, understand the problem, and try to predict a likely outcome of the experiment before you actually carry out the experiment in the laboratory. Your prediction, stated clearly in writing, becomes your *working hypothesis*. In many cases, the most likely outcome will become apparent after you read the experiment, especially if you apply the concepts you have learned in the organic chemistry lecture. In other cases, there may be several reasonable outcomes, and you will have to make an educated guess about the most likely outcome. During the experiment, you will need to gather evidence that may support your hypothesis—or prove it wrong. That means making careful observations and gathering data that relate to the problem. As you evaluate the evidence, you may decide that your original hypothesis was wrong, or at least incomplete, and needs to be revised or replaced by a new one. By the time you finish the experiment, you will have tested your hypothesis and arrived at a conclusion. In this way, each experiment will help you develop your observational and critical thinking skills—as well as your lab skills—as you apply them to the solution of the problem posed in that experiment. The next section will tell you, in more detail, how to approach and solve a scientific problem.

Scientific Methodology

If you are taking an organic chemistry course, you are probably planning a career in some field of science or technology or a field that is based on scientific knowledge and principles, such as medicine. To succeed in such a field, you must learn to think and work like a scientist. Scientists follow certain basic principles that are often lumped together under the expression "the scientific method." In fact, there is no universal scientific method that all scientists follow rigorously. However, most scientists take at least some of the following steps when faced with a scientific problem:

- Define the problem.
- Plan a course of action.
- Gather evidence.
- Evaluate the evidence.
- Develop a hypothesis.
- Test the hypothesis.

- Reach a conclusion.
- Report the results.

Defining the Problem. Most people think of a "problem" in a negative sense, as in "We've got a problem here" or "What's your problem?" To a scientist, a problem is not a perceived difficulty but an *opportunity* to explore and learn more about some aspect of the physical world. A problem may be inherent in an assigned task, or it may arise from anything that the scientist is curious about, such as an unexplained phenomenon or an unexpected observation. A problem is often defined in the form of a question: What is the identity of the liquid my instructor gave me? What is the mercury concentration in a Lake Michigan salmon? How do fireflies generate light? In this laboratory course, the problem associated with each experiment will be described in the Scenario that leads off the experiment.

Planning a Course of Action. A scientist must plan his or her own course of action for solving a scientific problem. This often requires that the scientist carry out a literature search to glean information and data relating to the problem, decide which experimental methods and instruments to use, and develop a detailed procedure to be followed. In most lab courses, the procedure is "in the book," and the student simply follows the procedure as if it were a recipe for baking a cake. That is true of a few basic experiments in this textbook, but for most of them, you will have to perform some calculations and develop your own experimental plan based on the information and directions given in the experiment. In a few cases, you may be required to develop a procedure of your own.

Gathering Evidence. Scientists will gather as much evidence as they feel is needed to solve a problem and convince other scientists that their solution is correct. Evidence is gathered by making careful *observations* and *measurements*.

To make valid observations, you must be *objective*—reporting only what you actually saw and not what you expected to see. A wildlife biologist who expects wild chimpanzees to behave just like chimpanzees at the zoo isn't likely to make any important discoveries about chimpanzees! Keep the following points in mind when you make observations.

1. Don't confuse an observation with an *inference*. An observation is whatever you perceive with your senses (sight, smell, touch, taste, or hearing) during an event. An inference is a guess about the *cause* of the event. Writing "The solution turned brown upon addition of 0.1 M $KMnO_4$" records an observation. Writing "The solution must have contained an alkene because it turned brown upon addition of 0.1 M $KMnO_4$" is an inference.
2. Be prepared to be surprised. If you observe something you didn't expect, don't simply disregard the observation or report what you thought you should have seen. Consider an unexpected observation an opportunity to learn something you didn't know before—something that might lead to a new discovery.
3. Write down your observations as you make them or shortly thereafter. If you wait too long, you are likely to leave out important details.
4. Record your observations clearly, completely, and systematically. For example, if you are doing repetitive measurements or carrying out the same test on a series of samples, record your observations in a table.

Making accurate measurements, such as determining the mass or melting point of the product of a chemical synthesis, requires a certain amount of skill and know-how. You can obtain such skills by, for example, watching your instructor demonstrate the operation of an instrument, and then practicing with the instrument until you obtain consistent and accurate results *before* you use it to make a measurement you intend to report. If you aren't sure how to use an instrument properly, ask the instructor to show you.

Evaluating the Evidence.   Evaluating the evidence involves assessing the reliability of your experimental results and looking for clues among your results that may point to a solution to the problem. For example, searching the infrared spectrum of an unknown liquid for evidence of a specific functional group and comparing its boiling point with the boiling points of known compounds may help you solve the problem "What is the identity of the liquid my instructor gave me?" Solving such problems requires clear and logical thinking; in other situations, a more creative, intuitive approach can be valuable. In either case, all of your reasoning and intuition may be fruitless if your experimental results are unreliable. The validation of experimental results requires first asking yourself whether the results make sense physically. If you obtain a melting point that is much lower than the literature value, a product mass that is higher than the theoretical yield for a synthesis, or any other result that seems suspect, you need to find out whether the result is, in fact, erroneous. You should review everything you did that led to the result, using notes from your lab notebook to jog your memory as necessary. Perhaps you only need to repeat a melting point or dry a product longer, but in any case, you should find out what you did wrong and correct it. For some kinds of experiments (there are none in this book), validation of results may also require a statistical analysis of experimental data. If you perform such an experiment, your instructor will tell you how to do that.

Developing and Testing Hypotheses.   A hypothesis can be regarded as an educated guess about the cause of some phenomenon or the outcome of an experiment. Hypotheses can help us see the significance of an object or event that would otherwise mean little. For example, the movements of the planets seemed erratic and mysterious before Copernicus developed his hypothesis that the Earth revolves around the sun. A hypothesis must be *testable* to have validity; that is, it must be formulated in such a way that experiments can be devised whose outcome might prove the hypothesis *wrong*. John Dalton's hypothesis that atoms are indivisible was proved wrong after it was shown that bombarding uranium atoms with neutrons caused them to split into smaller atoms. But Dalton's more fundamental hypothesis—that all matter is made of atoms—has been tested repeatedly over the years and has never been proven wrong, so it is generally accepted as true.

Most of the experiments in this book require you to formulate and test a working hypothesis based on a problem outlined in the Scenario. A working hypothesis can be a prediction about the outcome of an experiment based on information available to the experimenter, which, for your lab course, will usually be found in the write-up for the experiment. Such a hypothesis can be proposed and revised at any time during the course of an experiment. An appropriate working hypothesis and the method of testing it may become apparent upon reading the experiment. For example, after reading Experiment 9, you should be able to develop a working hypothesis such as "The red pigment in Brand X tomato paste was chemically altered when the tomatoes were processed," and then test your hypothesis by recording a spectrum of the isolated pigment in solution.

One drawback of a working hypothesis is that the scientist may become so attached to it that he or she will overlook or ignore evidence that contradicts it. For this reason, some scientists prefer to explore a problem without any preconceived ideas about the outcome—which isn't always easy to do. For most of the experiments in this book, you can formulate a working hypothesis after reading the experiment, but a few experiments require that you gather some experimental evidence first. In either case, if the experimental evidence does not support your initial hypothesis, you should be ready to revise or abandon it without regret.

Reaching Conclusions.   If a hypothesis passes all of the tests you carry out, then you are ready to state a conclusion, such as "The liquid my instructor gave me is benzaldehyde." This doesn't necessarily mean that your conclusion is correct; you may not have carried out enough tests, or perhaps some of your test results are faulty. But if you have performed an experiment carefully and reasoned logically, you will probably arrive at a valid conclusion.

Reporting Results.   You should report all results of an experiment as clearly, completely, and unambiguously as possible. Write up your results in correct English, using complete sentences and accurate spelling. Be as specific as you can, avoiding such generalities as "My yield was lower than expected due to human error." Label any tables clearly, giving names or standard abbreviations for all physical properties and the units in which they are measured.

If an experiment requires that you graph your data, use accurately ruled graph paper—never notebook paper or paper you have ruled yourself. Plot the dependent variable on the *y*-axis and the independent variable on the *x*-axis. Label both axes with the physical quantities being graphed and their units, if any. Select appropriate, uniform scale intervals so that your data points extend most of the way up and across the graph paper. If the relationship you are graphing is linear, draw the straight line that best fits the data points.

Applying Scientific Methodology

How can you apply scientific methodology in your organic chemistry lab course? Consider Experiment 5 in this book, which involves the reaction of isopentyl alcohol with acetic acid. By reading the Scenario, you learn that you are expected to prepare isopentyl acetate (also known as "banana oil") by this reaction and then analyze your product by gas chromatography to see whether it meets the specified outcome of containing less than 10% isopentyl alcohol and 2% acetic acid. Using this information, you can state the problem as, for example: "When isopentyl alcohol is heated with acetic acid in the presence of a catalyst, will the reaction yield isopentyl acetate containing less than 10% isopentyl alcohol and 2% acetic acid?" You can then formulate one or more working hypotheses, sometimes by simply restating the problem in a form that predicts the outcome of the experiment. Such a hypothesis might be, for example: "The reaction of isopentyl alcohol with acetic acid *will* yield isopentyl acetate containing less than 10% isopentyl alcohol and 2% acetic acid." This statement actually contains two predictions: (1) that there will be a chemical reaction that yields some isopentyl acetate, and (2) that the product's purity will meet the specifications stated. Thus, you will have to gather evidence to help you prove or disprove each prediction.

As you read the directions for the experiment, consider the kinds of evidence you can gather by measurement or observation. During the experiment itself, make careful observations of everything that might provide evidence relating to the problem. What changes occur when the chemicals are combined and heated together? Do the changes indicate that a chemical reaction is taking place? Do they give any clues about the possible identity of the product? What physical properties of the product can you observe (such as odor) or measure (such as boiling point) during the experiment, and what bearing do they have on the identity and purity of the product? What do your results from the analysis of the product by gas chromatography tell you about the purity of the product?

After you have completed the experiment, you can evaluate the evidence, decide whether the results confirm or disprove your hypothesis, arrive at a conclusion that answers the question proposed in your problem statement, and write a report that describes your findings. Appendixes II and III suggest ways to record and report your experimental results. Your instructor will let you know what kind of report he or she prefers.

Organization of This Book

Multiscale Operational Organic Chemistry is divided into five parts. Part I contains 12 experiments whose main purpose is to help you learn basic laboratory operations by applying them to the solution of a scientific problem. In the dictionary, an *operation* is defined as a process or series of acts performed to effect a certain purpose or result. For example, the *recrystallization* operation, which is used to purify a solid substance, involves at least four separate steps: (1) *heating* the solid in a boiling solvent until it dissolves, (2) *cooling* the resulting solution until the solid crystallizes, (3) *filtering* the crystals to separate them from the solvent, and (4) *washing* the crystals to remove residual impurities. Such operations are often called *techniques,* but the latter term is also used to refer to a single step, such as filtration, in a multi-step operation. In Part I, you will perform most of the operations in this book while carrying out experiments designed to accomplish other outcomes. For example, you will measure a melting point not just to learn how to measure melting points but also to establish the identity of a substance you have isolated or synthesized.

Once you have mastered the operations in Part I, you will apply them in experiments from Part II, which are correlated with topics in your lecture textbook. Performing these experiments will increase your proficiency in the laboratory and also give you the opportunity to apply—in a hands-on environment—what you have learned in the organic chemistry lecture course to the solution of specific scientific problems. In the process, you should find that learning by doing can be much more effective and enjoyable than learning by memorization and other purely mental processes.

Each experiment in Parts I and II contains information under most or all of the following headings.

Operations. This heading is followed by a list of the operations to be used in the experiment, each preceded by an operation number, such as OP-28 for recrystallization. The description for each operation can be located quickly by noting the large operation numbers in the right-hand corners of the odd-numbered pages in Part V as you flip through the pages. Operations being used for the first time are emphasized by boldface type in an experiment's list of operations; you should read their descriptions thoroughly before you come to the laboratory. After you have used an operation once or twice, you shouldn't have to reread the entire description the next time you use it, but you should at least read the Summary and review the "Directions" section (if provided) to refresh your memory. Eventually, you shouldn't need to refer to the operation description at all, unless you are applying the operation in a new situation or unexpected problems arise. If you do run into problems while carrying out an operation, read *When Things Go Wrong,* a troubleshooting guide that is included with most of the operations.

Before You Begin. Under this heading, you will find a *prelab assignment:* a list of things to do before you come to the laboratory. The prelab assignment always includes reading the experiment and reading or reviewing the operations. Starting with Experiment 5, you will also be expected to write an experimental plan for each experiment, as described in Appendix V, and you will usually need to carry out some calculations. Your instructor may require that you have your experimental plan and calculations approved before you begin an experiment.

Scenario. The Scenario presents a hypothetical situation involving the scientific problem you are to solve. A typical Scenario will describe a chemistry-related problem posed by a company or an individual and tell you what role you will play in its solution.

Applying Scientific Methodology. This section is intended to help you formulate and solve the problem posed in the Scenario by following the approach described in the previous sections, "Problem Solving in the Organic Chemistry Lab" and "Scientific Methodology."

Background Essay. Each background essay appears under a different descriptive heading, such as "Crime and Chemistry." The essay will often show the relation between the lab work and concepts from the lecture course. It may also relate historical sidelights or interesting facts that show the "real-world" relevance of the experiment.

Understanding the Experiment. This section describes the main purpose of the experiment, explains the theoretical basis of the experiment (when appropriate), and helps you understand the experimental methodology. It may also provide information that will help you interpret your results or cope with unexpected complications as they arise.

Reactions and Properties. For most experiments, this section gives balanced equations for synthetic reactions and tabulates the relevant physical properties of reactants, products, and other chemicals. The Properties table usually contains any data needed for the prelab calculations.

Directions. This section describes the course of action you will follow to carry out the experiment. You shouldn't follow it mechanically, as you would a recipe, but try to understand the purpose of each operation you are performing. The section entitled "Understanding the Experiment" will help you do so. The Directions for most Part I experiments are more detailed than those for Part II. By the time you get to Part II, you will be expected to know how to perform most lab operations proficiently without the aid of frequent reminders.

Safety Notes. Characteristics of some hazardous chemicals and precautions for their use are described in the Directions under this heading. See the following "Laboratory Safety" section for general information about laboratory hazards.

Exercises. Your instructor will assign exercises to be completed and turned in with your laboratory report.

Other Things You Can Do. These suggestions may include additional experiments or minilabs that you can perform, or library research projects that you can complete. You must have your instructor's permission to start any project marked by an asterisk. Read the relevant sections of Appendix VII, "The Chemical Literature," and scan the Bibliography for possible sources before you begin a library research project.

Part III of the text contains 46 short experiments called minilabs. Minilabs take only part of a lab period and don't require extensive reports. They are designed to add flexibility to the lab course and "fill in the gaps" when, for example, a two-week experiment can be finished in less than two full lab periods.

Part IV is a comprehensive, self-contained introduction to qualitative organic analysis that will help you learn how to identify organic compounds using chemical and spectral methods.

Part V contains descriptions of all of the operations, which are referred to in each experiment's directions by number, in the form [OP-28].

Appendix I contains illustrations of standard scale and microscale laboratory equipment. Appendixes II and III tell you how to keep a lab notebook and write lab reports. Appendix IV will help you perform calculations used in carrying out and writing up experiments. Appendix V tells you how to develop experimental plans and write flow diagrams for experimental procedures. Appendix VI contains tables of properties for qualitative organic analysis. Appendix VII is a guide to the chemical literature that describes important works in organic chemistry, directs you to citations for them in the Bibliography, and, in some cases, tells you how to use them.

The Bibliography lists a large number of useful works in organic chemistry, ranging from enormous multivolume sets such as *Chemical Abstracts* to short papers from the *Journal of Chemical Education*. References to entries listed in the Bibliography are made throughout this book in the form [Bibliography, F20], where the letter refers to a category and the number to a location within that category; for example, F20 is the twentieth book listed under Category F, Spectrometry. Citations to journal articles are given in the form *J. Chem. Educ.* **2002**, *79*, 721, where the abbreviated journal name (the *Journal of Chemical Education* in this example) is followed by the date, volume number, and page number.

A Guide to Success in the Organic Chemistry Lab

What to Expect in Your Organic Chemistry Lab Course

Students are sometimes apprehensive about having to work in an organic chemistry lab. They may have heard that organic chemistry is difficult or that the lab is a dangerous place because of the hazardous nature of organic chemicals. Although some students do find the subject matter of organic chemistry difficult, most of them have little trouble completing the laboratory experiments successfully. In fact, many students enjoy the lab far more than the lecture course, and they generally receive higher grades in lab than in lecture.

It is true that some organic chemicals are quite hazardous and can cause serious injury, or even death, if not handled properly. However, if the chemistry lab were a very dangerous place to work, you would expect professional chemists to have short life spans. In fact, chemists tend to live longer than professionals in most other fields; in one listing of occupational risks, chemists rank near the bottom (lowest risk), right between school administrators and ticket agents. In my 35 years of teaching organic chemistry, I've observed only a few lab accidents that caused significant injury, most of them involving broken glass. Only a handful of students were injured by contact with chemicals, and none of them suffered permanent injury. That is not to say that you can afford to be careless in the lab—the potential for a serious accident is always there. But if you follow the safety rules in the following "Laboratory Safety" section and take reasonable precautions when handling chemicals, you should have little reason for concern about lab accidents.

Getting Started

By the end of the first week of your organic chemistry course, you should have read the "Laboratory Safety" section of this book and any other safety rules or data provided by your instructor. Before you begin working in the laboratory, your instructor should review the safety rules and tell you what safety supplies, such as safety goggles and protective gloves and aprons, you will need to use in the lab. During the first laboratory period, the instructor will show you where safety equipment is located and tell you how to use it. As you locate each item, check it off the following list and make a note of its location. (Your instructor may suggest additions or changes to the list.)

- Fire extinguishers
- Fire blanket
- Safety shower
- Eyewash fountain
- First aid supplies
- Spill cleanup supplies

You should also learn the locations of chemicals, consumable supplies (such as filter paper and boiling chips), waste containers, and various items of equipment such as balances and drying ovens.

Your instructor will assign you a locker and provide a list of locker supplies. You will then need to check into the laboratory. This usually involves

chip on lip
of test tube

crack

star fracture

Glassware defects

getting a locker key or a combination lock and checking your locker for missing or damaged items. You will find illustrations of typical locker supplies in Appendix I at the back of this book. If you find any glassware items with chips, cracks, or star fractures, you should have them replaced; they may cause cuts, break on heating, or shatter under stress. If necessary, clean up any dirty glassware in your locker (see OP-1) and organize it neatly at this time.

Working Efficiently

Because of wide variations in individual working rates, it is usually not possible to schedule experiments so that everyone can finish in the allotted time. If all labs were geared to the slowest student, the objectives of the course could not be accomplished in the limited time available. If you fall behind in the lab, you may need to put in extra hours outside your scheduled laboratory period in order to complete the course. The following suggestions should help you work more efficiently and finish each experiment on time.

1. *Be prepared to start the experiment the moment you reach your work area.* Don't waste precious minutes at the start of a laboratory period doing calculations, reading the experiment, washing glassware, or carrying out other activities that should have been done at the end of the previous period or during the intervening time. The first half hour of any lab period is the most important—if you use it to collect the necessary materials, set up the apparatus, and get the initial operation (reflux, distillation, etc.) under way, you should have no trouble completing the experiment on time.

2. *Organize your time efficiently.* Schedule a time each week to read the experiment and operation descriptions and to complete the prelab assignment—an hour before the lab period begins is too late! Plan ahead so that you know approximately what you will be doing at each stage of the experiment. A written experimental plan, prepared as described in Appendix V, is invaluable for this purpose.

3. *Organize your work area.* Before performing any operation, arrange all of the equipment and supplies you will need during the operation neatly on your bench top, in the approximate order in which they will be used. Place small objects and any items that might be contaminated by contact with the bench top on a paper towel, laboratory tissue, or mat. After you use each item, move it to an out-of-the-way location where it can be cleaned and returned to its proper location when time permits; for example, put dirty glassware in a washing trough in the sink. Keep your locker well organized, placing each item in the same location after use so that you can immediately find the equipment you need. This will also help you notice whether any items are missing so that you can hunt for them before you leave the lab; otherwise, the items will probably disappear before the next lab period, and you may be charged for them.

Getting Along in the Laboratory

You will get along much better in the laboratory if you can maintain peace and harmony with your coworkers—or at least keep from aggravating them—and stay on good terms with your instructor. Following these commonsense rules will help you do that.

1. *Leave all chemicals where you found them.* You will understand the reason for this rule once you experience the frustration of hunting high and low for a reagent, only to find it at another student's station in a far corner of the lab. Containers should be taken to the reagent bottles to be filled; reagent bottles should never be taken to your lab station.

2. *Take only what you need.* Liquids and solutions should ordinarily be obtained using bottle-top dispensers, automatic pipets, or other measuring devices so that you will take no more than you expect to use for a given operation. Solids can be weighed out directly from stock bottles.

3. *Prevent contamination of chemicals.* Don't use your own pipet or dropper to remove liquids from stock bottles, and don't return unused chemicals to stock bottles. Be sure to close all bottles tightly after use—particularly those that contain anhydrous chemicals and drying agents.

4. *If you must use a burner, inform your neighbors*—unless they are already using burners. This will allow them to cover any containers of flammable solvents and take other necessary precautions. In some circumstances, you may have to use a different heat source, move your operation to a safe location (for instance, under a fume hood), or find something else to do while flammable solvents are in use.

5. *Return all community equipment to the designated locations.* This may include ring stands, lab kits, clamps, condenser tubing, and other items that aren't in your own locker. Because such items will be needed by students in other lab sections, they should always be returned to the proper storage area at the end of the period.

6. *Clean up for the next person.* Few experiences are more annoying than finding that the lab kit you just checked out is full of dirty glassware or that your lab station is cluttered with paper towels, broken glass, and spilled chemicals. The last 15 minutes or so of every laboratory period should be set aside for cleaning up your lab station and the glassware used during the experiment. Put things away so that your work station is uncluttered. Clean off the bench top with a towel or wet sponge; remove condenser tubing, other supplies, and debris from the sink; and thoroughly wash any dirty glassware that is to be returned to the stockroom, as well as that from your locker. Clean up any spills and broken glassware immediately. If you spill a corrosive or toxic chemical, such as sulfuric acid or aniline, inform the instructor before you attempt to clean it up.

7. *Heed Gumperson's Second Law,* which advises you to maximize the labor and minimize the oratory while in the **labor**a**tory**. This doesn't mean that all conversation must come to a halt. Quiet conversation during a lull in the experimental activity is okay, but a constant stream of chatter directed at a student who is performing a delicate operation is distracting and can lead to an accident. For the same reason, radios, MP3 players, and other audio devices should not be brought into the laboratory.

Laboratory Safety

thermometers into stoppers or thermometer adapters, and when removing them. Grasp the glass close to the stopper or thermometer adapter and gently twist it in or out. Remember that hot glass remains hot for some time; after you have fire-polished a glass rod or completed another glass-working operation, give the glass plenty of time to cool before you touch it. Refer to OP-3 for more information about safe glass-working procedures.

5. *Wear appropriate clothing in the laboratory.* Wear clothing that is substantial enough to offer some protection against accidental chemical spills, and shoes that can protect you from spilled chemicals and broken glass. Human hair is very flammable, so tie up your hair or wear a hair net while using a burner if you have long hair.

6. *Dispose of chemicals properly.* For reasons of safety and environmental protection, most organic chemicals should not be washed down the drain. Except when your instructor or an experiment's directions indicate otherwise, place used organic chemicals and solutions in designated waste containers. Some aqueous solutions can be safely poured down the drain, but consult your instructor if there is any question about the best method for disposing of a particular chemical or solution. See the section "Disposal of Hazardous Wastes" for additional information.

7. *Never work alone in the laboratory or perform unauthorized experiments.* If you wish to work in the laboratory when no formal lab period is scheduled, you must obtain written permission from the instructor and be certain that others will be present while you are working.

Reacting to Accidents: First Aid

Notice: Only qualified personnel trained in first aid care should treat serious injuries by any procedures described in this section.

If you have or witness a serious accident involving poisoning or injury, report it to the instructor immediately. Serious accidents should be treated by a competent physician, but applying some basic first aid procedures before a physician arrives can help minimize any damage.

If you have an accident that requires quick action to prevent permanent injury, take the appropriate action as described here, if you can, and see that the instructor is informed of the accident. If you *witness* an accident, call the instructor immediately and leave the first aid to him or her, unless (1) no instructor or assistant is in the laboratory area; (2) the victim requires immediate attention because of stopped breathing, heavy bleeding, or any other life-threatening condition; or (3) you have had appropriate emergency response training.

If an accident victim stops breathing or goes into shock as a result of any kind of accident, standard procedures for artificial respiration and treating shock should be applied. Descriptions of these procedures can be found in Chapter 2 of *The CRC Handbook of Laboratory Safety*, 4th ed. [Bibliography, C1].

Eye Injuries

If any chemical enters your eyes, *immediately* flush them with water from an eyewash fountain while holding your eyelids open. If you are wearing contact lenses, remove them first. Continue irrigation for at least 15 minutes (or until a nurse or a physician arrives), then have your eyes examined by a physician. If foreign bodies such as glass particles are propelled into your eye, seek immediate medical attention. Removal of such particles is a job for a specialist.

Chemical Burns

If a corrosive chemical is spilled on your skin or clothing, remove any contaminated clothing and *immediately* flush the affected area with a large amount of water until the chemical is completely removed. Use a safety shower if the area of injury is extensive or if it is not feasible to wash it from a tap. Speed and thoroughness in washing are the most important factors in reducing the extent of injury. Dry the area gently with a clean, soft towel. If you (or another victim) experience pain or if the skin is red or swollen, immerse the injured area in cold water or apply cold, wet dressings. Do not use neutralizing solutions, ointments, or greases on chemical burns unless they are specifically called for in a first aid procedure. Unless the skin is only reddened over a small area, a chemical burn should be examined by a nurse or physician. First aid procedures for burns caused by specific chemicals, such as bromine, are given in the *Sigma–Aldrich Library of Regulatory and Safety Data* [Bibliography, C4] and in the *First Aid Manual for Chemical Accidents* [Bibliography, C3].

If a chemical burn is very extensive or severe, the victim should lie down with the head and chest a little lower than the rest of the body. If the victim is conscious and able to swallow, he or she should be provided with plenty of nonalcoholic liquid to drink (water, tea, coffee, etc.) until a physician or an ambulance arrives.

Thermal Burns

If you are burned by hot glass, another hot object, or a flame, try to determine the type and extent of the burn and then take the appropriate action as described next.

- *First-degree burn.* The skin is reddened but there are no blisters or broken skin. Immerse the affected area in clean, cold water or apply ice to reduce the pain and facilitate healing.
- *Second-degree burn.* Blisters are raised. Immerse the burned area in clean, cold water or apply ice, then cover the area with sterile gauze or another clean dressing. If legs or arms are burned, keep them elevated above the trunk of the body. Never puncture blisters raised by a second-degree burn.
- *Third-degree burn.* The skin is broken and underlying tissue is damaged. Place a thick sterile dressing or clean cloth over the affected area and have the burn examined by a nurse or physician as soon as possible. Do not remove burned clothing, immerse the burned area in cold water, or cover the burn with greasy ointment. If legs or arms are burned, keep them elevated above the trunk of the body.

In case of an extensive thermal burn, the burned area should be covered with the cleanest available cloth material and the victim should lie down, with the head and chest lower than the rest of the body, until a physician or an ambulance arrives. If the injured person is conscious and able to swallow, he or she should be provided with plenty of nonalcoholic liquid to drink (water, tea, coffee, etc.).

Bleeding, Cuts, and Abrasions

In case of a cut or abrasion that doesn't involve heavy bleeding, cleanse the wound and the surrounding skin with soap and lukewarm water, applying it by wiping away from the wound. Try to remove embedded glass shards, if there are any, by using tweezers if necessary. Hold a sterile gauze pad over the wound until bleeding stops. Place a fresh gauze pad over the wound and secure it loosely with a triangular or rolled bandage. Replace the pad and bandage as necessary with clean, dry ones. Avoid contact between the wound and the mouth, fingers, handkerchiefs, or other unsterile objects. If the wound is deep or extensive, it should be treated further by a nurse or physician.

In case of a major wound that involves heavy bleeding, *immediately* apply pressure directly over the wound with a cloth pad (such as a clean handkerchief or other clean cloth) or sterile dressing, pressing firmly with one or both hands to reduce the bleeding as much as possible. Then call for assistance. A compression bandage should be applied on top of the original dressing if profuse bleeding continues. (Removing the original dressing may delay clotting.) The victim should lie down, with the bleeding part higher than the heart, and the dressing should be held in place using heavy gauze or other cloth strips. A physician or an ambulance should be called as soon as possible, and the victim should be kept warm with a blanket or coat. If the injured person is conscious and able to swallow, he or she should be provided with plenty of nonalcoholic liquid to drink (water, tea, coffee, etc.) until a physician arrives.

Poisoning

If, after contact with, inhalation of, or accidental ingestion of a chemical, you experience a burning sensation in the throat, discoloration of the lips or mouth, stomach cramps, nausea and vomiting, or confusion, seek treatment *immediately* for chemical poisoning.

If a poison has been ingested, an ambulance and a poison control center should be called immediately. If a victim of poisoning is conscious, loosen tight clothing around the neck and waist. If the poison is known, a sample of it should be saved for the physician.

If a poison has been inhaled, the victim must be taken to fresh air and a physician should be called immediately. Loosen any tight clothing around the neck and waist, and use a tongue depressor or other device, if necessary, to keep the victim's airway open. Keep the victim warm and as quiet as possible until a physician arrives. If the poison is a highly toxic gas, such as hydrogen cyanide, hydrogen sulfide, or phosgene, the persons attempting to rescue the victim should wear self-contained respirators while they are in contact with the vapors.

In case of skin contact with a toxic substance, follow the same general procedure as that for chemical burns. The *Sigma–Aldrich Library of Regulatory and Safety Data* [Bibliography, C4] or another appropriate source should be consulted for specific procedures to be used for injury by certain substances.

Reacting to Accidents: Fire

Most modern organic chemical laboratories use flameless heat sources for nearly all operations. However, burners may be used for special applications, such as bending glass, and some chemicals may ignite on a hot surface, such as the top of a hot plate. Hot plates can be particularly dangerous because the absence of an open flame makes them seem safe, but heating a volatile solvent on a hot plate can easily start a fire.

In case of fire, your first response should be to *get away* as quickly as possible and let the instructor deal with the fire. However, if a fire is small and confined to a container such as a flask or beaker, you may be able to put it out by placing a watch glass over the mouth of the container. If no instructor is present in the laboratory, obtain a fire extinguisher of the appropriate type and attempt to put out the fire by aiming the extinguisher at the base of the fire while maintaining a safe distance. Most labs should be equipped with class BC or ABC dry-chemical extinguishers, which are effective against solvent and electrical fires. A class D fire, which involves burning metals or metal hydrides such as sodium metal and lithium aluminum hydride, can be extinguished with an appropriate class D fire extinguisher or by smothering the fire in dry sand, sodium chloride, or sodium carbonate. If a fire is too large to be put out by a fire extinguisher, sound the nearest fire alarm and evacuate the area.

If your hair or clothing catches on fire, *do not panic*. *Walk* (don't run) directly to the nearest fire blanket or safety shower and attempt to extinguish the fire. Don't wrap yourself in a fire blanket while you are standing, as that may direct the flames around your face; instead, *drop* to the floor and *roll* as you wrap the blanket around your body. To use a safety shower, position yourself directly under the showerhead and pull the chain. If another person's hair or clothing has caught fire, try to prevent panic as you lead him or her to a safety shower or fire blanket.

Chemical Hazards

For your own health and safety, it is essential that you *exercise caution while handling chemicals* and *minimize your exposure to them*. Most academic chemistry departments have policies and procedures for dealing with hazardous chemicals, which should be incorporated into the institution's chemical hygiene plan. Your instructor will inform you of any departmental or institutional rules that relate to the safe handling and disposal of hazardous chemicals. The experiments and some of the operations in this book describe specific chemical hazards and handling precautions under the heading "Safety Notes." The hazard descriptions are meant to inform you of the potential danger posed by certain chemicals when they aren't handled properly. If you take reasonable precautions and follow the directions in the Safety Notes, you are unlikely to suffer ill effects from working with any chemical.

There are several different kinds of chemical hazards. A chemical may be toxic and therefore capable of causing illness or death when ingested, inhaled, or allowed to contact the skin. Certain chemicals can burn when exposed to a spark, an open flame, or a high temperature. A few chemicals can explode when they are heated, subjected to shock, or mixed with certain organic materials. Some chemicals may react spontaneously or when combined with other chemicals, generating heat that could cause a fire.

The severity of any hazards associated with a chemical can be indicated by a labeling system, such as the one established by the National Fire Protection Association (NFPA), which rates the health, flammability, and reactivity hazards of chemicals on a scale ranging from 0 to 4 (where 4 is the highest hazard rating). This book uses a similar system, in which the general health hazard number is usually replaced by two numbers that indicate the hazards posed by contact with and inhalation of a chemical. Hazard information on selected chemicals used in the experiments is provided in the form of octagonal signs that contain hazard index numbers. Each hazard index is a number from 0 to 4, where 0 indicates no known hazard and 4 indicates a very great health or safety hazard. Letters such as "W" are sometimes included to warn of other hazards, such as reactivity with water. The significance of the numbers and letters is explained in Table 1.

Table 1 Meanings of numbers and letters on hazard symbols

Symbol	Health (Contact or Vapor)	Fire	Reactivity
0	No known hazard	Will not burn	Stable
1	May cause irritation if not treated	Ignites after strong preheating	Unstable only at high temperature and pressure
2	May cause injury; requires treatment	Ignites after moderate heating	Unstable, but won't detonate
3	May cause serious injury despite treatment	Ignites at normal temperatures	Detonates or explodes with difficulty
4	May cause death or major injury despite treatment	Very flammable	Readily detonates or explodes
CA	Carcinogen (cancer-causing agent)		
OX			Strong oxidant; may react violently with combustible material
P			Polymerizes readily
W			Reacts violently with water

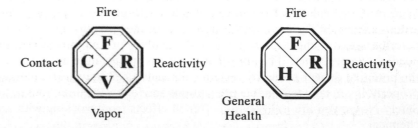

You should learn the location of each category on the hazard signs. Moving clockwise from the top, the order is Fire → Reactivity → Vapor → Contact. The *fire* index number in the upper quadrant rates the fire danger posed by the chemical. The *reactivity* index number in the right quadrant

assesses the danger of a violent reaction or explosion. The *vapor* index number in the lower quadrant rates the potential health effect of inhaling the vapors of the chemical. The *contact* index number in the left quadrant rates the adverse health effects that may result from skin contact (the eye-contact hazard, which is not rated, may be even greater in some cases). For some chemicals, the vapor and contact index numbers are replaced by a single *health* index number that represents the overall health hazard of the chemical. If any quadrant is left blank, it means that no hazard index number was reported in the sources consulted; it does *not* mean that no hazard exists.

The meaning of the hazard signs is illustrated by the examples in the margin. Carbon tetrachloride is nonflammable and thermally stable, so its fire and reactivity hazard index numbers are both zero. Inhaling its vapors may be extremely harmful, and there is a moderate risk of injury from skin contact. Carbon tetrachloride has also been identified as a carcinogen in tests using laboratory animals and is suspected of causing cancer in humans. For these reasons, carbon tetrachloride is not used in the experiments in this book. The second hazard sign shows that hexane is very flammable but very stable, and its health risk is comparatively low.

carbon   hexane
tetrachloride

Chemicals with a high fire hazard number should obviously be kept away from ignition sources, including flames, sparks, and hot surfaces. For example, diethyl ether will ignite if it is spilled on a hot plate at a temperature of 160°C or higher.

Chemicals with a high reactivity hazard number should be handled with great care, following any precautions given in the Safety Notes. Such chemicals may ignite or explode if subjected to shock or brought into contact with metal spatulas or materials that may catalyze their decomposition.

The value of a vapor or contact hazard number may suggest the appropriate response to inhalation of or contact with a chemical. If you inhale significant amounts of a chemical's vapor or the dust of a solid chemical, you should go to a window or other area where you can breathe fresh air, unless the chemical's vapor hazard number is zero. If the chemical has a high vapor hazard number, or if inhalation was prolonged, see your instructor to determine whether treatment is required. In case of skin contact with a chemical that has a contact hazard number other than zero, you should wash the area of contact with soap and water. If the chemical has a high contact hazard number, or if the exposure is extensive, see your instructor to determine whether treatment is required. If you get a chemical in your eyes, follow the procedures described under the heading "Eye Injuries" in the previous section on first aid. The higher the chemical's contact hazard number, the more likely it is that eye damage will result without prompt medical treatment.

Chemicals designated as strong oxidants (OX) must not be allowed to contact other chemicals, except for the ones specified in the experimental directions. In fact, you should never mix *any* chemicals together unless directed because mixing incompatible chemicals may result in the generation of toxic gases, fire, or an explosion.

Chemicals that polymerize readily (P) may sometimes undergo spontaneous, rapid polymerization, which generates heat. If this reaction occurs in a capped reagent bottle, it could cause the bottle to shatter violently. Most such chemicals are stabilized by the addition of a small amount of antioxidant or other stabilizer, so they are unlikely to react unless the stabilizer has been removed.

Water-sensitive chemicals (W) react violently and exothermically upon contact with water, often generating toxic fumes. Some water-sensitive chemicals generate toxic fumes even when exposed to moist air. Such chemicals should be kept in tightly closed containers that are opened only for transfers and closed immediately afterward. They should be used under fume hoods at some distance from any source of water.

Carcinogens

A few chemicals used in the experiments are potential *carcinogens*— agents suspected of causing cancer. Such chemicals are identified by the symbol CA in the hazard signs. Although this label certainly should not be disregarded, it is important to recognize that these chemicals present little risk of cancer to students if used as directed. The carcinogenic activity of a compound is generally established by animal tests in which high doses of the chemical are administered by various routes for prolonged periods. For example, phenacetin taken orally has been found to cause cancer in laboratory animals, but it is highly unlikely that anyone will ingest enough phenacetin during a laboratory experiment to incur a risk of cancer. Chromium(VI) compounds have been shown to cause cancer of the lungs, nasal cavity, and sinuses in humans, but most persons at risk are industrial workers who have been continuously exposed to the dust of chromium compounds in the workplace. In this course, you will use chromic acid solutions—prepared from chromium(VI) oxide—a drop or so at a time, so there will be no possibility of inhaling chromium dust.

When handling any potential carcinogen, it is only prudent to take appropriate precautions, such as wearing protective gloves and clothing and working under a hood. Some halogenated hydrocarbons are suspected of causing cancer if inhaled, so avoid breathing the vapors of dichloromethane, chloroform, and other chlorinated solvents. Compounds such as benzene and carbon tetrachloride, which might present a significant risk of cancer under conditions likely to be encountered in an undergraduate laboratory, are not used in this book.

Teratogens

If you are pregnant or think you may be pregnant, inform your instructor before you enter the organic chemistry lab for the first time. Some organic chemicals are known or suspected *teratogens*, meaning that they may harm a developing fetus. As is the case for carcinogens, handling a chemical designated as a teratogen does not necessarily represent a danger to the fetus. Ethanol (ethyl alcohol) is a teratogen when ingested, but people are far more likely to ingest ethanol in a bar, a restaurant, or at home than in a chemistry laboratory. Nevertheless, some chemicals that are routinely used in organic chemistry laboratories may represent a significant danger to a developing fetus. Therefore, it is important to contact your instructor, the laboratory coordinator, or a designated chemical hygiene officer to discuss your options if you are pregnant. The best option may be to take the laboratory course after your child is delivered. If you prefer to remain in the lab course, you should obtain the consent of your physician and then make arrangements with your instructor to minimize your exposure to potential teratogens. Such arrangements might include substituting less hazardous chemicals for teratogenic ones, performing alternative experiments that do not require the use of teratogens, or using gloves, protective clothing, and a hood when handling any teratogenic chemical.

Finding and Using Chemical Safety Information

Some basic hazard information on a number of organic compounds can be found in *The Merck Index* [Bibliography, A11]. More detailed information can be found in the *Sigma-Aldrich-Library of Regulatory and Safety Data* [Bibliography, C4], which compiles safety and regulatory information for more than 20,000 chemicals. Other useful sources of chemical hazard information include *Sax's Dangerous Properties of Industrial Materials* [Bibliography, C5], *Hazards in the Chemical Laboratory* [Bibliography, C6], and *Bretherick's Handbook of Reactive Chemical Hazards* [Bibliography, C8]. You can find hazard information about some common chemicals online at the *NIOSH Pocket Guide to Chemical Hazards* Web site, http://www.cdc.gov/niosh/npg/search.html.

The labels on the containers in which chemicals are originally received must include appropriate hazard warnings, and they may provide additional hazard information along with handling precautions and emergency management procedures. To reduce waste and contamination, chemicals are ordinarily transferred to stock bottles before being used in the chemistry laboratory, but some hazard warnings may be included on the stock-bottle labels.

This lab text includes hazard information and safe-handling procedures for hazardous chemicals used in the experiments. For example, Experiment 29 contains the following Safety Note about sodium borohydride, a reducing agent used in many chemical syntheses.

> Sodium borohydride is toxic and corrosive, and it can react violently with concentrated acids, oxidizing agents, and other substances. Aqueous $NaBH_4$ solutions with pH values below 10.5 have been known to decompose violently, so be sure that your reaction mixture (if aqueous) is sufficiently alkaline. Avoid contact with $NaBH_4$, do not breathe its dust, and keep it away from other chemicals.

The most complete source of information about the hazards associated with any chemical is its *Material Safety Data Sheet (MSDS)*, which is provided by the manufacturer or vendor of the chemical and is usually available on the manufacturer's Web site. The MSDSs for chemicals used in your organic chemistry laboratory should be available from the chemistry department office, the chemical hygiene officer, or some other designated source at your institution.

The MSDS for a chemical must include the following information:

- Identity of the chemical
- Physical properties and relevant chemical characteristics
- Information on potential physical hazards such as fire, explosion, reactivity, and chemical incompatibility
- Health hazards from both short- and long-term exposure
- Toxicology data such as LD_{50} values
- Significant exposure routes such as inhalation, ingestion, or contact
- Exposure limits set by OSHA and other agencies

- Cancer-causing potential
- Precautions for safe handling and storage
- Control measures for preventing accidents, such as the use of personal protection gear
- Emergency procedures in case of accidental exposure

The MSDS for benzoic acid is shown in Figure 1.

```
                          SIGMA-ALDRICH
```

```
                   MATERIAL SAFETY DATA SHEET
                                            Date Printed: 09/08/2006
                                            Date Updated: 01/31/2006
                                            Version   1.12
```

```
Section 1 - Product and Company Information
```

```
Product Name            BENZOIC ACID, >=99.5%, A.C.S. REAGENT
Product Number          242381
Brand                   SIAL

Company                 Sigma - Aldrich
Address                 3050 Spruce Street
                        SAINT LOUIS MO 63103 US
Technical Phone:        800-325-5832
Fax:                    800-325-5052
Emergency Phone:        314-776-6555
```

```
Section 2 - Composition/Information on Ingredient
```

```
Substance Name                    CAS #                    SARA 313
BENZOIC ACID                      65-85-0                  NO

Formula      C7H6O2
Synonyms     Acide benzoique (French) * Acido benzoico
             (Italian * Benzenecarboxylic acid *
             Benzeneformic acid * Benzenemethanoic acid *
             Benzoate * Benzoesaeure (German) * Carboxybenzene
             * Dracylic acid * E 210 * HA 1 (acid) * Kyselina
             benzoova (Czech) * Phenylcarboxylic acid *
             Phenylformic acid * Retarder BA * Retardex *
             Salvo liquid * Salvo powder * Tenn-Plas
RTECS Number:  DG0875000
```

```
Section 3 - Hazards Identification
```

```
EMERGENCY OVERVIEW
   Harmful.
   Harmful if swallowed. Irritating to eyes, respiratory system and
   skin.

HMIS RATING
   HEALTH: 2
   FLAMMABILITY: 1
   REACTIVITY: 0
```

Figure 1 Material Safety Data Sheet for benzoic acid (Reprinted with permission from Aldrich Chemical Co., Inc., Milwaukee, WI)

```
NFPA RATING
   HEALTH: 2
   FLAMMABILITY: 1
   REACTIVITY: 0
```

For additional information on toxicity, please refer to Section 11.

Section 4 - First Aid Measures

ORAL EXPOSURE
   If swallowed, wash out mouth with water provided person is
   conscious. Call a physician.

INHALATION EXPOSURE
   If inhaled, remove to fresh air. If not breathing give
   artificial respiration. If breathing is difficult, give oxygen.

DERMAL EXPOSURE
   In case of skin contact, flush with copious amounts of water for
   at least 15 minutes. Remove contaminated clothing and shoes.
   Call a physician.

EYE EXPOSURE
   In case of contact with eyes, flush with copious amounts of
   water for at least 15 minutes. Assure adequate flushing by
   separating the eyelids with fingers. Call a physician.

Section 5 - Fire Fighting Measures

FLASH POINT
   250 °F   121 °C   Method: closed cup

AUTOIGNITION TEMP
   572 °c

FLAMMABILITY
   N/A

EXTINGUISHING MEDIA
   Suitable: Water spray. Carbon dioxide, dry chemical powder, or
   appropriate foam.

FIREFIGHTING
   Protective Equipment: Wear self-contained breathing apparatus
   and protective clothing to prevent contact with skin and eyes.
   Specific Hazard(s): Emits toxic fumes under fire conditions.

Section 6 - Accidental Release Measures

PROCEDURE TO BE FOLLOWED IN CASE OF LEAK OR SPILL
   Evacuate area.

PROCEDURE(S) OF PERSONAL PRECAUTION(S)
   Wear respirator, chemical safety goggles, rubber boots, and
   heavy rubber gloves.

METHODS FOR CLEANING UP
   Sweep up, place in a bag and hold for waste disposal. Avoid
   raising dust. Ventilate area and wash spill site after material
   pickup is complete.

Figure 1 (*continued*)

Section 7 - Handling and Storage

HANDLING
    User Exposure: Do not breathe dust. Avoid contact with eyes,
    skin, and clothing. Avoid prolonged or repeated exposure.

STORAGE
    Suitable: Keep tightly closed.

Section 8 - Exposure Controls / PPE

ENGINEERING CONTROLS
    Safety shower and eye bath. Mechanical exhaust required.

PERSONAL PROTECTIVE EQUIPMENT
    Respiratory: Use respirators and components tested and approved
    under appropriate government standards such as NIOSH (US) or CEN
    (EU). Where risk assessment shows air-purifying respirators are
    appropriate use a dust mask type N95 (US) or type P1 (EN 143)
    respirator.
    Hand: Compatible chemical-resistant gloves.
    Eye: Chemical safety goggles.

GENERAL HYGIENE MEASURES
    Wash thoroughly after handling.

EXPOSURE LIMITS

Country	Source	Type	Value
USA	ACGIH	TLV	10 mg/m3
Remarks: inhalable particulate			
USA	ACGIH	TLV	3 mg/m3
Remarks: respirable dust in air			
USA	OSHA.	PEL	15 mg/m3
Remarks: total dust			
USA	OSHA.	PEL	5 mg/m3
Remarks: respirable dust			

Section 9 - Physical/Chemical Properties

Appearance	Physical State: Solid
	Color: White
	Form: Fine crystals

Property	Value	At Temperature or Pressure
Molecular Weight	122.12 AMU	
pH	N/A	
BP/BP Range	248.9 °C	760 mmHg
MP/MP Range	121.0 - 125.0 °C	
Freezing Point	N/A	
Vapor Pressure	10 mmHg	132 °C
Vapor Density	4.21 g/l	
Saturated Vapor Conc.	N/A	
SG/Density	1.32 g/cm3	
Bulk Density	N/A	
Odor Threshold	N/A	
Volatile%	N/A	
VOC Content	N/A	
Water Content	N/A	

Figure 1 (*continued*)

```
Solvent Content        N/A
Evaporation Rate       N/A
Viscosity              N/A
Surface Tension        N/A
Partition Coefficient  N/A
Decomposition Temp.    N/A
Flash Point            250 °F 121 °C        Method: closed cup
Explosion Limits       N/A
Flammability           N/A
Autoignition Temp      572 °C
Refractive Index       N/A
Optical Rotation       N/A
Miscellaneous Data     N/A
Solubility             N/A
```

N/A = not available

Section 10 - Stability and Reactivity

STABILITY
    Stable: Stable.
    Materials to Avoid: Strong oxidizing agents, Strong bases, Strong
    reducing agents.

HAZARDOUS DECOMPOSITION PRODUCTS
    Hazardous Decomposition Products: Carbon monoxide, Carbon dioxide.

HAZARDOUS POLYMERIZATION
    Hazardous Polymerization: Will not occur

Section 11 - Toxicological Information

ROUTE OF EXPOSURE
    Skin Contact: May cause skin irritation.
    Skin Absorption: May be harmful if absorbed through the skin.
    Eye Contact: Causes eye irritation.
    Inhalation: Material may be irritating to mucous membranes and
    upper respiratory tract. May be harmful if inhaled.
    Ingestion: Harmful if swallowed.

SIGNS AND SYMPTOMS OF EXPOSURE
    To the best of our knowledge, the chemical, physical, and
    toxicological properties have not been thoroughly investigated.

TOXICITY DATA

    Oral
    Man
    500 mg/kg
    LDLO

    Oral
    Rat
    1700 mg/kg
    LD50

    Inhalation
    Rat

Figure 1 (*continued*)

```
> 26 mg/m3
LC50
Remarks: Sense Organs and Special Senses (Nose, Eye, Ear, and
Taste) : Eye: Lacrimation. Behavioral:Somnolence (general depressed
activity).

Intraperitoneal
Rat
1600 MG/KG
LD50

Intravenous
Rat
1700 MG/KG
LD50

Oral
Mouse
1940 mg/kg
LD50

Remarks: Behavioral:Somnolence (general depressed activity).
Lungs, Thorax, or Respiration:Respiratory depression.
Gastrointestinal:Other changes.

Intraperitoneal
Mouse
1460 MG/KG
LD50

Skin
Rabbit
> 10000 mg/kg
LD50

IRRITATION DATA
   Eyes
   Rabbit
   Remarks: Mild irritation effect

   Skin
   Human
   22 mg
   3D
   I
   Remarks: Moderate irritation effect

   Skin
   Rabbit
   500 mg
   24H
   Remarks: Mild irritation effect

   Eyes
   Rabbit
   100 mg
   Remarks: Severe irritation effect
```

Figure 1 (*continued*)

CHRONIC EXPOSURE - MUTAGEN

    Species: Human
    Dose: 5 MMOL/L
    Cell Type: lymphocyte
    Mutation test: DNA inhibition

Section 12 - Ecological Information

Section 13 - Disposal Considerations

APPROPRIATE METHOD OF DISPOSAL OF SUBSTANCE OR PREPARATION
    Contact a licensed professional waste disposal service to dispose
    of this material. Dissolve or mix the material with a combustible
    solvent and burn in a chemical incinerator equipped with an
    afterburner and scrubber. Observe all federal, state, and local
    environmental regulations.

Section 14 -Transport Information

DOT
    Proper Shipping Name: Environmentally hazardous
    substances, solid, n.o.s.
    UN#: 3077
    Class: 9
    Packing Group: Packing Group III
    Hazard Label: Class 9
    PIH: Not PIH

IATA
    Non-Hazardous for Air Transport: Non-hazardous for air
    transport.

Section 15 - Regulatory Information

EU ADDITIONAL CLASSIFICATION
    Symbol of Danger: Xn
    Indication of Danger: Harmful.
    R: 22—36
    Risk Statements: Harmful if swallowed. Irritating to eyes.
    S: 26
    Safety Statements: In case of contact with eyes, rinse
    immediately with plenty of water and seek medical advice.

US CLASSIFICATION AND LABEL TEXT
    Indication of Danger: Harmful.
    Risk Statements: Harmful if swallowed. Irritating to eyes,
    respiratory system and skin.
    Safety Statements: In case of contact with eyes, rinse
    immediately with plenty of water and seek medical advice.

UNITED STATES REGULATORY INFORMATION
    SARA LISTED: No
    TSCA INVENTORY ITEM: Yes

Figure 1 (*continued*)

CANADA REGULATORY INFORMATION
    WHMIS Classification: This product has been classified in
    accordance with the hazard criteria of the CPR, and the MSDS
    contains all the information required by the CPR.
    DSL: Yes
    NDSL: No

Section 16 - Other Information

DISCLAIMER
    For R&D use only. Not for drug, household or other uses.

WARRANTY
    The above information is believed to be correct but does not
    purport to be all inclusive and shall be used only as a guide. The
    information in this document is based on the present state of our
    knowledge and is applicable to the product with regard to
    appropriate safety precautions. It does not represent any
    guarantee of the properties of the product. Sigma-Aldrich Inc.,
    shall not be held liable for any damage resulting from handling or
    from contact with the above product. See reverse side of invoice
    or packing slip for additional terms and conditions of sale.
    Copyright 2006 Sigma-Aldrich Co. License granted to make unlimited
    paper copies for internal use only.

Figure 1 (*continued*)

Note that section 3, Hazards Identification, includes NFPA hazard ratings of the chemical. Section 8, Exposure Controls, gives Threshhold Limit Values (TLVs) and Permissible Exposure Limits (PELs) in milligrams of the chemical per cubic meter of ambient air. The TLV of a chemical reflects the level that a typical worker can experience without an unreasonable risk of disease or injury when the worker is exposed to the vapor or dust of the chemical for 8 hours a day, 5 days a week. The PEL value is the maximum concentration of a chemical that a worker may be exposed to under OSHA regulations. Section 11, Toxicological Information, gives LD_{50} values for different methods of exposure to a chemical, in which its LD_{50} (lethal dose, 50%) is the amount of the chemical—usually expressed in milligrams per kilogram of body weight—that it takes to kill 50% of a tested group of rats, mice, or other experimental animals.

Chemical manufacturers, for reasons related to legal liability, tend to list every possible mishap that might result from the use of their chemicals, no matter how unlikely. Because MSDSs are intended primarily for chemical and industrial workers, whose exposure to chemicals may be intense and prolonged, the manufacturers often recommend protective apparatus and measures that may not be necessary when chemicals are used in small quantities for short periods of time. This makes it difficult to determine which hazards associated with the chemicals used in a given organic chemistry experiment are truly significant. Nevertheless, the MSDS for a given chemical can be very helpful if the information it provides is used appropriately.

Chemistry and the Environment

chloride or another salt so that it forms a distinct layer, it may be possible to separate the product directly from the aqueous layer in good yield, eliminating the need for an extraction solvent.

Reduce the Energy Requirements of a Reaction.   Some reactions can be carried out in the chemistry lab at a lower temperature, or even at ambient temperature, by using a more reactive reagent or an appropriate catalyst. Other reactants can be carried out in a microwave oven rather than by direct heating. Microwave radiation is an efficient heat source because it can be tuned to heat up some substances (especially water) and not others.

Use Renewable Resources.   Some reactions can be carried out using chemicals derived from plants and other natural materials rather than chemicals synthesized from petroleum products and other nonrenewable resources. For example, aspirin is synthesized commercially from benzene, but in a chemistry lab it can be synthesized from methyl salicylate (the major ingredient in wintergreen oil) using the procedures followed in Experiments 4 and 34. Unfortunately, most methyl salicylate is also synthesized from nonrenewable petroleum products, but wintergreen oil from natural sources such as sweet birch trees can be obtained from various suppliers.

Mastering
the Operations

The experiments in Part I will help you learn the basic laboratory operations of organic chemistry and become proficient in their use. The first time an operation is used in Part I, its number is highlighted in boldface type in the **Operations** list at the beginning of the experiment. The symbol (SS) after an operation's listing means that the operation is used only for the standard scale procedure; (μS) means that it is used only for the microscale procedure. The section titled **Before You Begin** lists some prelab assignments that you must complete before you arrive at the laboratory to start the experiment. If you have standard scale equipment, use the numbers accompanied by (SS) for prelab calculations (if there are any), and follow the directions flagged by a round-bottom flask. If you have microscale equipment, use the numbers accompanied by (μS) for prelab calculations, and follow the directions flagged by a conical vial. Any directions flagged by both a round-bottom flask and a conical vial can be used with either kind of equipment.

PART I

Learning Basic Operations
The Effect of pH
on a Food Preservative

EXPERIMENT 1

Laboratory Orientation. Acid–Base Reactions. Reaction Stoichiometry.

Operations

OP-1   Cleaning and Drying Glassware
OP-4   Weighing
OP-5   Measuring Volume
OP-6   Making Transfers
OP-16   Vacuum Filtration
OP-26   Washing and Drying Solids

Before You Begin

1. Read the Introduction and the "Laboratory Safety" section of this book.
2. Read the experiment carefully, particularly the section titled "Understanding the Experiment" and the Directions.
3. Read the sections in Part V describing operations OP-l, OP-4, OP-5, OP-6, OP-16, and OP-26. Most of the descriptions are quite brief.
4. If you are required to write up your experiments in a formal laboratory notebook, prepare the notebook as directed by your instructor after reading Appendix II.

Scenario

For this and the other experiments in this book, you will play the role of a consultant in a Consulting Chemists Institute operated by your college or university, with your instructor serving as the laboratory supervisor and the other students in your lab section as members of your project group. Most of the Scenarios in this book describe purely hypothetical situations. Except where otherwise indicated, any similarity between a person or organization named herein and an actual person or organization is coincidental.

Fresh Foods Incorporated (FFI) is a small, family-owned chemical company that manufactures sodium benzoate and other food preservatives for sale to food processors. One of its competitors has launched an ad campaign claiming that FFI's sodium benzoate changes to a different chemical in the stomach, implying that the chemical may be harmful or ineffective. D. K. Little, FFI's marketing director, has asked your institute to find out whether the competitor's claim is valid. Your assignment is to place sodium benzoate into a medium that simulates stomach acid, which is an aqueous hydrochloric acid solution with a pH range of 1–3, to see whether or not a new substance forms in that environment. Since this is your first day on the job, your supervisor will show you around the laboratory and help you develop some basic lab skills involving measurements of mass and volume.

Applying Scientific Methodology

Read "Scientific Methodology" in the Introduction before you read this section.

As in the other experiments in this book, the scientific *problem* to be solved is described in the Scenario. In this experiment the fundamental problem, stated as a question, is "Does a new substance form when sodium benzoate is placed into a simulated stomach acid?" After reading the experiment thoroughly, you should be ready to formulate a *working hypothesis* such as "A new substance will (or will not) form when sodium benzoate is placed into a simulated stomach acid." Your *course of action*, described in detail in the Directions, is then fairly obvious: You will have to place some sodium benzoate in an aqueous solution of hydrochloric acid that has a pH in the range of 1–3. You can do this by dissolving the sodium benzoate in water and adding enough dilute hydrochloric acid (aqueous HCl) to lower the pH to about 2. During this process, you will have to *gather evidence* about whether or not a chemical reaction has occurred. Evidence for a chemical reaction may include a color change, formation of a gas, formation of a precipitate, evolution of heat, or any combination of these. As you *evaluate the evidence* (i.e., think about what you've observed), you may decide to stay with your working hypothesis (if the evidence supports it), modify it, or discard it and formulate a new one. You then should be able to *arrive at a conclusion* based on the experimental evidence and any clues you came across while reading the experiment. You will *report your results* after referring to the "Report" section that follows the Directions.

Sodium Benzoate as a Food Preservative

When resin from the Sumatran tree *Styrax benzoin* is heated to 100°C, white vapors rise and condense to form needlelike crystals of benzoic acid, which was named for the tree and its resin, gum benzoin. Benzoic acid can easily be converted to its salt, sodium benzoate, which is used widely as a food preservative, particularly in acidic foods such as fruits and fruit juices. Benzoic acid is so widely distributed in plants that the urine of all plant-eating animals (including humans) contains hippuric acid, a compound synthesized in the kidneys by the combination of benzoic acid with the amino acid glycine. Significant amounts of benzoic acid can be isolated from such diverse natural sources as anise seed, cranberries, prunes, cherry bark, cloves, and the scent glands of the beaver. In cranberries and other plant products, benzoic acid is a natural preservative that inhibits the growth of bacteria, yeasts, and molds, and thus retards spoilage.

If you read the labels on cans and bottles in a grocery store, you will find sodium benzoate (sometimes called benzoate of soda) listed on many of them. Sodium benzoate is used as a preservative in such food products as jams and jellies, soft drinks, fruit juices, pickles, condiments, margarine, and canned and frozen seafood, and even in such nonfood items as toothpaste and tobacco. Benzoic acid is also an effective food preservative, but sodium benzoate is a more popular food additive because it is much more soluble in water than is benzoic acid, making it easier to blend into water-containing food products.

A hexagon with a circle in it represents a benzene ring, whose molecular formula in these compounds is C_6H_5.

benzoic acid   sodium benzoate

hippuric acid   glycine

Understanding the Experiment

This experiment will help you become familiar with the laboratory environment and with some fundamental laboratory operations, such as measuring mass and volume, separating solids from liquids by vacuum filtration, and drying solids.

In part **A**, you will add hydrochloric acid to a solution of sodium benzoate and, if a different substance forms, recover it and measure its mass. This is a "green" reaction because the only solvent used is water and the only by-product is nontoxic sodium chloride. Although concentrated hydrochloric acid is quite hazardous, the dilute solution of HCl used here is relatively nontoxic and safe to handle.

To understand what is happening in the reaction, you need to know something about the properties of the substances involved and remember what you have previously learned about acid-base chemistry and stoichiometry. When sodium benzoate dissolves in water, it dissociates into benzoate ions (which are weakly basic) and sodium ions, according to the reaction equation:

$$C_6H_5COONa \longrightarrow C_6H_5COO^- + Na^+$$
$$\text{benzoate ion}$$

Hydrochloric acid is a solution of hydrogen chloride (HCl) in water. The strongest acid present in this solution is the hydronium ion, formed by the transfer of a proton from an HCl molecule to a water molecule.

$$HCl + H_2O \longrightarrow Cl^- + H_3O^+$$
$$\text{hydronium ion}$$

Key Concept: In a Lowry-Brønsted acid-base reaction under standard conditions, the stronger acid transfers protons to a stronger base to yield a weaker acid and a weaker base.

If the hydronium ion concentration is high enough, protons will be transferred from the strong acid H_3O^+ to the basic benzoate ions. This will yield benzoic acid, which, being quite insoluble in water (sodium benzoate is about 200 times more soluble), should precipitate from solution. The reaction is

$$C_6H_5COO^- + H_3O^+ \longrightarrow C_6H_5COOH + H_2O \quad \quad \textbf{(1)}$$
$$\text{benzoic acid}$$

The net reaction is the sum of these three reaction steps.

$$C_6H_5COONa + HCl \longrightarrow C_6H_5COOH + NaCl \quad \quad \textbf{(2)}$$

Stop and Think: What is the relationship between hydronium ion concentration and pH?

The hydronium ion concentration depends on the pH of the solution; the lower the pH, the higher $[H_3O^+]$ will be. By carrying out the experiment, you will discover whether or not the pH of stomach acid is low enough to cause the conversion of sodium benzoate to benzoic acid.

In any experiment that involves the conversion of one substance to another, it is important to understand the stoichiometry of the reaction. (Read Appendix IV if you need a review of stoichiometric calculations.) Equation **2** shows that, if the reaction were complete at the pH used, a mole of benzoic acid would be formed for each mole of sodium benzoate in the reaction mixture. If you are following the standard scale procedure, you will start with about 2.00 g of sodium benzoate, which is 13.9 mmol (0.0139 mol), so the theoretical yield of benzoic acid (if any forms) should be 13.9 mmol, which corresponds to a mass of 1.70 g. For the microscale procedure, the corresponding amounts are 0.400 g (2.78 mmol) of sodium benzoate and 0.339 g of benzoic acid. Keep in mind that you will probably not measure out *exactly* the mass of sodium benzoate specified, in which case you will need to calculate the theoretical yield (to the appropriate number of significant figures) based on your measured mass of sodium benzoate.

Whether or not your yield approaches the theoretical value will depend on a number of factors, including the following:

- You may make errors in measuring mass or volume.
- The proposed reaction may not occur or, if it does, it may not be complete.
- Some of the product may remain dissolved in the reaction mixture and may not be recovered.
- You may lose some product while transferring it from one vessel to another.

Always try to minimize your losses by taking great pains to perform accurate measurements and to make nearly *quantitative transfers*; that is, to scrape or rinse the last traces of product from its container and from anything (such as a stirring rod or a spatula) that comes into contact with it. Making efficient transfers is particularly important for a microscale experiment; losing 20 mg of product from a standard scale experiment designed to yield 4.0 g of product represents a loss of only 0.5%, but losing the same amount from a microscale experiment designed to yield 0.20 g of product will result in a 10% loss. Although you can't possibly scrape the last molecule of product from one vessel to another, you should try to transfer virtually all of the product that is visible to the naked eye. Get into the habit of doing the kind of careful, meticulous work that will increase your yields and save you time and effort in the long run.

The product of a chemical preparation should always be dried to *constant mass*, meaning that its mass after drying should not change significantly between two successive weighings. For most preparations in this book, you can assume that a product is sufficiently dry if—following the initial drying period—its mass does not decrease by more than 0.5% after an additional five minutes of oven drying. If the product is being dried at room temperature in a desiccator, the interval between weighings should be longer.

In part **B**, you will determine the density of an unknown liquid by using a graphical method. The validity of your results will depend on the care you take in measuring the mass and volume of the liquid and in graphing your results.

Laboratory Safety and Orientation

Before coming to lab, you should have read the Introduction, which includes a section entitled "A Guide to Success in the Organic Chemistry Lab," and the "Laboratory Safety" section of this book. Before you begin to work in the laboratory, your instructor will review the safety rules and tell you what safety supplies you must have, such as safety goggles and protective gloves and aprons. During the first laboratory period, the instructor will show you where safety equipment is located and tell you how to use it. You should also learn the locations of chemicals, consumable supplies (such as filter paper and boiling chips), waste containers, and various items of equipment such as balances and drying ovens. Obtain a locker and a supply list and check into the laboratory as directed by your instructor. You will find illustrations of typical locker supplies in Appendix I at the back of this book. If necessary, clean up (see OP-1) any dirty glassware and replace any damaged glassware in your locker at this time (see Figure 1.1).

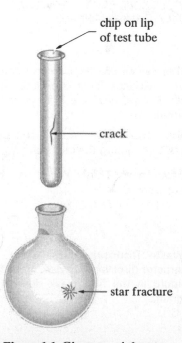

Figure 1.1 Glassware defects

Reactions and Properties

O
‖
CO⁻Na⁺

+ HCl ⟶

O
‖
COH

+ NaCl

Table 1.1 Physical properties

	mol wt	mp	Water solubility
benzoic acid	122.1	122	0.34
sodium benzoate	144.1	—	61.2

Note: mol wt = molecular weight; melting points (mp) are in °C; solubilities are in grams of solute per 100 mL of water at room temperature (usually 25°C).

DIRECTIONS

Your instructor should demonstrate the operation of balances, automatic pipets, and any other special equipment you will use during this experiment.

A. *The Effect of pH on Sodium Benzoate*

Safety Notes

> Sodium benzoate and benzoic acid are mild irritants. Do not get them in your eyes or on your skin or clothing.

Standard Scale

Reaction. Weigh [OP-4] approximately 2.00 g of sodium benzoate to the maximum accuracy of your balance, and transfer [OP-6] it quantitatively to a 30-mL (or larger) beaker. Measure [OP-5] 10 mL of water with a graduated cylinder, pour it into the beaker, and stir with a glass rod until the sodium benzoate dissolves. Measure 5.0 mL of 3 *M* hydrochloric acid and add it slowly, while stirring, to the sodium benzoate solution until you have added about 4.0 mL. Then, while stirring, add more 3 *M* HCl drop by drop—testing the solution frequently with pH paper—until its pH is 2. To test the pH, use your stirring rod to transfer a drop of the supernatant liquid (liquid near the surface) to a strip of pH paper. Adding a little excess HCl will do no harm. Cool the solution to 10°C or below by setting the 30-mL beaker in a larger beaker containing cracked ice and a small amount of tap water.

When "water" is specified in a procedure, use distilled or deionized water unless otherwise indicated.

Observe and Note: Can you detect any evidence for a chemical reaction? If so, describe it in your lab notebook.

Stop and Think: What is the purpose of cooling the solution?

Stop and Think: What is the substance?

Separation. If a new substance has formed, separate it from the reaction mixture by vacuum filtration [OP-16]. Use about 5 mL of ice-cold water to transfer any solid that adheres to the walls of the beaker, and wash the solid on the filter [OP-26a]. Let the solid air-dry on the filter for a few minutes with the vacuum turned on, then dry [OP-26b] it to constant mass. If an oven is used for drying, its temperature should be 90°C or lower because the solid may sublime above that temperature. Weigh [OP-4] the dry product in a tared (preweighed) vial. Label the vial with the experiment number, the name of the product, its mass, your name, the current date, and any other information required by your instructor. Unless your instructor indicates otherwise, always turn in your product

Waste Disposal: Unless your instructor directs otherwise, wash the liquid in the filter flask down the drain.

when you finish an experiment. If you don't, you may not get credit for the experiment.

Microscale

Reaction.   Obtain a short ($5\frac{3}{4}$-inch) Pasteur pipet, attach a latex rubber bulb to it, and calibrate the pipet as described in OP-5. Weigh [OP-4] approximately 0.400 g of sodium benzoate to the maximum accuracy of your balance, and transfer [OP-6] it quantitatively to a 5-mL conical reaction vial. Measure [OP-5] 3 mL of water into the vial, and stir with a thin glass stirring rod until the sodium benzoate dissolves. Measure [OP-5] 1.0 mL of 3 M hydrochloric acid with your calibrated Pasteur pipet and transfer [OP-6] it slowly, while stirring, to the vial until you have added about 0.8 mL. Then, while stirring, add more 3 M HCl drop by drop—testing the solution frequently with pH paper—until its pH is 2. To test the pH, use your stirring rod or the closed end of a capillary melting-point tube to transfer a small drop of the supernatant liquid (liquid near the surface) to a strip of pH paper. Adding a little excess HCl will do no harm. Cool the solution for five minutes or more by setting the reaction vial in a small beaker containing cracked ice and a small amount of tap water. To keep the vial from tipping over, attach an air condenser to it and clamp the condenser to a ring stand.

Separation.   If a new substance has formed, separate it from the reaction mixture by vacuum filtration [OP-16] with a Hirsch funnel. Use about 1 mL of ice-cold water to transfer any solid that adheres to the walls of the vial, and wash the solid on the filter [OP-26a]. Let the solid air dry on the filter for a few minutes with the vacuum turned on, then dry [OP-26b] it to constant mass. If an oven is used for drying, its temperature should be 90°C or lower, because the solid may sublime above that temperature. Weigh [OP-4] the dry product in a tared (preweighed) 1-dram screw-cap vial. Label the vial with the experiment number, the name of the product, its mass, your name, the current date, and any other information required by your instructor. Unless your instructor indicates otherwise, *always* turn in your product when you finish an experiment. If you don't, you may not get credit for the experiment.

B. *Measuring the Density of an Unknown Liquid*

> **The unknown liquid may be harmful if inhaled or absorbed through the skin. Avoid contact with the liquid and do not breathe its vapors.**

Standard Scale and Microscale

At your instructor's request, first measure the density of room-temperature water by the procedure described here. If your measured density is not within 2% of the expected density of water (~0.997 g/mL at room temperature), repeat the measurement.

Have ready two clean, dry, 1-dram screw-cap vials. Use a measuring pipet or a bottle-top dispenser to measure [OP-5] about 1.1 mL of the unknown liquid into one of the vials, and take both vials to a balance. Weigh [OP-4] the

When "water" is specified in a procedure, always use distilled or deionized water unless otherwise indicated.

Observe and Note: Can you detect any evidence of a chemical reaction? If so, describe it in your lab notebook.

Stop and Think: What is the purpose of cooling the solution?

Stop and Think: What is the substance?

Waste Disposal: Unless your instructor directs otherwise, wash the liquid in the filter flask down the drain.

Safety Notes

Take Care! Avoid contact with the liquid and do not breathe its vapors.

empty vial and its cap to the nearest milligram (0.001 g), and record the mass. (Alternatively, zero the balance with the empty capped vial and record the mass of the liquid directly.) If one is available, use an automatic pipet set at 200 μL (0.200 mL) to measure the volume [OP-5] of the liquid; otherwise, use a 1-mL measuring pipet. (Don't try to adjust the automatic pipet! If it doesn't read 200 μL, see your instructor.) Use the pipet to accurately measure 0.200 mL of the liquid into the empty vial, cap it immediately, and record the mass. Without delay, measure an additional 0.200-mL portion of the liquid into the vial, cap it, and again record the mass. Repeat this process until you have added a total of five 0.200-mL portions. Use the same balance for all readings.

Prepare a graph of your data, plotting cumulative volume on the x-axis and cumulative mass (of the liquid only) on the y-axis. Draw the best straight line through the data points. From the slope of the graph, calculate the density of the liquid to three decimal places. Show your graph and your calculated density to your instructor; if either is unacceptable, you may be asked to repeat your measurements or redraw your graph.

Waste Disposal: Put the liquid in a solvent recovery container as directed by your instructor.

The cumulative volume (or mass) is the total volume (or mass) added up to a particular time; for example, after three additions the cumulative volume is 3 × 0.200 mL, or 0.600 mL.

Stop and Think: What is the relationship between the slope of your graph and the density? Does your calculated density make sense physically?

Cleanup Routine.   After completing this and all subsequent experiments, you should:

- Clean [OP-1] the glassware you used during the experiment.
- Clear off your work area, wipe the bench top with a sponge or wet towel, and remove any refuse or equipment from the sink.
- Turn in any items you may have checked out of the stockroom, and return any community supplies to their proper locations.
- Turn in your labeled product to the instructor, when applicable.
- See that all the items on the locker list are safely inside your locker (you may have to pay for missing supplies), then lock it.

Report.   Read Appendix III before your write your report. (Your instructor may ask you to write up your results as if you were submitting them to D. K. Little of Fresh Foods Incorporated.) Unless your instructor directs otherwise, you should do the following for this and all subsequent reports:

- State any scientific problem posed in the Scenario in your own words, and write down your working hypothesis (or hypotheses).
- Report and interpret the relevant evidence, which may include observations, lists or tables of numerical data, and so forth.
- State your conclusion, and tell how the evidence supports it.

For a synthesis, as in part **A** of this experiment, calculate the theoretical yield of the product based on the measured mass of the reactant, and the percent yield of your preparation. For part **B** of this experiment, include the density of your unknown liquid, a table showing your data, and your graph. Follow your instructor's directions regarding other items from Appendix III to include in your report.

Exercises

1. You can confirm that a substance has been converted to a different substance by showing that the substances have different properties. Your observations should have revealed a difference in at least one property

of sodium benzoate and benzoic acid. What property was that, and what observation revealed the difference?

2. Label the stronger acid, stronger base, weaker acid, and weaker base in Equation **1** for the proton transfer reaction in part **A** of the experiment.

3. (a) Based on information in the "Chemistry and the Environment" section, calculate the atom economy and reaction efficiency of the reaction you carried out in part **A**. (b) Describe some green features of your synthesis, and any that aren't so green.

4. When you lower the pH of a solution containing aqueous sodium benzoate, a precipitate eventually forms. (a) What will happen if you then raise the pH by adding aqueous NaOH? Why will this happen? (b) Write a balanced equation for the proton-transfer reaction involved and label the stronger acid, stronger base, weaker acid, and weaker base.

5. The water solubilities of oxalic acid and sodium oxalate at room temperature are 10 g/100 mL and 3.7 g/100 mL, respectively. Could you prepare oxalic acid by adding HCl to a solution of sodium oxalate, cooling it to room temperature, and filtering the resulting mixture? Explain why or why not.

6. The equation for a straight line can be written in the form $y = mx + b$, where x and y are variables, m is the slope, and b is the intercept. Write an equation for the straight line you obtained in your graph for part **B**, and show how it yields the equation for density $d = m/v$. (Remember that m in this equation stands for mass, not the slope.)

7. (a) Calculate the ratio of dissolved benzoic acid to benzoate ion that will exist in solution at equilibrium at a pH of 2.00. The acid equilibrium constant (K_a) for benzoic acid is 6.46×10^{-5}. Note that this calculation doesn't account for the benzoic acid that has precipitated from solution, but you can assume that the higher the ratio, the more benzoic acid will precipitate. (b) Carry out the same calculation for a pH of 4.00, and explain why it was important to reduce the pH to below 4 in this experiment.

oxalic acid

sodium oxalate

Other Things You Can Do

(Starred items require your instructor's permission.)

*1. Make a flat-bottomed stirring rod and other useful laboratory items as described in Minilab 1 in Part III of this book.

*2. Try converting some other salts of organic acids, such as sodium salicylate and sodium oxalate, to the corresponding acids. You may need to look up the solubilities of the substances involved to explain your results.

3. To test the preservative effect of sodium benzoate, prepare a solution containing 0.15 g of sodium benzoate in 1 mL of water. Cut an apple into halves and use a brush to apply the solution to *one* of the cut surfaces. Leave the apple halves at room temperature and observe them over a period of several days.

4. Write a short research paper about food additives after consulting such sources as the *Kirk-Othmer Encyclopedia of Chemical Technology* [Bibliography, A8] and appropriate sources listed in section L of the Bibliography.

Extraction and Evaporation
Separating the Components of "Panacetin"

Separation Methods.

Operations

OP-7   Heating
OP-15 Gravity Filtration (SS)
OP-17 Centrifugation (μS)
OP-18 Extraction
OP-19 Evaporation
OP-4   Weighing
OP-5   Measuring Volume
OP-6   Making Transfers
OP-16 Vacuum Filtration
OP-26 Washing and Drying Solids

Before You Begin

Operations used only for a standard scale procedure are indicated by (SS), and operations used only for a microscale procedure are indicated by (μS).

1. Read the experiment carefully.
2. Read operations OP-15 (SS), OP-17 (μS), OP-18, OP-19, and the section titled "Heat Sources" in OP-7. Review the other listed operations as necessary.

Scenario

See Experiment 1 if you don't understand the purpose of the Scenarios.

Your supervisor has been e-mailed the following message from a drug watchdog agency, the Association for Safe Pharmaceuticals (ASP).

Greetings:
   Our roving agent in Southern California, Sam Surf, recently purchased some Panacetin—an analgesic drug preparation—at a drugstore in San Diego. According to the label on the bottle, the Panacetin tablets were manufactured in the United States by a legitimate pharmaceutical company, but Sam detected some discrepancies on the label and flaws in the tablets themselves that made him suspect they might be counterfeit. Such illegal knockoffs of a domestic drug can be manufactured cheaply elsewhere and smuggled into the United States, where they are sold at a big profit margin.
   The label on the bottle lists the ingredients per tablet as aspirin (200 mg), acetaminophen (250 mg), and sucrose (50 mg). Aspirin and acetaminophen are presumably the active ingredients, while sucrose is an inactive ingredient used to make the tablets more palatable to children. But counterfeit drugs may contain less of an active ingredient than claimed, the wrong active ingredient, or no active ingredients at all. We have reason to believe that Panacetin does contain

aspirin, sucrose, and another active component, but we're not sure what that component is or whether the amounts listed on the label are accurate. The unknown component is probably a chemical relative of acetaminophen, either acetanilide or phenacetin. Both of these kill pain as effectively as acetaminophen, so the consumer wouldn't notice their presence in an analgesic drug. But acetanilide and phenacetin are banned in the United States because of their toxicity, and we would like to keep them off the market.

We want your Consulting Chemists Institute to analyze this drug preparation to find out what percentages of aspirin, sucrose, and the unknown component it contains, and whether the unknown is acetanilide or phenacetin. You have two weeks to complete your investigation.

Les Payne, Director of Operations, ASP

Applying Scientific Methodology

The Scenario presents two problems for you to solve in this experiment and the next: (1) Is the composition of Panacetin as stated on the label accurate? (2) What is the identity of the unknown component in Panacetin? You will concentrate on the first problem in this experiment, following the course of action described in the Directions. Because of possible material losses, you must allow some margin for error in deciding whether the percentage composition derived from the label (10% sucrose, 40% aspirin, 50% unknown component) is accurate. If you follow the standard scale procedure, ranges of 8–12% sucrose, 35–45% aspirin, and 45–55% of the unknown component are close enough to indicate that the label is reasonably accurate. If you follow the microscale procedure, acceptable ranges are 6–14% sucrose, 30–50% aspirin, and 40–60% of the unknown component. As in the previous experiment, you should start with a working hypothesis, gather and interpret evidence, change your hypothesis if the evidence doesn't support it, arrive at a conclusion, and report your results.

Painkilling Drugs, from Antifebrin to Tylenol

Analgesic drugs reduce pain; *antipyretic* drugs reduce fever. Some drugs, including aspirin and acetaminophen, do both. Many of the common over-the-counter analgesic–antipyretic drug preparations contain aspirin, acetaminophen, or combinations of these substances with other ingredients. For example, acetaminophen is the active ingredient of Tylenol, and Extra Strength Excedrin contains aspirin, acetaminophen, and caffeine. From their molecular structures, you can see that acetaminophen is chemically related to both acetanilide and phenacetin, whose painkilling effects were discovered late in the nineteenth century.

In 1886, two clinical assistants named Arnold Cahn and Paul Hepp were looking for something that would rid their patients of a particularly unpleasant intestinal worm. The trick was to find a drug that would kill the worm but not the patient, and their method—not a very scientific one—was to test the chemicals in their stockroom until they found one that worked. When they came across an ancient bottle labeled NAPHTHALENE, they tried it out on a patient who had every malady in the book, including worms. It didn't faze the worms, but it reduced the patient's fever dramatically. Before

Some compounds with analgesic–antipyretic properties

naphthalene

NH$_2$

p-aminophenol

OH

NH$_2$

O—CH$_2$CH$_3$ ethyl "masking" ← group

NHCOCH$_3$ acetyl group

OCH$_2$CH$_3$

phenacetin

Synthesis of phenacetin

Cahn and Hepp went out on a limb and endorsed naphthalene as a cure-all for fevers, someone noticed that the white substance in the bottle was nearly odorless. Since naphthalene has a strong mothball-like odor, Hepp suspected that the bottle was mislabeled and sent it to his cousin, a chemist at a nearby dye factory, for analysis. The tests showed that the new drug was not naphthalene at all, but acetanilide.

Acetanilide proved to have painkilling as well as fever-reducing properties and was soon being marketed under the proprietary name Antifebrin. Unfortunately, some patients who used Antifebrin developed a serious form of anemia called methemoglobinemia, in which hemoglobin molecules are altered in a way that reduces their ability to transport oxygen through the bloodstream. Even though Antifebrin is now considered too toxic for medicinal use, its discovery did much to stimulate the development of safer and more effective analgesic–antipyretic drugs.

About six months after the discovery of Antifebrin, a similar drug was developed as the result of a storage problem. Carl Duisberg, director of research for the Friedrich Bayer Company, had to get rid of 50 tons of *para*-aminophenol—a seemingly useless yellow powder that was a by-product of dye manufacturing. Rather than pay a teamster to haul the stuff away, Duisberg decided to change it into something Bayer could sell. After reading about Antifebrin, he reasoned that a compound with a similar molecular structure might have similar therapeutic uses. Duisberg knew that a hydroxyl (OH) group attached to a benzene ring is characteristic of many toxic substances (for example, phenol), so he decided to "mask" the hydroxyl group in *para*-aminophenol with an ethyl (CH$_3$CH$_2$—) group, as shown in the margin. Incorporation of an acetyl (CH$_3$CO—) group then yielded phenacetin, which proved to be a remarkably effective and inexpensive analgesic–antipyretic drug. Until recently, phenacetin was used in APC tablets (which contained aspirin, phenacetin, and caffeine) and in other analgesic–antipyretic drug preparations. It is no longer approved for medicinal use in the United States because it may cause kidney damage, hemolytic anemia, or even cancer in some patients.

Ironically, the substance Duisberg would have obtained had he not masked the hydroxyl group is acetaminophen, which has proven to be a safer drug than either acetanilide or phenacetin. In the body, acetanilide and phenacetin are both converted to acetaminophen, which is believed to be the active form of all three drugs.

Understanding the Experiment

Most natural products and many commercial preparations are mixtures that contain a number of different substances. To obtain a pure compound from such a mixture, the desired compound is separated from the other components of the mixture by taking advantage of differences in physical and chemical properties. For example, substances with very different solubilities in a given solvent may be separated by extraction or filtration, and liquids with different boiling points can be separated by distillation. Acidic or basic substances are often converted to water-soluble salts, which can then be separated from the water-insoluble components of a mixture.

In this experiment, you will separate the components of a simulated pharmaceutical preparation, Panacetin, making use of their solubilities and

Key Concept: *The separation of substances from one another is based on differences in their physical and chemical properties.*

acid-base properties. Panacetin contains aspirin, sucrose, and an unknown component that may be either acetanilide or phenacetin. These substances have the following characteristics:

- Sucrose is insoluble in the organic solvent dichloromethane (CH_2Cl_2, also called methylene chloride).
- Aspirin, acetanilide, and phenacetin are soluble in dichloromethane but relatively insoluble in water.
- Aspirin reacts with bases such as sodium bicarbonate to form a salt, sodium acetylsalicylate, which is insoluble in dichloromethane and soluble in water.
- Acetanilide and phenacetin are not converted to salts by sodium bicarbonate.

Mixing the Panacetin with dichloromethane should therefore dissolve the aspirin and the unknown component, leaving the sucrose behind as an insoluble solid that can be removed by gravity filtration or centrifugation. Aspirin can be removed from the dichloromethane solution by extraction with an aqueous solution of sodium bicarbonate. The base converts aspirin to its sodium salt, as shown in the margin. This salt will migrate from the dichloromethane layer, in which it is insoluble, to the aqueous layer, in which it is soluble. The unknown component will stay behind in the dichloromethane layer. After separation of the layers, aspirin can be recovered by the same method you used in Experiment 1 to prepare benzoic acid from its salt: precipitation from the aqueous layer with hydrochloric acid followed by vacuum filtration. The unknown component can then be isolated by evaporating the solvent from the dichloromethane solution.

This separation process is summarized by the following flow diagram:

*A **Greener Way:** Diethyl ether is less harmful to health and the environment than is dichloromethane, so it can be used as the solvent in place of dichloromethane. Just remember that an ether layer separates above an aqueous layer rather than below it. If you use dichloromethane, it is best to evaporate the organic layer under vacuum and recover the solvent, which can then be recycled.*

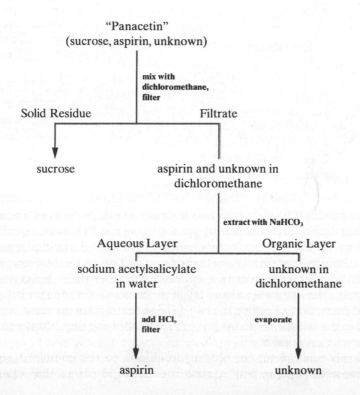

aspirin   sodium
                           acetylsalicylate

Minilab 2 in Part III will help you understand how the extraction operation works; you can carry out this minilab at your instructor's request.

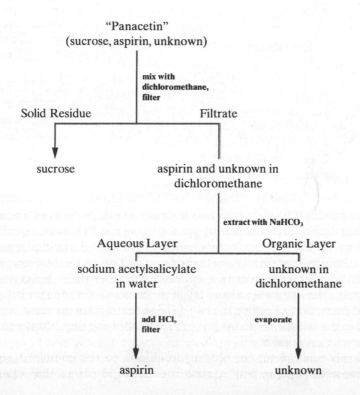

You can estimate the percentage composition of Panacetin from the masses of the dried components. Note that the actual composition may or may not be the same as the composition given in the Scenario. Careful work is required to obtain accurate results in this experiment; errors can arise from incomplete mixing with dichloromethane, incomplete extraction or precipitation of aspirin, incomplete drying of the recovered components, and losses in transferring substances from one container to another.

Dichloromethane may be harmful to the environment, especially when released into groundwater. The Environmental Protection Agency (EPA) classifies it as a priority pollutant and has established a maximum contaminant level (MCL) of 5 parts per billion (ppb) for its concentration in drinking water. See the "Chemistry and the Environment" section for information about priority pollutants, MCLs, and other environmental topics.

DIRECTIONS

Dichloromethane may be harmful if ingested, inhaled, or absorbed through the skin. There is a possibility that prolonged inhalation of dichloromethane may cause cancer.
Minimize contact with the liquid, and do not breathe its vapors.

See "Chemical Hazards" in the "Laboratory Safety" section for an explanation of the hazard symbols.

 ## Standard Scale

Separation of Sucrose. Accurately weigh [OP-4] about 3.00 g of Panacetin and transfer it to a clean, *dry* 125-mL Erlenmeyer flask. Add 50 mL of dichloromethane to the flask. Stir the mixture thoroughly with a glass stirring rod to dissolve as much solid as possible, and use the rod to break up any lumps or granules. Using a preweighed fluted filter paper, filter the mixture by gravity [OP-15] into a small flask, saving the filtrate (the liquid that goes through the filter paper) for the next step. Set the filter paper aside, being careful not to lose any of the sucrose, and reweigh it when it is completely dry. Record the mass of the sucrose in your laboratory notebook. If requested, submit the sucrose to your instructor in a tared (preweighed) and labeled vial.

Separation of Aspirin. Transfer [OP-6] the filtrate to a separatory funnel and extract [OP-18] it with two *separate* 30-mL portions of 5% sodium bicarbonate. For each extraction, use a stirring rod to stir the liquid layers until any fizzing subsides before you stopper and shake the separatory funnel. Because the dichloromethane layer will be on the bottom, you will have to transfer each layer to a different container (label the containers) and return the dichloromethane layer to the separatory funnel before the second extraction. Combine the two aqueous extracts in the same container and save the dichloromethane layer for the following step, "Isolation of the Unknown Component."

Slowly add 7.0 mL of 6 *M* hydrochloric to the combined aqueous extracts while stirring with a glass rod. Test the pH of the solution as

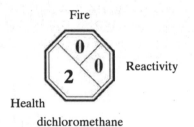

described in Experiment 1, and add more acid, if necessary, to bring the pH down to 2 or lower. Cool the mixture in an ice/water bath for at least 10 minutes, collect the aspirin by vacuum filtration [OP-16], and wash it on the filter [OP-26a] with cold water. Let the aspirin dry on the filter for a few minutes with the aspirator running, then dry [OP-26b] it to constant mass. Weigh the aspirin and record its mass in your lab notebook. Submit the aspirin to your instructor in a vial labeled as described in Experiment 1.

Isolation of the Unknown Component.   Use a filter flask attached to a trap and aspirator to evaporate [OP-19] the solvent from the dichloromethane solution. Heating and swirling the solution over a steam bath or in a hot-water bath [OP-7] will increase the evaporation rate. Cool the trap in a beaker of ice water to recover the dichloromethane. Discontinue evaporation when only a solid residue remains in the flask or when no more solvent evaporates. Transfer the unknown component to a tared vial and let it dry [OP-26b] to constant mass. Weigh it before you begin Experiment 3. Calculate your percent recovery, dividing the sum of the masses of all components by the mass of Panacetin that you started with. Calculate the approximate percentage composition of Panacetin, based on the total mass of components recovered. (These percentages should add up to 100%.) In your report, be sure to include the information specified in the "Report" section of Experiment 1 and any other information requested by your instructor.

Microscale

Separation of Sucrose.   Accurately weigh [OP-4] about 0.400 g of Panacetin and transfer it to a clean, *dry* 15-mL screw-cap centrifuge tube (tube **A**) that has been tared (preweighed). Measure [OP-5] 8.0 mL of dichloromethane into the centrifuge tube. Dissolve as much solid as possible in this solvent by shaking it vigorously for a minute or so. If necessary, use the pointed end of a flat-bladed microspatula to break up any solid lodged in the tip. Balancing the centrifuge tube against one of equal mass, centrifuge [OP-17] the mixture for at least three minutes. Next, transfer [OP-6] the liquid to a second screw-cap centrifuge tube (tube **B**), leaving all of the solid behind. Leave centrifuge tube **A** (uncapped) under a fume hood until you have finished the rest of the experiment, to allow any traces of dichloromethane to evaporate. Then weigh it and calculate the mass of the sucrose it contains. Record the mass of the sucrose in your laboratory notebook. If requested, submit the sucrose to your instructor in a tared and labeled vial.

Separation of Aspirin.   Extract [OP-18] the dichloromethane in centrifuge tube **B** with two *separate* 4-mL portions of 5% sodium bicarbonate. For each extraction, use a stirring rod to stir the liquid layers until any fizzing subsides before you stopper and shake the centrifuge tube. After the first extraction, transfer [OP-6] the bottom (dichloromethane) layer to a labeled 20-mL beaker, transfer the top (aqueous) layer to a second small beaker, and return the bottom layer to the centrifuge tube without delay. After the second extraction, transfer the dichloromethane layer to a tared 4-dram screw-cap vial, and combine the second aqueous layer

Waste Disposal: Unless your instructor directs otherwise, wash the filtrate down the drain.

If it is quite impure, the unknown may remain liquid after all of the solvent is removed. It should solidify upon cooling.

Waste Disposal: Put the recovered dichloromethane in a designated chlorinated solvent recovery container.

Take Care! Avoid contact with dichloromethane; do not breathe its vapors.

Stop and Think: Does all of the solid dissolve? If not, why not?

Stop and Think: What components of Panacetin are in the transferred liquid?

Take Care! A gas is evolved, so don't shake too vigorously.

Stop and Think: Which component of Panacetin is in the aqueous layer? In the dichloromethane layer? If you don't shake the centrifuge tube long enough, how might that affect your results?

Observe and Note: Can you detect any evidence for a chemical reaction upon adding HCl? If so, describe it in your lab notebook.

Waste Disposal: Unless your instructor directs otherwise, wash the filtrate down the drain.

A Greener Way: You can recover the dichloromethane by evaporating it under vacuum using a cold trap (see OP-16) and placing it in an appropriate waste container.

If it is quite impure, the unknown may remain liquid after all of the solvent is removed. It should solidify upon cooling.

with the first one. Save the dichloromethane solution in the vial for the following step, "Isolation of the Unknown Component."

Slowly add 1.0 mL of 6 *M* hydrochloric acid to the combined aqueous extracts while stirring with a glass rod. Test the pH of the solution with pH paper as described in Experiment 1, and add more acid, if necessary, to bring the pH to 2 or lower. Cool the mixture in an ice/water bath for at least five minutes, collect the aspirin by vacuum filtration [OP-16] with a Hirsch funnel, and wash it on the filter [OP-26a] with cold water. Let the aspirin dry on the filter for a few minutes with the aspirator running, then dry [OP-26b] it to constant mass. Weigh the aspirin and record its mass in your lab notebook. Submit the aspirin to your instructor in a vial labeled as described in Experiment 1.

Isolation of the Unknown Component. *Under the hood,* evaporate [OP-19] the solvent from the dichloromethane solution while heating [OP-7] it in a warm water bath. Discontinue evaporation when only a solid residue remains in the vial or when no more solvent evaporates. Let the unknown component dry [OP-26b] to constant mass. Weigh it before you begin Experiment 3.

Calculate your percent recovery, dividing the sum of the masses of all components by the mass of Panacetin that you started with. Calculate the approximate percentage composition of Panacetin, based on the total mass of components recovered. (These percentages should add up to 100%.) In your report, be sure to include the information specified in the "Report" section of Experiment 1 and any other information requested by your instructor.

Exercises

1. (a) Describe any evidence that a chemical reaction occurred when you added 6 *M* HCl to the solution of sodium acetylsalicylate. (b) Explain why the changes that you observed took place.
2. Describe and explain the possible effect on your results of the following experimental errors or variations. In each case, specify the component(s) whose percentage(s) would be too high or too low. (a) After adding dichloromethane to Panacetin, you didn't stir or shake the mixture long enough. (b) During the $NaHCO_3$ extraction, you failed to mix the aqueous and organic layers thoroughly. (c) You mistakenly extracted the dichloromethane solution with 5% HCl rather than 5% $NaHCO_3$. (d) Instead of using pH paper, you neutralized the $NaHCO_3$ solution to pH 7 using litmus paper.
3. Although acetanilide and phenacetin are not appreciably acidic, acetaminophen (like aspirin) is a stronger acid than water. What problem would you encounter if the unknown component were acetaminophen rather than acetanilide or phenacetin, and you extracted the aspirin with 5% NaOH? Explain, giving equations for any relevant reactions.
4. Acetaminophen is a weaker acid than carbonic acid (H_2CO_3), but aspirin is a stronger acid than carbonic acid. Prepare a flow diagram, like the one in this experiment, showing a procedure for separating a mixture of sucrose, aspirin, and acetaminophen.

5. Write balanced reaction equations for the reactions involved (a) when aspirin dissolves in aqueous $NaHCO_3$, and (b) when aspirin is precipitated from a sodium acetylsalicylate solution by HCl. Assuming that both reactions are spontaneous under standard conditions, label the stronger acid, stronger base, weaker acid, and weaker base in each equation.

Other Things You Can Do

(Starred items require your instructor's permission.)

*1. Carry out Minilab 2 in Part III to help you visualize what happens during an extraction.
2. Write a short research paper about the chemistry and physiological effects of analgesic–antipyretic drugs using such sources as the *Kirk–Othmer Encyclopedia of Chemical Technology* [Bibliography, A8] and titles from section L of the Bibliography.

Recrystallization and Melting-Point Measurement
Identifying a Constituent of "Panacetin"

Purification Methods.

Operations

OP-28 Recrystallization
OP-33 Melting Point
OP-4   Weighing
OP-7   Heating
OP-16 Vacuum Filtration
OP-26 Washing and Drying Solids

Before You Begin

1. Read the experiment and operations OP-28 and OP-33. Review the other operations as necessary.
2. Read "Using the Bibliography" in Appendix VII, and familiarize yourself with the layout of the Bibliography.
3. Calculate the minimum volume of boiling water that will be needed to dissolve all of your unknown compound if it is acetanilide *and* if it is phenacetin (see "Understanding the Experiment").

Scenario

The Scenario for this experiment is given in Experiment 2.

Applying Scientific Methodology

The problem you will be trying to solve in this experiment is "What is the identity of the unknown component of Panacetin?" Your course of action is described in the Directions. During the experiment, you should gather and evaluate evidence that can help you solve the problem. No working hypothesis can be more than a guess, so you might want to wait until you carry out the *Purification* step before you formulate your initial hypothesis. You will then test your hypotheses in the *Analysis* step, which will enable you to reach a conclusion. Keep a careful record of your observations and your interpretation of the evidence so that you will be able to describe them in your report.

Using Chemical Reference Books

Knowing the physical properties of a compound—such as its melting or boiling point, refractive index, and spectral absorption bands—can help you identify the compound and estimate its degree of purity. Whenever a new compound is discovered or synthesized, its physical properties are measured and reported in one or more scientific journals to enable future investigators to identify that compound when they encounter it. Physical properties and other information about the more familiar compounds are reported in chemical handbooks and other reference books. For instance, from its entry in *The Merck Index,* we learn that acetaminophen is known by at least 8 chemical names and 45 proprietary drug names, including Alpiny, Bickiemol, Cetadol, Dial-a-gesic, Enelfa, Finimal, Gelocatil, Homoolan, and so on throughout the alphabet. The same source lists the compound's important physical properties and uses, provides references that describe its preparation from various starting materials, and tells where to find more information about it. For example, *The Merck Index* refers to an evaluation of acetaminophen's effect on the kidneys located on page 1238 of volume 320 (published in 1989) of the *New England Journal of Medicine,* as indicated by the following entry:

This and other general reference books are described under Category A in Appendix VII.

Evaluation of renal effects: D. P. Sandler *et al., N. Engl. J. Med.* **320**, 1238 (1989).

In such citations, the abbreviated journal name is followed by the volume number, the page number on which the article begins, and the year of publication. Currently the preferred convention is to list the abbreviated journal name, the year of publication (in boldface type), the volume number (in italics), and the page number, as illustrated by the following citation to an article in the *Journal of Organic Chemistry.*

| *J. Org. Chem.* | **1994**, | *59*, | 2546 |
| journal abbrev. | year | volume | page |

The full names of scientific periodicals can be found in the *Chemical Abstracts Service Source Index* (*CASSI*) [Bibliography, A5].

Figure 3.1 reproduces the entry for acetanilide from *Lange's Handbook of Chemistry.* This handbook reports that acetanilide has a melting point of 114°C and that it is only slightly soluble in water (aq) at 25°C, dissolving to the extent of 0.56 g per 100 mL of water at that temperature. *The Merck Index* reports that a gram of acetanilide dissolves in about 185 mL of cold (near room temperature) water or 20 mL of boiling water, and that a gram of phenacetin dissolves in 1310 mL of cold water or 82 mL of boiling water. Such entries often tell you what you need to know in order to purify a compound and identify or characterize the pure substance. These and other physical properties of acetanilide and phenacetin are summarized in Table 3.1 (see "Structures and Properties"), in which solubilities from *The Merck Index* are expressed in grams of solute per 100 mL of water.

No.	Name	Formula	Formula weight	Beilstein reference	Density, g/mL	Refractive index	Melting point, °C	Boiling point, °C	Flash point, °C	Solubility in 100 parts solvent
a18	Acetanilide	$CH_3CONHC_6H_5$	135.17	12, 237	1.219_4^{15}		114	304–305	173	0.56 aq^{25}; 25 acet; 29 alc; 2 bz; 27 chl; 5 eth

Figure 3.1 *Lange's Handbook of Chemistry* entry for acetanilide (Reprinted with permission from *Lange's Handbook of Chemistry,* 15th ed., by N. A. Lange, edited by J. A. Dean. Copyright McGraw-Hill, Inc., New York, 1999.)

Understanding the Experiment

In this experiment, you will purify and identify the unknown component of Panacetin from Experiment 2.

No separation is perfect; traces of impurities will always remain in a substance that has been separated from a mixture. Therefore, some kind of purification process is needed to remove them. Solids can be purified by such operations as recrystallization, chromatography, and sublimation; liquids are usually purified by distillation or chromatography. The solubility information from Table 3.1 indicates that both acetaminophen and phenacetin are relatively soluble in boiling water but insoluble in cold water. This suggests that the unknown component can be purified by recrystallization, in which an impure solid dissolves in a hot (usually boiling) solvent and then crystallizes from the cooled solution in a purer form.

Key Concept: The solubilities of most substances decrease as the temperature is lowered.

Based on the mass of unknown that you recovered from Experiment 2, you can estimate the volume of boiling water needed to dissolve that mass of either acetanilide or phenacetin. For example, suppose your unknown is acetanilide, and you recovered 0.18 g of the crude solid using the microscale procedure. Table 3.1 shows that the solubility of acetanilide in boiling water is 5.0 g per 100 mL water, so the volume of boiling water you will need to dissolve it is approximately 3.6 mL.

$$0.18 \text{ g acetanilide} \times \frac{100 \text{ mL water}}{5.0 \text{ g acetanilide}} = 3.6 \text{ mL water}$$

The standard scale procedure requires more solvent; 23.0 mL of water is needed to dissolve 1.15 g of acetanilide.

Phenacetin, which is less soluble in boiling water, will require more water to dissolve. You should begin the recrystallization operation using the smaller volume of water (don't add it all at once; see OP-28), and add more only if your compound doesn't dissolve in that amount of water at its boiling point.

After a compound has been purified, it should be *analyzed* to establish its identity and degree of purity. Although sophisticated instruments such as nuclear magnetic resonance (NMR) spectrometers and mass spectrometers are now used to determine the structures of most newly discovered organic compounds, an operation as simple as a melting-point measurement can help identify a compound whose properties have already been reported in the chemical literature. By itself, the melting point of a compound is not sufficient proof of its identity because thousands of compounds may share the same melting point. But when an unknown compound is thought to be one of a small number of possible compounds, its identity can often be determined by mixing the unknown with an authentic sample of each known compound and measuring the melting points of the mixtures. The use of a *mixture melting point* for identification is based on the fact that the melting point of a pure compound is lowered and its melting-point range broadened when it is combined with a different compound. For example, if your unknown is phenacetin, it should melt sharply near 135°C, and a mixture of the unknown with an authentic sample of phenacetin should have essentially the same melting point. But a 1:1 mixture of phenacetin with acetanilide should melt at a considerably lower temperature over a much broader range.

Key Concept: Impurities lower the melting point of a pure substance.

The melting point of a compound can also give a rough indication of its purity. If your compound melts over a narrow range (1–2°C or less) at a temperature close to the literature value, it is probably quite pure. If its melting-point range is broad and substantially lower than the literature value, it is probably contaminated by water or other impurities.

The only solvent used in this experiment is dihydrogen oxide (H_2O), also known as water. It has been established that H_2O can cause serious injury or death by inhalation (in its liquid state), thermal burns (in its gaseous state), and hypothermia (in its solid state). Nevertheless, H_2O is not officially classified as a hazardous chemical and may be released into the environment.

Structures and Properties

Table 3.1 Physical properties

	mol wt	mp	Solubility, c.w.	Solubility, b.w.
acetanilide	135.2	114	0.54	5.0
phenacetin	179.2	135	0.076	1.22

Note: Melting points are in °C; solubilities are in grams of solute per 100 mL of cold water (c.w.) or boiling water (b.w.).

acetanilide   phenacetin

DIRECTIONS

Acetanilide and phenacetin can irritate the skin and eyes, so minimize contact with your unknown compound.

     ## Standard Scale and Microscale

Purification.   Recrystallize [OP-28] the unknown drug component from Experiment 2 by boiling [OP-7] it with just enough water to dissolve it completely, then letting it cool slowly to room temperature. Use a container (such as a test tube or a small Erlenmeyer flask) that will easily accommodate the largest volume of recrystallization solvent that you calculated. If necessary, induce crystallization by scratching the sides of the container with a glass stirring rod. Then cool the container further in a beaker containing ice and tap water to increase the yield of product. Collect the solid by vacuum filtration [OP-16], and wash it [OP-26a] with a small amount of ice-cold water. Dry [OP-26b] the product to constant mass and weigh [OP-4] it in a tared vial.

Analysis.   Grind a small amount of the dry unknown component to a fine powder on a watch glass using a spatula or a flat-bottomed stirring rod (see OP-3). Divide the solid into four nearly equal portions. Combine portions 1 and 2. Thoroughly mix portion 3 with an approximately equal amount of finely ground acetanilide, and thoroughly mix portion 4 with an approximately equal amount of finely ground phenacetin. Measure the melting-point ranges [OP-33] for the purified unknown (portions 1 + 2), the mixture with acetanilide, and the mixture with phenacetin. In each case, record the temperature at which you see the first trace of liquid and the temperature at which the sample is completely liquid. Unless your instructor indicates otherwise, you should carry out at least two measurements with each of these. Turn in the remaining product to your instructor in a vial labeled as shown by the example in the margin (or as directed by your instructor), giving the actual name of the product as indicated by your results.

Safety Notes

Observe and Note: How much water was needed to dissolve it? What happens as the solution cools?

Waste Disposal: Unless your instructor directs otherwise, wash the filtrate down the drain.

> *Exp. 3*
> *phenacetin*
> *0.183 g*
> *mp 112–114°C*
> *Ann A. Liszt*
> *9/23/08*

Stop and Think: Is your unknown reasonably pure? If not, what should you do?

Exercises

1. (a) What is the minimum volume of boiling water needed to dissolve 0.200 g of phenacetin (see Table 3.1)? (b) About how much phenacetin will remain dissolved when the water is cooled to room temperature? (c) Calculate the maximum mass of solid (undissolved) phenacetin that can be recovered when the cooled solution is filtered.
2. An unknown compound **X** is one of the four compounds listed in Table 3.2. A mixture of **X** with benzoic acid melts at 89°C, a mixture of **X** with phenyl succinate melts at 120°C, and a mixture of **X** with *m*-aminophenol melts at 102°C. Give the identity of **X** and explain your reasoning.

Table 3.2 Melting points for Exercise 2

Compound	mp, °C
o-toluic acid	102
benzoic acid	121
phenyl succinate	121
m-aminophenol	122

3. Tell how each of the following experimental errors will affect your experimental results (yield, purity, or both), and explain why. (a) You failed to dry the product completely. (b) You used enough water to recrystallize phenacetin, but your unknown was acetanilide. (c) In Experiment 2, you didn't extract all of the aspirin from the dichloromethane solution.
4. Tell whether each of the experimental errors in Exercise 3 will affect the melting point of the unknown component. If it will, tell how it will affect the melting point, and explain why.
5. Using one or more of the reference books listed in Appendix VII, give the following information about the analgesic drug ibuprofen: chemical names, molecular weight, molecular formula, structural formula, melting point, and a suitable recrystallization solvent.
6. Locate citations for one or more journal articles that give procedures for preparing (a) aspirin and (b) propoxyphene (Darvon). Give the full name of each journal, the volume number, the page number(s), and the year.

Other Things You Can Do

(Starred items require your instructor's permission.)

*1. Purify an unknown solid by recrystallization as described in Minilab 3.
*2. Carry out the purification and melting-point analysis of an acetanilide–salicylic acid mixture as described in *J. Chem. Educ.* **1989**, *66*, 1063.
3. Calibrate your thermometer by measuring the melting points of compounds listed in Table F1 of OP-33.
4. Look up the properties of a common organic compound in at least five different reference books, and compare the kind of information provided by each.

Heating Under Reflux
Synthesis of Salicylic Acid from Wintergreen Oil

Preparation and Purification of Solids.

Operations

OP-2 Using Specialized Glassware
OP-4 Weighing
OP-7 Heating
OP-16 Vacuum Filtration
OP-26 Drying Solids
OP-28 Recrystallization
OP-33 Melting Point

Before You Begin

1. Read the experiment and operation OP-2. Read "Smooth Boiling Devices" and "Heating Under Reflux" in OP-7, and review the other operations as necessary.
2. Read Appendix IV, "Calculations for Organic Synthesis." Then calculate the mass and volume of 10.0 mmol (SS) or 2.00 mmol (μS) of methyl salicylate, the theoretical yield of salicylic acid from that much methyl salicylate, and the minimum volume of water needed to recrystallize that much salicylic acid.
3. Complete the experimental plan that follows the "Reactions and Properties" section by specifying all sizes and quantities indicated by asterisks in the Chemicals and Supplies list. Note that reaction flasks (pear shaped and round bottom) come in 10-, 25-, 50-, 100-, 250-, and 500-mL sizes; conical vials in 3- and 5-mL sizes; Erlenmeyer flasks in 10-, 25-, 50-, 125-, and 250-mL sizes; and beakers in 10-, 20-, 30-, 50-, 150-, 250-, and 400-mL sizes.

Be sure to distinguish millimoles (mmol) from moles (mol); most prelab assignments will specify amounts of chemicals in millimoles.

Scenario

The new-age pharmaceutical company Natural Nostrums manufactures drugs from "natural" starting materials. For example, the company manufactures a painkilling drug it advertises as "organic aspirin" starting with methyl salicylate, which occurs naturally in wintergreen oil. Most commercially marketed aspirin is manufactured starting with benzene, a product of petroleum refining. An intermediate in both of these syntheses is salicylic acid.

Natural Nostrums claims that its aspirin, which is supposedly more natural than aspirin made from benzene, has fewer side effects than ordinary aspirin. Critics have accused the company of false and misleading advertising,

Simple Distillation, Gas Chromatography
EXPERIMENT 5   Preparation of Synthetic Banana Oil

Preparation, Purification, and Analysis of Liquids. Gas Chromatography.

Operations

OP-10 Mixing
OP-24 Washing Liquids
OP-25 Drying Liquids
OP-30 Simple Distillation
OP-37 Gas Chromatography
OP-2   Using Specialized Glassware
OP-4   Weighing
OP-6   Making Transfers (μS)
OP-7   Heating
OP-15   Gravity Filtration (SS)

Before You Begin

1. Read the experiment and operations OP-10, OP-24, OP-25, OP-30, and OP-37. Review the other operations as necessary. (Reading OP-30 and OP-37 may be deferred until the second lab period for this experiment.)
2. Calculate the mass and volume of 150 mmol (SS) or 20.0 mmol (μS) of isopentyl alcohol and the theoretical yield of isopentyl acetate from this amount of the alcohol.
3. Read Appendix V, "Planning an Experiment," and then write an experimental plan like the one you used in Experiment 4.

Scenario

Your supervisor has just received the following message from the Cavendish Distilling Company.

Greetings:

   We have a problem. Cavendish Distilling Company markets the popular liqueur Banana Elixir, which is flavored with a natural banana extract from fruit grown on our Caribbean banana plantations. Last June, Hurricane Floyd blew down all of our banana trees. Our stock of banana extract is running low, and we have no alternative source of bananas at this time. As a temporary solution, we have decided to add a synthetic banana flavoring to our remaining stock of the natural extract until our plantations start producing again.

   Synthetic banana flavorings are formulated mainly from isopentyl acetate, with smaller amounts of other esters. I understand that esters

banana tree

can be prepared economically by a process called the Fischer esterification, which involves the combination of an acid, such as acetic acid, with an alcohol. According to our technical staff, one problem with this method is that Fischer esterifications do not go to completion, leaving considerable amounts of starting material in the product. We can tolerate up to 10% isopentyl alcohol in our isopentyl acetate, since the alcohol is a component of natural banana extract. But we cannot tolerate more than 2% acetic acid, because it would tend to degrade the flavor of the liqueur. Will you have your consulting chemists prepare some isopentyl acetate and analyze it to see if it falls within our tolerances?

Amy Lester, CEO

The banana plant (Musa cavendishii and other species) is actually a gigantic herb and not a true tree. Each year, the foliage-bearing part withers away and is replaced by new growth from an underground stem.

Applying Scientific Methodology

By now, you should be familiar with the steps involved in applying scientific methodology to the solution of a problem, so they will not all be repeated in subsequent experiments. In this experiment, the problem described in the Scenario involves the purity of the product—not its identity—so your course of action will include the use of an instrumental method, gas chromatography, to determine the composition of the product.

Esters and Artificial Flavorings

The word *flavor* is used to describe the overall sensory effect of a substance taken into the mouth. Flavor may involve tactile, temperature, and pain sensations, as well as smell and taste. Many fruits, flowers, and spices contain esters that contribute to their characteristic flavors—an *ester* is an organic compound that contains the functional group (characteristic combination of atoms) shown in the margin.

$$-\overset{\overset{\displaystyle O}{\|}}{C}-O-R$$

functional group
of an ester

Most volatile esters have strong, pleasant odors that can best be described as "fruity." Some esters with flavors characteristic of real and "fantasy" fruits are shown in Table 5.1. The ester you will prepare in this experiment, isopentyl acetate, has a strong banana odor when undiluted and an odor reminiscent of pears in dilute solution. It is used as an ingredient in artificial coffee, butterscotch, and honey flavorings, as well as in pear and banana flavorings.

Many different esters are included in the basic repertoire of the flavor chemist, who combines natural and synthetic ingredients to prepare artificial flavorings. These ingredients may include natural products, synthetic organic compounds identical to those found in nature, and synthetic compounds not found in nature but accepted as safe for use in food. Each flavor ingredient is characterized by one or more flavor *notes* that suggests the predominant impact the ingredient makes on the senses of taste and smell. Although the flavor note of a single ingredient may seem unrelated to the overall character of a natural flavor, the combination of carefully selected ingredients in the right proportions can often yield a good approximation of that flavor. A high-boiling *fixative,* such as glycerine or benzyl benzoate, is usually added to an artificial flavoring to retard vaporization of volatile components, and the flavor notes of the individual components are blended

$$\underset{\underset{\displaystyle CH_3}{|}}{CH_3COCH_2CH_2CHCH_3}$$

with the O above the second C.

isopentyl acetate

Some food products, such as cola beverages and Juicy Fruit gum, are characterized by fantasy flavors that have no counterparts in nature, but most artificial flavorings are meant to resemble natural flavors.

Table 5.1 Flavor notes of some esters used in artificial flavorings

Name	Structure	Flavor note
propyl acetate	$\overset{\displaystyle O}{\overset{\|}{CH_3C}} - OCH_2CH_2CH_3$	pears
octyl acetate	$\overset{\displaystyle O}{\overset{\|}{CH_3C}} - O(CH_2)_7CH_3$	oranges
benzyl acetate	$\overset{\displaystyle O}{\overset{\|}{CH_3C}} - OCH_2 \bigcirc$	peaches, strawberries
isopentenyl acetate	$\overset{\displaystyle O}{\overset{\|}{CH_3C}} - OCH_2CH = \overset{\overset{\displaystyle CH_3}{\|}}{C} - CH_3$	"Juicy Fruit"
isobutyl propionate	$\overset{\displaystyle O}{\overset{\|}{CH_3CH_2C}} - OCH_2\overset{\overset{\displaystyle CH_3}{\|}}{CH} - CH_3$	rum
ethyl butyrate	$\overset{\displaystyle O}{\overset{\|}{CH_3CH_2CH_2C}} - OCH_2CH_3$	pineapples

Fixatives

$$\overset{\overset{\displaystyle OH\ OHOH}{\|\ \ \|\ \ \|}}{CH_2CHCH_2}$$

glycerine

$\bigcirc - \overset{\displaystyle O}{\overset{\|}{C}}OCH_2 \bigcirc$

benzyl benzoate

Vehicle

CH_3CH_2OH

ethyl alcohol

by dissolving them in a solvent called the *vehicle*. The most frequently used vehicle is ethanol (ethyl alcohol).

The formulation of artificial flavorings is perhaps as much an art as a science. The components of a strawberry flavoring, for example, may vary widely depending on the manufacturer and the specific application. Because natural flavors are usually very complex, a cheap artificial flavoring may be a poor imitation of its natural counterpart, but advances in flavor chemistry have made possible the production of superior flavorings that reproduce natural flavors very closely. Superior flavorings may contain natural oils or extracts that have been fortified with a few synthetic ingredients to enhance the overall effect and to replace flavor elements lost during the distillation or extraction process. Even the most experienced flavor chemist can't hope to do as well as a strawberry plant, which may combine several hundred different flavor components in its berries. But a superior strawberry flavoring with a few dozen ingredients may be hard to distinguish from the real thing—except by the most discriminating of strawberry aficionados.

Understanding the Experiment

In this experiment you will prepare synthetic banana oil, which is known by several chemical names, including isopentyl acetate, isoamyl acetate, and 3-methylbutyl ethanoate. Esters are often prepared by the Fischer esterification method, which involves heating a carboxylic acid with an alcohol in the presence of an acid catalyst, as shown by the following general equation:

$$\underset{\substack{\text{carboxylic} \\ \text{acid}}}{\overset{\displaystyle\text{O}}{\overset{\displaystyle\|}{\text{RCOH}}}} \; + \; \underset{\text{alcohol}}{\text{HOR}'} \; \overset{\text{H}^+}{\rightleftharpoons} \; \underset{\text{ester}}{\overset{\displaystyle\text{O}}{\overset{\displaystyle\|}{\text{RCOR}'}}} \; + \; \text{H}_2\text{O}$$

The acid catalyst is used to increase the rate of the reaction, which would otherwise require a much longer reaction time.

You will synthesize isopentyl acetate by combining isopentyl alcohol (3-methyl-1-butanol) with acetic acid and sulfuric acid and then heating the reaction mixture under reflux for an hour. The alcohol is the limiting reactant, so it should be weighed; the acids can be measured by volume. The esterification reaction is reversible, and it has an equilibrium constant of approximately 4.2. If you were to start with equimolar amounts of acetic acid and isopentyl alcohol, only about two-thirds of each reactant would be converted to isopentyl acetate by the time equilibrium was reached. Your highest attainable yield in that case would be only 67% of the theoretical value. Thus, despite having a high atom economy, the reaction efficiency of the synthesis could be rather low. To increase the reaction efficiency, you will apply Le Châtelier's principle by using a 100% excess of acetic acid — the less expensive reactant — to shift the equilibrium toward the products. Even then, the reaction will not be complete at equilibrium, so the reaction mixture will contain some unreacted isopentyl alcohol as well as the excess acetic acid.

Key Concept: For a reaction at equilibrium, adding more of a reactant or removing a product will shift the equilibrium to favor the products.

As you learned in Experiment 2, a pure component can be obtained from a mixture by separating it from all other components of the mixture, using procedures that take advantage of differences in solubility, boiling points, acid-base properties, and other characteristics of the components. Because isopentyl acetate is a liquid, the separation and purification operations will differ from those used previously for solid products.

At the end of the reflux period, the reaction mixture will contain (in addition to the ester) unreacted acetic acid, sulfuric acid, water, unreacted isopentyl alcohol, and some unwanted by-products (see Figure 5.1). Isopentyl acetate is quite insoluble in water, whereas both acetic acid and sulfuric acid are water soluble and acidic. This makes it easy to separate the two acids from the product by washing the reaction mixture with water and then with aqueous sodium bicarbonate. Water doesn't remove the acids entirely because they are somewhat soluble in the ester as well, but it removes the bulk of them and thus helps prevent a violent reaction with sodium bicarbonate in the second washing step. The aqueous sodium bicarbonate converts the acids to their salts, sodium acetate and sodium sulfate, which are insoluble in the ester but very soluble in water; these salts migrate to the aqueous layer, where they can be removed. The rule of thumb given in OP-24 will help you estimate the quantity of aqueous sodium bicarbonate needed.

Reactions carried out with acid catalysts often yield polymeric, tarlike by-products that have high boiling points and are insoluble in water.

The water that forms during the reaction will be separated from the ester along with the wash liquids. Any traces of water that remain are then removed by a drying agent, either magnesium sulfate or sodium sulfate. The rule of thumb in OP-25 will help you estimate the amount of drying agent needed.

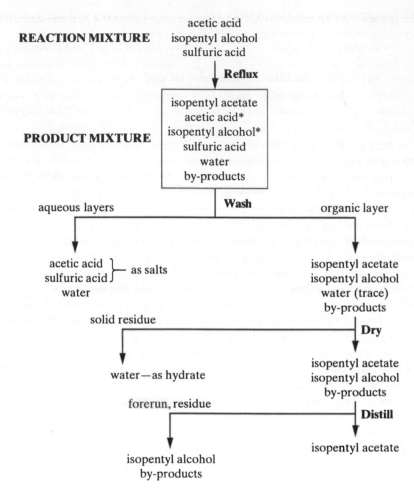

REACTION MIXTURE

acetic acid
isopentyl alcohol
sulfuric acid

Reflux

PRODUCT MIXTURE

isopentyl acetate
acetic acid*
isopentyl alcohol*
sulfuric acid
water
by-products

aqueous layers   **Wash**   organic layer

acetic acid ⎱
sulfuric acid ⎰ — as salts
water

isopentyl acetate
isopentyl alcohol
water (trace)
by-products

solid residue   **Dry**

water — as hydrate

isopentyl acetate
isopentyl alcohol
by-products

forerun, residue   **Distill**

isopentyl alcohol
by-products

isopentyl acetate

*unreacted starting materials

Figure 5.1 Flow diagram for the synthesis of isopentyl acetate

Because isopentyl alcohol has a lower boiling point than that of isopentyl acetate, and the by-products have higher boiling points, it should be possible—in principle—to remove the alcohol and by-products from the ester by distillation. Isopentyl alcohol should distill first, followed by the ester, and any by-products should remain behind in the pot—the vessel in which the reaction mixture is boiled. For the reasons described in OP-30, the separation is incomplete, so you will still have some isopentyl alcohol in your isopentyl acetate after the purification step.

You will determine the composition of your distillate by injecting a very small amount into an instrument called a gas chromatograph. (Your instructor will demonstrate the operation of this instrument.) Inside the gas chromatograph, the liquid will vaporize, and the vapors of different components will travel through a packed column at different rates. As the vapors exit the column, their presence will be detected and recorded on a graph called a gas chromatogram, which should display several peaks of different sizes. The area under the peak for each component will be proportional to the amount of that component present, so by measuring the peak areas you can estimate the percentage of each component in the distillate. This will tell you how much (if any) isopentyl alcohol and acetic acid remain in your product.

This should be a green synthesis because it has a high atom economy, no organic solvents are used, and the catalyst reduces energy consumption and improves the yield. Acetic acid is expected to be slightly toxic to aquatic life, but it is a naturally occurring substance that readily breaks down to carbon dioxide and water in the environment. Isopentyl alcohol and isopentyl acetate are not considered to be serious environmental contaminants.

The procedure for the synthesis of isopentyl acetate is summarized in the flow diagram in Figure 5.1, which illustrates the transformations or separations that occur during each operation. Appendix V tells you how to interpret such a flow diagram.

Isopentyl acetate is known to be an *alarm pheromone* of the honeybee. A pheromone is a "molecular messenger" that produces a response, such as mating behavior or aggression toward a perceived threat, in another member of the same species. When a worker honeybee stings someone, it releases a tiny amount (about 1 μg) of isopentyl acetate in its stinger, which attracts more honeybees to the scene. Although isopentyl acetate alone doesn't cause the bees to sting (other pheromones in the stinger do that), it agitates them and puts them on guard. So it might be wise to steer clear of beehives on your way home from the lab!

Reactions and Properties

$$\underset{\text{acetic acid}}{CH_3\overset{\overset{\displaystyle O}{\|}}{C}-OH} + \underset{\text{isopentyl alcohol}}{HOCH_2CH_2\overset{\overset{\displaystyle CH_3}{|}}{C}HCH_3} \underset{}{\overset{H_2SO_4}{\rightleftharpoons}} \underset{\text{isopentyl acetate}}{CH_3\overset{\overset{\displaystyle O}{\|}}{C}-OCH_2CH_2\overset{\overset{\displaystyle CH_3}{|}}{C}HCH_3} + H_2O$$

Table 5.2 Physical properties

	mol wt	bp	d	Solubility
acetic acid	60.1	118	1.049	miscible
isopentyl alcohol	88.1	130	0.815	2.7
isopentyl acetate	130.2	142	0.876	0.25
sulfuric acid	98.1	290	1.84	miscible

Note: Boiling points are in °C; densities are in g/mL; solubilities are in g/100 mL water.

DIRECTIONS

Acetic acid causes chemical burns that can seriously damage skin and eyes; its vapors are highly irritating to the eyes and respiratory tract. Wear gloves, dispense under a hood, avoid contact, and do not breathe its vapors.

Sulfuric acid causes chemical burns that can seriously damage skin and eyes. Wear gloves and avoid contact.

Isopentyl alcohol and isopentyl acetate can irritate the skin, eyes, and respiratory tract.

Safety Notes

acetic acid   sulfuric acid

Standard Scale

Reaction.   Accurately weigh 150 mmol of isopentyl alcohol into a round-bottom flask of appropriate size, and add boiling chips or a magnetic stir bar [OP-10]. *Under a hood,* add 17 mL (~300 mmol) of glacial acetic acid, and then carefully mix in 1.0 mL of concentrated sulfuric acid while stirring or swirling. Connect a West condenser to the reaction flask, turn on the cooling water, start the stirrer (if you are using one), and heat the reaction mixture under reflux [OP-7] for one hour after boiling begins.

Separation.   When the reaction time is up, allow the reaction mixture to cool to about room temperature. Turn off the cooling water and remove the reflux condenser. Transfer the reaction mixture to a separatory funnel, leaving the stir bar or boiling chips behind, and wash [OP-24] the mixture with 50 mL of water. Drain the aqueous layer, and leave the organic layer in the separatory funnel. Then carefully wash the organic layer with two successive portions of 5% aqueous sodium bicarbonate, draining the aqueous layer after each washing. (**Take Care!** Pressure may build up in the stoppered separatory funnel.) During the first washing, stir the layers until gas evolution subsides before you stopper the separatory funnel, and vent it frequently thereafter. Dry [OP-25] the crude isopentyl acetate with anhydrous magnesium sulfate or sodium sulfate, and filter it by gravity [OP-15].

Purification and Analysis.   Using standard-taper glassware [OP-2], assemble an apparatus for standard scale simple distillation [OP-30]. Be sure the thermometer bulb is positioned as shown in Figure E8, OP-30, and have your instructor check your setup before you start. Distill the crude product, collecting any liquid that distills between 137°C and 143°C. Record the actual boiling range you observe; wait until the entire thermometer bulb is moist with condensing vapors, liquid is distilling into the receiver, and the temperature is stable before you record the initial temperature reading. Stop the distillation when only a drop or so of liquid remains in the pot *or* when the temperature reaches 143°C. If the distillate is cloudy or contains water droplets, dry it [OP-25]. Weigh [OP-4] the distillate in a tared, labeled vial. Using a Carbowax column or another suitable column, obtain a gas chromatogram [OP-37] of the distillate and measure the peak areas as directed by your instructor. Unless your instructor indicates otherwise, assume that the components of the distillate appear on the gas chromatogram in the order (1) isopentyl alcohol, (2) isopentyl acetate, and (3) acetic acid. From the peak areas, calculate the percentage of each component in the distillate, then calculate your percent yield of isopentyl acetate based on its percentage in the distillate.

Microscale

Reaction.   Accurately weigh 20.0 mmol of isopentyl alcohol into an appropriate reaction flask and add a magnetic stir bar [OP-10]. *Under a hood,* add 2.3 mL (~40 mmol) of glacial acetic acid; stir the mixture as you carefully add 0.15 mL (or about 6 drops) of concentrated sulfuric acid. Connect a water-cooled condenser to the reaction flask, turn on the cooling water, and heat the reaction mixture under reflux [OP-7] with magnetic stirring [OP-10] for one hour after boiling begins. Reduce the heating rate if the reflux ring rises to within 2 cm of the top of the condenser.

Separation.   When the reaction time is up, allow the reaction mixture to cool to about room temperature. Turn off the cooling water and remove the condenser, then remove the stir bar with a forceps and rinse it over the reaction flask with a few drops of water. Transfer the reaction mixture to a screw-cap centrifuge tube, and add 6 mL of water, using some of the water for the transfer. Wash [OP-24] the reaction mixture with the water and remove the aqueous layer, leaving the organic layer in the centrifuge tube. Then carefully wash the organic layer with two separate portions of 5% aqueous sodium bicarbonate, removing the aqueous layer after each washing. During the first washing, stir the layers until gas evolution subsides before you cap the centrifuge tube, and vent it frequently thereafter. Try to remove all of the aqueous layer after the last washing to minimize the amount of water in the product. Dry [OP-25] the crude isopentyl acetate by adding a small amount of anhydrous sodium sulfate (about as much as you can get on the grooved end of a Hayman-style microspatula), shaking the capped tube vigorously, and letting the mixture stand for at least 10 minutes. Carefully transfer [OP-6] the liquid to a dry 5-mL conical vial using a dry filter-tip pipet. Try not to transfer any drying agent with the liquid.

Stop and Think: What is the density of isopentyl acetate? Which layer should initially be on top, the aqueous layer or the organic layer?

Stop and Think: What gas is evolved during the $NaHCO_3$ wash?

Take Care! Pressure may build up in the capped centrifuge tube.

Waste Disposal: Unless your instructor directs otherwise, dissolve the spent drying agent in the combined wash solvents and flush the mixture down the drain.

Purification and Analysis.   Using Mayo–Pike-style microware [OP-2], assemble an apparatus for microscale simple distillation [OP-30] that incorporates a Hickman still equipped with a water-cooled condenser and a thermometer. Be sure the thermometer bulb is positioned as shown in Figure E12, OP-30, and have your instructor check your setup before you start. Distill the crude product *slowly,* collecting any liquid that distills between 137°C and 143°C. Record the actual boiling range you observe; wait until the entire thermometer bulb is moist with condensing vapors, liquid has begun to appear in the well of the Hickman still, and the temperature is stable before you record the initial temperature reading. As the well fills with distillate, use a Pasteur pipet to transfer it to a tared, labeled 1-dram vial. Stop the distillation when only a drop or so of liquid remains in the pot *or* when the temperature reaches 143°C. If the distillate is cloudy or contains water droplets, dry it [OP-25]. Weigh [OP-4] the distillate. Using a Carbowax column or another suitable column, obtain a gas chromatogram [OP-37] of the distillate and measure the peak areas as directed by your instructor. Unless your instructor indicates otherwise, assume that the components of the distillate appear on the gas chromatogram in the order (1) isopentyl alcohol, (2) isopentyl acetate, and (3) acetic acid. From the peak areas, calculate the percentage of each component in the distillate, then calculate your percent yield of isopentyl acetate based on its percentage in the distillate.

Stop and Think: What does the boiling range of the distillate tell you about the purity of your product?

Waste Disposal: Put any forerun and any residue left in the boiling flask into a designated waste container.

Exercises

1. (a) Calculate the amount of isopentyl acetate (isoamyl acetate) that should be present in the reaction mixture at equilibrium, based on the quantities of starting materials you used and a value of 4.2 for the equilibrium constant. (Use the quadratic equation; because volumes cancel out, moles can be used in place of molar concentrations.)
    (b) Estimate the mass of isopentyl acetate that was lost (1) as a result of incomplete reaction, (2) during the washings, and (3) during the

Isoamyl acetate equilibrium

$i\text{-AmOH} + \text{HOAc} \rightleftharpoons$
$ i\text{-AmOAc} + H_2O$

$$K = \frac{[i\text{-AmOAc}][H_2O]}{[i\text{-AmOH}][\text{HOAc}]}$$

$Ac = \text{acetyl}, CH_3CO —$
$i\text{-Am} = \text{isoamyl}, CH_3CHCH_2CH_2 —$
$ |$
$ CH_3$

distillation (see OP-30). Assume that the ester's solubility in aqueous $NaHCO_3$ is about the same as in water. Compare the sum of these estimated losses with your actual product loss, and try to account for any significant differences.

2. What gas escaped during the sodium bicarbonate washing? Write balanced equations for two reactions that took place during this operation.

3. (a) Calculate the atom economy and reaction efficiency of your synthesis of isopentyl acetate. (b) Tell how the procedure for the preparation of isopentyl acetate might be modified to increase the reaction efficiency. (c) Describe some green features of your synthesis, and any that aren't so green.

4. Describe and explain how each of the following experimental errors or variations might affect your results. (a) You failed to dry the reaction flask after washing it with water. (b) You forgot to add the sulfuric acid. (c) You used twice the amount of acetic acid specified in the procedure. (d) You left out the sodium bicarbonate washing step. (e) Your thermometer bulb was 1 cm higher than it should have been.

5. (a) In the "Understanding the Experiment" section, it was stated that the reaction of an equimolar mixture of isopentyl alcohol and acetic acid will produce, at most, 67% of the theoretical amount of isopentyl acetate. Verify this with an equilibrium constant calculation, using $K = 4.2$. (b) Compare this with the corresponding percentage for the conditions used in this experiment (see Exercise 1). Are your results consistent with Le Châtelier's principle? Explain.

6. Based on the procedure that you used in this experiment, and using the same molar quantities of reactants, develop a procedure that would be suitable for the preparation of isobutyl propionate. Specify the amounts of all materials required and a distillation range for the product. Obtain the necessary physical properties from one of the reference books listed in the Bibliography.

$$\overset{\displaystyle O}{\overset{\displaystyle \|}{CH_3CH_2C}} — OCH_2\overset{\displaystyle CH_3}{\overset{\displaystyle |}{CHCH_3}}$$

isobutyl propionate

Other Things You Can Do

(Starred items require your instructor's permission.)

*1. You and your coworkers can prepare a series of esters and compare their odors as described in Minilab 5.

*2. Prepare another ester of a primary alcohol, such as butyl acetate or isobutyl propionate, by the general method described for isopentyl acetate. Work out a procedure for the synthesis (see Exercise 6) and have it approved by your instructor. In some cases, a longer reflux time may be necessary for satisfactory results.

3. Read about the isolation of isopentyl acetate (isoamyl acetate) in the alarm pheromone of the honeybee in *Nature* **1962**, *195*, 1018.

4. Read about various types of pheromones in *Chemical Communication: The Language of Pheromones* [Bibliography, L3].

Fractional Distillation
Separation of Petroleum Hydrocarbons

Separation Methods.

Operations

OP-32 Fractional Distillation
OP-4   Weighing
OP-7   Heating
OP-37   Gas Chromatography

Before You Begin

1. Read the experiment and operation OP-32. Review the other operations as necessary.
2. Prepare a brief experimental plan following the directions in Appendix V.

Scenario

The Northern Pines Chemical Company specializes in manufacturing chemicals from wood products such as turpentine. For example, they use a major component of turpentine, α-pinene, to prepare organic compounds such as isobornyl acetate and terpineol, which impart a "piney" note to perfumes. To obtain pure α-pinene, it must be separated from the other major component of turpentine, β-pinene. They have been carrying out this separation by fractional distillation using an expensive column-packing material that has to be replaced frequently. They would like to switch to a cheaper and longer-lasting packing material, but because the new packing material will be less efficient than their current type, they will need to purchase a longer column. Based on the difference between the boiling points of the pinenes (10°C), they estimate that such a column will need to have at least 20 theoretical plates (hypothetical column segments) to provide adequate separation. However, the height of each theoretical plate, and thus the total length of the column, depends on the efficiency of the packing material.

Forrest Greenwood, the operations engineer at Northern Pines, has sent your supervisor some of the new packing material for testing. Your assignment is to determine its height equivalent to a theoretical plate (HETP; a measure of column efficiency) and to estimate how long their new column must be to separate α-pinene from β-pinene efficiently. To do this, you will fractionally distill a mixture of two petroleum hydrocarbons, toluene and cyclohexane, and measure the composition of the fractions by gas chromatography.

See OP-32 for information about fractional distillation and distilling columns.

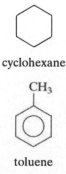

cyclohexane

toluene

Applying Scientific Methodology

This experiment differs from the previous ones in that no hypothesis is being tested; your job is to determine the value of a physical quantity, the HETP of the column, and to report the value as your conclusion. The accuracy of your results, and thus the validity of your conclusion, will depend on the care you take in performing the distillation.

Distillation in Petroleum Refining

Distillation has been used since antiquity to separate the components of mixtures—the ancient Egyptians were distilling wood to make an embalming fluid more than 3500 years ago. Today, distillation is used to manufacture perfumes, flavor ingredients, liquors, charcoal, coke, and a host of organic chemicals, but its most important application is in the refining of petroleum to produce fuels, lubricants, and petrochemicals.

The first step in petroleum refining is the separation of petroleum into different hydrocarbon fractions by distilling it through huge fractionating columns, called distillation towers, which may be up to 200 feet high. Since components that have different numbers of carbon atoms usually have significantly different boiling points, this process separates the petroleum into fractions containing hydrocarbons of similar carbon content. Thus, a lower-boiling fraction might contain hydrocarbons with 5 or 6 carbon atoms, while a higher-boiling fraction contains hydrocarbons with 12 to 18 carbon atoms. Vapors from the lower-boiling hydrocarbons rise to the top of the tower, where they are condensed and collected as "top fractions." Hydrocarbons in top fractions, such as the one called straight-run gasoline, can be chemically modified and used in gasoline. The less volatile middle fractions are collected partway down the tower; these include kerosene and a gas–oil fraction used to produce diesel fuel, jet fuel, and home heating oil. The bottom fraction is usually subjected to vacuum distillation to produce vacuum gas oils, which can be used as fuel oils or converted to hydrocarbons suitable for gasoline. Such petroleum products as paraffin wax, lubricating grease, and asphalt also come from this fraction.

With an overall octane number range of 30–50, straight-run gasoline is not a suitable motor fuel, but its octane number can be increased to nearly 100 by a process known as catalytic reforming. In this process, the straight-run gasoline is heated to about 500°C at high pressure in the presence of a suitable catalyst. Catalytic reforming converts alkanes to cycloalkanes and cycloalkanes to aromatic compounds; the result is a mixture rich in high-octane aromatics. For example, hexane may be *cyclized* to yield cyclohexane, which may then lose hydrogen atoms in a process called *dehydrogenation* to yield the aromatic compound benzene. Cyclohexane cannot easily be separated from petroleum by distillation alone, so pure cyclohexane is generally obtained by catalytic hydrogenation of benzene, the reverse of the second step shown here.

The octane number of a fuel is a measure of its antiknock properties. Most gasolines have octane numbers that range from 85 to the low 90s.

$$CH_3CH_2CH_2CH_2CH_2CH_3 \longrightarrow$$

hexane   cyclohexane   benzene

Toluene is obtained by dehydrogenation of methylcyclohexane, which can be formed by cyclization of heptane and other alkanes.

$$CH_3CH_2CH_2CH_2CH_2CH_2CH_3 \longrightarrow \overset{CH_3}{\bigcirc} \longrightarrow \overset{CH_3}{\bigcirc}$$

heptane   methylcyclohexane   toluene

Understanding the Experiment

In this experiment, you will separate the components of an equimolar mixture of cyclohexane and toluene by fractional distillation and assess the efficiency of the separation by measuring the composition of the fractions. The more completely the cyclohexane and toluene are separated from each other, the more efficient the separation. The degree of separation depends not only on the column packing you use but also on such factors as the stability of the heat source, the rate of distillation, and the way the column is packed. Good separation requires a low rate of distillation to maintain a high *reflux ratio*— the ratio of liquid returned to the boiling flask to liquid that distills into the receiving vessel—so patience is required if you are to obtain good results. The efficiency of the column will be reduced if it isn't packed uniformly, so it is important to distribute the packing material as evenly as possible.

You will measure the composition of each fraction you collect by gas chromatography. Your gas chromatograms should display two peaks, the cyclohexane peak being the first to appear. The areas of the peaks can be converted to relative masses by multiplying them by the appropriate correction factors from Table 6.1.

Table 6.1 Gas chromatography correction factors for cyclohexane and toluene

	TC detector	FI detector
cyclohexane	1.11	0.942
toluene	1.05	1.02

Note: Benzene = 1.00. Your instructor will tell you what kind of detector your gas chromatograph has.

You will then determine the HETP of the column packing from the composition of the first few drops of liquid you collect, the *HETP sample*. The number of theoretical plates provided by your distillation apparatus can be calculated using the Fenske equation, expressed as follows for an equimolar mixture of two components, A and B:

$$\text{total number of theoretical plates} = \frac{\log \dfrac{n_A}{n_B}}{\log \alpha} \qquad (1)$$

See OP-32 for definitions of theoretical plate and HETP and for a discussion of the Fenske equation.

In Equation 1, n_A/n_B is the ratio of the number of moles of cyclohexane to the number of moles of toluene in the HETP sample. The volatility factor, α, for the cyclohexane–toluene mixture is 2.33. The boiling flask furnishes one theoretical plate, so you will have to subtract 1 from the total number of theoretical plates to obtain the number of plates provided by the column itself. From this number and the length of your column packing, you can calculate the HETP of the column packing; the lower the HETP, the more efficient the packing.

*A **Greener Way:** The combined distillation fractions are collected in a waste container at the end of the experiment. This mixture should contain nearly equimolar amounts of cyclohexane and toluene, so the recovered "waste" from previous labs can be dried if necessary and used in subsequent ones.*

The MCL of a contaminant is the highest level of the contaminant that is allowed in drinking water.

According to Environmental Protection Agency (EPA) reports, cyclohexane and toluene by themselves aren't likely to cause environmental harm at levels normally found in the environment. Toluene, on the other hand, is quite toxic, with a maximum contaminant level (MCL) of 0.5 parts per billion (ppb); it can contribute to the formation of photochemical smog when it reacts with other volatile organic substances in air. Release of either hydrocarbon into the environment should be avoided.

Properties

Table 6.2 Physical properties of cyclohexane and toluene

	mol wt	bp	*d*
cyclohexane	84.2	81	0.774
toluene	92.2	111	0.867

Note: Boiling points are in °C, and densities are in g/mL.

DIRECTIONS

Safety Notes

cyclohexane

toluene

Cyclohexane is very flammable and may irritate the skin, eyes, and respiratory tract.
Do not use open flames during the experiment.
Toluene is flammable, and inhalation, ingestion, or skin absorption may be harmful. Avoid contact with the liquid, and do not breathe its vapors.

Standard Scale

Take Care! Avoid contact with the liquid mixture, and do not breathe its vapors.

Stop and Think: Will the thermometer record the boiling temperature of the liquid as soon as it begins to boil? Why or why not?

Observe and Note: When does the thermometer begin to record the true boiling temperature? Record that temperature, and describe what you observe at that point.

Separation.   All components of the fractional-distillation apparatus must be clean and dry. Pack a distilling column uniformly with the column packing provided, and measure the height of the packing in centimeters to the nearest 0.1 cm; the column need not be insulated. Obtain five clean, dry fraction collectors, such as a 1-dram screw-cap vial and four 4-dram screw-cap vials. Label the smaller vial "HETP," and number the other vials from 1 to 4. Then weigh vials #1–4 with their caps on. Measure 40 mL of an equimolar mixture of cyclohexane and toluene into a 100-mL round-bottom flask (keep the flask stoppered to prevent evaporation) and add some boiling chips (or a stir bar). Clamp the flask to a ring stand over an appropriate heat source [OP-7] and assemble an apparatus for fractional distillation [OP-32], using the HETP vial as the receiver.

Heat the mixture to a gentle boil (with the stirrer turned on, if you are using one) and adjust the heating rate so that the vapors rise slowly up the column. Reduce the heating rate if the column begins to flood (fill with liquid); the packing should be moistened by condensing vapors but should not contain any flowing liquid. Distillate should begin collecting not long after the rising vapors reach the still head (connecting adapter). Collect the first five drops of distillate in the HETP vial, then cap the vial tightly. Quickly replace the HETP vial with vial #1, record the distillation temperature (it should be ~81°C or higher), and adjust the heating rate as necessary so that no more than 20 drops distill per minute. You may have to gradually increase the heating rate to keep the distillation rate more or less uniform. Begin collecting in vial #2 when the temperature reaches 85°C, and in vial #3 when it reaches 97°C. When the temperature reaches 107°C, remove the heat source and let all the liquid that remains in the column drain into the boiling flask. When the boiling flask has cooled, transfer its contents to vial #4. At this point, you should have four fractions covering the following approximate boiling ranges:

Stop and Think: Why does the boiling temperature rise during the distillation?

1. 81–84°C
2. 85–96°C
3. 97–106°C
4. 107–111°C

Analysis. Weigh [OP-4] fractions #1–4 (or whichever fractions your instructor specifies), and analyze them and the HETP sample by gas chromatography [OP-37]. Measure the peak areas on each gas chromatogram and use the appropriate correction factors to convert the areas to relative masses. Calculate the percentage (by mass) and the actual mass of cyclohexane and toluene in each fraction you analyzed, the number of theoretical plates provided by your fractional-distillation apparatus, the HETP of your column, and the length of the column (in cm) that will provide 20 theoretical plates. At your instructor's request, plot the component masses for each fraction (on the *y*-axis) as a function of boiling temperature, using the midpoints of the appropriate boiling ranges on the *x*-axis (use different symbols, such as × and •, for different components). Draw a smooth curve connecting the data points for cyclohexane, and draw another one (overlapping the first) connecting the data points for toluene.

Waste Disposal: Combine all fractions and place them in the hydrocarbon solvent recovery container.

Microscale

Separation.   All components of the fractional-distillation apparatus must be clean and dry. Pack an air condenser uniformly with stainless-steel sponge (see OP-32) or another packing material specified by your instructor, and measure the height of the packing to the nearest millimeter. Insulate the column as directed by your instructor. Obtain five clean, dry fraction collectors, such as 1-dram screw-cap vials. Label one vial "HETP," number the other vials from 1 to 4, then weigh vials #1–4 with their caps on. Measure 5.0 mL of an equimolar mixture of cyclohexane and toluene into a 10-mL round-bottom flask (keep the flask stoppered to prevent evaporation) and add a stir bar. Clamp the flask to a ring stand over an appropriate heat source [OP-7] and assemble an apparatus for microscale fractional distillation [OP-32], taking care to place the thermometer bulb correctly.

Heat the mixture to a gentle boil with the stirrer turned on, and adjust the heating rate so that the vapors rise slowly up the column. Reduce the heating rate if the column begins to flood (fill with liquid); the packing should be moistened by condensing vapors but should not contain any flowing liquid. Distillate should begin collecting not long after the rising vapors reach the top of the column. Adjust the heating rate as necessary so that liquid collects *slowly* in the well of the Hickman still. Use a Pasteur pipet to transfer distillate from the well to the appropriate collecting vial. Collect the first 2–4 drops of distillate in the HETP vial, cap it tightly, and then

Take Care! Avoid contact with the liquid mixture, and do not breathe its vapors.

Stop and Think: Will the thermometer record the boiling temperature of the liquid as soon as it begins to boil? Why or why not?

Observe and Note: When does the thermometer begin to record the true boiling temperature? Record that temperature, and describe what you observe at that point.

begin collecting in vial #1. Record the distillation temperature (it should be ~81°C or higher) and continue to distill slowly. You may have to gradually increase the heating rate to keep the distillation rate more or less uniform. Begin collecting in vial #2 when the temperature reaches 85°C, and in vial #3 when it reaches 97°C. When the temperature reaches 107°C, remove the heat source and let the liquid that remains in the column drain into the boiling flask. When the boiling flask has cooled, transfer its contents to vial #4. At this point, you should have four fractions covering the following approximate boiling ranges:

1. 81–84°C
2. 85–96°C
3. 97–106°C
4. 107–111°C

Analysis.   Weigh [OP-4] fractions #1–4 (or whichever fractions your instructor specifies), and analyze them and the HETP sample by gas chromatography [OP-37]. Measure the peak areas on each gas chromatogram and use the appropriate correction factors to convert the areas to relative masses. Calculate the percentage (by mass) and the actual mass of cyclohexane and toluene in each fraction you analyzed, the number of theoretical plates provided by your fractional-distillation apparatus, the HETP of your column, and the length of the column (in cm) that will provide 20 theoretical plates. At your instructor's request, plot the component masses for each fraction (on the *y*-axis) as a function of boiling temperature, using the midpoints of the appropriate boiling ranges on the *x*-axis (use different symbols, such as $\times$ and •, for different components). Draw a smooth curve connecting the data points for cyclohexane, and draw another one (overlapping the first) connecting the data points for toluene.

Exercises

1. A certain fractional-distillation apparatus contains a 24-cm Vigreux column stacked on top of a 30-cm glass tube that is half-filled with 4×4-mm porcelain saddles. This assembly is inserted into a boiling flask. How many theoretical plates does the entire apparatus provide if the HETP of the saddles is 5 cm, the HETP of the Vigreux column is 8 cm, and the HETP of the empty glass tube is 15 cm?

2. Describe and explain how each of the following experimental errors or variations would affect your HETP value and the efficiency of your separation. (a) You didn't collect the HETP sample until midway through the distillation. (b) All of your liquid distilled within 5 minutes of the time you began heating. (c) You stacked two packed columns over the boiling flask rather than using one.

3. Using the data in Table 6.3, construct a temperature–composition diagram like that shown in Figure E19 of OP-32. (a) From your diagram, estimate the initial composition of the distillate obtained by simple distillation of a mixture containing 20 mole percent cyclohexane and 80 mole percent toluene. (b) Estimate the initial composition if the same mixture is distilled through a three-plate column.

4. If you were to return your 97–106°C fraction to the empty boiling flask and redistill it, you might expect it all to distill between 97°C and 106°C, as it did the first time. It actually yields some distillate in all four boiling ranges. Explain.

5. Derive Equation **1** (for an equimolar mixture of two components) from the Fenske equation in OP-32.

6. Suggest a chemical method that could be used to remove small amounts of toluene from cyclohexane.

7. Show how nylon 6,6 can be synthesized using cyclohexane as the starting material.

Other Things You Can Do

(Starred items require your instructor's permission.)

*1. Analyze some or all of your fractions with a refractometer [OP-35] rather than a gas chromatograph, using a graph that plots refractive index versus mole fraction. (Assume a linear relationship between these variables.) The refractive indexes at 20°C of pure cyclohexane and toluene are 1.4260 and 1.4968, respectively.

*2. Carry out a gas chromatographic analysis of commercial xylene as described in Minilab 6.

3. Write a research paper about distillation and its uses based on information from *Kirk-Othmer* [Bibliography, A8] and other sources listed in the Bibliography.

Table 6.3 Temperature–composition data for cyclohexane–toluene

T, °C	Mol % cyclohexane	
	Liquid	Vapor
110.7	0	0
108.3	4.1	10.2
105.5	9.1	21.2
103.9	11.8	26.4
101.8	16.4	34.8
99.5	21.7	42.2
97.4	27.3	49.2
95.5	32.3	54.7
93.8	37.9	59.9
91.9	45.2	66.2
89.8	53.3	72.4
88.0	59.9	77.4
86.6	67.2	81.1
84.8	76.3	86.4
83.8	81.4	89.5
82.7	87.4	92.6
81.1	96.4	97.3
80.7	100.0	100.0

The penetrating "camphoraceous" odor of camphor is shared by many compounds of similar molecular shape and size. Compounds as diverse in structure as the ones shown here all have roughly spherical molecules and similar camphoraceous odors:

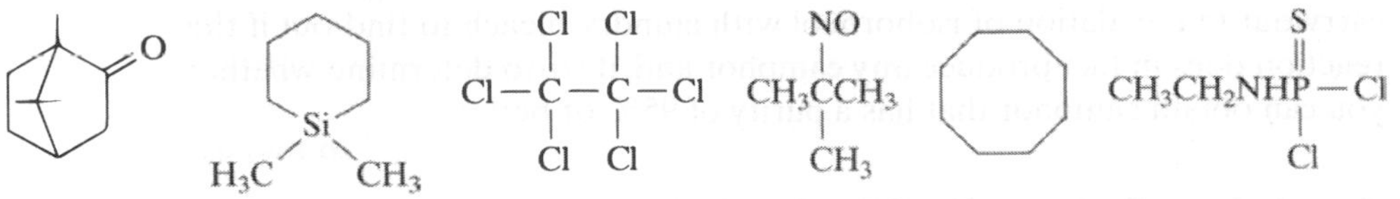

Most scientists believe that the sense of smell is based on the presence in the nasal passageways of a large number of odor receptors, each of which is programmed to detect a specific kind of odor. This idea gained support in 1996, when scientists who had induced bacteria to grow an odor receptor normally found in rats discovered that molecules of two compounds with floral odors, lilial and lyral, became strongly attached to the receptors. The similarities among molecules that have camphoraceous odors suggest that the odor of a substance may, at least in part, depend on the size and shape of its molecules. A spherical molecule, for example, might fit nicely inside a hemispherically convex odor receptor, causing it to transmit a neural message that the brain interprets as a camphor-like odor. However, scientists still do not fully understand how humans and other animals can detect and recognize a multitude of different odors.

Understanding the Experiment

In this experiment, you will oxidize a secondary alcohol, isoborneol, to a ketone, camphor. Secondary alcohols can be converted to ketones by powerful oxidizing agents such as chromic acid, but many chromium compounds are highly toxic and corrosive, and some are known to cause cancer. They also present a difficult disposal problem because they cannot legally be discharged into waterways or other places where they might harm the environment. For these reasons, you will use a safer and more environmentally friendly oxidizing agent, the familiar household laundry bleach that is sold under such trade names as Clorox and Javex. Most chlorine bleaches contain either 5.25% or 6.0% sodium hypochlorite (NaOCl) in an aqueous solution. Adding a little acetic acid facilitates oxidation by converting sodium hypochlorite to hypochlorous acid (HOCl), which is probably the active oxidizing agent. Because sodium hypochlorite solutions evolve some chlorine gas, the reaction is carried out under a fume hood.

The bleach should be unscented and there should be no ingredient other than sodium hypochlorite listed on the label.

In some previous experiments, you heated the reaction mixture to speed up the reaction. In this experiment, you will need to slow it down instead, because the oxidation of isoborneol is exothermic and the heat evolved can lead to the formation of unwanted by-products such as camphoric acid. You will control the reaction rate by adding the sodium hypochlorite, a little at a time, from a separatory–addition funnel (SS) or a Pasteur pipet (μS) rather than combining all of the reactants at once. For the standard scale procedure, you will monitor the temperature with a thermometer, as described in OP-9, and you may use a cooling bath to keep down the temperature in the reaction flask.

Key Concept: Excessive heat can promote high-energy reaction paths that lead to the formation of unwanted by-products.

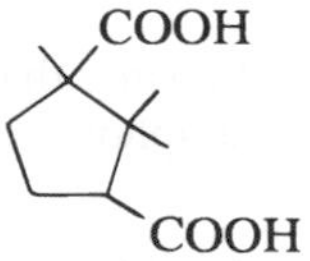

camphoric acid

When a reaction takes place under reflux, the boiling action helps mix the reactants. In this experiment, the reactants are mixed using a magnetic stirrer or by shaking and swirling the flask after each addition. If you are following the standard scale procedure, you will have to monitor the reaction temperature by holding a thermometer with the bulb immersed in the reactants as you mix them. The directions in OP-9 explain how to do this safely.

To ensure a complete reaction, you must add enough sodium hypochlorite solution to keep the oxidizing agent in excess throughout the reaction. Because the NaOCl concentrations of different chlorine bleaches may differ and will decrease with age, you can't be sure that the amount of bleach that you add at first will be enough, so you will have to test the reaction mixture periodically to see whether there is still excess oxidant present. When HOCl is present in excess, a drop of the acidic reaction mixture placed on an indicator paper impregnated with starch and potassium iodide will oxidize iodide ions to iodine, which turns the starch a deep blue-black color. The color near the center of the drop may be bleached white, but some color should remain around its edges. Any excess HOCl that remains after the reaction is over can be destroyed by treatment with the reducing agent sodium bisulfite, according to the following equation:

$$HOCl + HSO_3^- \longrightarrow HCl + HSO_4^-$$

Because of its compact molecular structure, camphor changes directly from a solid to a vapor when heated, which allows it to be purified by sublimation. Isoborneol also sublimes at elevated temperatures, so the sublimed camphor will probably contain some unreacted isoborneol. Assuming that isoborneol is the only significant impurity in the product, its purity can be estimated with good accuracy from its melting point because camphor has an unusually large freezing-point depression constant. The product can be regarded as a solid solution with camphor as the solvent and isoborneol as the solute, so you can use the following equation to calculate the molal concentration (m) of isoborneol in the product:

The melting point of a solid equals the freezing point of the corresponding liquid.

$\Delta T = K_f \times m$

ΔT = melting-point depression (reported mp – observed mp)

K_f = freezing-point depression constant for camphor = $40°C \, kg \, mol^{-1}$

m = molal concentration of isoborneol (mol isoborneol/kg camphor)

Knowing m, the number of moles of isoborneol per kilogram of camphor, you can calculate the mass percent of isoborneol and camphor in the product.

This experiment has several green features in addition to the use of a more benign oxidizing agent. It uses no solvents other than the water present in the laundry bleach, its atom economy is fairly high, and the only by-products are water and sodium chloride. Because sodium hypochlorite is used widely to disinfect water, it is often present in municipal drinking water, and the EPA has concluded that such uses present no unreasonable adverse effects on the environment. It is toxic to freshwater fish and invertebrates, however, so its release into the environment should be avoided.

Reactions and Properties

isoborneol   camphor

Table 7.1 Physical properties

	mol wt	mp	bp	d
isoborneol	154.3	212		
camphor	152.2	179	204	
sodium hypochlorite	74.4			
acetic acid	60.1	17	118	1.049

Note: mp and bp are in °C; d is in g/mL.

DIRECTIONS

Safety Notes

> Acetic acid causes chemical burns that can seriously damage skin and eyes; its vapors are highly irritating to the eyes and respiratory tract. Wear gloves, avoid contact with the acid, do not breathe its vapors, and dispense it under a hood.
> Aqueous sodium hypochlorite can irritate the skin, eyes, and respiratory tract. Avoid contact, and do not breathe its vapors.
> The reaction mixture may evolve some chlorine gas, which can irritate the eyes and respiratory tract, so carry out the reaction under a fume hood.

```
   ┌─2─┐           ┌─2─┐           ┌─0─┐
   2 ✕ 1           2 ✕ 0           ✕ 1
   └─2─┘           └─1─┘           3
```

acetic acid   camphor   chlorine

 Standard Scale

Reaction. *Under the hood,* combine 25.0 mmol of isoborneol with 2.0 mL of glacial acetic acid in a 125-mL Erlenmeyer flask. Mix in 5.0 mL of 5.25% (or 4.4 mL of 6%) sodium hypochlorite solution (Clorox or another hypochlorite laundry bleach). Measure another 40 mL of 5.25% (or 35 mL of 6%) sodium hypochlorite solution into a separatory–addition funnel, stopper the funnel, and support it over the flask. Place a strip of filter paper between the addition funnel's neck and the stopper to prevent a vacuum. Add [OP-11] the NaOCl solution to the reaction mixture in small portions, with vigorous swirling or magnetic stirring [OP-10], for a period of 10 minutes or more. Use a thermometer to monitor the temperature

Take Care! Wear gloves, avoid contact with acetic acid and the NaOCl solution, and do not breathe their vapors.

[OP-9] of the reaction mixture, and control the rate of addition so that the temperature remains below 50°C. Have an ice/water bath handy to cool [OP-8] the reaction mixture if its temperature reaches 50°C.

When the addition is complete, seal the flask with Parafilm and stir [OP-10] the reactants (or swirl the flask frequently) at room temperature for 30 minutes or more. Every 5 minutes or so, test the reaction mixture for excess hypochlorite by transferring a drop of the solution to a strip of starch–iodide paper. If, at any time, the test is negative, add enough sodium hypochlorite solution (about 1 mL at a time) to the reaction mixture to give a *positive* test. When the reaction period is over, again test the reaction mixture with starch–iodide paper. If the test is positive, add enough saturated sodium bisulfite solution dropwise to give a *negative* test.

Separation.   Cool [OP-8] the reaction mixture to 5°C or below in an ice/water bath. Collect the product by vacuum filtration [OP-16], washing it on the filter [OP-26a] with two portions of ice-cold water. Dry [OP-26b] the crude product at room temperature, *not* in an oven. (At your instructor's request, weigh the crude product and save a small amount of it for a melting-point measurement.)

Purification and Analysis.   Purify the crude product by sublimation [OP-29], taking care not to char the solid by overheating. Weigh [OP-4] the sublimate, dry [OP-26b] it at room temperature (if necessary), and measure its melting point [OP-33]. Taking as its melting point the temperature at which the solid was completely liquefied, calculate the mass percentages of isoborneol and camphor in your purified product. Include a calculation of percent yield in your report.

Microscale

Reaction: *Under the hood,* combine 2.50 mmol of isoborneol with 0.20 mL of glacial acetic acid in a small Erlenmeyer flask, and drop in a stir bar. Measure 5.0 mL of sodium hypochlorite solution (Clorox or another hypochlorite laundry bleach) into a screw-cap vial, and keep the vial capped when not in use. While stirring the reaction mixture, use a calibrated Pasteur pipet to add [OP-11] about 4.5 mL of the NaOCl solution, a few drops at a time, at a rate of about 1 mL per minute.

When the addition is complete, seal the flask with Parafilm and stir [OP-10] the reactants at room temperature for 30 minutes. Every 5 minutes or so, test the reaction mixture for excess hypochlorite by transferring a drop of the solution to a strip of starch–iodide paper. If, at any time, the test is negative, add enough sodium hypochlorite solution (a few drops at a time) to the reaction mixture to give a *positive* test. When the reaction period is over, again test the reaction mixture with starch–iodide paper. If the test is positive, add enough saturated sodium bisulfite solution dropwise to give a *negative* test.

Separation.   Cool [OP-8] the reaction mixture for 5 to 10 minutes in an ice/water bath. Collect the product by vacuum filtration [OP-16], washing it on the filter [OP-26a] with two portions of ice-cold water. Dry [OP-26b] the crude product at room temperature, *not* in an oven. (At your instructor's request, weigh the crude product and save a small amount of it for a melting-point measurement.)

Observe and Note: Can you detect any evidence that a reaction is taking place?

Waste Disposal: If you have any unused sodium hypochlorite solution, place it in an appropriate waste container.

Stop and Think: What is the purpose of the sodium bisulfite addition?

Waste Disposal: Unless your instructor directs otherwise, wash the filtrate down the drain.

Your instructor may request that you purify only part of the crude camphor.

Take Care! Wear gloves, avoid contact with acetic acid and the NaOCl solution, and do not breathe their vapors.

Observe and Note: Can you detect any evidence that a reaction is taking place?

Waste Disposal: If you have any unused sodium hypochlorite solution, place it in an appropriate waste container.

Stop and Think: What is the purpose of the sodium bisulfite addition?

Waste Disposal: Unless your instructor directs otherwise, wash the filtrate down the drain.

Your instructor may request that you purify only part of the crude camphor.

Purification and Analysis.   Purify the crude product by sublimation [OP-29], taking care not to char the solid by overheating. Weigh [OP-4] the sublimate, dry [OP-26b] it at room temperature (if necessary), and measure its melting point [OP-33]. Taking as its melting point the temperature at which the solid was completely liquefied, calculate the mass percentages of isoborneol and camphor in your purified product. Include a calculation of percent yield in your report.

Exercises

1. In this experiment, you started with a white, strong-smelling solid and ended up with a white, strong-smelling solid. What evidence leads you to conclude that these two solids are in fact different compounds and that you did not just isolate the unreacted starting material?

2. Following the format in Appendix V, construct a flow diagram for the synthesis of camphor.

3. The equation in the "Reactions and Properties" section shows only one isoborneol enantiomer and the camphor enantiomer it forms. Find out from your instructor if the isoborneol you used was the right-handed (*R*) enantiomer shown, the left-handed (*S*) enantiomer, or an equimolar mixture of both. Then rewrite the equation showing the correct stereochemistry of the reactants and products.

4. (a) Calculate the atom economy and reaction efficiency of this synthesis. (b) Describe some green features of your synthesis, and any that aren't so green.

5. Describe how each of the following experimental errors or variations might affect your results. (a) You omitted the 30-minute reaction period after the addition step. (b) You added the sodium hypochlorite solution all at once. (c) You mistook a negative starch–iodide test for a positive one and stopped adding sodium hypochlorite solution midway through the reaction period.

6. Write a balanced net ionic equation for the reaction of the acidified sodium hypochlorite solution with iodide ion from the starch–iodide paper, assuming that HOCl is reduced to HCl.

7. Show which carbon–carbon bond of camphor must be broken to form camphoric acid. Use molecular models if necessary.

Other Things You Can Do

(Starred projects require your instructor's permission.)

*1. Isolate an expectorant from cough capsules as described in Minilab 7.

*2. Oxidize cyclohexanol to cyclohexanone as described in *J. Chem. Educ.* **1985**, *62*, 519.

3. Write a research paper about camphor and its applications, using sources listed in the Bibliography.

Boiling Point, Refractive Index
Identification of a Petroleum Hydrocarbon

Physical Properties of Liquids. Alkanes and Cycloalkanes.

Operations

OP-34 Boiling Point
OP-35 Refractive Index
OP-4 Weighing
OP-5 Measuring Volume
OP-30 Simple Distillation

Before You Begin

1. Read the experiment and the descriptions for OP-34 and OP-35, and review the other operations as needed.
2. Prepare a brief experimental plan for this experiment following the directions in Appendix V.

Scenario

An investigative organization known as The Consumer's Advocate (TCA) publishes a monthly magazine, *Caveat Emptor*, which evaluates consumer products and exposes scams. TCA is currently investigating an auto-supplies manufacturer that markets Thrust, a gasoline additive claimed to improve engine performance. TCA's preliminary tests show that the additive has no measurable effect on either power or mileage, and they suspect that the additive is nothing more than a hydrocarbon that burns along with the gasoline. To support its case against the company, TCA needs to know the identity and octane number of the hydrocarbon. If its octane number is higher than that of a typical regular no-lead gasoline (about 87), then the company's claim that the additive improves engine performance might have some validity—although the amount of improvement would be negligible when the additive is used in the quantity recommended on the can.

Because their own chemists are busy with other projects, TCA's technical director, Patsy Haven, has farmed out the job to your institute. Your assignment is to identify the hydrocarbon in Thrust and determine whether or not its octane number is greater than 87.

Applying Scientific Methodology

You should evaluate the evidence and formulate tentative hypotheses as you go along. For example, if you measure a boiling point of 79°C, your tentative hypothesis might be "The alkane in Thrust is 2,4-dimethylpentane" (see Table 8.2). If you then measure its density as 0.79 g/mL, you might have to change your hypothesis to "The alkane in Thrust is cyclohexane."

Measuring a refractive index of 1.4262 would then confirm your second hypothesis and lead you to the conclusion that the alkane is indeed cyclohexane, whose octane number you can look up in Table 8.1.

Table 8.1 Octane numbers of some petroleum hydrocarbons

Hydrocarbon	Octane no.	Hydrocarbon	Octane no.
nonane	−45	2,4-dimethylpentane	82
octane	−17	methylcyclopentane	82
heptane	0	cyclopentane	83
2-methylheptane	24	2,3-dimethylpentane	89
hexane	26	2-methylbutane	89
3-methylheptane	35	butane	92
2-methylhexane	45	2,3-dimethylbutane	95
pentane	61	2,2-dimethylbutane	96
3-methylhexane	66	2,2,3-trimethylbutane	100
methylcyclohexane	71	2,2,4-trimethylpentane	100
2-methylpentane	73	2,2,3-trimethylpentane	102
3-methylpentane	75	toluene	104
cyclohexane	77	benzene	106

Gasoline—A Chemical Soup

Gasoline is a kind of "chemical soup" that contains an incredibly large number of ingredients that are carefully selected and blended to produce a fuel with the desired properties. Virtually all of the main fuel components of gasoline are derived either directly or indirectly from petroleum, which must be refined before a usable fuel is obtained. The word *refine* suggests a simple separation and purification process, but the refining of petroleum is a more complex operation that involves chemical as well as physical changes. As you learned in Experiment 6, petroleum is first fractionated in a distillation tower, which separates its components according to their boiling-point ranges. The fraction that boils between approximately 50°C and 150°C, straight-run gasoline, is not a good motor fuel by itself because it contains a large proportion of straight-chain hydrocarbons such as heptane and hexane (see Figure 8.1). Straight-chain hydrocarbons burn very rapidly, generating a shock wave in the combustion chamber that reduces power and can damage the engine. This "knocking" doesn't occur with highly branched hydrocarbons, which burn more slowly and uniformly.

The octane number of a motor fuel is a measure of its antiknock qualities. The highly branched alkane 2,2,4-trimethylpentane (sometimes called "isooctane") is a very good motor fuel and has arbitrarily been assigned an octane number of 100. Heptane, with no branching, has an octane number of 0. The performance of a particular motor fuel is measured relative to these two alkanes; for example, a fuel that performs as well as a mixture containing 70% 2,2,4-trimethylpentane and 30% heptane is assigned an octane number of 70. Table 8.1 lists the octane numbers of selected hydrocarbons found in gasoline.

A major objective of petroleum refining is to convert the low-octane components of petroleum into higher-octane compounds. This can be accomplished by a variety of chemical processes, such as *isomerization*, which converts straight-chain alkanes to branched alkanes; *cracking*, which breaks down large molecules into smaller ones; *alkylation*, which combines short-chain alkane and alkene molecules to form longer, branched molecules; and

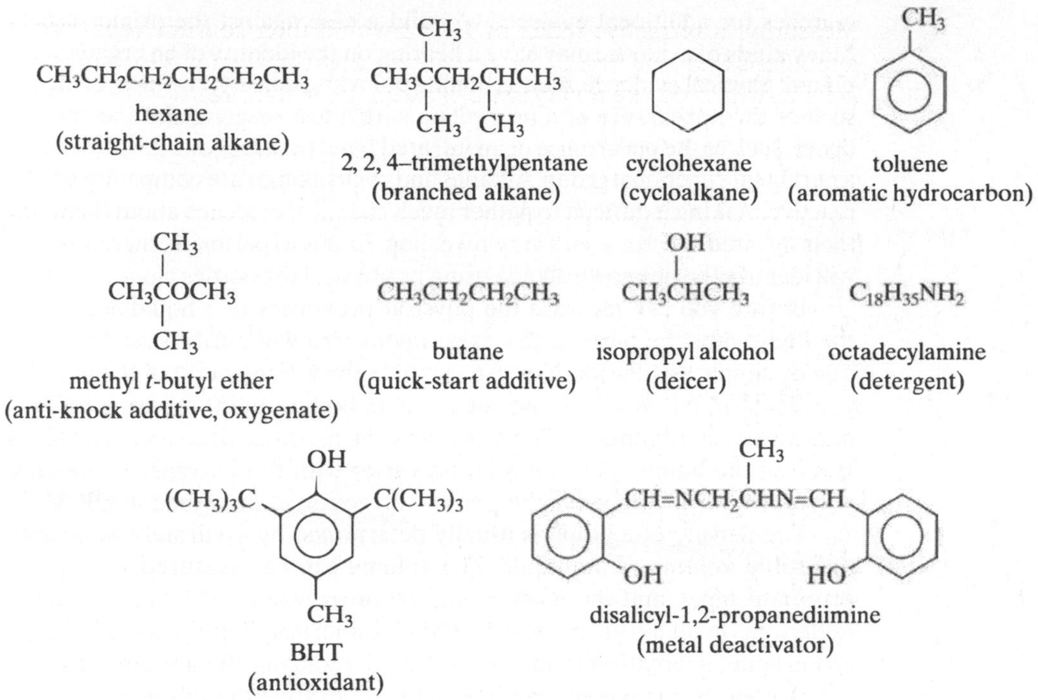

CH₃CH₂CH₂CH₂CH₂CH₃
hexane
(straight-chain alkane)

2, 2, 4–trimethylpentane
(branched alkane)

cyclohexane
(cycloalkane)

toluene
(aromatic hydrocarbon)

methyl *t*-butyl ether
(anti-knock additive, oxygenate)

butane
(quick-start additive)

isopropyl alcohol
(deicer)

octadecylamine
(detergent)

BHT
(antioxidant)

disalicyl-1,2-propanediimine
(metal deactivator)

Figure 8.1 Some components of a typical gasoline

catalytic reforming, which converts alkanes to cycloalkanes and aromatic compounds. Aromatic hydrocarbons such as toluene have particularly high octane numbers and are used to increase the octane rating of no-lead fuels.

Gasoline for use in automobile engines is prepared by combining varying amounts of straight-run gasoline, cracked gasoline, alkylated gasoline, reformate, and other hydrocarbon mixtures in the right proportions to give the desired boiling-point range and octane number. The properties of the fuel are then further adjusted with a variety of additives. Antiknock additives, such as methyl *t*-butyl ether (MTBE), may be included to boost the octane rating. MTBE is also an *oxygenate* (oxygen-containing fuel) that reduces the amount of carbon monoxide produced by combustion. Quick-start additives, such as butane, facilitate cold-weather starting. Antifreeze additives, such as isopropyl alcohol, reduce icing. Antioxidants, such as butylated hydroxytoluene (BHT), help improve fuel stability and reduce gum formation, particularly in fuels that contain appreciable amounts of alkenes. Certain metals, such as copper and iron, can catalyze gum-forming reactions, so chelating compounds such as disalicyl-1,2-propanediimine may be added to deactivate these metals. Cars with fuel injectors require detergent additives, such as octadecylamine, to keep their intake systems clean. Dyes are added for identification and visual appeal.

The chemistry involved in these reactions is described in many organic chemistry textbooks.

The use of MTBE in gasoline is prohibited in some places because of its adverse environmental effects.

Understanding the Experiment

In this experiment, you will attempt to identify an unknown hydrocarbon that is one of the compounds listed in Table 8.2. Identifying an unknown organic compound is somewhat like identifying the perpetrator of a crime. The investigator compiles a list of suspects, hunts for clues that might have a bearing on the case, sifts through the evidence to eliminate most of the suspects, and then searches for additional evidence to build a case against the prime suspect. Many kinds of evidence may have a bearing on the identity of an organic compound: physical evidence, such as boiling point and density; chemical evidence, such as the appearance of a precipitate with a test reagent; and spectral evidence, such as the occurrence of an infrared band that suggests the presence of a particular functional group. Alkanes and cycloalkanes are comparatively unreactive, making it difficult to gather much chemical evidence about them, and their infrared spectra aren't very revealing. In this experiment, therefore, you will identify the unknown alkane using its physical properties alone.

Before you can measure the physical properties of a liquid accurately, the liquid must be pure. In this experiment, you will purify your hydrocarbon by simple distillation. You can estimate the boiling point of the liquid as you distill it, but you will also measure its boiling point by using either a microscale or semimicroscale boiling-point method, described in OP-34. Because the boiling point of a liquid varies with the barometric pressure, you may have to apply a boiling-point correction as described in OP-34.

The density of a liquid is usually determined by accurately weighing a measured volume of the liquid. The volume can be measured with an appropriate pipet, and the mass should be measured to at least the nearest milligram on an accurate balance. Using a microcapillary pipet for the microscale determination requires less liquid, reducing the amount of waste.

A good refractometer can be used to determine the refractive index of a pure liquid with great accuracy. With reasonable care, you should be able to measure the refractive index of your unknown to within 0.05% or better, so this value may be the most important clue to the identity of your hydrocarbon. The refractive index of a liquid is very sensitive to temperature, however, so you will need to correct your observed value if the temperature at the refractometer is above or below 20°C.

The physical constants of the hydrocarbons listed in Table 8.2 are different enough that an accurate determination of all three constants should allow for the certain identification of an unknown. Your instructor may add more hydrocarbons to your list of possibilities. If so, he or she will provide you with the appropriate physical constants or ask you to look them up.

*A **Greener Way:** If the unknown hydrocarbons don't require purifying, and your instructor agrees, you can omit the distillation and measure your hydrocarbon's boiling point using only the capillary method. If you also use the alternative microscale method for measuring density, as described in the Directions, this will reduce the amount of hydrocarbon needed to a few drops.*

Properties

Table 8.2 List of possible hydrocarbons

Name	bp	n_D^{20}	d^{20}
cyclopentane	49	1.4065	0.746
2,2-dimethylbutane	50	1.3688	0.649
2,3-dimethylbutane	58	1.3750	0.662
3-methylpentane	63	1.3765	0.664
hexane	69	1.3749	0.659
methylcyclopentane	72	1.4097	0.749
2,4-dimethylpentane	80	1.3815	0.673
cyclohexane	81	1.4266	0.779
2,3-dimethylpentane	90	1.3919	0.695
heptane	98	1.3877	0.684
2,2,4-trimethylpentane	99	1.3915	0.692
methylcyclohexane	101	1.4231	0.769

Note: Boiling points are in °C; n_D^{20} = refractive index at 20°C using sodium D line; d^{20} = density at 20°C.

Aliphatic hydrocarbons are toxic to some forms of aquatic life, so their release into the environment should be avoided.

DIRECTIONS

Your instructor may suggest additional tests to carry out on your hydrocarbon.

> **Your unknown hydrocarbon is flammable; keep it away from flames and hot surfaces.**

Standard Scale and Microscale

Purification and Boiling-Point Determination.   Obtain a sample of the unknown hydrocarbon from your instructor. Record its identification number and the ambient barometric pressure in your laboratory notebook. Select a suitable heat source and assemble an apparatus for small-scale or microscale simple distillation [OP-30]. Add some boiling chips and be sure that the thermometer bulb is positioned correctly in the still head (connecting adapter) or Hickman still. Distill the liquid slowly, setting aside a low-boiling forerun or high-boiling fraction, if any, for later disposal. Record its boiling range and the temperature when about half of it has distilled (the median boiling point). Then carry out a semi-microscale or microscale boiling-point measurement [OP-34] on the hydrocarbon using a capillary-tube method. The resulting boiling point should be within 1–2° of the median distillation boiling point. If it is not, repeat the boiling point measurement or redistill the hydrocarbon. Apply a correction to the boiling point if the atmospheric pressure was below 750 torr.

Density Measurement.   The temperature of the purified hydrocarbon should be close to 20°C. Accurately measure [OP-5] 1.00 mL (SS) or 0.200 mL (µS) of the liquid into a clean, dry, tared vial using a measuring pipet or an automatic pipet. (**Take Care!** Do not pipet by mouth.) Stopper the vial immediately, and weigh [OP-4] it to the nearest milligram on an accurate balance. Calculate the density of your hydrocarbon from your results.

Alternatively (µS), you can weigh a 100 µL Drummond Microcap on an analytical balance, fill it with your liquid (according to the directions provided with the Microcaps), and reweigh it. The masses should be measured to the nearest tenth of a milligram. Be sure to handle the Microcap with a forceps and not your fingers, which produce enough heat to skew the results.

Refractive Index Measurement.   Measure the refractive index [OP-35] of the purified hydrocarbon as directed by your instructor, and record the temperature of the measurement. Apply a correction to the refractive index if the temperature of the measurement was not 20°C. Identify your unknown hydrocarbon and find its octane number.

Safety Notes

alkanes and cycloalkanes of five to eight carbons

Take Care! Keep the hydrocarbon away from flames or hot surfaces.

A hydrocarbon that boils over a broad range should be redistilled, and a pure fraction (collected over a range of 1–2°C) should be used for analysis.

Stop and Think: What do you think will happen if you put one or two drops of your hydrocarbon in a test tube containing a small amount of water and then shake the test tube? Do it. Was your prediction correct?

Waste Disposal: Put your hydrocarbon and any liquid saved from the distillation in a designated hydrocarbon solvent recovery container.

Exercises

1. The following properties were measured for an unknown hydrocarbon in a laboratory with an ambient temperature of 28°C and a barometric pressure of 28.9 inches of mercury (1 inch Hg = 25.4 torr):

   boiling point: 78.2°C
   refractive index: 1.3780
   mass of 0.200 mL: 0.133 g

   Correct the refractive index and boiling point to 20°C and 1 atmosphere, and calculate the density of the unknown. If the unknown is one of the hydrocarbons listed in Table 8.2, what is its probable identity?
2. Give names and structural formulas for all structural (constitutional) isomers of your unknown hydrocarbon.
3. Describe and explain the possible effect on your results of the following experimental errors or variations. In each case, tell whether the resulting physical property (bp, density, or refractive index) will be too high or too low. (a) You read the temperature when the unknown liquid began to boil and recorded that temperature as its boiling point. (b) To obtain 0.200 mL of the liquid, you filled a Mohr pipet to the 0.200-mL mark and drained it completely into the weighing vial (you can ask your instructor to show you a Mohr pipet). (c) The liquid was at a temperature of 25° when you measured its mass and volume. (d) The liquid was at a temperature of 25° when you measured its refractive index, but you forgot to correct it.
4. A large oil spill that resulted from the 1989 shipwreck of the *Exxon Valdez* caused considerable damage to Alaska's wildlife. Do you think a comparable spill of a water-insoluble liquid that has a density of 1.20 g/mL would have been as harmful to waterfowl and aquatic mammals, assuming that the toxicity of the liquid was comparable to that of petroleum? Explain your answer.
5. (a) Write a balanced equation for the complete combustion of 2,2,4-trimethylpentane in an engine's combustion chamber. (b) Show how butane can be converted to 2,2,4-trimethylpentane using petroleum-refining processes mentioned in this experiment.
6. (a) Dioxane has a boiling point of 101°C. Could you separate dioxane from methylcyclohexane by distillation? Explain why or why not, based on the liquid and vapor compositions during the distillation. (b) How might these liquids be separated?

dioxane

Other Things You Can Do

(Starred projects require your instructor's permission.)

*1. Solve the missing-label puzzle described in Minilab 8.
*2. With your coworkers, obtain and compare gas chromatograms of different grades of gasoline, such as leaded, unleaded, and "gasahol." Refer to *J. Chem. Educ.* **1972**, *49*, 764 and *J. Chem. Educ.* **1976**, *53*, 51 for information and references that will help you interpret the gas chromatograms and identify some of the components.

*3. Test for lead in gasoline as follows: saturate a piece of filter paper with gasoline and expose it to strong sunlight for several hours. Moisten the paper with 3 M acetic acid followed by a few drops of aqueous potassium iodide solution (16.5 g/100 mL). A yellow color that appears after several minutes indicates the presence of lead.

4. Write a research paper about gasoline and petroleum refining using references cited in the Bibliography.

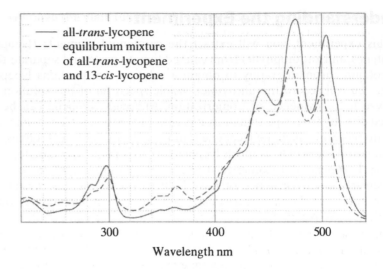

Figure 9.3 Ultraviolet–visible spectra of lycopene stereoisomers

- Measure the height of both peaks from that line, and call the heights *a* and *b*.
- Divide the smaller height (*b*) by the larger (*a*), subtract 0.40, multiply by 100%, and divide the product by 0.40, as shown by the following equation.

$$\frac{\left(\dfrac{b}{a} - 0.40\right) \times 100\%}{0.40}$$

If the percentage of all-*trans*-lycopene is significantly lower than 90%, the lycopene in your tomato paste may have isomerized while the tomatoes were being processed into tomato paste, during your isolation of the lycopene, or both. Before drawing any definite conclusion about the quality of your tomato paste, you should compare your results with those of the other members of your team. Such a comparison should help you select the result that was least affected by the experimental conditions.

Partial isomerization of all-*trans*-lycopene to 13-*cis*-lycopene is also catalyzed by iodine. To show the effect of isomerization, you can add a dilute solution of iodine to your lycopene solution and again obtain its spectrum (or your instructor may demonstrate the isomerization to the class).

Although this experiment requires the use of organic solvents, it features a nontoxic natural product, and the majority of the solvents used can be recovered. The acetone used in the extraction ends up in the wash solvents and may not be recovered. Acetone is slightly toxic to aquatic life, but it does not bioaccumulate and isn't considered a serious environmental contaminant.

DIRECTIONS

Students may work together in small research teams, with each team working on a specific brand of tomato paste, agreeing on a conclusion, and comparing its results with those of other groups working with different brands.

Acetone and petroleum ether are very flammable, and their vapors can irritate the eyes and upper respiratory tract. Keep petroleum ether and the petroleum ether–acetone mixture away from flames and hot surfaces, and do not breathe their vapors.

The hexanes solvent is flammable, so keep it away from flames and hot surfaces.

Safety Notes

petroleum ether   acetone

Standard Scale

Preparing the Chromatography Column. Pack a column for chromatography [OP-21] with neutral Brockmann grade II–III alumina in a 25-mL buret or other appropriate chromatography column, using hexanes as the column-packing solvent (use the method for packing with dry adsorbent described in OP-21). See that the surface of the alumina is uniform and as horizontal as possible. Obtain a 50-mL beaker and a clean, dry 4-dram screw-cap vial to collect the eluates. Clamp the column to a ring stand over the beaker, making sure that it is as vertical as possible.

Take Care! Keep the solvent away from flames and hot surfaces.

Extraction of Pigments from Tomato Paste. Protect the pigment from undue exposure to light throughout the remainder of this experiment. Weigh about 4.0 g of tomato paste into a small beaker. Extract [OP-18c] the solid material three times with successive 10-mL portions of a 50% (by volume) mixture of acetone and low-boiling petroleum ether, each time filtering [OP-15] the extract through fluted filter paper into a small Erlenmeyer flask. After each extraction, decant the liquid extract onto the filter, pressing the residue in the beaker with a flat-bladed spatula to squeeze out as much liquid as possible. After the third extraction, transfer the residue to the filter and wash it with 5 mL of the extraction solvent, combining the wash liquid with the extracts. Wash [OP-24] the combined extracts with 20 mL of 10% aqueous potassium carbonate, followed by 20 mL of saturated sodium chloride solution. Dry [OP-25] the lycopene-containing organic layer with anhydrous sodium sulfate or magnesium sulfate. Concentrate the pigment solution to a volume of about 0.5 mL by evaporating [OP-19] most of the petroleum ether *without* heating. If you inadvertently evaporate the solution to dryness, dissolve the residue in 0.5 mL of hexanes.

Take Care! Keep the extraction mixture away from flames and hot surfaces.

Stop and Think: What is the purpose of the K_2CO_3 wash?

Waste Disposal: Unless your instructor directs otherwise, flush the wash solvents down the drain.

Separation and Isolation of Lycopene. Fill the chromatography column with the first eluant, hexanes, and let the liquid drain until its surface *just* disappears into the sand layer. Immediately transfer the pigment extract to the top of the column with a Pasteur pipet, using a few drops of eluant to rinse any remaining extract onto the column. When the extract surface just disappears into the sand, fill the column nearly to the top with the first eluant and continue to add eluant to keep its level more or less constant. When the yellow carotene band begins to drain out of the column, fill the column with the second eluant, 10% acetone in hexanes (or in high-boiling petroleum ether), and continue to replenish the eluant as before. When the orange–red lycopene band begins to leave the column, replace the beaker by the collection vial and elute the lycopene band, collecting a

Observe and Note: Describe what you see as the bands pass down the column.

5.0-mL sample of eluate from the center of this band. (You can save the rest of the lycopene eluate and evaporate it to obtain the pigment, as described in "Other Things You Can Do".) Then replace the vial by the beaker you used before, and let any remaining eluate drain into the beaker. Use the midband lycopene sample for spectral analysis as soon as possible. If you can't record its spectrum on the same day, store your sample in a tightly closed container in a refrigerator or freezer.

Spectral Analysis and Isomerization of Lycopene.   Using an appropriate 1-cm sample cell and 10% acetone/hexanes in the reference cell, record a spectrum [OP-41] of the midband lycopene sample over the 600–400 nm range (with your instructor's permission, you can scan the 400–250 nm UV range as well). If necessary, dilute the lycopene solution with 10% acetone/hexanes to keep the strongest peak (at ~475 nm) on scale.

Your instructor may demonstrate the isomerization of lycopene. To do it yourself, mix a drop of a 0.025% solution of iodine in hexanes into the lycopene solution and leave the solution in the sample beam at 475 nm, monitoring its absorbance until it remains constant (about 2 minutes). (Alternatively, leave it in bright sunlight for 15 minutes or more.) Then record another spectrum over the same wavelength range as before. Turn in your lycopene solution in a labeled vial.

Estimate the percentage of all-*trans*-lycopene in your midband sample before isomerization, as well as its percentage in your (or your instructor's) sample after isomerization. After consulting with other students who analyzed the same brand of tomato paste, decide whether the lycopene in that brand was isomerized significantly as a result of processing. (Read Exercise 1 before you do this.)

 Microscale

Preparing the Chromatography Column.   Dry pack a column for chromatography [OP-21] using neutral Brockmann grade II–III alumina in a short Pasteur pipet. This should take about 1.5 to 2.0 g of alumina; the top of the alumina layer should be about 1 cm below the upper constriction in the pipet. See that the surface of the alumina is as horizontal as possible. Obtain a 10-mL beaker and a clean, dry, 1-dram screw-cap vial to collect the eluates. Clamp the column to a ring stand over the beaker, making sure that it is as vertical as possible.

Extraction of Pigments from Tomato Paste.   Protect the pigments from undue exposure to light throughout the remainder of this experiment. Weigh about 1.0 g of tomato paste into a 15-mL screw-cap centrifuge tube. Extract [OP-18c] the solid material by shaking the capped tube with 4 mL of a 50% (by volume) mixture of acetone and low-boiling petroleum ether until the solid residue looks dry and fluffy. Then use a flat-bladed microspatula to rub and crush it against the sides of the tube. Repeat the shaking and crushing steps several times. Separate the extract by centrifugation [OP-17] or with a filter-tip pipet, and transfer [OP-6] it to a second 15-mL centrifuge tube. Then repeat the extraction of the solid residue with another 4-mL portion of 50% acetone/petroleum ether, and combine the extracts in the second centrifuge tube. Wash [OP-24] the combined extracts with 5 mL of saturated aqueous sodium chloride, followed by 5 mL of 10% aqueous potassium carbonate and another 5-mL portion of saturated NaCl solution. Dry [OP-25] the lycopene-containing organic layer with anhydrous sodium sulfate or magnesium sulfate, collect it in a 5-mL conical vial, and concentrate it to a volume of 0.1–0.2 mL by evaporating [OP-19] most of the solvent *without* heating. If you inadvertently evaporate the solution to dryness, dissolve the residue in 0.1 mL of hexanes.

Stop and Think: What is the purpose of the K_2CO_3 wash?

Waste Disposal: Unless your instructor directs otherwise, flush the wash solvents down the drain.

Separation and Isolation of Lycopene.
Fill the chromatography column [OP-21] with the first eluant, hexanes, and let the liquid drain until its surface *just* disappears into the alumina layer (or the upper sand layer, if there is one). Immediately transfer the lycopene extract to the top of the column with a Pasteur pipet, using a drop or two of eluant to rinse any remaining extract onto the column. When the extract surface just disappears into the alumina (or sand), fill the column nearly to the top with eluant and continue to add eluant to keep its level more or less constant. When the yellow carotene band begins to drain out of the column, fill the top of the column with the second eluant, 10% acetone in hexanes, and continue to replenish the eluant as before. When the orange–red lycopene band begins to leave the column, replace the beaker underneath it by the collection vial and collect the eluate until nearly all of this band has drained from the column (do not collect any of the subsequent yellow xanthophyll band in this vial). Then replace the vial by the beaker you used before, and let any remaining eluate drain into the beaker. Use the lycopene sample for spectral analysis as soon as possible. If you can't record its spectrum on the same day, store your sample in a tightly closed container in a refrigerator or freezer.

Observe and Note: Describe what you see as the bands pass down the column.

Stop and Think: Why do the bands move down the column at different rates?

Waste Disposal: Place all eluates except the lycopene eluate in a designated solvent recovery container.

Spectral Analysis of Lycopene.
Transfer the lycopene eluate to an appropriate 1-cm sample cell, and add enough 10% acetone/hexanes to fill the cell about three-quarters full. Cap the cell and swirl it gently to mix the contents. Use 10% acetone/hexanes in the reference cell. Record a spectrum [OP-41] of the lycopene sample over the 600–400 nm range. (With your instructor's permission, you can scan the 400–250 nm UV range as well.) If necessary, dilute the lycopene solution with 10% acetone/hexanes to keep the strongest peak (at ~475 nm) on scale.

Your instructor may demonstrate the isomerization of lycopene. To do it yourself, mix a drop of a 0.025% solution of iodine in hexanes into the lycopene solution and leave the solution in the sample beam at 475 nm, monitoring its absorbance until it remains constant (about 2 minutes). (Alternatively, leave it in bright sunlight for 15 minutes or more.) Then record another spectrum over the same wavelength range as before. Turn in your lycopene solution in a labeled vial.

Estimate the percentage of all-*trans*-lycopene in your sample before treatment with iodine, as well as its percentage in your (or your instructor's) sample after treatment. After consulting with the other members of your research team, decide whether the lycopene in your brand of tomato paste was significantly isomerized as a result of processing (read Exercise 1 before you do this). Compare your team's results with those of the other research teams, and attempt to assess the relative quality of different brands of tomato paste.

Observe and Note: Do you see any differences in the spectra? If so, describe them.

Exercises

1. To estimate the percentage of all-*trans*-lycopene present in the original tomato paste, should you average the percentages obtained by all the members of your team? If not, what should you do, and why?

2. (a) Calculate the concentration of the lycopene solution in the spectrophotometer cell before isomerization, given that the molar absorptivity of lycopene at 471 nm is 1.86×10^4. (b) Calculate the mass of lycopene in 3.0 mL of the solution that has the concentration you calculated in (a).

3. (a) Draw the structures of the 7-*cis*, 11-*cis*, and 13-*cis* isomers of lycopene. (b) Linus Pauling predicted that 13-*cis*-lycopene should be considerably more stable than the other two isomers. Explain.

4. Describe some green features of this experiment, and any that aren't so green.

5. Describe and explain the possible effect on your results of the following experimental errors or variations. (a) You used a can of tomato paste that had been left open in a refrigerator for several days. (b) You recorded the second spectrum immediately after adding the iodine solution. (c) You used acid-washed alumina for the chromatographic separation.

6. (a) Explain why some hydrocarbons (such as lycopene and β-carotene) are colored, whereas most other hydrocarbons are not. (b) The color of a lycopene solution fades and may disappear entirely if it is treated with a larger amount of iodine than you used in this experiment. Explain this, and give an equation for a possible reaction.

7. (a) Write an equation for the reaction that occurred during the addition of iodine to all-*trans*-lycopene in this experiment. (b) Write a feasible mechanism for this reaction.

Other Things You Can Do

(Starred projects require your instructor's permission.)

*1. Concentrate some lycopene-containing eluate to a small volume by evaporation [OP-19] at room temperature, and cool it in ice water to obtain crystalline lycopene. Its melting point should be about 175°C.

*2. Separate the dyes in Kool-Aid by paper chromatography as described in Minilab 9.

*3. Make a "tomato-juice rainbow" that shows the effect of conjugation on color as described in *J. Chem. Educ.* **1986**, *63*, 1092.

4. Write a research paper about vitamin A and vision using sources from the Bibliography.

Steam Distillation, Infrared Spectrometry
Isolation and Identification of the Major Constituent of Clove Oil

EXPERIMENT **10**

Isolation of Natural Products. Infrared Spectrometry.

Operations

OP-20 Steam Distillation
OP-39 Infrared Spectrometry
OP-4   Weighing
OP-18 Extraction
OP-19 Evaporation
OP-25 Drying Liquids

Before You Begin

1. Read the experiment and operations OP-20 and OP-39. Review the other operations as necessary.
2. Write an experimental plan following the directions in Appendix V.

Scenario

Professional aromatherapist Rose Otto uses the essential oil from cloves as a treatment for toothache, muscle pain, ringworm, flatulence, warts, and general exhaustion. However, the latest batch of clove oil from her current supplier is darker than usual, has a harsh odor, and appears to be less effective than the oil she received previously. She suspects that the supplier has substituted some clove leaf oil for true clove oil, which is distilled from clove buds, the dried calyxes left after the flowers of the clove tree have fallen off.

Ms. Otto has asked you to provide her with an authentic sample of freshly distilled clove oil and tell her what's in it, so that she can compare the authentic clove oil with the product she has on hand. Your assignment is to isolate clove oil from ground cloves and identify its major constituent, which is known to have the molecular formula $C_{10}H_{12}O_2$. Your supervisor believes that you can identify the constituent by using infrared (IR) spectrometry.

clove bud

Applying Scientific Methodology

Reading the experiment carefully should yield a clue or two about the identity of the unknown, which is one of those illustrated in Figure 10.1. Then you should be able to develop a working hypothesis that will be tested when you obtain and interpret the infrared spectrum.

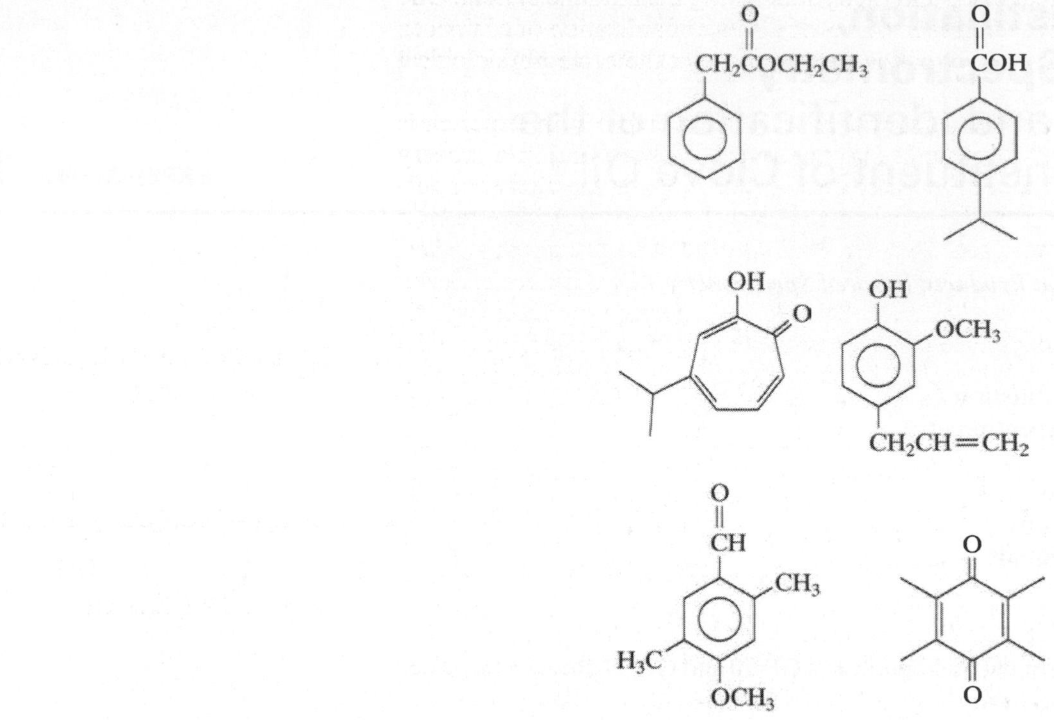

Figure 10.1 Compounds with the molecular formula $C_{10}H_{12}O_2$

Plants and Healing

As people seek alternatives to traditional medical practices, which emphasize the use of drugs and surgery to treat illness, various fields of alternative medicine are gaining adherents around the world. These include *aromatherapy,* the use of essential oils to maintain health and treat illness; *naturopathy,* a system of treating diseases using special diets, herbs, vitamins, and other natural healing methods; and *homeopathy,* which originally relied on the use of minute doses of drugs to cure illness but now utilizes carefully formulated mixtures of herbal medicines. Although some alternative medical practices may be associated with scientifically questionable theories—such as the idea (still accepted by some homeopathic practitioners) that the potency of a drug increases with dilution—many fields of alternative medicine utilize plant-based medicines that have a long history of healing efficacy.

At a time when most physicians prescribe commercial drugs for medical conditions, we may tend to associate herbal medicine—the use of plants to treat and prevent illness—with witch doctors, shamans, or far-out medical cults. But herbal remedies have gained popularity in recent years, as more and more people turn to echinacea, goldenseal, and even garlic to help them stay healthy and cope with illness. Europe is well ahead of the United States in conducting scientific research on herbal medicines. In fact, the popularity of six of the ten top-selling herbs in the United States has resulted mainly from European research. For example, a scientific team at the University of Dusseldorf, Germany, recently studied the active principles and biological effects of the purple coneflower, *Echinacea purpurea,* which is used to treat colds and flu by stimulating the immune system. One objective of their research was to improve the standardization of echinacea extracts, helping to ensure that each dose provides the same physiological activity.

After echinacea, the most widely used herbal remedy in America is garlic—one of the few remedies you are more likely to find in a grocery store than a drugstore. Although researchers disagree on the virtues of garlic, there is evidence that it lowers cholesterol and triglyceride levels in blood, helps prevent blood clots that could lead to heart attacks or strokes, and lowers blood pressure. The active ingredient in garlic was once believed to be a sulfur compound called allicin, which is formed by an enzymatic reaction when garlic is bruised or otherwise damaged and contributes to its distinctive and powerful aroma. However, recent research has shown that allicin is highly unstable and can't be detected in the body after garlic is consumed. Other components of garlic, including *S*-allylcysteine, are now believed to be responsible for garlic's medicinal properties. Cooking garlic tends to destroy its active consitituents, so most of the alleged benefits of garlic are obtained only from the raw cloves or garlic capsules. Eating lots of raw garlic could limit your social life, but that may be a small price to pay for good health!

Legend has it that Achilles, during the siege of Troy, used yarrow to treat the wounded Greeks. Its botanical name, *Achillea millefolium,* recognizes that tradition. The bruised leaves of yarrow help to stop bleeding, heal cuts, and relieve the pain of a wound, so the plant has been used in medical emergencies by backpackers and other outdoor adventurers. The ancients supposedly used St. John's wort (*Hypericum perforatum*) to drive away evil spirits; today it is touted as a natural alternative to Prozac for treating mild to moderate depression. The indigenous North American weed boneset (*Eupatorium perfoliatum*) provides a bitter tea that was a favorite Native American remedy for fevers and other ailments. The closely related joe-pye weed (*Eupatorium purpureum*) was named after a Native American who gained fame by using it to cure typhus. It is an effective diuretic for the treatment of kidney and bladder ailments. Other popular herbal medicines include goldenseal root for treating peptic ulcers, infected gums, sore throats, and skin infections; saw palmetto berries for treating nonmalignant prostate disease; gingko leaf to improve blood flow in capillaries and arteries; aloe vera gel to heal burns, cuts, and wounds; ephedra stems to treat asthma and hay fever; and ginseng root to enhance one's general well-being and revitalize people weakened by old age or illness.

It should not surprise us that natural medicines can be effective. There are, after all, far more molecules in the world's natural life forms than have been synthesized in all the world's pharmaceutical laboratories. Many natural molecules are already known to have medicinal properties, and there must be at least as many more whose properties are yet to be discovered. Most of the drugs now prescribed by physicians were either derived from natural sources or developed by modifying the molecular structures of natural substances. For example, the heart stimulant digitalis is obtained from the foxglove plant, and the molecular structure of aspirin (acetylsalicylic acid) is similar to that of natural salicylates such as salicin from willow bark, which has been used for centuries by Native Americans to treat fevers.

$$CH_2{=}CHCH_2\overset{\overset{\displaystyle O}{\|}}{S}{-}SCH_2CH{=}CH_2$$

allicin

$$CH_2{=}CHCH_2SCH_2\underset{\underset{\displaystyle NH_2}{|}}{CH}\overset{\overset{\displaystyle O}{\|}}{C}OH$$

S-allylcysteine

The six-carbon substituent in salicin is a glucose unit.

$$CH_2OH$$

$$OC_6H_{11}O_5$$

salicin

$$CO_2H$$

$$OCOCH_3$$

aspirin

Although herbal medicines are generally milder and have fewer side effects than traditional prescription drugs, they are not all harmless. According to the U.S. Food and Drug Administration (FDA), herbal preparations containing *Ephedra sinica* (also known as Ma huang) can cause heart attacks, strokes, seizures, and even death if used improperly. Unlike most prescription drugs, different preparations that contain the same herb may vary widely in potency and physiological effect, and since the FDA doesn't regulate them, there is no guarantee that herbal preparations will contain the ingredients claimed. However, when used responsibly by well-informed individuals, herbal medicine may provide a viable alternative to the use of traditional drugs for maintaining good health and treating some medical conditions.

Understanding the Experiment

The *essential oil* of a plant is a volatile mixture of water-insoluble components that exhibits the odor and other characteristics of the plant. In this experiment, you will isolate an essential oil from cloves, which are obtained from a small evergreen tree (*Syzygium aromaticum*) that grows in places such as Indonesia, Madagascar, and Zanzibar. The essential oil of cloves is a pale yellow liquid with a sweet, spicy aroma. Clove oil is unusual among essential oils in that it has only one major component, which makes up about 85% of the oil.

Because ground cloves lose their volatile components over time, it is best to grind fresh whole cloves just before use. Essential oils are usually isolated by steam distillation, in which steam forced through the plant material vaporizes the essential oil, which is then condensed into a receiver along with water from the condensed steam. For microscale work, it is not practical to use externally generated steam, so steam is generated internally by boiling water that contains the plant material. A mixture of ground cloves and water has a tendency to froth up under these conditions, but you should be able to prevent frothing by applying a vacuum to the boiling flask as described for the microscale procedure.

Steam distillation is preferable to ordinary distillation because the volatile components distill at temperatures below their normal boiling points, reducing or preventing decomposition due to overheating. During your steam distillation, the distillate should be cloudy or contain oily droplets at first and become clearer when most of the clove oil has distilled. Clove oil is separated from the distillate by extraction with dichloromethane. It is possible to separate the major component of clove oil from its minor components by extraction with aqueous sodium hydroxide, in which only the major component dissolves. This process is not very practical with microscale quantities because of material losses, but the nature of the process provides a clue that may help you solve the problem posed in the Scenario. The dichloromethane is removed by evaporation, leaving the strong-smelling oil behind.

The major component of clove oil is a liquid that has the molecular formula $C_{10}H_{12}O_2$. The structures of some natural compounds that have this formula are shown in Figure 10.1. Because these compounds have different sets of functional groups, it is possible to distinguish them using IR spectrometry. By detecting the presence or absence of IR absorption bands that correspond to specific functional groups, you should be able to arrive at the correct structure for the major component. The section "Interpretation of Infrared Spectra" in OP-39 describes the characteristic bands of organic compounds that have various functional groups. If you do not carry out the step "Separation of Minor Components," your IR spectrum will contain a weak carbonyl ($C{=}O$) band belonging to one of the minor components. This band, which provides a clue to the structure of the minor component (see Exercise 3), should be disregarded when you try to deduce the structure of the major component.

This is a comparatively green experiment because the clove oil is obtained from a natural product by codistillation with water, and the dichloromethane used to extract clove oil from the aqueous distillate can be recovered by evaporation under vacuum. The EPA classifies dichloromethane as a priority pollutant and has established a maximum contaminant level (MCL) of 5 parts per billion (ppb) for its concentration in drinking water.

*A **Greener Way:** You can recover the dichloromethane by evaporating the extracts under vacuum using a cold trap (see OP-16).*

__Key Concept:__ Different covalent bonds vibrate at different frequencies, producing IR absorption bands at those frequencies. Thus, a functional group that contains a particular set of bonds produces a characteristic set of IR bands, from which it can often be identified.

DIRECTIONS

Live steam (used only in the standard scale procedure) can cause serious thermal burns. Make sure all steam hoses are connected tightly, and turn off the steam before you withdraw the steam inlet tube from the apparatus.
Dichloromethane may be harmful if ingested, inhaled, or absorbed through the skin. There is a possibility that prolonged inhalation of dichloromethane may cause cancer. Minimize contact with the liquid, and do not breathe its vapors.
Clove oil irritates the skin, eyes, and respiratory tract. Avoid contact, and do not breathe its vapors.

Safety Notes

dichloromethane

 ## Standard Scale

Steam Distillation of Cloves.   If fresh whole cloves are provided, use a spice mill or a mortar and pestle to grind enough cloves to provide about 5 g of the ground spice. Weigh [OP-4] 5.0 g of ground cloves in a tared weighing dish. Assemble an apparatus for steam distillation [OP-20] using a large (250–500 mL) boiling flask and a steam trap, and have your instructor check your apparatus. Combine the ground cloves with 50 mL of water in the boiling flask, then steam distill the mixture to obtain the clove oil. Continue the distillation until a drop or two of the emerging distillate, collected on a watch glass, is odorless and water clear, with no oily droplets.

Observe and Note: How does the appearance of the distillate change during the distillation?

Take Care! Turn off the steam before you completely remove the inlet tube from the apparatus.

Waste Disposal: Filter the clove residue through glass wool and place it in a solid-wastes container.

Take Care! Avoid contact with dichloromethane, and do not breathe its vapors.

Stop and Think: What does this separation procedure suggest about the nature of the major component?

Waste Disposal: Unless your instructor directs otherwise, pour the aqueous layers from all extractions down the drain. Place the recovered dichloromethane in a chlorinated solvents recovery container.

If the solution is evaporated without heating, the clove oil may solidify.

If a suitable one is available, use a 20-or 25-mL round-bottom flask. Fill the flask half full with water at the start (after adding the cloves), and add no more water during the distillation.

Observe and Note: How does the appearance of the distillate change during the distillation?

You may need to distill 150 mL of liquid or more before the distillate becomes completely clear. Be sure to vent the steam line or raise the steam inlet tube above the liquid level in the boiling flask before you turn off the steam.

Extraction of Clove Oil.   Extract [OP-18] the clove oil from the distillate with two 20-mL portions of dichloromethane (which layer is the dichloromethane layer?), and combine the extracts.

Separation of Minor Components.   (Optional) Extract [OP-18] the active component of clove oil from the dichloromethane solution with two 15-mL portions of 1 *M* aqueous sodium hydroxide, and combine the aqueous layers. Acidify the aqueous solution to blue litmus paper with 10 mL or more of 3 *M* hydrochloric acid. Extract this aqueous solution with two 15-mL portions of dichloromethane, and combine the extracts.

Isolation and Analysis of the Major Component.   Dry [OP-25] the dichloromethane solution with anhydrous magnesium sulfate or sodium sulfate. Evaporate [OP-19] the dichloromethane under vacuum, using a cold trap, until the boiling stops and the volume of the residue remains constant. Weigh the liquid residue and leave it in an open container for a few minutes, then reweigh it. If its mass decreases significantly between weighings, continue evaporating until the mass is nearly constant. Measure the final mass [OP-4], and obtain an infrared spectrum [OP-39] of your clove oil. Calculate the percent recovery of clove oil based on the mass of cloves you started with. Identify as many bands in the IR spectrum as you can, and deduce the identity of the major component of clove oil. Turn in your IR spectrum along with the product.

 Microscale

Steam Distillation of Cloves.   If whole cloves are provided, use a spice mill or a mortar and pestle to grind enough cloves to provide about 1 gram of ground cloves, grinding them into *coarse* particles to reduce frothing. Weigh [OP-4] 1.0 g of coarsely ground cloves into a 10-mL round-bottom flask. Assemble an apparatus for internal steam distillation [OP-20] using the round-bottom flask, a Hickman still, and a condenser. Calibrate a 15-mL screw-cap centrifuge tube at the 6-mL and 8-mL levels by adding the appropriate volumes of water and marking the position of each meniscus (discard the water). Add enough cold water to the boiling flask to fill it *no more* than half full, and mark the water level with a marking pen. Insert a stopper or thermometer adapter fitted with a bent, fire-polished glass tube in the mouth of the flask, and apply a vacuum to draw any air bubbles out of the cloves. If the mixture foams up near the top of the flask, release the vacuum and let the foam go down, then repeat the process until there is no more foaming. Reattach the flask to the apparatus, and begin heating the mixture to codistill the clove oil with water. During the distillation, use a 9-inch Pasteur pipet to add water through the condenser, keeping the water level relatively constant throughout the distillation; the flask should never be more than half full. Heat rapidly enough to maintain a good distillation rate, collecting about 1 mL every 5–10 minutes. If the liquid mixture threatens to froth up into the neck of the Hickman still, immediately raise the apparatus above the heat source and adjust the heating rate so that any foam stays within the flask. If liquid that contains solid residue boils up into the well of the Hickman still, remove it with a long Pasteur pipet and return it to the boiling flask through the condenser. As the well fills with distillate, transfer the distillate to the calibrated centrifuge tube. Keep distilling until you have collected 6–8 mL of distillate.

Isolation and Analysis of Clove Oil.   Use about 1 mL of dichloromethane to rinse out the well of your Hickman still, and transfer it to the centrifuge tube. Add another 2 mL of dichloromethane, and shake the centrifuge tube to extract [OP-18] clove oil from the distillate, saving both layers. Extract the aqueous layer in the centrifuge tube with two separate 3-mL portions of dichloromethane, and combine all of the dichloromethane extracts. Dry [OP-25] the dichloromethane layer with anhydrous sodium sulfate or magnesium sulfate. *Under the hood,* evaporate [OP-19] the dichloromethane while heating it in a warm-water bath. Weigh the liquid residue, and then reweigh it after another minute or so of evaporation. If its mass decreases significantly between weighings, evaporation should be continued until the mass is essentially constant. Measure the final mass [OP-4], and obtain an infrared spectrum [OP-39] of your clove oil. Calculate the percent recovery of clove oil based on the mass of cloves you started with. Identify as many bands in the IR spectrum as you can, and deduce the identity of the major component of clove oil. Turn in your IR spectrum along with the product.

Waste Disposal: Filter the clove residue through glass wool and place it in a solid-wastes container.

Take Care! Avoid contact with dichloromethane, and do not breathe its vapors.

Waste Disposal: Unless your instructor directs otherwise, wash the aqueous layer down the drain.

If the solution is evaporated without heating, the clove oil may solidify.

Exercises

1. Derive a systematic name for the active component of clove oil, and use this to find its common name in *The Merck Index* [Bibliography, A11] or another reference book.
2. (a) The active component of clove oil can be separated from the minor components by the extraction process described in the standard scale procedure. What property of the active component makes this separation possible? Is this consistent with the structure you chose for it? Explain. (b) Write equations for the chemical reactions involved in the extraction and subsequent acidification of the extract.
3. (a) Clove oil contains about 10% of a minor component that can be hydrolyzed to yield the major component and acetic acid. Deduce the structure of the minor component, which has the molecular formula $C_{12}H_{14}O_3$. (b) The percentage of the major component of clove oil actually increases as the cloves are steam distilled. Explain why, and give an equation for the reaction involved.
4. Describe some green features of this experiment, and any that are not so green.
5. Describe and explain the possible effect on your results of the following experimental errors or variations. (a) You stopped the steam distillation after collecting 3 mL (μ5) or 75 mL (55) of distillate. (b) You forgot to wash the boiling flask, which contained a residue of sodium hydroxide left over from Experiment 4. (c) You didn't evaporate the dichloromethane long enough.

6. (a) Clove oil also contains a small amount of a substance whose systematic name is (*E*)-4,11,11-trimethyl-8-methylenebicyclo[7.2.0]undec-4-ene. Write the structure of this compound and find its common name in *The Merck Index* or another reference book.

7. Following the format in Appendix V, construct a flow diagram for this experiment. If you followed the standard-scale procedure, show how the active component is separated from the solid part of the cloves and the component mentioned in Exercise 3.

Other Things You Can Do

(Starred items require your instructor's permission.)

*1. Analyze your product by gas chromatography, and estimate the percentage of the major component. If your instructor provides a sample of the major component, compare its IR spectrum with that of your product.

*2. Obtain and analyze an essential oil from orange peel as described in Minilab 10.

*3. Steam distill the essential oils from anise seed, caraway seed, or cumin seed following the procedure in this experiment. (Omit the "Separation of Minor Components" step.) Each of these essential oils contains a single major component that can be characterized by IR spectrometry.

4. Write a research paper about herbal medicine after referring to sources cited in the Bibliography.

Thin-Layer Chromatography, NMR Spectrometry
Identification of Unknown Ketones

Qualitative Analysis. Thin-Layer Chromatography. NMR Spectrometry. Ketones.

Operations

OP-22 Thin-Layer Chromatography
OP-40 Nuclear Magnetic Resonance Spectrometry
OP-4　Weighing
OP-5　Measuring Volume
OP-16　Vacuum Filtration
OP-26　Washing and Drying Solids
OP-28　Recrystallization
OP-33　Melting Point

Before You Begin

1. Read the experiment and operations OP-22, OP-28b, and OP-40. Review the other operations as necessary.
2. Prepare a brief experimental plan following the directions in Appendix V.

Scenario

A nearby machine shop in your city was recently destroyed by fire under conditions that strongly suggest arson. A residue recovered at the fire's point of origin was found to contain traces of methyl ethyl ketone (MEK), one of several commercial degreasing solvents that shop employees use to clean the machinery. The primary suspect is a disgruntled ex-employee who was recently fired for sleeping on the job. While searching the suspect's garage, police discovered two unlabeled cans containing flammable liquids, which the suspect claims are charcoal starters for his grill. However, most charcoal-starting fluids are mixtures of petroleum hydrocarbons, and preliminary tests indicate that the liquids found in the suspect's possession are both ketones.

Local police detective Spike Burns has asked your institute to help him solve the crime. Detective Burns provided your supervisor with samples of the two ketones. Matching one of them with the solvent recovered at the fire's point of origin will help the police discredit the suspect's claim and may result in his conviction. Your assignment is to identify the ketones and determine whether either one of them matches the solvent found at the scene of the crime. Your supervisor has requested that you use two different methods to identify your ketones.

Applying Scientific Methodology

You will, in effect, be performing two separate experiments. Your working hypothesis for the first experiment might be, for example, "The first unknown solvent is (or is not) methyl ethyl ketone." You will then gather evidence to prove or disprove the hypothesis. In part **A**, the evidence used to test the hypothesis will be obtained by thin-layer chromatography (TLC) analysis and a melting-point determination. In part **B**, the only evidence will be provided by the nuclear magnetic resonance (NMR) spectrum of the second solvent, which should lead you to its structure. There is, of course, no guarantee that either of the two solvents will be methyl ethyl ketone.

Crime and Chemistry

Forensic chemistry is chemistry applied to the solution of crimes. It deals with the analysis of materials that were used to commit a crime or that were inadvertently left at the crime scene. Materials used to commit a crime might include the ink on a forged document, an explosive used in a terrorist bombing, a toxic substance used in a fatal poisoning, or a flammable liquid used to start a fire. Such materials can be identified and sometimes traced to a particular source. Materials found at the scene of a crime might include paint chips, pieces of fiber from clothing, and particles of dust or soil, as well as any materials that were used to commit the crime. Chips of paint or glass found at the scene of a hit-and-run accident can be analyzed both chemically and under a microscope to determine the make and model of the car involved. Clothing can be traced by the dyes contained in fibers, and dust or soil particles may link a criminal to a particular occupation or location.

Bringing a suspect to trial requires that evidence be presented to establish, first, that a crime has actually been committed, and second, that the suspect is connected with the crime. In an arson case, for example, this requires proof that the fire was deliberately set as well as evidence implicating the suspect. One way to establish that a fire was deliberately set is to prove that an *accelerant* (a flammable substance that causes a fire to intensify and spread rapidly) was used to start and spread the fire. Because fires burn upward from the point of origin, some of the accelerant may soak downward into flooring, rags, paper, or other porous materials. When an investigator traces a fire to its point of origin, he or she can often collect samples of materials containing the accelerant, which are placed in airtight containers and sent to a forensic laboratory for analysis.

In the laboratory, a forensic chemist can separate an accelerant from debris collected at the crime scene by steam distillation or extraction. Once the accelerant has been isolated, it is usually classified according to chemical type (gasoline, turpentine, etc.) by an instrumental method such as gas chromatography or spectrometry. The forensic chemist may then try to match the accelerant sample with a control material, such as a liquid in the suspect's possession or a commercial material. Some flammable liquids, such as the industrial solvent MEK—whose IUPAC name is 2-butanone—contain only one major component and can be compared to the control material using chemical or spectrometric methods. If the original accelerant was a mixture of different components, such as gasoline, its more volatile components will evaporate and burn more rapidly in a fire. For this reason, a sample of accelerant taken from the crime scene will probably not have the same composition as the original accelerant. Therefore, various control materials related to the accelerant are evaporated slowly and analyzed repeatedly by gas chromatography to determine whether the composition of a control material at any stage of evaporation matches that of the recovered material. With this procedure, it is often possible to determine the brand and grade of gasoline or other accelerant used.

Thin-layer chromatography is another important technique used by forensic chemists. TLC provides a rapid, sensitive means of analyzing many of the materials associated with various crimes. The dyes used to color gasoline can be characterized by the pattern of spots they produce on a TLC plate, making it possible in some cases to trace an arson accelerant to its source. The U.S. Treasury Department maintains a library of pen inks that are catalogued according to their TLC dye patterns, allowing an investigator to match the ink on a document with one on file. In a few cases, TLC analysis has proven that the ink used to fraudulently backdate a document did not even exist on the date in question! Substances suspected of being illicit drugs are frequently screened by TLC; most drugs that are mixtures of several substances, such as marijuana, produce telltale patterns that are easily recognized. A thin-layer chromatogram alone may not be sufficient to establish the identity of a suspect material, but it can narrow down the list of possibilities and thus lead to positive identification of the material by other means.

Understanding the Experiment

In this experiment, you will attempt to identify one of the unknown ketones using TLC and the other using NMR spectrometry. TLC can be used in the identification of pure compounds, as well as complex mixtures such as drugs and dyes. When a TLC plate (see OP-22) spotted with structurally similar organic compounds is developed with an appropriate solvent, the R_f values obtained vary more or less regularly with chain length. This correlation is illustrated in Table 11.1 for a homologous series of carboxylic acids. When an unknown compound is known to be one of a limited number of

Key Concept: The R_f value of a substance depends on its relative affinities for the adsorbent on the TLC plate and the developing solvent. A substance with a higher affinity for the adsorbent spends most of its time stuck to the adsorbent and has a low R_f value. A substance with a higher affinity for the solvent spends most of its time dissolved in the solvent and has a high R_f value.

Table 11.1 TLC R_f values for carboxylic acids

Carboxylic acid	# Carbon atoms	R_f
methanoic (formic) acid	1	0.07
ethanoic (acetic) acid	2	0.13
propanoic acid	3	0.30
butanoic acid	4	0.40
pentanoic acid	5	0.50
hexanoic acid	6	0.57
heptanoic acid	7	0.60
octanoic acid	8	0.66

Note: Developed on silica gel using a 19:1 mixture of methyl acetate and 2.5% ammonia.

Vacuum Distillation, Optical Rotation
The Optical Activity of α-Pinene:
A Chemical Mystery

Separation of Liquids. Optical Activity. Stereoisomerism. Terpenes.

Operations

OP-31 Vacuum Distillation
OP-36 Optical Rotation
OP-4   Weighing
OP-10   Mixing
OP-34   Boiling Point

Before You Begin

1. Read the experiment and operations OP-31 and OP-36.
2. Prepare a brief experimental plan following the directions in Appendix V.

Scenario

Dick Hawkshaw, a private investigator, has called on you to help him solve a mystery. A wealthy American entrepreneur named Aldo Hyde was recently found murdered in his chalet in Cannes, France. Although the house was set on fire in an apparent attempt to cover up the murder, firefighters were able to extinguish the fire before the evidence was destroyed. Inside the house, a half-filled can of paint thinner was found; it had no label, but the word TURPENTINE was written on one side with a felt-tip pen. The housekeeper informed Hawkshaw that there was no turpentine in the house before the night of the fire, so the murderer must have brought it there. Gas-chromatographic analysis of a flammable residue found at the fire's point of origin revealed that liquid from this can was used to start the blaze.

The only suspects in the case are Aldo Hyde's widow, Dr. Jacqueline Hyde, a talented but unpredictable talk-show psychologist; and Guy Framboise, a hot-tempered French businessman. Aldo and Jacqueline Hyde had lived separately for more than a year, she in New York and he in Cannes. He was planning to change his will—and leave her out of it—when his untimely death intervened, so Jacqueline stands to inherit most of his fortune. Dr. Hyde arrived in Cannes from New York on the night of the murder and checked into a hotel at 10:05 p.m., approximately two hours before the murder took place, but there are no witnesses who can place her at the scene of the crime. Guy Framboise made threats against Aldo's life after a joint business operation failed, and a reliable witness saw the Frenchman's Peugeot parked near Hyde's chalet on the night of the murder.

Dick Hawkshaw just shipped your supervisor a sample of the turpentine used in the crime. Now it is up to you to discover the crucial evidence that will identify the murderer of Aldo Hyde.

Applying Scientific Methodology

The problem, of course, is "Who murdered Aldo Hyde?" As you read the experiment, you should find some clues that will help you solve the mystery—after you have gathered the experimental evidence.

Turpentine and the Terpenes

Terpenes are among the most widely distributed natural products, occurring in nearly all plants. They are compounds that can, in principle, be broken down into two or more isopentane (2-methylbutane) units. For example, the carbon skeleton of geraniol can be separated in the middle to yield two isopentane units connected head to tail; that is, the "head" end of one unit—the end nearest the side chain—is connected to the "tail" end of the next.

Terpenes that have oxygen-containing functional groups are sometimes called terpenoids.

These isopentane units are also called isoprene units, after a diene that has the same carbon skeleton.

Geraniol, with its rose-blossom aroma, is an important constituent of the essential oil known as rose otto. It also plays an important role in the biosynthesis of terpenes. This process involves the enzymatic isomerization of isopentenyl pyrophosphate and a subsequent reaction with its isomer to yield geranyl pyrophosphate, from which the other terpenes are produced.

Many terpenes, especially the ones that contain oxygen, have pleasant odors and flavors and are therefore important flavoring and perfume ingredients.

Other Things You Can Do

(Starred items require your instructor's permission.)

*1. Determine the percentage composition of turpentine by measuring its optical rotation as described in Minilab 12.
*2. Purify technical grade (85–90%) α-terpineol, whose normal boiling point is 220°C, by vacuum distillation. Cool the purified product in ice, if necessary, to see if it will solidify (pure α-terpineol is said to solidify around 30°C).
3. Write a research paper about terpenes, starting with sources cited in the Bibliography.

PART II

Correlated Laboratory Experiments

The directions in Part I were quite detailed, to help you carry out the operations and complete the experiments successfully. Now that you have learned how to use the major laboratory operations of organic chemistry, you should be able to apply them proficiently to the experiments in Part II, which provide somewhat less detailed directions. It will be increasingly important to *plan ahead* and decide exactly how you will carry out each operation in advance. Continue to refer to the operation descriptions as necessary, particularly when an operation is to be carried out by a different method or in a different context than before. Note that frequently used elementary operations, such as weighing and measuring volume, will no longer be listed at the beginning of an experiment or flagged in the directions. Unless your instructor directs otherwise, assume that your lab reports should include the same information as for the Part I experiments, including yield calculations for all preparations.

The following experiments are correlated with topics discussed in most introductory textbooks of organic chemistry. Correlations are indicated by the list of topics that begins each experiment.

4. Write resonance structures for the following compounds, and predict their relative C=O vibrational frequencies, listing them in order from lower to higher frequency.

5. (a) Outline a synthesis of phenylethyl alcohol (2-phenylethanol) starting with benzene and ethylene oxide. (b) Outline a synthesis of benzyl acetate starting with toluene and ethanol.

Other Things You Can Do

(Starred items require your instructor's permission.)

1. Construct molecular models of some representative organic molecules as described in Minilab 13.
2. Interpret one or more of your IR spectra by indicating what kind of bond is responsible for each significant IR band.
*3. Use a molecular mechanics program to determine the preferred geometry for one or more of your compounds or for another compound suggested by your instructor.
4. Write a research paper about perfumes, starting with sources listed in the Bibliography.

Properties of Common Functional Groups

EXPERIMENT **14**

Functional Group Chemistry. Qualitative Analysis. Infrared Spectrometry.

Operations

OP-5   Measuring Volume
OP-30   Simple Distillation
OP-34   Boiling Point
OP-39   Infrared Spectrometry

Before You Begin

1. Read the experiment, read or review the operations, and write a brief experimental plan.
2. Read or review the section "Interpretation of Infrared Spectra" in OP-39.

Scenario

Marvelous Molecules Incorporated (MMI) manufactures fine chemicals for use by research chemists in educational institutions and industry. One of their sales representatives, Albert Keene, just flew in from Milwaukee to meet an important client. He brought along samples of some representative chemicals to demonstrate the quality of MMI's products. Federal regulations prevented him from transporting the chemicals on the airplane, so he had them sent ahead by freight carrier. On arrival, he discovered—to his dismay—that the bottles of chemicals had been exposed to high heat and humidity during transit, which caused all of their labels to fall off. The labels were salvaged, but he has no idea which label belongs to which bottle, so he placed a desperate phone call to your supervisor asking for help. Your assignment is to match each chemical with the correct label. Fortunately, Al Keene selected chemicals from different families of organic compounds, so you will only have to identify the functional group present in each compound to find out what it is.

Applying Scientific Methodology

At your instructor's discretion, you can work in teams, with each member of the team responsible for the identification of one compound. After you observe some of your compound's physical and chemical properties, you should be able to formulate a tentative hypothesis about the identity of its functional group. You will then record the infrared (IR) spectrum of your compound to test your hypothesis and arrive at a conclusion.

Chemical Taxonomy

A botanist attempting to identify an unknown flowering plant may first examine the flowering parts to detect features that suggest the family of plants to which it belongs, and then study the whole plant systematically to determine its genus and species. For example, a botanist coming across a plant with four symmetrical flower petals and six stamens (four long and two short) might tentatively classify it as a member of the mustard family (*Cruciferae*). Further observation of white flower petals, lyre-shaped leaves, and a red, globular root might then lead the botanist to the conclusion that the plant is a specimen of *Raphanus sativus*. On the other hand, an experienced gardener might immediately recognize the same specimen as a radish plant, based only on its general appearance.

Similarly, people experienced in handling chemicals may learn how to recognize a familiar organic compound from its odor and general characteristics, but a systematic approach is needed for positive identification of a range of organic compounds. Qualitative organic analysis—the identification of organic compounds based on their physical and chemical properties—is analogous in some ways to the identification of plants according to their *taxonomy*—their structural features and presumed natural relationships. Classifying an organic compound into a given family requires first detecting a specific functional group (characteristic set of atoms) in the molecules of the compound. Table 14.1 lists some functional groups found frequently in organic compounds.

Because functional groups influence the physical, chemical, and spectral properties of an organic compound, a chemist can usually identify a compound's functional group by a process that may involve measuring certain physical properties, observing its chemical behavior with different classification reagents, and studying its infrared spectrum. The chemical name and structure of the compound can then be determined by methods described in Part IV of this book.

Table 14.1 Common functional groups and their families

Functional group	Functional group name	Family
$-C=C-$	carbon-carbon double bond	alkene
$-Cl$	chlorine atom	alkyl chloride
$-OH$	hydroxyl group	alcohol (also phenol)
$\overset{O}{\overset{\|}{-C}}-H \ (-CHO)$	carbonyl group, with H on carbonyl carbon	aldehyde
$\overset{O}{\overset{\|}{-C}}- \ (-CO-)$	carbonyl group, no H on carbonyl carbon	ketone
$\overset{O}{\overset{\|}{-C}}-OH \ (-COOH)$	carboxyl group (*carb*onyl + hydr*oxyl*)	carboxylic acid
$-NH_2$	amino group	amine (primary)

Note: Condensed representations of some of the functional groups are given in parentheses.

Understanding the Experiment

In this experiment, you will investigate some physical, chemical, and spectral properties of a compound that belongs to one of the families listed in Table 14.1. Then you will share your results with your coworkers, who will be assigned the remaining compounds. All of the compounds have molecules of about the same size and mass, so differences in their properties will depend primarily on their functional groups.

Physical properties that are affected by functional groups include boiling point, density, and water solubility.

Molecular Structure and Boiling Points

Boiling of a liquid occurs when the kinetic energy of its component molecules becomes high enough to overcome the forces between them, allowing them to leave the surface of the liquid and enter the gaseous state (see Figure 14.1). Since the kinetic energy of molecules increases with temperature, and the energy required to separate molecules depends on the strength of the forces between them, we can expect liquids that have strong intermolecular forces to have high boiling points as well.

The important kinds of intermolecular forces occurring between organic molecules are, in order of increasing strength, (1) dispersion forces (sometimes called van der Waals forces), (2) dipole–dipole interactions, and (3) hydrogen bonding. Dispersion forces are caused by alternating transient charge separations on the surfaces of molecules. They occur among all kinds of molecules, polar or nonpolar, causing them to "stick together" on contact — somewhat like the Styrofoam peanuts used as packing material, which cling to one another by static electricity. Dipole–dipole interactions result when molecules that have permanent bond dipoles line up so that the negative end of one molecule's dipole is opposite the positive end of another's, and vice versa. Hydrogen bonding is a special kind of dipole–dipole interaction that involves the attraction of a highly polarized hydrogen atom for an electron-donating atom (such as oxygen or nitrogen) on another molecule.

Among compounds of similar molecular shape and molecular weight, those capable of forming hydrogen bonds tend to have the highest boiling points, followed by compounds with polar groups capable of dipole–dipole interactions. Hydrogen bonding makes an important contribution to the boiling point only for organic compounds that contain O—H and N—H bonds, with OH groups forming the strongest hydrogen bonds. Compounds with no polar groups, whose molecules are held together only by dispersion forces, tend to have the lowest boiling points.

You will distill your liquid to remove impurities that might affect your results. You can estimate its boiling point during the distillation if it is reasonably pure; otherwise, you may need to redistill it or carry out an alternative boiling-point determination.

Molecular Structure and Density

The density of an organic compound depends, to some extent, on the mass/volume ratio of its constituent atoms. Atoms that have a high nuclear mass confined within a small atomic volume, such as those in the top right-hand corner of the periodic table, have a high atomic density (atomic mass/atomic volume), so compounds whose molecules contain such atoms tend

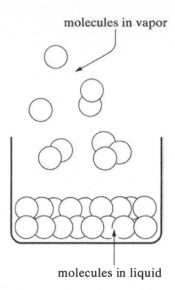

molecules in vapor

molecules in liquid

Figure 14.1 Boiling of a liquid

dipole-dipole
interaction
(formaldehyde)

hydrogen
bonding
(water)

to have comparatively high densities. Among the atoms encountered in this experiment (other than hydrogen), oxygen has the highest atomic density, followed by chlorine, nitrogen, and carbon.

Atomic density of some "heavy" atoms, relative to carbon = 1.00

O: 1.50   Cl: 1.35   N: 1.26

The density of an organic liquid will thus depend, in part, on the number and kind of these "heavy" atoms it contains and on the fraction of its molecular weight they contribute. For example, chlorobenzene (C_6H_5Cl) has a higher density than phenol (C_6H_5OH), even though chlorine has a lower atomic density than oxygen, because the chlorine atom makes a greater contribution to the molecular weight of chlorobenzene than the oxygen atom of phenol makes to its molecular weight.

You will determine the density of your liquid by weighing a precisely measured volume of the liquid.

Molecular Structure and Solubility

Key Concept: *"Like dissolves like." Polar compounds tend to dissolve in polar solvents, and nonpolar compounds in nonpolar solvents.*

$$CH_3CH_2CH_2CH_2CH_2CH_3$$

hexane

benzene

A compound will generally be soluble in a given solvent if the forces holding its own molecules together are similar to the forces holding the molecules of the solvent together *or* if the compound can form hydrogen bonds with the solvent. Thus, hexane dissolves readily in benzene because both compounds are hydrocarbons whose molecules are held together by dispersion forces. Ethanol dissolves in water because both compounds contain OH groups capable of forming hydrogen bonds. Formaldehyde, although it cannot form hydrogen bonds among its own molecules, can hydrogen bond to solvents that contain OH groups, so it is also soluble in water.

Hydrogen bonding interactions

ethanol
and water

formaldehyde
and water

Keep in mind that "solubility" is a relative term; there are varying degrees of solubility. Terms commonly used to indicate the extent to which one compound dissolves in another are, in order of decreasing solubility: miscible (∞), very soluble (v), soluble (s), sparingly soluble (δ), and insoluble (i).

You will measure the solubility of your liquid by shaking it with water in a small test tube. For the purposes of this experiment, a liquid will be classified as *miscible* if it dissolves in an equal volume of water, and as *soluble* if 0.20 mL of the liquid dissolves in about 6 mL of water. If the liquid dissolves, the resulting solution should be clear, like water itself. If it does not dissolve, you should observe a second liquid layer, cloudiness, or liquid droplets (not air bubbles) in the water. Because low-boiling liquids may evaporate rapidly, you should keep the test tube stoppered while you make your observations.

Classification Tests for Functional Groups

Chemists have developed a number of simple chemical tests that are positive only for compounds that have certain kinds of functional groups. A litmus test, for example, can be used to detect acidic and basic functional groups. When dissolved in water, carboxylic acids turn blue litmus paper red, and amines turn red litmus paper blue. Compounds that are easily oxidized react with a solution of chromium(III) oxide in sulfuric acid, commonly referred to as "chromic acid." Primary and secondary alcohols react within 2–3 seconds to form an opaque blue–green suspension. Aldehydes give the same result, but they usually take 10 seconds or more to react. Aldehydes and ketones both react with 2,4-dinitrophenylhydrazine (DNPH) reagent to yield yellow or orange precipitates. Alkenes and aldehydes react with dilute aqueous potassium permanganate ($KMnO_4$) to form a brown precipitate as the purple color of the permanganate disappears. Alkyl halides give a green flame in the Beilstein test, which involves heating a copper wire moistened with the unknown in a burner flame.

The test results and their interpretations are summarized as follows.

A Greener Way: In place of chromic acid, ceric ammonium nitrate can be used to test for alcohols, and Schiff's reagent for aldehydes. Your instructor will provide directions for conducting such tests. Alternatively, alcohols and aldehydes can be identified from their infrared spectra alone.

- Blue litmus paper turns red $\Rightarrow$ carboxylic acid
- Red litmus paper turns blue $\Rightarrow$ amine
- Chromic acid forms blue–green suspension in 2–3 seconds $\Rightarrow$ 1° or 2° alcohol
- Chromic acid forms blue–green suspension in 10 seconds or more $\Rightarrow$ aldehyde
- DNPH yields orange or yellow precipitate $\Rightarrow$ aldehyde or ketone
- $KMnO_4$ yields brown precipitate $\Rightarrow$ alkene or aldehyde
- Burner flame turns green $\Rightarrow$ alkyl halide

Conflicting or ambiguous results may be produced with some tests because of impurities in the unknown or because the tests themselves may be open to misinterpretation. For example, an aldehyde often contains traces of the corresponding carboxylic acid as an impurity, leading to a false-positive litmus test. In such cases, it may be necessary to repeat a test or redistill the unknown. For additional information and general equations for the reactions involved, see the "Classification Tests" section of Part IV.

Although only very small quantities of chromic acid and potassium permanganate are used for their tests, both can harm the environment and must be disposed of properly. The chromium(VI) in chromic acid is classified by the Environmental Protection Agency (EPA) as a priority pollutant; it is very toxic and can cause cancer and genetic mutation in some organisms. Potassium permanganate is harmful to aquatic life. 2-4-Dinitrophenylhydrazine is not a common environmental contaminant, so there is little information on its effects on the environment. But similar hydrazines are very toxic, so DNPH and its derivatives should not be released into the environment.

Infrared Spectra

Each kind of functional group is associated with one or more characteristic IR bands that can reveal its presence. A carboxyl group (COOH), for example, contains $C=O$, $C-O$, and $O-H$ bonds, all of which give rise to

one with those groups on *opposite* sides is a *trans* isomer. Maleic acid is thus *cis*-2-butenedioic acid, and fumaric acid is *trans*-2-butenedioic acid.

Understanding the Experiment

Friedrich Wöhler prepared urea by several different methods. One method involved mixing ammonium chloride and silver cyanate and then evaporating the resulting ammonium cyanate solution to dryness. When heated, ammonium cyanate decomposes to ammonia and cyanic acid, which combine to form urea.

$$NH_4Cl + AgOCN \longrightarrow NH_4OCN + AgCl$$

ammonium
cyanate

$$NH_4OCN \xrightarrow{\text{heat}} NH_3 + HOC \equiv N \longrightarrow H_2N\overset{\overset{\displaystyle O}{\|}}{C}NH_2$$

cyanic   urea
acid

You will attempt to isomerize the phenyl derivative of ammonium cyanate by a similar reaction. As shown in the "Reactions and Properties" section, aniline reacts with hydrochloric acid to form the organic salt phenylammonium chloride. By combining an aqueous solution of phenylammonium chloride with potassium cyanate, you can prepare a solution that contains phenylammonium cyanate. Then you will see whether heating this solution yields a different product. If it does, a melting-point determination should tell you whether you have synthesized phenylurea, a constitutional isomer of phenylammonium cyanate.

Sometimes, one of a pair of geometric isomers can be converted to the other under conditions that cause temporary cleavage of a pi bond. When maleic acid is heated with a trace of bromine in the presence of light, some of the bromine molecules break apart into bromine atoms. A bromine atom then adds to one end of the double bond of a maleic acid molecule, breaking the pi bond. This allows the molecule to rotate freely about the remaining sigma bond. If the bromine atom is ejected when the COOH groups are opposite one another, the pi bond is regenerated to yield a molecule of fumaric acid.

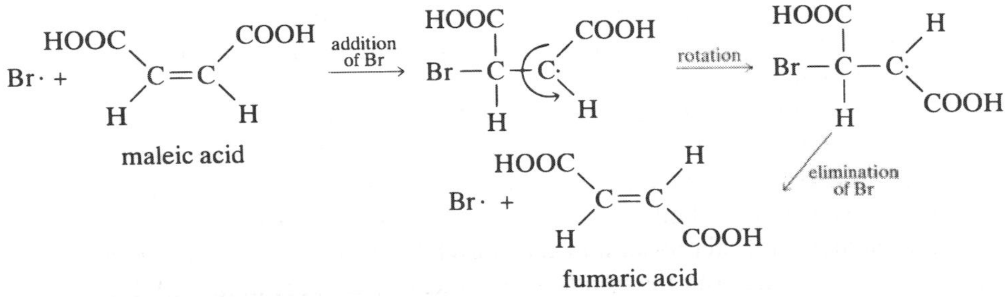

Mechanism of the isomerization of maleic acid

Maleic acid and fumaric acid are both solids, so this reaction must be run in solution, and the fumaric acid cannot be separated from the starting material by filtration. However, dimethyl maleate (the methyl ester of maleic acid) is a liquid, and dimethyl fumarate is a solid. Therefore, if dimethyl maleate can be induced to isomerize to dimethyl fumarate, the liquid *cis* isomer should change to a solid *trans* isomer that can be separated by filtration. If molecular model sets are available, you can simulate the isomerization of dimethyl maleate after building a molecular model of it.

Aniline is highly toxic to aquatic life and is classified as a hazardous air pollutant, so it should not be released into the environment. Potassium cyanate is slightly toxic to fish but is not considered a serious environmental contaminant. Bromine is toxic to marine organisms, but no water quality standards for bromine have been issued by the U.S. government.

Reactions and Properties

A $PhNH_2 + HCl \longrightarrow PhNH_3Cl$
  aniline   phenylammonium
                        chloride

$PhNH_3Cl + KOCN \longrightarrow PhNH_3OCN + KCl$
                       phenylammonium
                             cyanate

$$PhNH_3OCN \longrightarrow PhNH\overset{\overset{\displaystyle O}{\|}}{C}NH_2$$
                    phenylurea

B
$$\underset{\text{dimethyl maleate}}{\overset{\displaystyle CH_3OOC}{\underset{\displaystyle H}{}}C=C\overset{\displaystyle COOCH_3}{\underset{\displaystyle H}{}}} \quad \xrightarrow{Br_2} \quad \underset{\text{dimethyl fumarate}}{\overset{\displaystyle CH_3OOC}{\underset{\displaystyle H}{}}C=C\overset{\displaystyle H}{\underset{\displaystyle COOCH_3}{}}}$$

Table 17.1 Physical properties

	mol wt	mp	bp	*d*
aniline	93.1	−6	184	1.022
potassium cyanate	81.1	800 d		
phenylurea	136.2	147	238	
dimethyl maleate	144.1	8	205	1.151
dimethyl fumarate	144.1	104	193	

Note: mp and bp are in °C; *d* is in g/mL.

DIRECTIONS

A. Isomerization of Phenylammonium Cyanate

Aniline is poisonous and may be carcinogenic. It can cause serious injury or death if swallowed, inhaled, or absorbed through the skin. Wear protective gloves, and dispense under a fume hood; avoid contact, and do not breathe its vapors.

aniline

Safety Notes

EXPERIMENT 18

Structures and Properties of Stereoisomers

Isomerization Reactions. Stereoisomerism. Infrared Spectrometry.
Gas Chromatography.

Operations

OP-7   Heating
OP-10 Mixing
OP-18 Extraction
OP-19 Evaporation
OP-25 Drying Liquids
OP-34 Boiling Point
OP-35 Refractive Index
OP-36 Optical Rotation
OP-37 Gas Chromatography
OP-39 Infrared Spectrometry

Before You Begin

1. Read the experiment, read or review the operations as necessary, and write an experimental plan.
2. Before beginning this experiment, you should know how to draw stereochemical structural formulas, how to designate configurations at stereocenters, and how to classify stereoisomers as enantiomers and diastereomers. Review the sections of your lecture textbook on stereochemistry if you need help in any of these areas.

Scenario

The new-age herbalist Basil Wormwood explores the composition and uses of natural products from plants. For example, he isolates and analyzes essential oils from various plants using techniques he learned in his college organic chemistry course. While pursuing his studies, he observed several phenomena that puzzled him, so he has contacted the institute to see if its consulting chemists can explain them.

- While Basil was away, his assistant accidentally spilled some vinegar in a batch of peppermint oil. When he returned, he removed the vinegar by extraction, but the aroma of the oil had changed markedly.
- After isolating the major component of caraway oil (from caraway seeds) and the major component of spearmint oil (from spearmint leaves), Basil discovered that these substances, whose odors are very different, have virtually identical physical and chemical properties.
- When examined under a microscope, the tartaric acid crystals he received from a supplier looked different from the crystals of natural tartaric acid that he had used before.

caraway plant   spearmint plant

Your assignment, then, is threefold:

- To find out what happens when menthone from peppermint oil is treated with acid
- To find out how the major components of caraway and spearmint oils differ (if they do)
- To find out whether the tartaric acid provided is natural L-(+)-tartaric acid or an "unnatural" tartaric acid stereoisomer

Applying Scientific Methodology

You should find enough information in the experiment to formulate working hypotheses for the first two problems. You will need to gather some experimental evidence before you can develop a meaningful hypothesis for the third problem.

Alice Through the Looking Glass: Dissymmetry and Life

In Lewis Carroll's *Through the Looking Glass,* Alice—contemplating the world she views in her mirror—wonders aloud to her cat whether looking-glass milk would be good to drink. Such an inquiry might seem naive, even to a cat. If you hold a glass of milk in front of a mirror, the milk and its reflection look exactly alike, so why should "mirror-image milk" be any different from the milk we ordinarily drink? You may be surprised to learn that mirror-image milk would not be very good to drink; it would be quite indigestible, and its taste would be bitter and unpleasant. To understand why, let's take an imaginary trip to a looking-glass world.

Imagine yourself onboard the spaceship *Icarus,* bound for the planetary system of Barnard's star. Arriving on the surface of its earthlike third planet, called *Arret* by the inhabitants, your landing party is invited to a feast by some friendly Arretians. You are served their standard banquet fare: roast *krop,* overdone *iloc'corb,* crusty *yawarac* seed rolls, and an aromatic *t'nim* tea. You had been looking forward to a change from the monotonous space diet, but you soon lose your appetite. Most of the food tastes flat or bitter, the seeds on the roll have a minty flavor, and the tea smells like caraway seeds! After politely declining a second helping of *krop,* you return to your shuttlecraft with the rest of the landing party. Before long, you and the rest of the crew are suffering from indigestion, which causes a serious breach in interplanetary relations.

Earthly organisms are composed mostly of *chiral* molecules, such as the D-monosaccharides in complex carbohydrates and the L-amino acids that make up proteins and enzymes. It is conceivable that somewhere in the universe there exists a mirror-image planet, otherwise similar to Earth, where carbohydrates are composed of L-monosaccharides and proteins of D-amino acids, and the configurations of other chiral compounds are reversed as well. On such a planet, many foods would taste different from their earthly counterparts, and we earthlings would find them indigestible. The chiral compounds on that planet would still be optically active; that is,

A proposed expedition to Barnard's star was described in New Scientist **1974,** *63, 522.*

Key Concept: *A chiral compound is one that exhibits "handedness." Like a glove, a chiral molecule lacks a plane of symmetry and cannot be superposed on its mirror image.*

Reaction of Iodoethane with Sodium Saccharin, an Ambident Nucleophile

EXPERIMENT 20

Nucleophilic Substitution. NMR Spectrometry. Carboxylic Acid Derivatives. Heterocyclic Compounds.

Operations

OP-38 High-Performance Liquid Chromatography (optional)
OP-16 Vacuum Filtration
OP-26 Washing and Drying Solids
OP-33 Melting Point
OP-40 Nuclear Magnetic Resonance Spectrometry

Before You Begin

1. If you will be doing the optional HPLC analysis, read OP-38. Read the experiment, read or review the other operations, and write a brief experimental plan.
2. Calculate the mass of 10.0 mmol (SS) or 2.00 mmol (μS) of sodium saccharin, and the theoretical yield of ethylsaccharin.

Scenario

A nutritional Calorie (the C should be capitalized) is 1000 times as large as a scientific calorie.

Saccharin is a nonnutritive sweetener, meaning that it is not metabolized by the body to produce energy. Saccharin is usually mixed with fructose or other Calorie-laden sweeteners to mask its bitter aftertaste, giving the mixture about half as many Calories as sucrose and thus making it less attractive as a sugar substitute. Dulcinea Petty IV directs a product development team at Sweet Nothings Ltd., which manufactures saccharin. She has learned that substances with N—H bonds often have bitter tastes, so she wonders if converting the N—H bond of saccharin to an N—C bond by alkylating it will mask the bitter taste and thus yield a better sweetener. Saccharin is converted to its more nucleophilic sodium salt prior to alkylation, but resonance structures of the salt reveal that it is an ambident nucleophile; that is, it has two potentially nucleophilic atoms: the nitrogen atom and an oxygen atom.

saccharin   resonance structures of sodium saccharin

Before their quest for a better sweetener can be pursued, Sweet Nothings needs to know whether or not alkylation will occur mainly on the nitrogen atom. Your assignment is to carry out the alkylation of sodium saccharin with iodoethane and analyze the product mixture to determine the structure of the major product.

Applying Scientific Methodology

You should be able to formulate a working hypothesis (or at least a reasonable guess) after reading the experiment, and then test it by either nuclear magnetic resonance (NMR) or high-performance liquid chromatography (HPLC) analysis of your product. You will not taste the product, but you can ask your instructor about its taste after completing the experiment.

Saccharin, an Accidental Sweetener

One rule that most chemists follow scrupulously is to never, *ever* taste anything they make in the laboratory. A chemist should not even eat or drink anything while working in the lab because of possible contamination by toxic chemicals. During the nineteenth century, however, chemists were not so fastidious. It was a common practice to perform a "taste test" on any new chemical, sometimes with unfortunate results; but occasionally, an accidental or deliberate tasting paid off with a new discovery.

Ira Remsen, a Johns Hopkins University chemistry professor, studied chemistry under a protégé of the "father of organic chemistry," Friedrich Wöhler, and became the most famous American chemist of the nineteenth century. In 1878, a German student working in Remsen's research group, Constantin Fahlberg, prepared some white crystals of a previously unknown compound from *o*-toluenesulfonamide. He later ate a piece of bread and was astonished to find that it tasted intensely sweet. It didn't take Fahlberg long to trace the sweet taste to the new compound he had just handled, which he named saccharin after the Latin word for sugar, *saccharum*.

Saccharin is about 300 times sweeter than sucrose (common table sugar). Its sweetness came as a surprise because no one was looking for a synthetic sweetener at the time—most scientists believed that only natural compounds could be sweet. Fahlberg recognized the commercial possibilities of a nonfattening sweetener, so he applied for a patent and began to manufacture saccharin. Despite its somewhat bitter aftertaste, saccharin was the most popular artificial sweetener during most of the twentieth century, outselling other synthetic sweeteners such as dulcin (from the Latin *dulcis*, meaning "sweet"), which was discovered just six years after saccharin.

Concerns about the safety of saccharin cropped up from time to time, inspiring Theodore Roosevelt to proclaim, "Anyone who says saccharin is injurious to health is an idiot!" Roosevelt, who liked to sweeten his chewing tobacco with saccharin, was no authority on the safety of commercial products, but his words must have reassured many Americans about saccharin. Then, in a Canadian study carried out in 1977, some rats developed bladder tumors when fed a diet that contained 5% saccharin. Although the rats' diet was equivalent to a human consuming about 1000 cans of diet soda per day, saccharin was promptly removed from the GRAS (generally recognized as safe) list and later banned in the United States. Reacting to protests by diabetics and overweight Americans, for whom consuming sugar was a greater health risk than the remote possibility of saccharin-induced cancer, Congress suspended the ban in 1979, but foods containing saccharin were still required to carry a warning label. Saccharin was finally removed from the U.S. government's list of suspected carcinogens in 1999 in response to evidence that the rat-bladder tumors arose from mechanisms that are not relevant to humans.

Because of the cancer scare and competition from other synthetic sweeteners, such as aspartame and sucralose, saccharin use has declined sharply in recent years. Sucralose (in Splenda), which like aspartame (in NutraSweet and Equal) lacks the bitter aftertaste of saccharine, has become the world leader in the $1.5 billion artificial sweetener market. Approximately 600 times sweeter than sucrose and 4 times sweeter than aspartame, sucralose is manufactured by selectively chlorinating glucose, converting three of its hydroxyl groups to chlorine atoms. Aspartame, the previous leader among artificial sweeteners, is still popular, but a French sweetener called superaspartame is 300 times sweeter than aspartame and—unlike aspartame—can be used in baking and frying. The natural sweetener thaumatin, which is extracted from the West African ketemfe plant, is reported to be nearly 100,000 times sweeter than sucrose, making it the sweetest natural substance ever discovered. It is also (like aspartame) a flavor enhancer, so it has been used to persuade farm animals to eat more—pigs gain up to 10% more weight when thaumatin is added to their feed!

Understanding the Experiment

DMF

Key Concept: Solvation reduces the strength of a nucleophile and therefore decreases the rates of its nucleophilic substitution reactions.

In this experiment, you will carry out the reaction of sodium saccharin with iodoethane in the solvent *N,N*-dimethylformamide (DMF). This is a nucleophilic substitution reaction in which the nucleophilic atom can be either nitrogen or oxygen, and the leaving group is iodide ion (I^-). The rate of a nucleophilic substitution reaction can be very sensitive to the solvent used. Polar protic solvents (solvents capable of hydrogen bonding), such as water and ethanol, form bulky solvation shells around a charged nucleophile, reducing its nucleophilic strength. Polar aprotic solvents, such as DMF, do not solvate the nucleophile strongly, leaving it free to attack the substrate. Thus, they accelerate the rates of many substitution reactions, particularly S_N2 reactions, in which the strength of the nucleophile has a large effect on the reaction rate.

As shown in the "Reactions and Properties" section, nucleophilic attack by nitrogen on iodoethane yields *N*-ethylsaccharin, whereas nucleophilic attack by oxygen yields *O*-ethylsaccharin. Thus, your product will be either *N*-ethylsaccharin, *O*-ethylsaccharin, or a mixture of the two, depending on whether saccharin's nitrogen atom or oxygen atom (or both) acts as the nucleophilic atom. Predicting the most likely product is not easy because several competing factors may come into play. *N*-Ethylsaccharin is more stable than *O*-ethylsaccharin, so it should be the major (or only) product if the reaction reaches thermal equilibrium. However, the oxygen atom of sodium saccharin has a higher partial negative charge than the nitrogen atom because oxygen is more electronegative than nitrogen, so a reaction involving oxygen as the nucleophile should occur faster than one involving nitrogen. For example, the reaction of potassium saccharin with 2-bromopropane in DMF yields mainly *O*-isopropylsaccharin.

You can determine the identity or composition of your product by using proton nuclear magnetic resonance (^{1}H NMR) spectrometry. An oxygen atom has a stronger deshielding effect on nearby protons than does a nitrogen atom, so the signal for the methylene protons (highlighted) of an $-OCH_2CH_3$ group will appear farther downfield ($\delta \approx 4.7$ ppm) than the corresponding signal for an $-NCH_2CH_3$ group ($\delta \approx 3.9$ ppm). Because the methylene protons have three methyl protons as neighbors, their signal in either case will be a quartet. If your product is either N-ethylsaccharin or O-ethylsaccharin, you can identify it from the chemical shift of its methylene quartet. If it is a mixture, you can measure the integrated signal areas for both quartets, calculate the percentages of N-ethylsaccharin and O-ethylsaccharin present, and decide which one is the major product.

At your instructor's discretion, you can analyze your product using HPLC in addition to or instead of NMR spectrometry.

Although iodoethane is toxic, it is not considered a highly hazardous chemical and is not regulated by the EPA or other U.S. agencies. N,N-Dimethylformamide can harm aquatic organisms, but it biodegrades readily in soil and water and does not bioaccumulate; it is listed as a hazardous air pollutant by the EPA.

Reactions and Properties

Table 20.1   Physical properties

	mol wt	bp	mp	d
sodium saccharin	205.2			
iodoethane	156.0	72		1.950
N,N-dimethylformamide	73.1	153		0.945
N-ethylsaccharin	211.2		95	
O-ethylsaccharin	211.2		211	

Note: bp and mp are in °C; density is in g/mL.

DIRECTIONS

Iodoethane severely irritates the eyes, skin, and respiratory tract. Wear gloves, avoid contact, and do not breathe its vapors.
N,N-Dimethylformamide is harmful by inhalation, ingestion, and absorption through the skin. Avoid contact, and do not breathe its vapors.
Deuterochloroform is harmful if inhaled, ingested, or absorbed through the skin, and it may be carcinogenic. Avoid contact, and do not breathe its vapors.

Safety Notes

N,N-dimethylformamide

Standard Scale

Reaction. *Carry out the reaction under the hood.* Weigh 10.0 mmol of sodium saccharin and add it to 5.0 mL of *N,N*-dimcthylformamide in a 125-mL Erlenmeyer flask. Heat the mixture in an 80°C water bath, with swirling, until the solid dissolves. Next, add 0.80 mL (~10 mmol) of iodoethane using a dispenser or an automatic pipet. Cover the mouth of the flask with Parafilm and heat the mixture in the water bath, with occasional swirling, for 10 minutes; keep the water temperature close to 80°C during this period.

Separation. Let the reaction mixture cool to room temperature, add 40 mL of water, and shake the stoppered flask until any liquid residue that forms has solidified. Cool the flask in an ice/water bath, and break up the solid with a spatula or stirring rod until it is finely divided. Collect the solid by vacuum filtration [OP-16], washing it twice with 5-mL portions of ice-cold water [OP-26a]. Dry [OP-26b] the product, but do *not* taste it!

Analysis. Measure the mass and melting-point range [OP-33] of the product. Obtain an integrated ^{1}H NMR spectrum [OP-40] of the product in deuterochloroform. (At your instructor's discretion, you can analyze the product mixture by HPLC [OP-38]; the instructor will demonstrate the operation of the instrument.) If the product is a single compound, deduce its identity. If it is a mixture, calculate its percentage composition and decide whether *N*-ethylsaccharin or *O*-ethylsaccharin is the major product.

 Microscale

Reaction. *Carry out the reaction under the hood.* Weigh 2.00 mmol of sodium saccharin and add it to 1.0 mL of *N,N*-dimethyl formamide in a 25-mL Erlenmeyer flask. Heat the mixture in an 80°C water bath, with swirling, until the solid dissolves. Next, add 0.16 mL (~2.0 mmol) of iodoethane using an automatic pipet or graduated syringe. Cover the mouth of the flask with Parafilm and heat the mixture in the water bath, with occasional swirling, for 10 minutes; keep the water temperature close to 80°C during this period.

Separation. Let the reaction mixture cool to room temperature, add 8.0 mL of water, and shake the stoppered flask until any liquid residue that forms has solidified. Cool the flask in an ice/water bath, and break up the solid with a flat-bladed microspatula until it is finely divided. Collect the solid by vacuum filtration [OP-16], washing it twice with ice-cold water [OP-26a]. Dry [OP-26b] the product, but do *not* taste it!

Analysis. Measure the mass and melting-point range [OP-33] of the product. Obtain an integrated ^{1}H NMR spectrum [OP-40] of the product in deuterochloroform. (At your instructor's discretion, you can analyze the product by HPLC [OP-38]; the instructor will demonstrate the operation of the instrument.) If the product is a single compound, deduce its identity. If it is a mixture, calculate its percentage composition and decide whether *N*-ethylsaccharin or *O*-ethylsaccharin is the major product.

Take Care! Wear gloves, avoid contact with DMF and iodoethane, and do not breathe their vapors.

Waste Disposal: Put the filtrate in a designated solvent recovery container.

Stop and Think: Is the product a single compound or a mixture? How can you tell?

Waste Disposal: Put the deuterochloroform solution in a designated solvent recovery container.

Take Care! Avoid contact with CDCl$_3$, and do not breathe its vapors.

Take Care! Wear gloves, avoid contact with DMF and iodoethane, and do not breathe their vapors.

Waste Disposal: Put the filtrate in a designated solvent recovery container.

Stop and Think: Is the product a single compound or a mixture? How can you tell?

Waste Disposal: Put the deuterochloroform solution in a designated solvent recovery container.

Take Care! Avoid contact with CDCl$_3$ and do not breathe its vapors.

Exercises

1. (a) Assuming that the reaction was S_N2, which atom appears to be more nucleophilic: N or O? (b) Write a mechanism showing the transition state of the reaction that led to your major product.
2. Describe and explain the possible effect on your results of the following experimental errors or variations. (a) The reagent bottle labeled "sodium saccharin" contained saccharin instead. (b) You used water as the reaction solvent rather than DMF. (c) You heated the reaction mixture for 3 hours under reflux.
3. Following the format in Appendix V, construct a flow diagram for this experiment.
4. (a) Calculate the atom economy and reaction efficiency of your synthesis. (b) Describe some green features of your synthesis, and any that are not so green.
5. Most compounds that contain N—H bonds are basic, but saccharin is acidic. Explain why, using resonance structures.
6. Outline a synthesis of saccharin from o-toluenesulfonamide.
7. One objection raised to the use of aspartame is that it decomposes in the presence of moisture to produce phenylalanine, which must be avoided by people who have the genetic condition phenylketonuria, and methanol, which can have an effect on mental behavior. Write an equation for a hydrolysis reaction of aspartame that yields both of these products.

$$\underset{\text{aspartame}}{{}^{-}\text{OCCH}_2\text{CHCNHCHCOCH}_3}$$

Other Things You Can Do

(Starred items require your instructor's permission.)

*1. Add some aqueous sodium bicarbonate to a solution of saccharin (not sodium saccharin) and explain the result, writing an equation for the reaction.
*2. Carry out an S_N1 reaction of trityl bromide with ethanol as described in Minilab 17.
3. Write a research paper about artificial sweeteners, starting with sources listed in the Bibliography.

EXPERIMENT **21**

Dehydration of Methylcyclohexanols and the Evelyn Effect

Reactions of Alcohols. Preparation of Alkenes. Elimination Reactions. Carbocations. Regioselectivity.

Operations

OP-10   Mixing
OP-24   Washing Liquids
OP-25   Drying Liquids
OP-30   Simple Distillation
OP-37   Gas Chromatography

Before You Begin

1. Read the experiment, read or review the operations as necessary, and write an experimental plan.
2. Calculate the mass and volume of 150 mmol (SS) or 20.0 mmol (µS) of 2- and 4-methylcyclohexanol, and the theoretical yield of methylcyclohexenes from each alcohol.

Scenario

(Unlike most other Scenarios in this book, this one describes a real chemical mystery, which is documented in the *Journal of Chemical Education,* **1994**, *71*, 440. Not even the names of the characters have been changed.)

For many years, the dehydration of 2-methylcyclohexanol to a mixture of alkenes has been carried out in college organic chemistry labs to demonstrate the application of Zaitzev's rule and the occurrence of the E1 mechanism in alcohol dehydration reactions. In 1994, David Todd (then a chemistry professor at Pomona College) carried out this reaction and was distilling the product alkenes from the reaction mixture when he received an invitation to lunch with the chemistry department secretary, Evelyn Jacoby. Dr. Todd stopped the distillation, which was about half done, and saved the distillate in its receiver. Upon returning from lunch, he decided to collect the rest of the distillate in a new receiver, giving him two separate fractions. He then worked up both fractions and analyzed them by gas chromatography. Much to his surprise, the second fraction contained a markedly lower percentage of the expected product, 1-methylcyclohexene, than did the first. Because his decision to replace the receiver with a new one was a direct result of the secretary's invitation, Professor Todd named this unexpected result the "Evelyn Effect."

Although several mechanistic hypotheses have been proposed to explain the Evelyn Effect, it is by no means certain that any of them are correct. Your project group's assignment is to verify the existence of the Evelyn Effect for the dehydration of 2-methylcyclohexanol and to see if a

similar effect exists for 4-methylcyclohexanol. You may then want to specu-
late about some possible causes of the Evelyn Effect.

Applying Scientific Methodology

As in the previous experiments, you need to state the problem as a question, formulate a working hypothesis, follow the course of action described
in the Directions, gather and evaluate evidence, test your hypothesis, arrive
at a conclusion, and report your findings.

Zaitzev's Rule and the Evelyn Effect

More than a century ago, at the University of Kazan, Vladimir Vasilevich
Markovnikov and Alexander Zaitzev were investigating a chemical reaction both forward and backward: Markovnikov was adding hydrogen iodide
to alkenes to prepare alkyl iodides, and Zaitzev was removing hydrogen
iodide from alkyl iodides to prepare alkenes. Markovnikov discovered that
hydrogen iodide adds to propene to form mainly 2-iodopropane.

$$CH_3CH = CH_2 + HI \longrightarrow CH_3\overset{\overset{\displaystyle I}{\displaystyle |}}{C}HCH_3$$

From this and other results, Markovnikov formulated his well-known rule,
which can be expressed as follows for a hydrogen-containing species represented by HZ:

> *Markovnikov's rule:* When HZ adds to the carbon–carbon double
> bond of an unsymmetrical alkene, hydrogen adds preferentially to
> the carbon atom that already has *more* hydrogens.

In the meantime, Zaitzev learned that dehydrohalogenation of 2-iodobutane
by alcoholic potassium hydroxide yields mainly 2-butene.

$$CH_3CH_2\overset{\overset{\displaystyle I}{\displaystyle |}}{C}HCH_3 \xrightarrow{\text{KOH}} CH_3CH = CHCH_3$$

He proposed an analogous rule for elimination reactions:

> *Zaitzev's rule:* When HZ is removed from a species to form an
> alkene, hydrogen is lost preferentially from the carbon atom that
> has *fewer* hydrogens.

Markovnikov's and Zaitzev's rules together can be paraphrased by the
well-known socioeconomic maxim "The rich get richer and the poor get
poorer."

These examples show that organic reactions can be selective, favoring
some products and not others—Zaitzev's reaction might have yielded as
much 1-butene as 2-butene, but it did not. When a reaction *could* produce
two or more different structural isomers but in fact yields mainly one of
them, the reaction is said to be *regioselective*. Zaitzev's rule works because,
in most cases, it predicts the formation of the most stable alkene. 2-Butene

was the major product of Zaitzev's reaction not because hydrogen-poor carbon atoms have some innate tendency to lose the hydrogens they have, but because 2-butene is more stable than 1-butene.

Although generalizations such as Zaitzev's rule can help us predict the products of many organic reactions, organic chemistry remains an empirical science—we cannot be certain that a rule that is valid for one system under a given set of conditions will apply equally well under different circumstances. Chemists must study each system experimentally to see if it behaves in the expected manner and, if it doesn't, try to find out why.

For example, neomenthyl chloride undergoes dehydrohalogenation in the presence of a strong base such as sodium ethoxide (CH_3CH_2ONa) to yield a product mixture that consists of mostly alkene **A**, the one predicted by Zaitzev's rule. But menthyl chloride, which differs only in the geometry of the C—Cl bond, yields 100% of alkene **B** and none of the Zaitzev product. It also reacts much more slowly than neomenthyl chloride.

neomenthyl chloride   **A**   **B**

menthyl chloride   **B**

E2 mechanism for elimination of HCl

This result can be explained by assuming that the reaction occurs by an E2 mechanism, which requires that the H and Cl atoms being eliminated lie in the same plane and on opposite sides of the C—C bond separating them; this is called *anti*-periplanar geometry.

Neomenthyl chloride, in its most stable ring conformation, has the desired *anti*-periplanar geometry for formation of either **A** or **B**. Because **A** is the more stable alkene, it is the major product.

In its more stable conformation (with all large groups equatorial), menthyl chloride does not have the geometry necessary to form either product. In its less stable conformation, the *anti*-periplanar geometry needed to form product **A** cannot be attained, because the isopropyl group rather than a hydrogen atom is *anti* to the chlorine atom. This conformation is suitable for the formation of product **B**, however, so it is the only product isolated.

The reaction is much slower than the reaction of neomenthyl chloride because only a small percentage of the menthyl chloride molecules are in the less stable conformation at any time. This example shows that, whenever a substrate yields the less stable alkene as a major product of an elimination reaction, there may be some stereochemical constraints inhibiting the formation of the Zaitzev product.

E2 reactions require a base strong enough to remove a proton from the carbon atom adjacent to the leaving group, but alcohols are ordinarily dehydrated in the presence of a strong acid such as sulfuric acid or phosphoric acid. Thus the acid-catalyzed dehydration of alcohols is generally believed to occur by an E1 (elimination, unimolecular) mechanism involving protonation of the hydroxyl group, loss of water to form a carbocation intermediate, and then loss of a proton.

Key Concept: For certain kinds of reactions, stereochemical constraints may lead to unexpected results.

Note that there are *no* stereochemical constraints in an E1 reaction because the leaving group leaves before the proton is lost. Thus, in the E1 dehydration of an alcohol, H and OH do not need to be *anti*-periplanar or in any other particular orientation for elimination to occur.

Unlike E2 reactions, E1 reactions may involve rearrangements in which the initial carbocation rearranges to a more stable carbocation before it loses H$^+$. A carbocation rearrangement may involve a *hydride shift*, during which a hydrogen next to the positively charged carbon moves to that carbon, taking its bonding electron pair along with it. Such rearrangements lead to alkenes whose double bond does not include the carbon atom that was originally bonded to the hydroxyl group. Postulating such a rearrangement can explain the formation of 2-methyl-2-butene in the dehydration of 2-methyl-1-butanol, for example.

$$\underset{\substack{\text{2-methyl-1-butanol}}}{\overset{\displaystyle\overset{\text{H}}{|}\;\overset{\text{OH}}{|}}{\text{CH}_3\text{CH}_2\text{C}-\text{CH}_2}}\;\;\xrightarrow[\text{(2 steps)}]{\text{H}^+,\,-\text{H}_2\text{O}}\;\;\underset{\text{1° carbocation}}{\overset{\displaystyle\overset{\text{H}}{|}}{\text{CH}_3\text{CH}_2\text{C}-\overset{+}{\text{CH}_2}}}$$

$$\xrightarrow{\text{H}^-\text{shift}}$$

$$\underset{\text{3° carbocation}}{\text{CH}_3\text{CH}-\overset{+}{\text{C}}-\text{CH}_2}\;\;\xrightarrow{-\text{H}^+}\;\;\underset{\substack{\text{2-methyl-2-butene}}}{\text{CH}_3\text{CH}=\text{CCH}_3}$$

This brings us to the Evelyn Effect. When Professor Todd carried out the dehydration of 2-methylcyclohexanol, he obtained the following mixture of alkenes.

The reaction is performed by distilling the alkenes as they are formed, and the distillate typically contains 75–80% of product **A**, the product predicted by Zaitzev's rule. However, when the distillate is collected in separate fractions and the fractions are analyzed separately, the first 10% of the distillate contains about 93% **A**, whereas the final distillate contains as little as 55% **A**. The remaining product in each case is mostly **B**, with only a trace of **C**. There is a clue to the origin of the Evelyn Effect in the catalog of the Aldrich Chemical Company, where the 2-methylcyclohexanol used by Professor Todd is described as a mixture of *cis* and *trans* isomers. In fact, it is a nearly equimolar mixture of the two isomers. Previous researchers had reported that the *cis* isomer reacts much faster than the *trans* isomer, so Todd reasoned that the initial product mixture—containing mostly **A**—formed mainly by dehydration of the *cis* isomer, whereas the final product mixture—with comparable amounts of **A** and **B**—formed mainly by dehydration of the *trans* isomer.

Since the *trans* isomer yields an unexpectedly large percentage of the less stable alkene, it appears that the dehydration of 2-methylcyclohexanol, like the E2 dehydrohalogenation of menthyl chloride, has some stereochemical constraints. The occurrence of E2 elimination from a protonated alcohol could explain a reduction in the amount of the expected product **A** because elimination involving an *anti*-periplanar geometry can yield only product **B** and not product **A**.

It could also explain the lower reactivity of the *trans* alcohol, which can achieve the *anti*-periplanar geometry only in its less stable *diaxial* conformation. However, it does *not* explain why the *trans* alcohol yields any **A** at all, nor does it explain the existence of a small amount of methylenecyclohexane (product **C**) in the product mixture. Product **C** might be obtained by an E1 mechanism involving a carbocation rearrangement, but not by an ordinary E2 mechanism.

Does the reaction proceed by both E1 and E2 mechanisms? That possibility, raised by Todd, has been questioned by two other researchers, John J. Cawley and Patrick E. Lindner, who proposed an "E2-like" mechanism involving bridged ions (*J. Chem. Educ.* **1997,** 74, 102). On the other hand, a recent senior thesis project carried out by Rachel M. Anderson under the direction of James O. Currie at Pacific University has provided evidence that either E1 or E2 elimination can occur during the phosphoric-acid catalyzed dehydration of 2-methylcyclohexanol, with the mechanism depending on the stereochemistry of the alcohol's conformations. Anderson postulates that an E2 reaction can occur because the dihydrogen phosphate ion, $H_2PO_4^-$, is a strong enough base to remove a hydrogen atom adjacent to the protonated OH group. The evidence for competing mechanisms, derived from both experimental results and molecular modeling, is convincing, but does it settle the issue? A mechanism is, after all, a scientific hypothesis about processes that we can't observe directly—the things that molecules do as they redistribute their atoms and change into new molecules—and may be revised or rejected as new evidence comes to light.

The Evelyn Effect illustrates how science often works. For decades, the results of alcohol dehydration reactions were adequately explained by the E1 hypothesis; no other explanation seemed necessary. Then, a chance observation showed the inadequacy of the accepted hypothesis. A different hypothesis—that both E1 and E2 mechanisms are involved—was proposed and contested, followed by another hypothesis, and so on. The road to scientific discovery is a rocky one, and there may be many detours along the way, but every failed hypothesis yields new information, new ideas, and often new applications. Science is not simply a body of established facts and theories; the facts and theories of science are always subject to further inquiry that may disprove or modify them. Science is a dynamic *process* by which knowledge is acquired, ideas are debated, theories are proposed, and new ways of doing things are discovered.

Understanding the Experiment

In this experiment, you and your coworkers will carry out the dehydration of 2-methylcyclohexanol and 4-methylcyclohexanol by heating the alcohols in the presence of phosphoric acid. Both alcohols will be mixtures of *cis* and *trans* isomers, so either one or both may exhibit an Evelyn Effect.

Dehydration of a secondary alcohol proceeds readily with about half a mole of phosphoric acid for every mole of the alcohol. By protonating an alcohol, the acid catalyst converts the poor leaving group —OH to a much better leaving group, —OH$_2^+$.

$$\underset{\substack{| \\ —C—C— \\ |}}{\overset{\substack{H \quad OH \\ | \quad |}}{}} + H_3PO_4 \rightleftharpoons \underset{\substack{| \\ —C—C— \\ |}}{\overset{\substack{H \quad OH^+ \\ | \quad |}}{\overset{H}{\overset{|}{}}}} + H_2PO_4^-$$

Elimination of H$^+$ and H$_2$O from the protonated alcohol yields an alkene, with the unprotonated alcohol serving as the reaction solvent.

According to Le Châtelier's principle, removing a product from a chemical system at equilibrium shifts the equilibrium in the direction that favors the formation of the products. You will carry out the dehydration reaction in a distillation apparatus so that the products (water and alkene) will continuously distill from the reaction mixture as they are formed. Their removal will shift the equilibrium to the right and thus increase the yield of alkene.

alcohol $\rightleftharpoons$ alkene ↑ + water ↑

The upward-pointing arrows in the equation indicate that the products are vaporized under the reaction conditions, not that they are gases at room temperature.

If the reaction mixture is heated to a temperature above the boiling points of the product alkenes but below that of the alcohol, most of the unreacted alcohol will remain in the reaction flask while the alkenes and water collect in the receiver, or in the well of a Hickman still for a microscale distillation.

You will follow the progress of the reaction by measuring the volume of alkene in the distillate, collecting two fractions of approximately equal volume. When the reaction is over, the residue in the reaction flask may begin to foam and emit white vapors. You should separate the apparatus from the heat source at this time because overheating the residue may form a black tar and generate toxic fumes.

After washing and drying the organic layer of each fraction, you will analyze the fractions by gas chromatography. If you started with 2-methylcyclohexanol, your gas chromatograms may show peaks for both 1- and

3-methylcyclohexene (the methylenecyclohexene peak will be resolved only if you use a capillary column). If you started with 4-methylcyclohexanol, you may obtain only 4-methylcyclohexene or a mixture of products including 3-methylcyclohexene and 1-methylcyclohexene. From the relative areas of your peaks, you can estimate the percentage composition of the product mixture in each fraction. A packed GC column may not separate 3- and 4-methylcyclohexene; in that case, you should calculate their combined percentage.

This is a comparatively green experiment because the reaction has a high atom economy, no solvents other than water are used, the catalyst reduces the energy requirements of the reaction, and distilling the product increases the reaction efficiency. Little or no information about the environmental toxicity of phosphoric acid and the methylcyclohexanols is available, but as a rule, phosphates should not be released into the environment.

Reactions and Properties

Table 21.1 Physical properties

	mol wt	bp	d
2-methylcyclohexanol*	114.2	166	0.930
4-methylcyclohexanol*	114.2	173	0.914
1-methylcyclohexene	96.2	110	0.813
3-methylcyclohexene	96.2	104	0.801
4-methylcyclohexene	96.2	102	0.799
phosphoric acid (85%)	98.0		1.70

*Mixture of *cis* and *trans* isomers

Note: bp is in °C; density is in g/mL. The molecular weight given for phosphoric acid is for the pure acid; 85% phosphoric acid is about 14.7 *M*.

DIRECTIONS

Students can work in pairs, with each student using one of the two methylcyclohexanols.

Safety Notes

> The methylcyclohexanols and alkenes are flammable, and inhalation, ingestion, or skin absorption may be harmful. Avoid contact, do not breathe their vapors, and keep them away from flames and hot surfaces.
> Phosphoric acid can cause serious burns, particularly to the eyes; avoid skin or eye contact.

Take Care! Avoid contact with the acid and alcohol, and do not breathe their vapors.

The water that codistills with the alkene reduces its boiling temperature, so the still-head temperature will be lower than the expected boiling point of the product.

Waste Disposal: Place the residue from the reaction flask into a designated waste container.

Stop and Think: What is the purpose of the sodium bicarbonate?

Waste Disposal: Unless your instructor directs otherwise, the aqueous layers can be washed down the drain.

Take Care! Avoid contact with the acid and alcohol, and do not breathe their vapors.

Standard Scale

Reaction. Accurately weigh 150 mmol of 2-methylcyclohexanol *or* 4-methylcyclohexanol (*cis–trans* mixtures) into a 50-mL round-bottom flask. Mix in 5.0 mL of 85% phosphoric acid, and drop in a stir bar or a few acid-resistant boiling chips. Clamp the flask to a ring stand over a suitable heat source and assemble an apparatus for simple distillation [OP-30]. Use a 10-mL graduated cylinder or another graduated container as the receiver. Have ready two clean, numbered 15-mL screw-cap centrifuge tubes.

Start the stirrer [OP-10] if you are using one, and then heat the reactants so that the product mixture distills at a rate of 1 drop per second or less. Record the vapor temperature after distillation begins, and observe it at intervals during the reaction. Monitor the volume of the alkene (top) layer in the distillate. When the alkene volume is about 8 mL, quickly pour the distillate into the first centrifuge tube, cap the tube, replace the graduated receiver, and continue distilling. After the alkene volume reaches about 6 mL, monitor the still-head temperature continually. Lower the heat source, and turn it off when you observe a marked temperature drop at the still head, which may be accompanied by foaming and dense white fumes in the reaction flask. Pour the distillate into the second centrifuge tube, and cap the tube.

Separation. For each separate fraction, wash [OP-24] the distillate by shaking it cautiously with two 5-mL portions of saturated aqueous sodium bicarbonate (a gas may be evolved) and carefully remove the aqueous (lower) layer with a Pasteur pipet. Dry [OP-25] each alkene mixture separately, in its centrifuge tube, with anhydrous calcium chloride or another suitable drying agent. Transfer the liquids to labeled, tared screw-cap vials. Measure the mass of each alkene fraction, and calculate the total mass of alkenes.

Analysis. Analyze both fractions by gas chromatography [OP-37] as directed by your instructor. Measure the area and retention time of each peak on your gas chromatograms. Identify the peaks by comparison with a chromatogram provided by your instructor or by spiking your product mixture with an authentic sample of 1-methylcyclohexene and obtaining a chromatogram of the resulting mixture. Assuming that the detector response factors for the alkenes are equal, calculate the percentage composition of each fraction and obtain the same data from a coworker who started with the other alcohol. Decide whether either or both alcohols exhibit an Evelyn Effect.

Microscale

Reaction. Accurately weigh 20.0 mmol of 2-methylcyclohexanol *or* 4-methylcyclohexanol into a 10-mL round-bottom flask. Mix in 0.70 mL of 85% phosphoric acid, and add a stir bar. Clamp the reaction vessel to a ring stand over a suitable heat source, and assemble an apparatus for simple distillation [OP-30] using a Hickman still, water-cooled condenser, and thermometer. Weigh and number two clean conical vials.

Start the stirrer [OP-10] and begin heating the reactants. Control the heating rate so that the product mixture collects *slowly* in the well of the Hickman still. Record the still-head temperature after distillation begins, and observe it at intervals during the reaction. Using a Pasteur pipet, transfer distillate frequently to the first conical vial until it is filled with liquid to the 1.0 mL mark, and then begin transferring distillate to the second vial. As the alkene volume in that vial approaches 1 mL, monitor the still-head temperature continually. Remove the apparatus from the heat source when you observe a marked temperature drop at the still head, which may be accompanied by foaming and dense white fumes in the reaction flask.

Separation.   For each separate fraction, wash [OP-24] the distillate with 1.5 mL of 5% aqueous sodium bicarbonate and carefully remove the aqueous (lower) layer with a Pasteur pipet. Dry [OP-25] each alkene mixture separately with anhydrous calcium chloride. Measure the mass of each alkene fraction, and calculate the total mass of alkenes.

Analysis.   Analyze both fractions by gas chromatography [OP-37] as directed by your instructor. Measure the area and retention time of each peak on your gas chromatograms. Identify each peak by comparison with a chromatogram provided by your instructor or by spiking your product mixture with an authentic sample of 1-methylcyclohexene and obtaining a chromatogram of the resulting mixture. Assuming that the detector response factors for the alkenes are equal, calculate the percentage composition of each fraction and obtain the same data from a coworker who started with the other alcohol. Decide whether either or both alcohols exhibit an Evelyn Effect.

The water that codistills with the alkene reduces its boiling temperature, so the still-head temperature will be lower than the expected boiling point of the product.

Waste Disposal: Place the residue from the reaction flask into a designated waste container.

Stop and Think: What is the purpose of the sodium bicarbonate?

Waste Disposal: Unless your instructor directs otherwise, the aqueous layers can be washed down the drain.

Exercises

1. (a) Which kind of mechanism can better account for the product mixture obtained from the dehydration of *cis-* and *trans-*4-methylcyclohexanol: E1, E2, or a combination of the two? (Keep in mind that the actual mechanism may be none of these.) (b) Based on your answer, write detailed mechanisms explaining the formation of all of the observed products.

2. Following the format in Appendix V, construct a flow diagram for this experiment.

3. Describe and explain the possible effect on your results of the following experimental errors or variations. (a) You forgot to add the phosphoric acid. (b) You collected all of the distillate in one container rather than in two. (c) The 2-methylcyclohexanol you used was the pure *trans* isomer rather than a mixture of isomers.

4. In "Understanding the Experiment," 1-methylcyclohexene and 3-methylcyclohexene were mentioned as possible products of the dehydration of 2-methylcyclohexanol. Why was 2-methylcyclohexene not mentioned as a possible product?

5. (a) Calculate the atom economy and the reaction efficiency of your synthesis. (b) Describe some green features of your synthesis, and any that are not so green.

6. Do you think the Evelyn Effect is more likely or less likely to occur during the dehydration of 2-methylcyclohexanol if the catalyst is sulfuric acid rather than phosphoric acid? Explain your answer.

7. (a) Predict the major alkene product that would result from dehydrating each of the following alcohols, with no carbocation rearrangements.

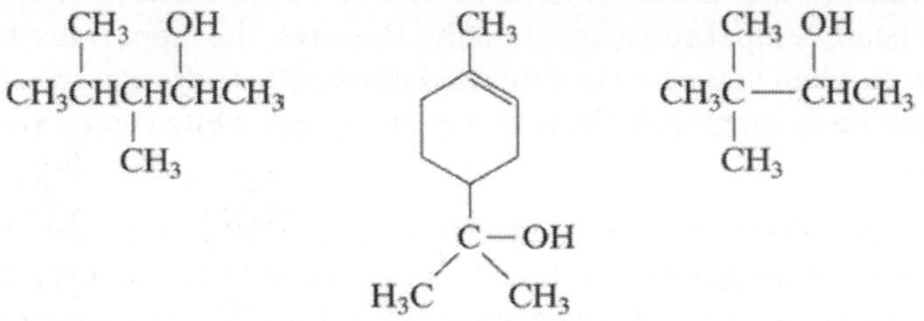

CH₃ OH
 | |
CH₃CHCHCHCH₃
         |
        CH₃

CH₃
 |

C—OH
H₃C   CH₃

CH₃ OH
 | |
CH₃C—CHCH₃
 |
CH₃

(b) In each case, predict the most stable dehydration product that could result after a single carbocation rearrangement.

Other Things You Can Do

(Starred items require your instructor's permission.)

*1. Prepare and test a gaseous alkene as described in Minilab 18.

*2. Test your product mixtures with bromine or potassium permanganate solution, and interpret the results. (See classification tests C-7 and C-19 in the "Classification" section of Part IV.)

*3. Dehydrate another alcohol, such as cyclohexanol, 3-methylcyclohexanol, or 4-methyl-2-pentanol, by the same procedure, adjusting the distillation temperature for the alkene or alkene mixture anticipated. Analyze the product mixtures by gas chromatography, and interpret the results.

4. The methylcyclohexanols used in this experiment are synthesized by catalytic hydrogenation of the corresponding cresols (methylphenols). Write a research paper about the production and uses of cresols, starting with sources listed in the Bibliography.

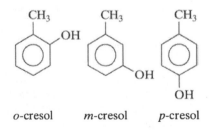

o-cresol   m-cresol   p-cresol

Testing Markovnikov's Rule   EXPERIMENT **22**

Addition to Alkenes. Preparation of Alcohols. Regioselectivity. Infrared Spectrometry.

Operations

OP-14 Trapping Gases (optional)
OP-7   Heating
OP-8   Cooling
OP-10   Mixing
OP-11   Addition of Reactants
OP-18   Extraction
OP-19   Evaporation
OP-24   Washing Liquids
OP-25   Drying Liquids
OP-30   Simple Distillation
OP-34   Boiling Point
OP-39   Infrared Spectrometry

Before You Begin

1. Read the experiment, read OP-14 and review the other operations as necessary, and write an experimental plan.
2. Calculate the mass and volume of 20.0 (SS) or 4.00 (μS) mmol of 1-hexene, and the masses of 4.0 (SS) or 0.8 (μS) mmol of iodine and 8.0 (SS) or 1.6 (μS) mmol of sodium borohydride. Calculate the theoretical yield or the product.

Scenario

At the University of Kazan in 1869, the Russian chemist Vladimir Vasilye-vich Markovnikov developed a rule for addition reactions of alkenes that can be expressed as:

> *When HZ adds to the carbon–carbon double bond of an unsymmetrical alkene, hydrogen adds preferentially to the carbon atom that already has more hydrogens.*

See Experiment 21 for a comparison of Markonikov's rule with Zaitzev's rule, which concerns the formation of alkene by elimination reactions.

Here, "Z" can stand for a halide, an OH group, and so forth. During the addition of hydrogen chloride to propene, for example, the H atom of HCl adds to the carbon atom that has two hydrogens, and the Cl ends up on the carbon that has only one.

$$CH_3CH = CH_2 + HCl \longrightarrow CH_3\overset{\overset{\displaystyle Cl}{|}}{C}H - \overset{\overset{\displaystyle H}{|}}{C}H_2$$

Note that the carbon atom that has the most hydrogen atoms is also the least substituted carbon. Markovnikov's rule works well for the direct addition of water, hydrogen halides, and similar reagents to carbon–carbon double bonds.

In 1959, a distinguished American chemist (known to his colleagues as HCB) discovered a new way of adding water indirectly to double bonds. His method involves initial addition of a compound that contains B—H bonds to an alkene's double bond, followed by oxidation and hydrolysis, as shown here for a general alkene.

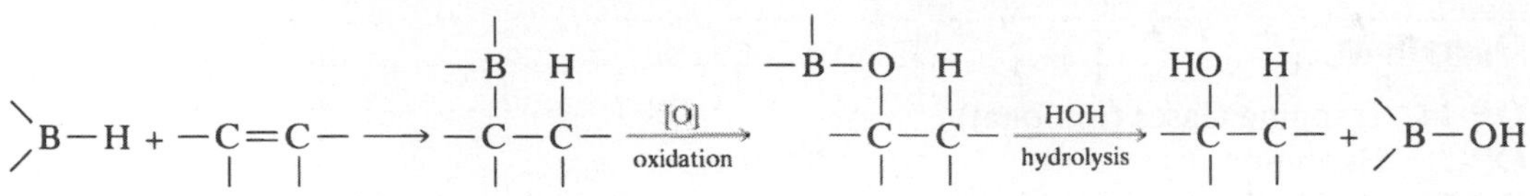

$$\begin{array}{c} \diagdown \\ \diagup \end{array} B-H + \begin{array}{c} | \\ -C=C- \\ | \end{array} \longrightarrow \begin{array}{c} -B \quad H \\ | \quad\quad | \\ -C-C- \\ | \quad\quad | \end{array} \xrightarrow[\text{oxidation}]{[O]} \begin{array}{c} -B-O \quad H \\ | \quad\quad\quad | \\ -C-C- \\ | \quad\quad\quad | \end{array} \xrightarrow[\text{hydrolysis}]{HOH} \begin{array}{c} HO \quad H \\ | \quad\quad | \\ -C-C- \\ | \quad\quad | \end{array} + \begin{array}{c} \diagdown \\ \diagup \end{array} B-OH$$

The other substituents on boron (not shown here) can be hydrogen atoms or various alkyl or aryl groups, and [O] refers to an unspecified oxidizing agent.

Markovnikov didn't anticipate such indirect addition reactions, so his rule may or may not apply in this case. Your assignment is to convert 1-hexene to an alcohol by this general method and to determine whether the reaction obeys or violates Markovnikov's rule.

Applying Scientific Methodology

You should be able to develop a working hypothesis about the structure of the product after reading the Scenario and "Understanding the Experiment." You will test your hypothesis by obtaining and interpreting an infrared spectrum of your product. Then you can arrive at a conclusion about the applicability of Markovnikov's rule in this case.

Markovnikov and His Rule

If you buy a bottle of rubbing alcohol at a drugstore, chances are it contains isopropyl alcohol (2-propanol) and not *n*-propyl alcohol (1-propanol).

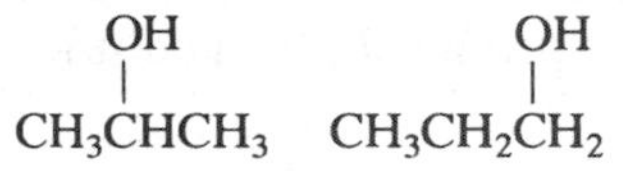

$$\begin{array}{cc} \text{OH} & \text{OH} \\ | & | \\ \text{CH}_3\text{CHCH}_3 & \text{CH}_3\text{CH}_2\text{CH}_2 \\ \text{2-propanol} & \text{1-propanol} \end{array}$$

These alcohols are isomers; each contains 3 carbon atoms, 8 hydrogen atoms, and 1 oxygen atom, and their physical properties are similar. There's no obvious reason that 2-propanol should be preferred to 1-propanol as a constituent of rubbing alcohol. However, if you check the prices of similar grades of the two alcohols, you'll find that 1-propanol costs about 40% more than 2-propanol. That's because the cheapest way to make an alcohol is often by acid-catalyzed hydration of an alkene. Hydration of 1-propene, which is obtained from petroleum refining, yields mainly 2-propanol and very little 1-propanol.

Isopropyl alcohol was the first organic compound made on a large scale from a petrochemical.

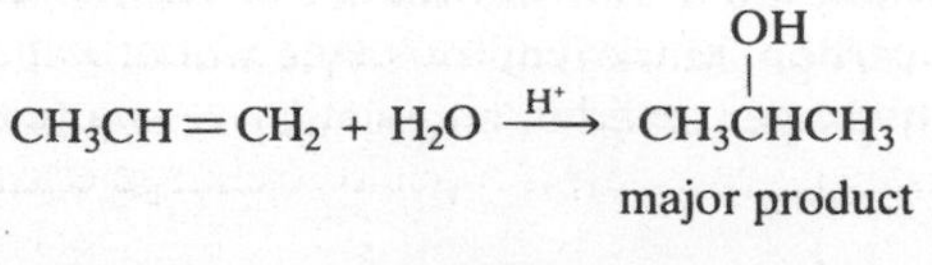

$$\text{CH}_3\text{CH}=\text{CH}_2 + \text{H}_2\text{O} \xrightarrow{\text{H}^+} \begin{array}{c} \text{OH} \\ | \\ \text{CH}_3\text{CHCH}_3 \end{array}$$
$$\text{major product}$$

This result can be predicted using a simple rule (stated in the Scenario) that was first advanced by Markovnikov in 1869. Markovnikov arrived at his famous rule after noticing that, when a hydrogen halide is added to an alkene, the hydrogen atom ordinarily attaches to the carbon that already has the *most* hydrogens. Any chemical reaction that, like this example, leads primarily or exclusively to the formation of one structural isomer rather than an alternative structural isomer is said to be *regioselective*.

Like most rules, Markovnikov's has exceptions. For example, in the presence of an organic peroxide, hydrogen bromide adds to alkenes in the "wrong" direction, yielding 1-bromopropane.

$$CH_3CH=CH_2 + HBr \xrightarrow{\text{peroxide}} CH_3CH_2\underset{\underset{\text{major product}}{|}}{\overset{\overset{Br}{|}}{CH_2}}$$

This kind of result is known as anti-Markovnikov addition. It occurs in this case because HBr addition in the presence of peroxides involves a free-radical intermediate rather than an ionic one. This is also a regioselective reaction because it could conceivably have yielded mainly 2-bromopropane but did not.

Key Concept: The outcome of a regioselective reaction is determined by the mechanism of the reaction.

Markovnikov was a remarkably productive chemist whose name might not be remembered at all were it not for his rule. Because he published only in Russian, his work was virtually unknown in the outside world for many years. Born in 1838 in Nizhny Novgorod, he studied and taught chemistry at the University of Kazan, which bills itself as "the birthplace of organic chemistry" based on research performed by Markovnikov, his mentor Aleksandr Butlerov, and others. He showed, for example, that butyric acid (butanoic acid) and isobutyric acid (2-methylpropanoic acid) are isomers. He was also the first to prove that cyclic organic compounds can contain fewer or more than six carbon atoms by synthesizing compounds that have four-membered and seven-membered rings. He was one of the first chemists who anticipated the need to know how atoms are arranged in space in order to understand the relationship between chemical reactions and structure. Shortly afterward, J. H. van't Hoff introduced his stereochemical theory, which proposed that carbon atoms can have a three-dimensional tetrahedral structure. While teaching at the University of Moscow, Markovnikov established his own school of chemists, thus insuring that his influence would extend well beyond his own lifetime.

Markovnikov also studied in Germany under Richard August Carl Emil Erlenmeyer, who is best known today for his flask.

Understanding the Experiment

In this experiment, you will be carrying out an indirect hydration of 1-hexene and identifying the product to determine whether or not the reaction follows Markovnikov's rule. Markovnikov's rule usually works, because alkyl (and aryl) groups can help stabilize a positive charge on a carbon atom. When H^+ adds to a carbon atom of an alkene, it strips away a pair of electrons from the pi bond, leaving the adjacent carbon atom with a positive charge. Therefore, when H^+ adds to the less substituted carbon atom (the one with more hydrogens), the positive charge ends up on the *more*

Stop and Think: What would the product be in each case?

substituted carbon, where it is stabilized by the substituents. This is shown in the following illustration, where R represents an alkyl substituent.

$$RCH = CH_2 + H^+ \longrightarrow R\overset{\oplus}{C}H - \overset{\overset{\displaystyle H}{|}}{C}H_2$$

In general, the more electropositive component of a reagent (such as the H in HCl) will tend to add to the less substituted double-bonded carbon atom of the alkene. In the following example, bromine is more electropositive (less electronegative) than chlorine, so "Br$^+$" adds to the less substituted carbon, leaving the positive charge on the more substituted carbon, to which Cl$^-$ then bonds.

$$RCH = CH_2 \xrightarrow{BrCl} R\overset{\oplus}{C}H - \overset{\overset{\displaystyle Br}{|}}{C}H_2 \xrightarrow{Cl^-} R\overset{\overset{\displaystyle Cl}{|}}{C}H - \overset{\overset{\displaystyle Br}{|}}{C}H_2$$

HCB's original method (described in the Scenario) used some chemicals that can be handled safely only by experienced chemists, but the method used here involves considerably less hazardous chemicals. In this experiment, the substance that adds to the double bond of 1-hexene is a hydride of boron, BH_3, which is generated by a reaction of sodium borohydride and iodine. The resulting boron-containing intermediate, a trialkylborane represented here by $(C_6H_{13})_3B$, is oxidized by hydrogen peroxide and hydrolyzed by aqueous NaOH. During these reaction steps, each alkyl group of the trialkylborane acquires an $-OH$ group at the site of its previous bond to boron (see the "Reactions and Properties" section).

BH$_3$ is ordinarily too unstable to exist as the pure substance, but it can be generated in the reaction mixture.

In the experiment, you will use a syringe or a separatory–addition funnel to add a solution of iodine in the solvent tetrahydrofuran to a reaction mixture containing sodium borohydride and 1-hexene in the same solvent. Each molecule of BH_3 produced in this reaction adds to the carbon–carbon double bonds of three molecules of 1-hexene. Hydrogen is evolved during the reaction, so a gas trap should be used to remove it unless you are working under an efficient fume hood. When the reaction is finished, you will add a concentrated solution of hydrogen peroxide (30% or 35%) and 3 M sodium hydroxide to bring about the oxidation and hydrolysis steps. Hydrogen peroxide is a strong oxidant that can cause severe burns and bleach your skin white, so it should be handled with care, using protective gloves. The organic layer from the reaction mixture, which contains the product in tetrahydrofuran, is separated by using potassium carbonate to salt it out (see OP-18b) from the aqueous layer and adding some hexanes to facilitate the separation. The two solvents are removed by evaporation, and the alcohol is purified by simple distillation. The alcohol can then be identified from its infrared spectrum. The section entitled "Characteristic Infrared Bands" in OP-39 will help you determine which alcohol you prepared.

A Greener Way: You can recover the solvents by distillation or by evaporating them under vacuum using a cold trap.

Iodine may be hazardous in the environment, especially to fish. Tetrahydrofuran is somewhat toxic to aquatic life but is not expected to bioaccumulate. Little information is available about the environmental effects of hydrogen peroxide, but it is expected to be converted to water in the environment.

Reactions and Properties

$$6CH_3(CH_2)_3CH\!=\!CH_2 + 2NaBH_4 + I_2 \longrightarrow 2(C_6H_{13})_3B + 2NaI + H_2$$
1-hexene

$$(C_6H_{13})_3B + 3H_2O_2 + NaOH \longrightarrow 3(C_6H_{13})OH + NaB(OH)_4$$

Note: $(C_6H_{13})OH = CH_3CH_2CH_2CH_2CH_2CH_2OH$ or $CH_3CH_2CH_2CH_2\overset{\overset{\displaystyle OH}{\displaystyle |}}{C}HCH_3$

                                    1-hexanol   2-hexanol

Table 22.1 Physical properties

	mol wt	mp	bp	d
1-hexene	84.2		64	0.678
iodine	253.8	113	184	4.93
sodium borohydride	37.8	300d		1.074
35% hydrogen peroxide	34.0	40	126	1.13*
tetrahydrofuran	72.1	−108	67	0.889
1-hexanol	102.2	−52	157.5	0.814
2-hexanol	102.2	−47	140	0.811

*The density of 30% hydrogen peroxide is 1.11 g/mL.

Note: mp and bp are in °C; density is in g/mL; d = decomposes at the melting point.

1-Hexene	$CH_3CH_2CH_2CH_2CH\!=\!CH_2$	2962.1	1466.1	909.2
		1821.3	1379.1	739.8
		1641.8	992.7	630.8

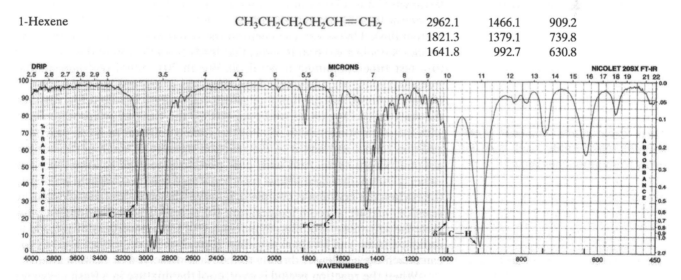

Figure 22.1 IR spectrum of 1-hexene

Stop and Think: What is the function of the potassium carbonate?

Heat the reaction mixture in a 30–40°C hot-water bath for 5 minutes or so, and then add 0.50 mL of 3 M sodium hydroxide with the syringe while stirring. Draw 0.80 mL of 30% or 35% hydrogen peroxide into the syringe and add it to the reaction mixture drop by drop. The reaction mixture will darken during the addition. Continue to heat the mixture at 30–40°C, with stirring, for 30 minutes.

Separation.   Transfer the reaction mixture to a conical centrifuge tube, add about 4 g of potassium carbonate (anhydrous or sesquihydrate), then cap the tube and shake it vigorously for a minute or so to dissolve the K_2CO_3. Rinse the reaction flask with 2.5 mL of hexanes and add the liquid to the centrifuge tube, then shake to extract [OP-18] all of the product into the organic layer. Separate the organic layer, and wash [OP-24] it with 2.5 mL or more of 30% sodium thiosulfate solution to remove most of the color (it may be light yellow even after washing). Then wash it with 2 portions of saturated aqueous sodium chloride. Dry the organic layer [OP-25] over anhydrous sodium sulfate and evaporate [OP-19] the solvent. You can transfer the organic solution in portions to a 5-mL conical vial if you use a stream of dry air or nitrogen for evaporation.

Purification and Analysis.   Purify the product by simple distillation [OP-30], and record its boiling point [OP-34a]. Weigh the product and record its infrared spectrum [OP-39]. Give the structure and name of your product, and tell how you arrived at that structure.

Exercises

1. Show how BH_3 must have added to the $C{=}C$ bond of 1-hexene, and explain why.
2. Find out who HCB was, and provide the name of the reaction sequence that you used in this experiment. (*Hint:* HCB won a Nobel Prize in chemistry.)
3. (a) Calculate the atom economy and reaction efficiency of your synthesis. (b) Describe some green features of your synthesis, and any that are not so green.
4. Write a balanced equation for a reaction that would cause the solution to darken when H_2O_2 is added.
5. Following the format in Appendix V, construct a flow diagram for this experiment.
6. Describe and explain the possible effect on your results of the following experimental errors or variations. (a) Instead of 1-hexene, you added hexanes (intended for the Separation step) to the reaction flask. (b) The lab assistant put 3% hydrogen peroxide in the reagent bottle labeled "30% H_2O_2." (c) You forgot to add potassium carbonate in the Separation step.
7. (a) In what form does BH_3 ordinarily exist? Give the name, molecular formula, and structure of this substance. (b) Write equations showing how this substance can be used to bring about the conversion of 1-hexene to the alcohol you obtained.

Other Things You Can Do

(Starred items require your instructor's permission.)

*1. Carry out the reaction of iodine with an alkene component of turpentine as described in Minilab 19.

*2. Write a procedure for converting 1-hexene to the alcohol you did *not* obtain in this experiment, have it approved by your instructor, and carry it out in the lab.

 3. Write a research paper about regioselectivity in addition reactions of alkenes, starting with sources listed in the Bibliography.

expected melting point doesn't indicate that both products are present.) From the identity of your product, you should be able to deduce whether the addition of bromine to *trans*-cinnamic acid involves *syn* or *anti* addition, or a mixture of the two. Molecular models will help you relate the configurations of the *syn* and *anti* addition products to the stereochemical structures shown for the *erythro*- and *threo*-dibromides.

Acetic acid is expected to be slightly toxic to aquatic life. Bromine is toxic to aquatic organisms, but no water quality standards for bromine have been issued by the U.S. government.

Reaction and Properties

H $\underset{\text{C}=\text{C}}{\overset{\text{COOH}}{}}$ + Br$_2$ $\xrightarrow{\text{HOAc}}$ —CHBrCHBrCOOH

trans-cinnamic acid   2,3-dibromo-3-phenylpropanoic acid

Table 23.1 Physical properties

	mol wt	mp	bp	d
trans-cinnamic acid	148.2	136		
bromine	159.8	−7	59	3.12
acetic acid	60.1	17	118	1.049
erythro-2,3-dibromo-3-phenylpropanoic acid	308.0	204		
threo-2,3-dibromo-3-phenylpropanoic acid	308.0	95		

Note: mp and bp are in °C; density is in g/mL.

DIRECTIONS

A. *Preparation of 2,3-Dibromo-3-phenylpropanoic Acid*

Safety Notes

acetic acid

bromine

> Bromine is highly toxic and corrosive, and its vapors can damage the eyes and respiratory tract. Wear gloves when handling the bromine solution, and dispense it under a hood. Avoid contact, and do not inhale its vapors. Acetic acid causes chemical burns that can seriously damage skin and eyes; its vapors are highly irritating to the eyes and respiratory tract. Wear gloves, and dispense it under a hood. Avoid contact, and do not breathe its vapors.

Standard Scale

Reaction. *Carry out the reaction under the hood, and wear gloves throughout.* In a 50-mL round-bottom flask, combine 10.0 mmol of *trans*-cinnamic acid with 6.0 mL of glacial acetic acid. Add a stir bar if you have a magnetic stirrer, or use boiling chips. Assemble an apparatus for addition [OP-11] under reflux using a separatory–addition funnel, reflux condenser, and

Take Care! Wear gloves, avoid contact with acetic acid and the bromine solution, and do not breathe their vapors.

Claisen connecting tube. Be sure the stopcock of the separatory–addition funnel is closed, then add 10 mL of a 1.0 *M* solution of bromine in acetic acid and stopper it immediately. Place the reaction mixture in a 50°C water bath and start the stirrer [OP-10] (or swirl the flask after each addition). Add the bromine/acetic acid solution in five or more portions, waiting until the color has faded to light orange before adding the next portion. The cinnamic acid should dissolve shortly after the addition of the first portion. After the last addition, heat the reaction mixture in a 50°C water bath for 15 minutes while stirring or occasionally swirling. If the mixture becomes colorless (or nearly so) during this period, add more of the bromine/acetic acid solution dropwise until the color just persists. If the mixture has a distinct orange color at the end of the reaction period, add a drop or so of cyclohexene to turn it light yellow.

Observe and Note: What evidence suggests that a reaction has occurred?

Separation.   Transfer the reaction mixture to an Erlenmeyer flask and cool it in an ice/water bath for 15 minutes or more, scratching the sides of the flask to induce crystallization, if necessary. Collect the product by vacuum filtration [OP-16] and wash it on the filter [OP-26a] with several portions of ice-cold water, until the acetic acid odor is hardly noticeable.

Stop and Think: What is the purpose of the cyclohexene? What reaction is involved?

Purification and Analysis.   Purify the product by recrystallization [OP-28] from 50% aqueous ethanol, washing it on the filter [OP-26a] with cold 50% ethanol. Dry [OP-26b] the 2,3-dibromo-3-phenylpropanoic acid and measure its melting point [OP-33]; then decide whether you have prepared the *erythro* or *threo* isomer, or a mixture of the two.

Waste Disposal: Unless your instructor directs otherwise, wash the filtrate down the hood's drain.

Stop and Think: Was the result what you expected? If not, why not?

Microscale

Reaction.   *Carry out the reaction under the hood, and wear gloves throughout.* Weigh 1.00 mmol of *trans*-cinnamic acid into a 3-mL conical vial, and add 0.8 mL of glacial acetic acid and a stirring device. Attach an air condenser and clamp the apparatus to a ring stand, then stir [OP-10] this mixture in a 50°C water bath until most of the cinnamic acid has dissolved. Measure 1.0 mL of a 1.0 *M* solution of bromine in acetic acid into a conical vial, and add [OP-11] this solution through the top of the condenser with a 9-inch Pasteur pipet. Heat the reaction mixture in the 50° hot water bath until the red–brown bromine color fades to light orange; then continue to heat the reaction mixture for 15 minutes. If the mixture becomes colorless (or nearly so) during this period, add more of the bromine/acetic acid solution dropwise until the color just persists. If the mixture has a distinct orange color at the end of the reaction period, add a drop or two of cyclohexene to turn it light yellow.

Take Care! Wear gloves, avoid contact with acetic acid and the bromine solution, and do not breathe their vapors.

Separation.   Cool the reaction mixture in an ice/water bath for 10 minutes or more, scratching the sides of the vial to induce crystallization, if necessary. Collect the product by vacuum filtration [OP-16] and wash it on the filter [OP-26a] with several portions of ice-cold water, until the acetic acid odor is hardly noticeable.

Stop and Think: What is the purpose of the cyclohexene? What reaction is involved?

Purification and Analysis.   Purify the product by recrystallization [OP-28] from 50% aqueous ethanol, washing it on the filter [OP-26a] with cold 50% ethanol. Dry [OP-26b] the 2,3-dibromo-3-phenylpropanoic acid and

Waste Disposal: Unless your instructor directs otherwise, wash the filtrate down the hood's drain.

Stop and Think: Was the result what you expected? If not, why not?

measure its melting point [OP-33]; then decide whether you have prepared the *erythro* or *threo* isomer, or a mixture of the two.

B. *Stereochemistry of Bromine Addition*

  Standard Scale and Microscale

Construct a molecular model of *trans*-cinnamic acid (to simplify matters, use a colored ball to represent the phenyl group). Simulate the *syn* addition of bromine by removing one of the C=C connectors and inserting two orange bromine atoms, with connectors, into the vacant holes. (You may want to replace the remaining flexible connector with a rigid one.) Rotate around the carbon–carbon single bond that remains until the model corresponds to the stereochemical projection for either *threo-* or *erythro*-2,3-dibromo-3-phenylpropanoic acid. Simulate the *anti* addition of bromine by removing the upper connector of the carbon–carbon double bond and moving one end of the lower connector from the hole it occupies to the vacant hole in the same carbon atom. Be careful not to rotate either carbon atom as you do so. Insert two bromine atoms, with connectors, into the vacant holes; then rotate the model as before, until it matches one of the stereochemical projections. Decide whether your product was formed by *syn* addition, *anti* addition, or a mixture of both. Write a mechanism that explains your results.

Exercises

1. (a) Write resonance structures showing how the aryl group of *trans*-anethole stabilizes the intermediate carbocation shown in "Understanding the Experiment." (b) Based on your results, explain any differences or similarities in the stereochemistry of the bromine addition reactions of *trans*-cinnamic acid and *trans*-anethole.

2. What product or products would you expect to obtain by the addition of bromine to *cis*-cinnamic acid, assuming that it reacts by the same mechanism as the *trans* acid?

3. (a) Write mechanisms showing why bromination of *trans*-cinnamic acid yields the product you obtained as a racemic mixture of enantiomers. (b) Draw a stereochemical projection for each enantiomer, and specify the configuration (*R* or *S*) at each stereocenter.

4. (a) Calculate the atom economy and reaction efficiency of your synthesis. (b) Describe some green features of your synthesis, and any that aren't so green.

5. Describe and explain the possible effect on your results of the following experimental errors or variations. (a) The cinnamic acid you used was actually a mixture of *cis* and *trans* isomers. (b) You added a total of 5 mL (SS) or 0.5 mL (μS) of the bromine solution. (c) You misread the label on a bottle of cyclohexane and used it in place of cyclohexene.

6. Following the format in Appendix V, construct a flow diagram for the synthesis that you carried out in this experiment.

7. Draw stereochemical projections for the products of bromine addition to maleic acid and fumaric acid (*cis* and *trans* HOOCCH=CHCOOH,

respectively), assuming that bromine adds to these compounds the same way it does to cinnamic acid.

8. (a) Would you expect the product from this experiment to be optically active? Could it be resolved into optically active constituents? Explain. (b) Would the product of the bromination of fumaric acid (see Exercise 7) be optically active? Could it be resolved into optically active constituents? Explain.

Other Things You Can Do

(Starred projects require your instructor's permission.)

*1. Test some commercial products for unsaturation as described in Minilab 20.

*2. Synthesize 3-phenylpropynoic acid from your product by scaling down the procedure given in *J. Am. Chem. Soc.* **1942**, *64*, 2510 (see Experiment 57 for information about scaling). Find a suitable recrystallization solvent to use in place of carbon tetrachloride.

3. Write a research paper about the industrial preparation and commercial uses of cinnamic acid and its derivatives, starting with sources listed in the Bibliography.

EXPERIMENT 24 A Green Synthesis of Adipic Acid

Green Chemistry. Oxidative Cleavage. Reactions of Alkenes. Preparation of Carboxylic Acids. Infrared Spectrometry.

Operations

OP-6 Making Transfers
OP-7 Heating
OP-8 Cooling
OP-10 Mixing
OP-16 Vacuum Filtration
OP-26 Washing and Drying Solids
OP-28 Recrystallization
OP-33 Infrared Spectrometry

Before You Begin

1. Read the experiment, read or review the operations as necessary, and write an experimental plan.
2. Calculate the mass and volume of 25.0 mmol (SS) or 5.00 mmol (μS) of cyclohexene, and the theoretical yield of the product.

Scenario

Mega Molecules, Inc. (MMI) prepares a variety of chemicals that are used to make such polymers as nylon and polystyrene. The polymers can then be used for manufacturing textiles and plastics. One of their products is adipic acid, which is used to manufacture the most common form of nylon, known as nylon 6,6.

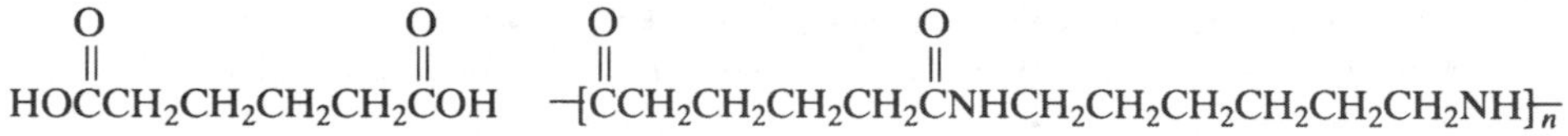
O
O
O
O
HOCCH2CH2CH2CH2COH
CCH2CH2CH2CH2CNHCH2CH2CH2CH2CH2CH2NH
n

adipic acid nylon 6,6

The main commercial process for manufacturing adipic acid involves the air oxidation of cyclohexane to a mixture of cyclohexanol and cyclohexanone, followed by nitric acid oxidation of this mixture.

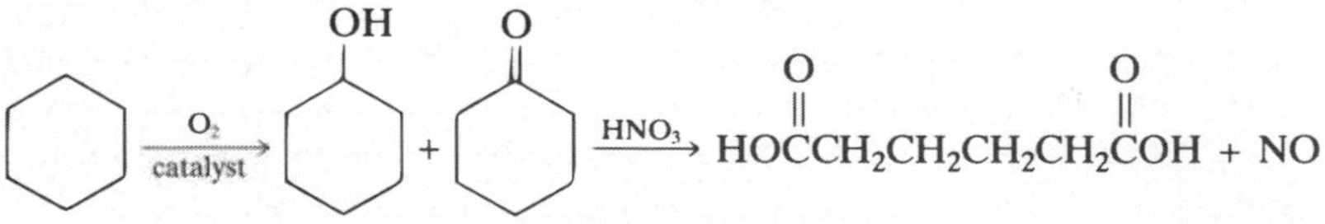
O2
catalyst
OH
O
+
HNO3
O
O
HOCCH2CH2CH2CH2COH + NO

The nitric oxide (NO) produced by this process contributes significantly to global warming and depletion of the ozone layer.

MMI would like to develop a greener method for the synthesis that produces no nitro oxides. One synthetic route they are considering involves the oxidation of cyclohexene using hydrogen peroxide in the presence of both a phase-transfer catalyst (PTC) and a sodium tungstate catalyst (see "Reactions and Properties"). This synthetic route would require no organic solvents, and its only significant by-product is water. Your assignment is to test this new procedure to find out whether it does, in fact, yield adipic acid of reasonable purity.

Applying Scientific Methodology

There are two scientific problems in this experiment: (1) to determine whether the reaction of cyclohexene yields adipic acid, and (2) to determine whether or not the adipic acid is reasonably pure. The first problem can be solved by obtaining the melting point and an infrared spectrum of your product. The melting point of pure adipic acid is 152°C, so a melting point within ±2°C of that value will suggest that the product is reasonably pure.

Crossing the Boundary—The Role of the Phase-Transfer Catalyst

In this experiment, you will be mixing the organic compound cyclohexene with an aqueous solution of hydrogen peroxide and a catalyst, sodium tungstate. Tungstate ion (WO_4^{2-}) is a good oxidizing agent, so presumably it is the oxidant that actually converts cyclohexene to adipic acid. The hydrogen peroxide then converts the reduced form of the ion back to WO_4^{2-}, which therefore acts as a true catalyst by promoting the reaction without being used up. Using such a catalyst makes the reaction even greener because the aqueous layer containing sodium tungstate can be recovered and reused in subsequent reactions.

In order for the reaction to work, tungstate ions have to come in contact with cyclohexene molecules; however, like most ionic compounds, sodium tungstate is soluble in water but not in organic phases. To get around this difficulty, we need to arrange for tungstate ions to somehow be "escorted" across the phase boundary that separates the organic cyclohexene phase from the aqueous hydrogen peroxide phase. This is where a different kind of catalyst, called a *phase-transfer catalyst*, comes in.

To understand the basic principles of phase-transfer catalysis, consider the nucleophilic substitution reaction of an alkyl halide with sodium cyanide to form a nitrile. If a high–molecular-weight halide such as 1-chlorooctane is heated with aqueous sodium cyanide, the reaction is extremely slow. Cyanide ions stay in the aqueous layer, and alkyl halide molecules stay in the organic layer, so the reactants only meet infrequently at the phase boundary. If, instead of sodium cyanide, a quaternary ammonium (Q) salt such as tetrabutylammonium cyanide [$(CH_3CH_2CH_2CH_2)_4N^+CN^-$] is used, the reaction proceeds quite readily and gives a high yield of product.

Reaction of 1-chlorooctane with sodium cyanide ($R = n\text{-}C_8H_{17}$)

$$RCl + Na^+CN^- \longrightarrow RCN + Na^+Cl^-$$

Improved reaction with a quaternary ammonium cyanide:

$$RCl + Q^+CN^- \longrightarrow RCN + Q^+Cl^-$$

$$[Q^+ = (CH_3CH_2CH_2CH_2)_4N^+]$$

There are several reasons for this enhanced reactivity of the cyanide. First, and most importantly, the sixteen carbon atoms of the $(CH_3CH_2CH_2CH_2)_4N^+$ cation make it soluble in the organic phase, and where the cation goes, the anion must follow. Second, the cyanide ion is more reactive in the organic phase than it would have been in the aqueous phase because it is not solvated by water molecules (a solvent shell would shield it from the alkyl halide and decrease its reactivity). Finally, the bulky alkyl groups around the positive nitrogen of the cation decrease the attractive forces between cation and anion and allow the cyanide ion more freedom to attack the alkyl halide. Therefore, substituting a quaternary ammonium ion for the sodium ion in the cyanide salt allows the desired reaction to proceed at a much higher rate. Its main drawback is that the quaternary ammonium cyanide is much more expensive than sodium cyanide.

The PTC technique gets around the high cost of quaternary ammonium salts by recycling them after each reaction step. If the quaternary ammonium cation in tetrabutylammonium chloride (represented in the previous equation by Q^+Cl^-) can be made to pick up more cyanide to react with the alkyl halide, it will function as a true catalyst, accelerating the reaction without being used up. All that is needed is a reservoir of cyanide ions and a small amount of quaternary ammonium salt to keep the reaction going. The reservoir can be provided by an aqueous layer that contains sodium cyanide.

Figure 24.1 diagrams the process, which occurs as follows: A catalytic amount of Q^+Cl^- combines with cyanide ion in the aqueous phase, and the Q^+CN^- that forms crosses over to the organic layer. There, it reacts with the alkyl halide to produce the nitrile (RCN) and form more Q^+Cl^-, which migrates across the interface, picks up more cyanide, shuttles it back into the organic layer to react with the alkyl halide and form more product and Q^+Cl^-, and so on, until the alkyl halide or the cyanide ion is used up.

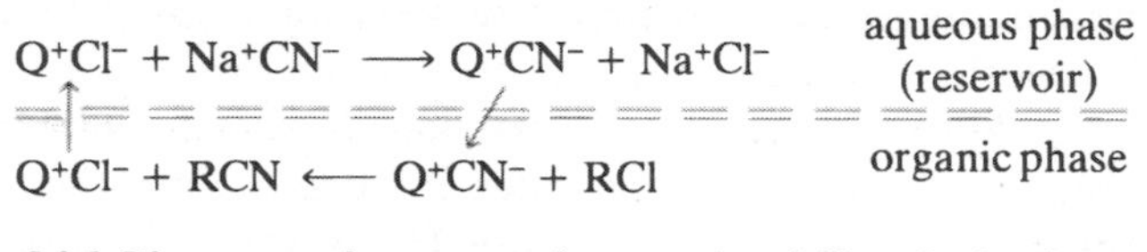

Key Concept: A phase-transfer catalyst speeds up a reaction by bringing together reactants that would otherwise remain in separate phases.

$$Q^+Cl^- + Na^+CN^- \longrightarrow Q^+CN^- + Na^+Cl^- \quad \text{aqueous phase (reservoir)}$$

$$Q^+Cl^- + RCN \longleftarrow Q^+CN^- + RCl \quad \text{organic phase}$$

Figure 24.1 Phase-transfer process for a nucleophilic substitution reaction

Understanding the Experiment

Hydrogen peroxide is a strong oxidant that can cause severe burns and bleach your skin white, so it should be handled with care, using protective gloves.

In this experiment, you will heat and stir cyclohexene with a mixture that contains 30% or 35% hydrogen peroxide, sodium tungstate dihydrate, a phase-transfer catalyst, and potassium bisulfate (potassium hydrogen sulfate, $KHSO_4$). A successful reaction requires a slightly acidic environment, so potassium bisulfate is used to lower the pH of the reaction mixture. The conversion of cyclohexene to adipic acid involves breaking the carbon–carbon double bond as well as oxidation of the doubly bonded carbon atoms, so it is classified as an *oxidative cleavage* reaction.

The phase-transfer catalyst you will use is a viscous liquid, tricaprylmethylammonium chloride, which is also known as Aliquat 336. The quaternary cation (Q^+) of this catalyst contains a methyl group and three 8-carbon alkyl attached to a nitrogen atom. The initial reaction mixture will consist of an organic phase containing cyclohexene and an aqueous phase containing sodium tungstate, hydrogen peroxide, and the other substances listed previously. The PTC reacts with sodium tungstate as shown.

$$2Q^+Cl^- + Na_2WO_4 \longrightarrow Q_2WO_4 + 2Na^+Cl^-$$

The resulting tricaprylmethylammonium tungstate (Q_2WO_4) is soluble in the organic phase, allowing the tungstate ions to react with cyclohexene molecules. The reduced form of tungstate then returns to the aqueous layer, where it is oxidized back to tungstate, and the process is repeated.

The product yield will depend on both the heating time and the stirring rate. The phases must be well mixed for a two-phase reaction to proceed, so the reaction mixture should be stirred as vigorously as possible throughout the reaction period. Enough product can be obtained for analysis after a minimum reaction time of one hour, but not all of the cyclohexene will have reacted; increasing the reaction time to two hours or more should improve the yield significantly. The solid product should crystallize out of solution upon cooling and can be collected by vacuum filtration. You can then purify it by recrystallizing it from boiling water. Once the product is dry, you can measure its melting point and obtain its infrared spectrum, which you can compare with a standard spectrum provided by your instructor or obtained from the library.

In the environment, cyclohexene should evaporate quickly; adipic acid is expected to be slightly toxic to aquatic life.

$[CH_3(CH_2)_7]_3NCH_3^+Cl^-$
tricaprylmethylammonium chloride (Aliquat 336)

Reactions and Properties

cyclohexene + $4H_2O_2$ $\xrightarrow[\text{PTC}]{\text{NaWO}_3\cdot2\text{H}_2\text{O}}$ HOCCH$_2$CH$_2$CH$_2$CH$_2$COH + $4H_2O$
adipic acid

Table 24.1 Physical properties

	mol wt	mp	bp	d
cyclohexene	82.15	−104	83	0.809
sodium tungstate dihydrate	329.9	696		3.245
35% hydrogen peroxide	34.0	−40	126	1.13
potassium bisulfate	136.1	197		2.24
adipic acid	146.1	152	338	1.36

Note: bp and mp are in °C; density is in g/mL.

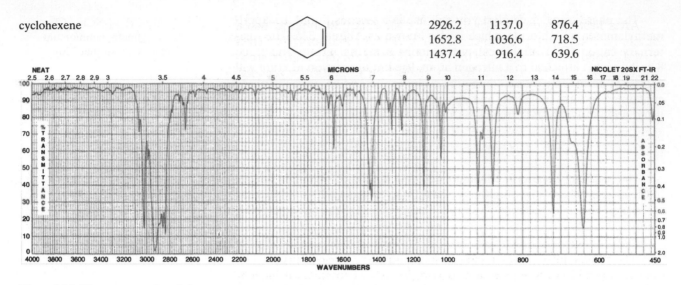

cyclohexene		2926.2	1137.0	876.4
		1652.8	1036.6	718.5
		1437.4	916.4	639.6

Figure 24.2 IR spectrum of cyclohexene

DIRECTIONS

Safety Notes

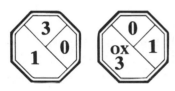

cyclohexene hydrogen peroxide

Cyclohexene is flammable, and inhalation or skin absorption may be harmful. Avoid contact, and do not breathe its vapors.

Concentrated hydrogen peroxide solutions are very corrosive and can cause severe burns. Hydrogen peroxide is a strong oxidant and can form explosive mixtures in the presence of certain organic compounds. Wear gloves, avoid eye and skin contact, do not breathe the vapors, and keep it away from other chemicals. In case of skin or eye contact, immediately flush thoroughly with water.

Sodium tungstate dihydrate irritates the skin and eyes and may be harmful by inhalation. Ingestion can be fatal. Avoid contact, and do not breathe its dust.

Potassium hydrogen sulfate is corrosive and can cause burns or other damage to the skin, eyes, and respiratory tract. Avoid contact, and do not breathe its dust.

Adipic acid causes moderate eye irritation and may irritate the skin and respiratory tract. Avoid contact, and do not breathe its dust.

 Standard Scale

Take Care! Hydrogen peroxide can cause severe burns; wear gloves, and avoid contact and inhalation. Avoid contact with sodium tungstate and potassium hydrogen sulfate, and do not breathe their dust.

Reaction.   Weigh 0.50 g of sodium tungstate dihydrate into a 50-mL round-bottom flask. Add about 0.50 g of Aliquat 336, and then add 10 mL of 35% hydrogen peroxide (or 12 mL of 30% H_2O_2) followed by 0.40 g of potassium hydrogen sulfate (potassium bisulfate); swirl to mix well. Add 25.0 mmol of cyclohexene and a stir bar (preferably the largest one that will fit), and heat the mixture under reflux [OP-7c] with *vigorous* stirring [OP-10]. Make sure that the reflux ring of condensing vapors stays below the midpoint of the condenser so that cyclohexene doesn't escape.

After heating and stirring under reflux for about 30 minutes, use a Pasteur pipet to rinse down the condenser with about 3 mL of water. Then dip the tip of a long glass rod into the reaction mixture and test with starch–iodide paper, if the paper doesn't turn blue–black within a few seconds, add hydrogen peroxide solution—about 1 mL at a time—until it does. Continue heating and stirring under reflux, testing the reaction mixture with starch–iodide paper every 15 minutes or so and adding more hydrogen peroxide if the test is negative. Carry out the reaction under reflux for a total time of at least one hour; if time permits, let it continue for another hour or so to improve your yield. By then, most or all of the oily top layer should have disappeared.

Stop and Think: What is in the top layer?

Separation.   While the reaction mixture is still hot, decant it (see OP-15) carefully into a beaker, leaving behind any Aliquat that separates as an oil (the oil may form a layer on the bottom of the flask or stick to its walls). It's better to leave a little solution behind than to contaminate it with Aliquat. Cool [OP-8] the reaction mixture in an ice/water bath for at least 30 minutes after a precipitate begins to form. Scratch the sides of the flask, if necessary, to induce crystallization. Collect the precipitate by vacuum filtration [OP-16], and wash it [OP-26a] with ice water.

Waste Disposal: Unless your instructor directs otherwise, wash the filtrate down the drain.

Purification and Analysis.   Recrystallize [OP-28] the product using a minimum volume of boiling water. Dry it [OP-26b] overnight (or longer) in a desiccator, and weigh it. Measure the melting point [OP-33] of the dried product, and record its infrared spectrum [OP-39].

Microscale

Reaction.   Weigh 0.10 g of sodium tungstate dihydrate into a 10-mL round-bottom flask. Using a Pasteur pipet, add about 0.10 g (5–6 drops) of Aliquat 336. Then add 2.0 mL of 35% hydrogen peroxide (or 2.4 mL of 30% H_2O_2) followed by 0.080 g of potassium hydrogen sulfate (potassium bisulfate); swirl to mix well. Add 5.00 mmol of cyclohexene and a stir bar (preferably the largest one that will fit), and heat the mixture under reflux [OP-7c] with *vigorous* stirring [OP-10]. Make sure that the reflux ring of condensing vapors stays below the midpoint of the condenser so that cyclohexene doesn't escape.

Take Care! Hydrogen peroxide can cause severe burns; wear gloves, and avoid contact and inhalation. Avoid contact with sodium tungstate and potassium hydrogen sulfate, and do not breathe their dust.

After heating and stirring under reflux for about 30 minutes, use a Pasteur pipet to rinse down the condenser with about 0.5 mL of water. Then dip the tip of a long, thin glass rod into the reaction mixture and test with starch iodide paper; if the paper doesn't turn blue–black within a few seconds, add hydrogen peroxide solution—5 to 10 drops at a time—until it does. Continue heating and stirring under reflux, testing the reaction mixture with starch–iodide paper every 15 minutes or so and adding more hydrogen peroxide if the test is negative. Carry out the reaction under reflux for a total time of at least one hour; if time permits, let it continue for another hour or so to improve your yield. By then, most or all of the oily top layer should have disappeared.

Stop and Think: What is in the top layer?

Separation.   While the reaction mixture is still hot, transfer [OP-6] it to a small beaker with a Pasteur pipet, leaving behind any Aliquat that separates

In the chain-propagating stage of the reaction, triphenylmethane should react with bromine atoms to produce trityl radicals. Thus, you could actually be making this radical twice during the experiment: once as an intermediate in the synthesis of bromotriphenylmethane, and later as a result of its reaction with zinc. Each trityl radical then reacts with a molecule of bromine, yielding a molecule of the product and another bromine atom that starts another cycle of chain-propagating steps.

$$Ph_3C-H + Br\cdot \longrightarrow Ph_3C\cdot + HBr$$

$$Ph_3C\cdot + Br_2 \longrightarrow Ph_3C-Br + Br\cdot$$

Key Concept: A chain reaction involves the initial formation of a reactive species that is regenerated after each cycle of product-forming steps and initiates the next cycle.

You will carry out the reaction by adding a solution of bromine in dichloromethane to a solution of triphenylmethane in the same solvent while heating the reaction mixture under reflux and irradiating it with light to generate bromine atoms. The reaction evolves hydrogen bromide, and bromine vapors may also escape from your apparatus, so you must either work under a fume hood or use a gas trap. When the reaction is complete, some excess bromine may remain that will color the reaction mixture. It can be removed by adding a drop or so of cyclohexene.

Removal of excess bromine

cyclohexene   1,2-dibromocyclohexane
                              (a liquid)

A Greener Way: Dichloromethane can be recovered by evaporating it under vacuum using a cold trap.

After you evaporate the solvent, you will purify the product by recrystallization from hexanes (a mixture of six-carbon alkanes). As always, you will want to minimize material losses by making nearly quantitative transfers, avoiding unnecessary transfers, and using minimal amounts of recrystallization and washing solvents. You can reduce the number of transfers by evaporating the solvent directly from the reaction flask and recrystallizing the product in the same flask.

You will attempt to prepare the triphenylmethyl radical by treating bromotriphenylmethane with metallic zinc in toluene. Exposing the solution to air may provide evidence for the existence of a dynamic equilibrium between the radical and its dimer.

The EPA classifies dichloromethane as a priority pollutant and has established a maximum contaminant level (MCL) of 5 ppb for its concentration in drinking water. Bromine is toxic to marine organisms, but no water quality standards for bromine have been issued by the U.S. government. Hexane and related hydrocarbons break down in air, water, and soil, and apparently do not persist for long in the environment. Toluene is a serious environmental contaminant that should not be released into the environment.

Reactions and Properties

A   triphenylmethane + $Br_2 \longrightarrow$ triphenylmethyl bromide + HBr

B   2 triphenylmethyl bromide + Zn $\xrightarrow{\text{toluene}}$ 2 triphenylmethyl radical + $ZnBr_2$

triphenylmethyl radical
(dimerizes in solution)

Table 25.1 Physical properties

	mol wt	mp	bp	d
triphenylmethane	244.3	94	359	
bromine	159.8	−7	59	3.12
dichloromethane	84.9	−97	40.5	1.326
bromotriphenylmethane	323.2	154		

Note: mp and bp are in °C; density is in g/mL.

DIRECTIONS

A. *Preparation of Bromotriphenylmethane*

Bromine is highly toxic and corrosive, and its vapors can damage the eyes and respiratory tract. Wear gloves when handling the bromine solution, and dispense it under a hood. Avoid contact, and do not inhale its vapors.
Dichloromethane may be harmful if ingested, inhaled, or absorbed through the skin. There is a possibility that prolonged inhalation of dichloromethane may cause cancer. Avoid contact with the liquid, and do not breathe its vapors.
Bromotriphenylmethane is harmful if inhaled or absorbed through the skin. Avoid contact with the product.
Hexanes and petroleum ether are highly flammable, so keep them away from flames and hot surfaces.

Safety Notes

the benzoyl peroxide. (b) So that it would dry faster, you washed the polystyrene with petroleum ether rather than methanol. (c) For the polymerization step of part **B**, you used commercial methyl methacrylate containing 50 ppm of 4-methoxyphenol.

4. (a) Calculate the atom economy and reaction efficiency of each polymerization reaction. (b) Describe some green features of each synthesis, and any that aren't so green.

5. Draw the structures of the monomers needed to prepare polymers that have the following repeating units.

a. $-(CHClCHCl)-$
b. $-(CF_2CFCl)-$
c. $-(CH_2CH_2NH)-$
d. $-(CH_2C=CHCH_2)-$
       $\quad\quad\quad\quad\quad |$
       $\quad\quad\quad\quad\quad CH_3$
e. $-(CH_2CH)-$
       $\quad\quad\quad |$
       $\quad\quad\quad CH_2CH_3$
f. $-(CH_2CH-CH_2CH)-$
       $\quad\quad\quad |$
       $\quad\quad\quad CN$

6. Show how the two monomers illustrated in the margin could combine to form a Diels–Alder addition polymer, and give the structure of the polymeric repeating unit.

7. Poly(ethylene glycol) can be prepared from either ethylene glycol or ethylene oxide. Write a balanced equation for each reaction, and classify each as addition or condensation polymerization.

8. Methyl methacrylate can be prepared commercially from acetone, hydrogen cyanide, and methanol. Propose a synthesis of methyl methacrylate from these starting materials, using any necessary inorganic reagents or solvents.

$-(CH_2CH_2O)-$
poly(ethylene glycol)

OH OH
$\;|\;\;\;|$
CH_2CH_2
ethylene glycol

O
$/\backslash$
CH_2CH_2
ethylene oxide

Other Things You Can Do

(Starred items require your instructor's permission.)

*1. You can attempt to prepare a polystyrene film from your product using the following method. Dissolve about 50 mg of the product in 0.5 mL of 2-butanone. This solution can be shared among several students. Use a Pasteur pipet to transfer about 10 drops of the solution to a *very clean* microscope slide, and tilt the slide to coat it evenly. Let the solvent evaporate completely under the hood. Carefully strip off the polymer film with a very sharp double-edged razor blade, and mount it between salt plates in an infrared cell holder.

*2. Three students can work together on part **B**—one using the standard procedure, the second using no *t*-butyl peroxybenzoate, and the third using 0.1 g (SS) or 40 mg (µS) of hydroquinone in place of the *t*-butyl peroxybenzoate. Compare and explain the results.

*3. Perform the "nylon rope trick" as described in Minilab 22.

4. Beginning with sources from the Bibliography, write a research paper on the use of Ziegler–Natta catalysts to synthesize stereoregular polymers, and describe some properties and uses of these polymers.

Synthesis of Ethanol by Fermentation

Reactions of Carbohydrates. Preparation of Alcohols. Biosynthesis of Organic Compounds.

Operations

OP-16   Vacuum Filtration (SS)
OP-17   Centrifugation (μS)
OP-32   Fractional Distillation
OP-34   Boiling Point

Before You Begin

1. Read the experiment, read or review the operations as necessary, and write an experimental plan.
2. Calculate the mass of 100 mmol (SS) or 5.00 mmol (μS) of sucrose, and the theoretical mass and volume of ethanol that can be produced from that much sucrose.

Scenario

The Great Plains Farm Cooperative helps farmers market their crops to help ensure that they receive a fair price. Recently, a bumper crop of sugar beets resulted in a surplus of beet sugar and drastically lowered the price of the product. The co-op has advised farmers to store their beets until the price rises; in the meantime, it is exploring alternative uses for the surplus beets. One alternative would be to convert the beet sugar to ethanol for use as an energy source in gasahol and other commercial fuels.

The co-op has sent your institute a quantity of beet sugar to see whether an ethanol conversion process would be feasible. To price the beet-sugar ethanol low enough to make it competitive with ethanol from corn and other sources, they require a product that is at least 180 proof. Your assignment is to ferment the sugar, distill it to concentrate the ethanol, and find out whether your product meets their specifications.

Applying Scientific Methodology

Whether or not you solve the problem in this experiment—that is, prepare ethanol that is 180 proof or higher—depends on your skill in performing the experiment.

The Chemistry of Brewing and Winemaking

The single-celled fungi called *yeasts* obtain the chemical energy they need to grow and reproduce by breaking down molecules of monosaccharides

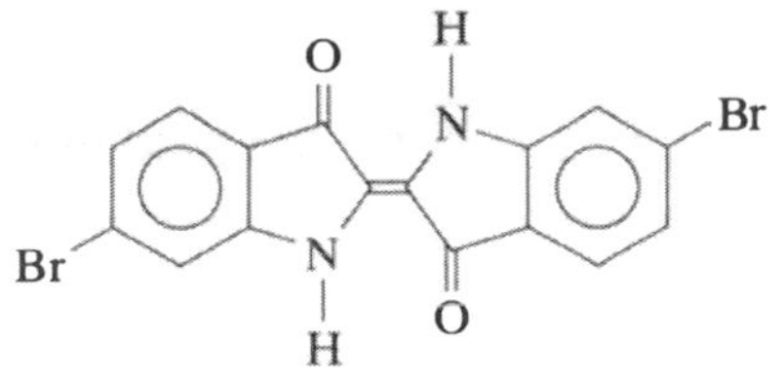

Tyrian purple (dibromoindigo)

Media reports on the issue tend to give the impression that all organohalogens are synthetic compounds that have never occurred naturally. In fact, there are a number of natural organohalogens. Tyrian purple is a bromine-containing dye derived from spiny carnivorous snails of the murex family. Because of its rarity—about 9000 snails are needed to produce one gram of the dye—Tyrian purple was a costly status symbol in the ancient world. Recently, a vial of 85-year-old whale oil collected during the last voyage of an old whaling ship was found to contain 11 halogenated organic compounds, including derivatives of polybrominated biphenyls and polybrominated diphenyl ethers. Because the whale oil was collected well before the production of similar synthetic halogen compounds, these compounds must have been produced naturally in the ocean. Some seaweeds produce trichloromethane (chloroform, $CHCl_3$) and tetrachloromethane (carbon tetrachloride, CCl_4), compounds that are also produced as by-products of water chlorination. Bromomethane (methyl bromide, CH_3Br), an important insect fumigant, is produced in large quantities by ocean algae. These and other organohalogens are, in part, responsible for the sharp smell of seawater. As various forest fungi break down dead trees and other plant materials, they produce about 200 times as much natural chloromethane (methyl chloride, CH_3Cl) as humans produce synthetically. Volcanoes also produce chloromethane, along with dichloromethane (methylene chloride) and chlorofluorocarbons such as dichlorodifluoromethane (Freon 12). Our own bodies utilize organic iodides in the form of thyroid hormones, and our white blood cells oxidize chloride ions in the blood to molecular chlorine, which kills invading bacteria and other microorganisms.

Polychlorodibenzodioxins (PCDDs) and polychlorodibenzofurans (PCDFs) are considered to be among the most hazardous organohalogens.

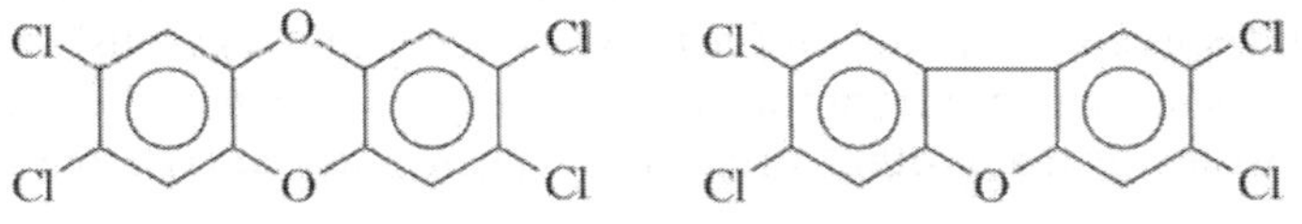

2,3,6,7-tetrachlorodibenzodioxin
(a PCDD)

2,3,6,7-tetrachlorodibenzofuran
(a PCDF)

2,3,6,7-Tetrachlorodibenzodioxin, called "dioxin" by the news media, occurs as a by-product when the herbicide 2,4,5-trichlorophenoxyacetic acid (2,4,5-T) is manufactured from 2,4,5-trichlorophenol.

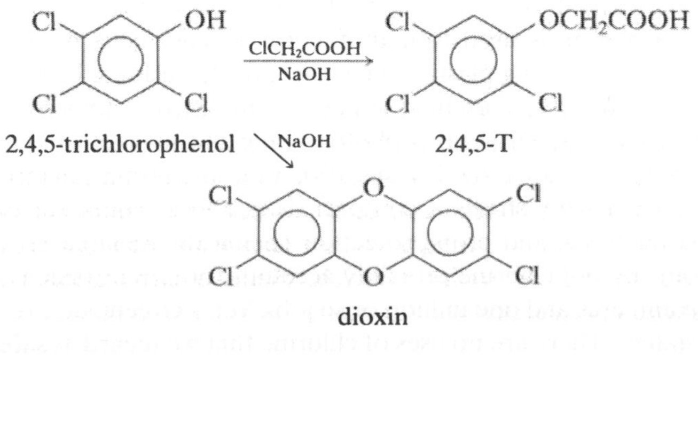

2,4,5-trichlorophenol   2,4,5-T

dioxin

Thus, 2,4,5-T is almost invariably contaminated with this chemical. Dioxin is regarded as one of the most toxic substances known, and some PCDFs may be even more toxic. Yet, both PCDDs and PCDFs are produced by burning wood, which contains natural chlorides, and some researchers believe that forest fires and brush fires are the major source of dioxins in the environment. Dioxins have been identified in ancient marine sediments from as early as 6000 B.C., and they are even produced in garden compost piles.

This is not to say that synthetic organohalogens aren't harmful because many of them also occur naturally. Many naturally occurring substances are hazardous to our health, and the levels of certain organohalogens in humans, including PCDDs and PCDFs, are considerably higher now than they were in preindustrial times, when the only sources of these substances were natural. Environmental groups and health organizations are concerned that they may already be causing reproductive problems, such as declining sperm counts, and other health problems in humans.

Most scientists agree that we should weigh the hazards and benefits of each organohalogen individually, rather than banning a whole family of compounds simply because it contains some bad actors. But those who support a chlorine ban believe we face a potential crisis that can't wait for a chemical-by-chemical study of all 15,000 or so chlorine-containing products that are now on the market. Meanwhile, measures are being taken to reduce the production of the most hazardous organohalogens. For example, the Environmental Protection Agency (EPA) is developing new regulations that should force pulp and paper mills—a major source of dioxin—to curtail their use of chlorine for bleaching. Nevertheless, the demand for many organohalogens has continued to grow, and there is little evidence to date of a slowdown in the production of industrial chlorine and its compounds.

2,4,5-T was the main constituent of Agent Orange, the Vietnam War defoliant believed to have caused health problems for many Vietnam veterans.

Key Concept: *A naturally occurring compound is not safe because it is natural, nor is a synthetic compound harmful because it is synthetic. The physiological effect of any substance, natural or synthetic, depends on its molecular structure, not on its source.*

Understanding the Experiment

In this experiment, you will convert either 1-butanol or 2-butanol to the corresponding alkyl bromide with HBr, using sulfuric acid as a catalyst. A *catalyst* is a substance that accelerates chemical reactions without being consumed in the process. For example, an alcohol cannot be converted to an alkyl bromide by sodium bromide, because hydroxide ion (OH^-) is too poor a leaving group to be displaced by bromide ion. A strong acid is needed to convert this poor leaving group to a better one, H_2O, by protonating it.

$$R-OH + H^+ \longrightarrow R-OH_2^+$$

Sulfuric acid catalyzes the overall reaction by increasing the concentration of the protonated alcohol, which can then react with bromide ion by either an S_N1 or S_N2 mechanism to form an alkyl bromide. Primary alcohols tend to react by the direct substitution (S_N2) mechanism; secondary and tertiary alcohols are more likely to form an intermediate carbocation, which then combines with halide ion.

See your lecture course textbook for a more detailed discussion of nucleophilic substitution reactions.

1.00 mL of sulfuric acid. Measure the quantities of all chemicals carefully for the cost analysis.

Reaction.   Assemble a microscale reflux apparatus [OP-7] using a 10-mL round-bottom flask, a water-cooled condenser, and a gas trap [OP-14]. The gas trap can be omitted if you are performing the reaction under an efficient fume hood. Add 18.0 mmol of your assigned alcohol (1-butanol or 2-butanol), accurately weighed, to the round-bottom flask and drop in a stir bar. *Under the hood,* cool the flask in ice water and cautiously add 2.5 mL (22 mmol) of 48% aqueous hydrobromic acid while stirring. Using a measuring pipet or an automatic pipet, add your assigned volume of concentrated sulfuric acid to the reaction mixture while stirring. Do not let either acid contact a plastic compression cap. Heat the mixture under reflux, with stirring [OP-10], for one hour from the time the solution starts to boil.

Separation.   Transfer the cooled reaction mixture to a 15-mL centrifuge tube using 5 mL of water for the transfer. Shake gently to mix the layers. Allow the layers to separate completely, rubbing the inside of the centrifuge tube with a wooden applicator stick to facilitate separation, if necessary. There should be only two layers at this point; if there are three, continue shaking. Ordinarily, the alkyl bromide is on the bottom and the aqueous layer on top, but occasionally the aqueous layer may be dense enough to end up on the bottom—in this case, the bottom layer will be the larger one. If you aren't sure which layer to save, test each one by adding a drop of water to a drop of the layer.

After separating it cleanly from the aqueous layer, wash [OP-24] the organic layer cautiously with 2 mL of cold, concentrated sulfuric acid, shaking gently with occasional venting. Remove the lower (H_2SO_4) layer, and then wash the alkyl bromide layer with a 2-mL portion of water followed by a 2-mL portion of saturated aqueous sodium bicarbonate, saving the organic (lower) layer each time. Dry [OP-25] the alkyl bromide with anhydrous sodium sulfate or calcium chloride. Transfer the crude product to a tared vial, weigh it, and report the yield to your instructor or coworkers.

Purification and Analysis.   Purify the alkyl bromide by microscale simple distillation [OP-30]. Collect the product over a 3–4°C range centered around the expected boiling point. Measure the mass and boiling point [OP-34] of the purified product. At your instructor's discretion, obtain its IR spectrum [OP-39]. Using prices provided by your instructor, calculate the total cost of all the chemicals (except water) that you used in the "Reaction" phase of the experiment. Divide the total cost in dollars by the mass of your crude product in kilograms, and obtain the cost/mass values reported by other members of your team. Because sulfuric acid can be recycled (at some cost), divide its cost by 3. Then determine the optimum catalyst/substrate ratio for each reaction.

Take Care! Wear gloves, avoid contact with the acids, and do not breathe their vapors.

Take Care! Possible violent reaction! Wear gloves, and avoid contact with the acid.

Waste Disposal: Put the sulfuric acid into an acid wastes container. Unless your instructor directs otherwise, wash all aqueous layers down the drain.

Stop and Think: What does the $NaHCO_3$ wash remove?

Exercises

1. Based on their structures, attempt to explain any differences in the optimum catalyst/substrate ratios for the two alcohols.

2. (a) Write structures for at least three by-products that might have formed during the reaction of 2-butanol. (b) Propose a mechanism for the formation of each by-product.

3. If you recorded the IR spectrum of your product, interpret the spectrum as completely as you can, and use the appropriate starting material spectrum in Figure 28.1 to show that the expected functional group conversion has taken place.

4. (a) Calculate the atom economy and reaction efficiency of your synthesis. (b) Describe some green features of your synthesis, and any that aren't so green.

5. Following the format in Appendix V, construct a flow diagram for this experiment.

6. Describe and explain the possible effect on your results of the following experimental errors or variations. (a) After adding water to the distillate (or the reaction mixture, if you used the microscale procedure) during the "Separation" step, you kept the bottom layer and discarded the smaller top layer. (b) You omitted the sulfuric acid wash. (c) You used a boiling-water bath to heat a reaction mixture containing 1-butanol.

7. Write balanced equations showing how HBr and SO_2 are consumed in a gas trap that contains NaOH.

8. Write a mechanism showing how 2,4,5-trichlorophenol is converted to 2,4,5-T.

Other Things You Can Do

(Starred items require your instructor's permission.)

*1. Obtain a nuclear magnetic resonance (NMR) spectrum of your product in deuterochloroform, and interpret it as completely as you can.

*2. Compare the nucleophilic substitution rates of some alcohols as described in Minilab 23.

3. Starting with sources from the Bibliography, write a research paper describing the manufacture, uses, and environmental effects of some chlorinated pesticides.

EXPERIMENT 29

Borohydride Reduction of Vanillin to Vanillyl Alcohol

Preparation of Alcohols. Reactions of Carbonyl Compounds. Reduction Reactions. Nucleophilic Addition.

Operations

The operations you use will depend on the procedure you develop.

Before You Begin

After reading the experiment, develop a procedure and an experimental plan for the sodium borohydride reduction of 25.0 mmol (SS) or 2.50 mmol (μS) of vanillin to vanillyl alcohol. Calculate or estimate the quantities of reactants and other chemicals you will need, and calculate the theoretical yield of vanillyl alcohol. Describe the reaction conditions, and tell how you intend to separate and purify the product. Your procedure should be clear and detailed enough so that anyone with sufficient background could carry it out successfully. (Alternatively, a group of students can work out a set of procedures in which some experimental parameters are varied to see how such variations alter the yield and purity of the product.)

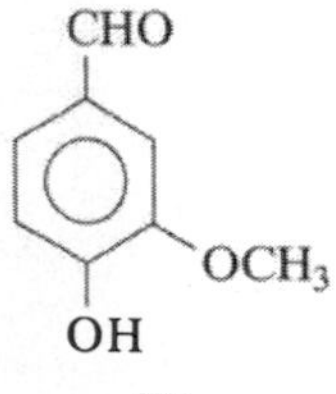

vanillin

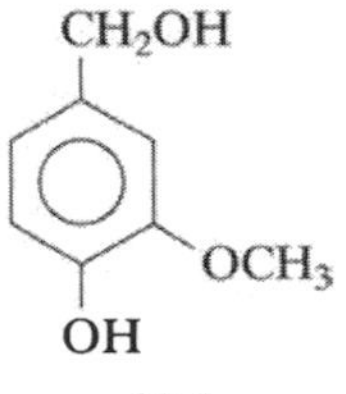

vanillyl alcohol

vanilla plant

Scenario

Pulpchem Inc., a subsidiary of a large paper company, produces useful chemicals from lignin and other by-products of paper production. Chemical treatment of lignin yields large quantities of vanillin, a white solid that is also responsible for the characteristic aroma of vanilla beans. Woody Aspin, Pulpchem's product development manager, has asked your institute to develop a method for reducing vanillin to vanillyl alcohol, which shows promise as a starting material for the synthesis of synthetic drugs and flavoring ingredients. A procedure for the preparation of vanillyl alcohol appeared in an obscure Swedish journal, *Acta Universitatis Lundensis,* which ceased publication in the 1960s. Unless you understand Swedish and can get your hands on a copy of the journal article, you will have to develop your own procedure for the synthesis.

Applying Scientific Methodology

The problem—whether vanillin can be converted to vanillyl alcohol by a procedure that you have developed yourself—will be solved when (and if) you obtain and characterize the product. You will test your working hypothesis by measuring the product's melting point, and you can record its infrared (IR) spectrum for confirmation.

Fragrant and Fiery Aromatics

Chemists recognized at an early date that certain compounds obtained from natural sources showed a higher ratio of carbon to hydrogen than did typical aliphatic compounds. These compounds also had distinctive chemical properties. Because many of them came from such pleasant-smelling sources as the essential oils of cloves, sassafras, cinnamon, anise, bitter almonds, and vanilla, they were called *aromatic* compounds. The name stuck, although it is no longer associated with the odors of such compounds but with their structures and properties. Many aromatic compounds do live up to the original meaning of the term, however. Among the most interesting and important of these are vanillin and the *vanilloids,* structurally related compounds that may exhibit vanillin's characteristic ring-substitution pattern.

In 1520, the Spanish conquistador Hernando Cortez was served an exotic drink by Montezuma II, emperor of the Aztecs, at his capital of Tenochtitlán on the site of modern Mexico City. Cortez enjoyed this *xocolatl,* a chocolate-based beverage flavored with honey and vanilla, and it soon found its way back to Europe. The vanilla plant (*Vanilla planifolia*), a climbing orchid, was also shipped back to the Old World in the hope that it could be cultivated there. The transported plants grew well but, mysteriously, would not fruit. This mystery remained unsolved for more than 300 years, until someone discovered that the plant was pollinated by a native Mexican bee with an exceptionally long proboscis. A method of hand pollination was soon developed, allowing the cultivation of vanilla outside of Mexico.

Vanilla flavoring comes from the fruit of the vanilla plant—a long, narrow pod that, after curing, looks somewhat like a dark brown string bean. The principal component of vanilla flavoring, vanillin (3-methoxy-4-hydroxybenzaldehyde), doesn't exist as such in the fresh vanilla bean, but is formed by the enzymatic breakdown of a glucoside during the curing process. Although the finest vanilla flavoring is still obtained from natural vanilla, synthetic vanillin is far less costly. It is used as a component of flavorings and perfumes and as a starting material for the synthesis of such drugs as L-dopa, which is used to treat Parkinson's disease.

At one time, synthetic vanillin was made mostly from isoeugenol, a naturally occurring phenol used widely as a perfume ingredient.

Most vanillin is now synthesized using lignin derived from wood pulp. Lignin is a complex polymer that gives rigidity to trees and other woody plants; after cellulose, it is the second most abundant organic material on

Earth. Many of the basic structural units of lignin are guiacylpropane units, and such units can be broken down chemically to yield vanillin.

guiacylpropane unit

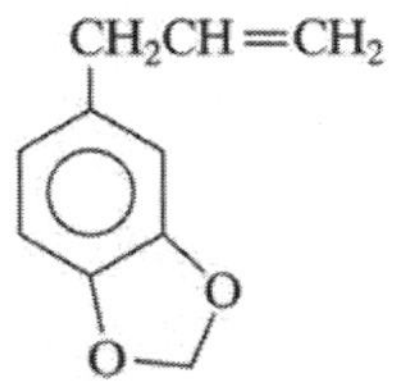

safrole

Safrole, a fragrant liquid derived from the roots and bark of the sassafras tree (*Sassafras albidum*), is structurally related to vanillin. Once widely used as a flavoring in root beer, toothpaste, and chewing gum, safrole can no longer be added to such products because of its toxic, irritant qualities and because it produces liver tumors in rats and mice. However, black pepper, anise, nutmeg, and other spices contain minute amounts of safrole, so you probably consume a little of it every day. Safrole has also been used by illicit-drug manufacturers to synthesize the dangerous designer drug "Ecstasy" (methylenedioxymethamphetamine), which can cause mental confusion, kidney failure, and death. For this reason, the sale of safrole is now strictly controlled.

Black pepper gets its "bite" from piperine, which contains the methylenedioxy ($-OCH_2O-$) unit also found in safrole.

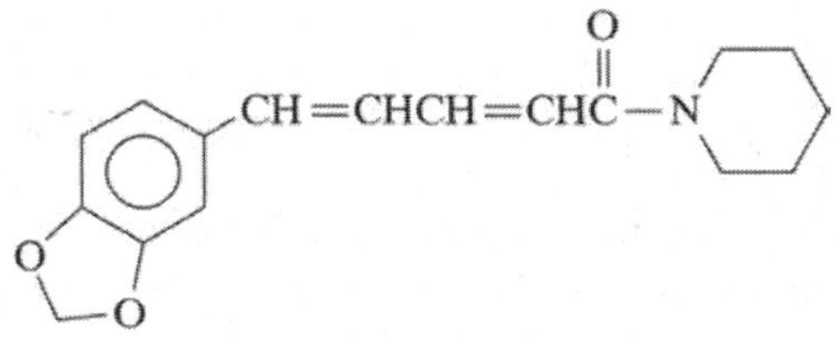

piperine (*trans* double bonds)

Another hot compound with the vanillin structural unit is zingerone, the pungent principle of ginger.

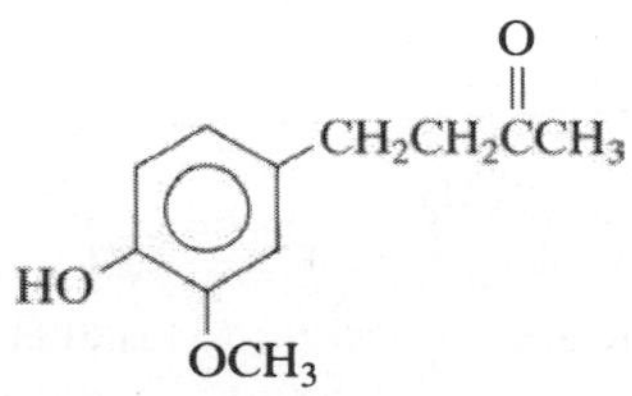

zingerone

Capsaicin, zingerone's much hotter cousin, is a fiery component of many *capsicums,* pungent peppers such as cayennes, jalapeños, and the ultrahot habaneros.

$$CH_2NHC(CH_2)_4CH=CHCHCH_3$$

capsaicin

Capsicum peppers are used to make Tabasco sauce, Jamaica Hell Fire, and other hot sauces, as well as most commercial salsas. Recent research has shown that the human tongue, in addition to containing receptors that detect sweet, sour, salty, bitter, and umami (MSG-like) tastes, also has vanilloid receptors that produce a sensation of heat when triggered by capsaicin and related vanilloids. As a result, the structural units that we associate with the pleasant flavor of vanillin contribute to a far different taste sensation in these fiery aromatics!

Understanding the Experiment

When organic chemists attempt to synthesize a new compound, they have no set procedure to follow. Instead, their options are to

- Adapt and modify an existing procedure for a similar synthesis
- Devise a procedure based on their knowledge of the substrate, reagent, product, and reaction involved
- Invent a new way of synthesizing the compound they wish to make

In this experiment, you will use the second option. You will develop your own procedure for reducing vanillin to vanillyl alcohol based on information that you will find in this section about the reducing agent, sodium borohydride, and the reaction, reduction of a carbonyl compound to an alcohol, as well as information in the "Reactions and Properties" section about the substrate and the product.

   Neither vanillin nor sodium borohydride is likely to be a significant environmental pollutant.

Key Concept: Developing a successful procedure for an organic synthesis requires a comprehensive knowledge of the characteristics of the reactants and a good understanding of the reaction.

Reduction Reactions.   In organic chemistry, *reduction* usually refers to a reaction that is accompanied by a gain of hydrogen atoms, a loss of oxygen atoms, or both. For example, a carbonyl compound is reduced to an alcohol when its carbonyl group gains two hydrogen atoms. The hydrogen is provided by an appropriate reducing agent.

Reducing Agents.   When lithium aluminum hydride ($LiAlH_4$) was introduced as a reducing agent in the late 1940s, it brought about a revolution in the preparation of alcohols by reduction. At that time, the two most popular reducing agents for carbonyl compounds were hydrogen and sodium metal. The greater simplicity and convenience of hydride reduction soon made it the preferred method for a broad spectrum of chemical reductions. Lithium aluminum hydride is a powerful reducing agent whose high reactivity is a disadvantage in some applications. Because it reacts violently with water and other hydroxylic solvents to release hydrogen gas, it can only be

Reduction of a carbonyl group

used in aprotic solvents, such as diethyl ether, under strictly anhydrous conditions. It is also expensive and somewhat hazardous to use—even grinding it in a mortar may cause a fire. By contrast, sodium borohydride ($NaBH_4$) is a much milder reducing agent that is comparatively safe to handle in its solid form. Unlike lithium aluminum hydride, it can even be used in aqueous or alcoholic solutions. $NaBH_4$ decomposes slowly in moist air, so its container should be tightly capped when it is not in use.

Sodium borohydride reductions involve nucleophilic addition of hydride ion ($H:^-$) to the carbonyl carbon, but apparently no free hydride ions are generated. Kinetic evidence suggests that one solvent molecule bonds to the boron atom while it is transferring hydride to the carbonyl compound, and another solvent molecule provides a proton to the carbonyl oxygen.

$$R-\overset{\frown}{O-}H + O=C\diagup + H^{\ominus}-B\diagdown + \overset{H}{\overset{|}{O}}-R \longrightarrow R-\overset{\ominus}{O} + H-O-\overset{|}{\underset{|}{C}}-H + \diagdown B^{\ominus}-OR + H^+$$

(R = alkyl or H)

This process can continue until all of the hydride ions from BH_4^- have been used up.

Reaction Stoichiometry.   The overall stoichiometry of the borohydride reduction of a carbonyl compound is given by the following general equation (R′ = alkyl or H):

$$4R\overset{O}{\overset{||}{C}}R' + NaBH_4 + 4H_2O \longrightarrow 4R\overset{OH}{\overset{|}{C}}HR' + H_3BO_3 + NaOH$$

In practice, it is best to use a 50–100% excess of sodium borohydride to compensate for any that reacts with the solvent or decomposes from other causes. Because the reaction is first order with respect to sodium borohydride (as well as the carbonyl compound), using an excess will also increase the reaction rate.

Reaction Solvents.   Sodium borohydride reductions are usually carried out in a dilute (~1 M) aqueous NaOH solution or in an alcohol, such as methanol, ethanol, or 2-propanol. The reagent is not stable at low pH, and even in a neutral aqueous solution it decomposes to the extent of about 4.5% per hour at 25°C. Acidic functional groups, such as COOH and the OH group of a phenol, may cause rapid decomposition of sodium borohydride. When a carbonyl compound having such a functional group is being reduced, enough 1 M NaOH should be used to neutralize the functional group *and* maintain a pH of 10 or higher. Sodium borohydride reacts slowly with alcohols, but ethanol and methanol are usually suitable solvents when there are no acidic functional groups and the reaction time is no more than 30 minutes at 25°C. For longer reaction times or reactions at higher temperatures, isopropyl alcohol is a better solvent, but it is more difficult to remove after the reaction is over.

Reaction Conditions.   In most reactions with sodium borohydride, the aldehyde or ketone is dissolved in the reaction solvent and a solution of sodium borohydride is added, with external cooling if necessary, at a rate slow enough to keep the reaction temperature below 25°C. Higher temperatures may decompose the hydride, and adding the carbonyl compound *to* the alkaline sodium borohydride solution may cause side reactions of base-sensitive substrates. The amount of solvent isn't crucial, but enough should be used to completely dissolve the reactants and facilitate the workup of the reaction mixture. The solubility of sodium borohydride per 100 g of solvent is reported to be 55 g in water at 25°C, 16.4 g in methanol at 20°C, and 4.0 g in ethanol at 20°C.

The time required to complete the reaction depends on the reaction temperature and the reactivity of the substrate. Kinetic studies of borohydride reduction in isopropyl alcohol have shown that aldehydes are considerably more reactive than ketones and that aliphatic carbonyl compounds are more reactive than aromatic ones. Most reactions of aldehydes and aliphatic ketones are complete in 30 minutes at room temperature, but those of aromatic ketones or particularly hindered ketones may require more time or higher reaction temperatures. For example, the comparatively reactive ketone 4-*t*-butylcyclohexanone is completely reduced at room temperature in 20 minutes, but benzophenone is reduced by boiling it in isopropyl alcohol for 30 minutes.

Et   = ethyl
i-Pr = isopropyl
t-Bu = *t*-butyl
r.t.   = room temperature

Reaction conditions in borohydride reductions

Workup of the Reaction Mixture.   After the reaction is complete, the excess sodium borohydride is decomposed by acidifying the reaction mixture to pH 6 or lower (slowly, while stirring) using dilute (~3 *M*) hydrochloric acid. Hydrogen gas is evolved as the excess sodium borohydride decomposes, so there must be no flames in the vicinity. Working under a hood is advisable. Addition of acid may also generate some diborane (B_2H_6), which can cause side reactions if other reducible groups, such as COOH, COOR, and C=C, are present.

Depending on the properties of the product and the reaction solvent used, the product can be separated from the reaction mixture by filtration, extraction, or partial evaporation of the solvent followed by extraction. If the product is a solid that crystallizes from the reaction mixture, it can be collected by vacuum filtration. The yield of the solid product can usually be increased by extracting the filtrate with diethyl ether or another suitable solvent, and then drying and evaporating the ether. Liquids or water-soluble products are generally separated from an aqueous reaction mixture by extraction with diethyl ether and recovered by evaporating the dried ether. If the reaction solvent is an alcohol, the reaction mixture is usually concentrated by evaporating most of the alcohol. Water is then added, and the product is extracted with a suitable solvent.

Purification.   The product can be purified by any appropriate method, based its physical state and properties. Vanillyl alcohol is reported to be soluble in hot and cold ethanol, hot and cold ether, and hot water. It is relatively insoluble in cold water, and it tends to form supersaturated solutions in water.

Reactions and Properties

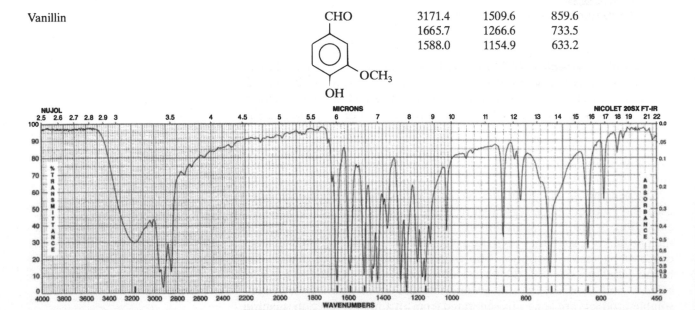

$$\underset{\text{vanillin}}{4\,\overbrace{}^{\text{CHO}}\underset{\text{OCH}_3}{}} + NaBH_4 + 4H_2O \longrightarrow 4\,\underset{\text{vanillyl alcohol}}{\overbrace{}^{\text{CH}_2\text{OH}}\underset{\text{OCH}_3}{}} + H_3BO_3 + NaOH$$

Table 29.1 Physical properties

	mol wt	mp	bp
vanillin	152.2	79	285
sodium borohydride	37.83	37	400d
vanillyl alcohol	154.2	115	d

Note: mp and bp are in °C; density is in g/mL; d = decomposes.

Vanillin

3171.4	1509.6	859.6
1665.7	1266.6	733.5
1588.0	1154.9	633.2

Figure 29.1 IR spectrum of vanillin

DIRECTIONS

Sodium borohydride is toxic and corrosive, and it can react violently with concentrated acids, oxidizing agents, and other substances. Aqueous $NaBH_4$ solutions with pH values below 10.5 have been known to decompose violently, so be sure that your reaction mixture (if aqueous) is sufficiently alkaline. Avoid contact with $NaBH_4$, do not breathe its dust, and keep it away from other chemicals.

Hydrogen is generated when the reaction mixture is acidified, so be sure that there are no flames nearby during this step.

Safety Notes

sodium borohydride

  Standard Scale and Microscale

Develop your own procedure for this experiment and submit it to your instructor for approval. Carry out the synthesis in the laboratory, measure the yield and melting point of the purified product, and turn it in. At your instructor's discretion, you can obtain the IR spectrum of your product and compare it with the spectrum of the starting material to confirm that the expected functional-group conversion has occurred. Dispose of any wastes as directed by your instructor. Calculate your percent yield, and compare your results with those of other students in your laboratory section.

Exercises

1. Write a mechanism for the reduction of vanillin by sodium borohydride under the reaction conditions you used.
2. Write a balanced equation for the decomposition of sodium borohydride in water to which HCl has been added.
3. Describe and explain the possible effect on your results of the following experimental errors or variations during a standard scale synthesis of vanillyl alcohol. (a) You used pure water as the reaction solvent. (b) You used 5 mL (SS) or 0.5 mL (μS) of 1 M NaOH for the $NaBH_4$ solution and 10 mL (SS) or 1.0 mL (μS) of 1 M NaOH for the vanillin solution. (c) Since you started with 25 mmol (SS) or 2.5 mmol (μS) of vanillin, you assumed that a 100% excess of $NaBH_4$ was 50 mmol (SS) or 5.0 mmol (μS) and used that amount.
4. (a) Calculate the atom economy and reaction efficiency of your synthesis. (b) Describe some green features of your synthesis, and any that aren't so green.
5. Following the format in Appendix V, construct a flow diagram for the experiment.
6. Sodium borohydride is a strong base as well as a reducing agent. Explain why it is better to add the $NaBH_4$ solution to a base-sensitive substrate than to add the substrate to the $NaBH_4$ solution.
7. (a) Draw the structure of the product you would have isolated if you had used $NaBD_4$ in D_2O in this experiment, and write a mechanism explaining the result. (b) Give the product structure for the same reaction

using $NaBD_4$ in H_2O. Assume that there is no hydrogen exchange between $NaBD_4$ and the solvent.

8. A careless student, Will Bobble, misread the label on a bottle of 10 M sodium hydroxide and used it (rather than 1 M NaOH) to dissolve his vanillin. Then he stored the solution and left the lab early to catch a ride home. During the next lab period, he added $NaBH_4$ and finished the experiment. Although his product was a white solid, it melted over a broad temperature range that was much lower than the melting point of vanillyl alcohol. His instructor suggested washing the product with dilute sodium bicarbonate; when he did so, about half of the product dissolved and the remainder melted at 115°C. Explain what happened, and write an equation for the reaction.

Other Things You Can Do

(Starred items require your instructor's permission.)

*1. Carry out the following tests from Part IV on vanillin and on your product: 2,4-dinitrophenylhydrazine (Test C-11), ferric chloride (Test C-13), and Tollens' test (Test C-23). Interpret the results, and comment on the purity of your product.

*2. Compare the oxidation rates of some alcohols in Minilab 25.

*3. Reduce another carbonyl compound (such as benzaldehyde or camphor) with sodium borohydride after developing a detailed procedure, and turn in a pure sample of the resulting alcohol. Your instructor must approve the procedure before you start.

4. Starting with sources listed in the Bibliography, write a research paper on the sources, nature, and uses of lignin, including a description of a commercial process for producing vanillin from the by-products of papermaking.

Synthesis of Triphenylmethanol and the Trityl Carbocation

*Reactions of Carbonyl Compounds. Reactions of Organic Halides.
Preparation of Alcohols. Nucleophilic Addition. Organometallic
Compounds. Carbocations. Infrared Spectrometry.*

Operations

OP-12 Excluding Water from Reaction Mixtures
OP-7   Heating
OP-10   Mixing
OP-11   Addition of Reactants
OP-15   Gravity Filtration (SS)
OP-16   Vacuum Filtration
OP-17   Centrifugation (µS)
OP-19   Evaporation
OP-24   Washing Liquids
OP-25   Drying Liquids
OP-26   Washing and Drying Solids
OP-28   Recrystallization
OP-33   Melting Point
OP-39   Infrared Spectrometry (optional)

Before You Begin

1. Read the experiment and operation OP-12, read or review the other operations as necessary, and write an experimental plan.
2. Calculate the mass of 22.0 mmol (SS) or 4.00 mmol (µS) of magnesium, the mass of 20.0 mmol (SS) or 3.80 mmol (µS) of benzophenone, the mass and volume of 22.0 mmol (SS) or 4.00 mmol (µS) of bromobenzene, and the theoretical yield of triphenylmethanol. Calculate the theoretical yield of trityl fluoborate from 1.00 g (SS) or 0.100 g (µS) of triphenylmethanol.

Scenario

The Complementary Colors Company manufactures synthetic dyes, including a number of triphenylmethane dyes. Gilda Lillie, product development director for the company, would like to develop some new colors to improve its market share in the dye industry. She has learned, for example, that having two *para*-dimethylamino groups on two of the three benzene rings in the parent structure yields a green dye (Malachite Green), while having three of them yields a violet dye (Crystal Violet).

carbocation structure   iminium ion structure

Two resonance structures for Malachite Green, a triphenylmethane dye

triphenylmethyl (trityl)
fluoborate

The company's technicians need to know how the kinds and positions of substituents on the parent triphenylmethyl ring structure affect the color of triphenylmethane dyes. For that, they need a sample of the unsubstituted parent compound of these dyes, the triphenylmethyl (trityl) carbocation. Your assignment is to prepare triphenylmethanol and convert it to trityl fluoborate, a salt that contains the trityl carbocation.

Applying Scientific Methodology

The main scientific problem—determining the color of trityl fluoborate—will be solved when you prepare this substance.

The Colorful Career of the Triphenylmethanes

The synthesis of quinine was not accomplished until 1944—88 years after Perkin had attempted it.

Reduced form of malachite green

Key Concept: When a substance cannot be represented satisfactorily by a single structural formula, its actual structure is regarded to be a composite of two or more contributing structures.

During his Easter vacation from London's Royal College of Chemistry, 18-year-old William Perkin was trying to synthesize quinine when he came up with an unpromising red-brown solid that had none of the properties of quinine. Undeterred, Perkin used similar methods to synthesize mauve, a light purple dye whose commercial success launched the synthetic dye industry. The first triphenylmethane dye, fuchsin, was synthesized a few years later, and it was followed soon after by Malachite Green, Crystal Violet, and other triphenylmethane dyes. The race to develop commercially marketable dyes also stimulated research into the molecular basis of color. Why, for example, is Malachite Green green and its reduced form colorless?

The *chromophore* of a compound is the part of its molecule over which electrons can be delocalized and which is responsible for its absorption of ultraviolet or visible light. Triphenylmethane dyes come in all colors of the rainbow, from the red of rosaniline through Malachite Green and Victoria Blue to Crystal Violet. The chromophores responsible for these colors appear to be nitrogen-substituted triphenylmethyl (trityl) cations, but they are not true carbocations because most of their positive charge is distributed to the nitrogen atoms, as in the iminium ion form of Malachite Green shown previously. According to resonance theory, the iminium ion and carbocation forms are contributing structures of a resonance hybrid that has some characteristics of each. The electron delocalization suggested by such structures is responsible for their colors. As a rule, compounds with extensive chromophores that allow electron delocalization over many atoms tend to be colored; the longer the chromophore, the higher the wavelength of light it absorbs. The reduced form of Malachite Green is not colored because the saturated carbon that connects the rings prevents electron delocalization over the three-ring system.

One resonance structure of the triphenylmethyl cation

Although it is nearly a trillion times less stable than Crystal Violet, the triphenylmethyl cation is unusually stable for a true carbocation. When protected from atmospheric moisture, trityl salts will keep almost indefinitely. The cation owes this unusual stability to delocalization of the positive charge about its three benzene rings. The cation is shaped somewhat like a propeller with the "blades" (benzene rings) pitched at a 32° angle, because steric interference between the *ortho* hydrogen atoms makes a planar configuration impossible.

Shape of triphenylmethyl cation

Understanding the Experiment

The year 1900 featured two milestones in organic chemistry: Moses Gomberg announced his discovery of the trityl free radical (see Experiment 25), and Victor Grignard reported his discovery of Grignard reagents. Just a year later, trityl carbocations were being prepared from triphenylmethanol, which is most easily synthesized using a Grignard reagent.

Grignard's original procedure for preparing a Grignard reagent was as follows: Approximately a mole of magnesium metal was placed in a dry, two-necked, round-bottom flask fitted with a reflux condenser and addition funnel. A mole of the organic halide was dissolved in diethyl ether, and 50 mL of this solution was added to the magnesium. When a white turbidity appeared at the metal surface and effervescence began, more ether was added in portions, with cooling, followed by drop-by-drop addition of the remainder of the halide/ether solution. The reaction was brought to completion by heating under reflux in a hot-water bath.

Although extensive studies of the reaction have led to some modifications of the reaction conditions, essentially the same method is used today to make most Grignard reagents. It is important that the reagents and apparatus be very dry because water not only reacts with Grignard reagents but also inhibits their formation. In a study using butyl bromide, it was found that the *induction period* (the time between the combination of reactants and the start of a noticeable reaction) for forming the Grignard reagent was $7\frac{1}{2}$ minutes using sodium-dried diethyl ether, 20 minutes using commercial absolute diethyl ether, and 2 hours using diethyl ether half saturated with water. It is apparent that careful drying of the reaction apparatus and reagents saves time in the long run; it should increase the yield of the desired product as well. An especially effective drying technique is to add the magnesium to the reaction flask and heat it (well away from any container of diethyl ether!) in a soft, blue Bunsen burner flame for 2–3 minutes, then set it on a cork ring or in a beaker to cool. If the bromobenzene/ether solution is then added, and the magnesium pieces are rubbed with a stirring rod for about 10 seconds, the reaction should start almost immediately.

The type and quantity of reagents and solvents used are also important. When magnesium metal is exposed to air, it forms a thin film of magnesium oxide on its surface. For the standard scale synthesis, you will crush dry magnesium turnings with a glass rod to remove some of the oxide film and provide a fresh surface for reaction. For the microscale synthesis, you will scrape a length of magnesium ribbon and then cut it into small pieces. Commercial anhydrous diethyl ether is suitable for most routine preparations, but the optimum quantity of ether depends on the kind of Grignard reagent being prepared. One study showed that the highest yields of phenylmagnesium bromide were obtained with 5 moles of diethyl ether per mole of bromobenzene.

In this experiment, you will prepare phenylmagnesium bromide by adding a solution of bromobenzene in anhydrous diethyl ether to magnesium metal. The Grignard reaction can usually be started by rubbing or crushing the magnesium with a stirring rod while cupping the reaction flask in the palm of the hand to warm the ether. The onset of the reaction is signaled by the formation of small bubbles on the surface of the magnesium accompanied by the appearance of a cloudy precipitate. You can sometimes jump-start a balky Grignard reaction by adding a small amount of previously prepared Grignard reagent to the reaction mixture; consult your instructor for help.

Using a high concentration of bromobenzene helps to get the reaction started, but it can promote the formation of an undesirable by-product, biphenyl, through a side reaction on the metal's surface. For this reason, the bromobenzene solution is diluted by adding diethyl ether as soon as the reaction gets under way. Phenylmagnesium bromide reacts rapidly with water to form benzene and more slowly with oxygen to form a magnesium salt of phenol. Therefore, the reaction apparatus must be protected from moisture, and the Grignard reagent should be used shortly after it is prepared.

When benzophenone is added to the Grignard reagent, a magnesium salt of triphenylmethanol precipitates from the reaction mixture, which usually turns pink during the addition. This salt is converted to triphenylmethanol by water, and dilute hydrochloric acid is added to dissolve the basic magnesium salts that form along with the product. The ether solution containing triphenylmethanol is washed to remove impurities, and the solvent is evaporated. The crude product is then *triturated* with hexanes or petroleum ether to remove biphenyl, and purified by recrystallization.

Carbocations can be prepared by mixing alcohols with a strong acid such as fluoboric acid (tetrafluoroboric acid); the fluoborate anion is a very weak nucleophile that doesn't react with the resulting carbocation. You will prepare trityl fluoborate by the reaction of triphenylmethanol with 48% fluoboric acid. The water in the aqueous fluoboric acid solution, as well as that produced during the carbocation-forming reaction, could prevent or

Trituration of a solid involves rubbing and grinding it, usually in the presence of a solvent.

Preparation of carbocations using fluoboric acid

$$ROH + HBF_4 \rightleftharpoons ROH_2^+ + BF_4^-$$
$$\longrightarrow R^+BF_4^- + H_2O$$

reverse the reaction. Acetic anhydride is added to consume the water by the following reaction:

$$\underset{\text{acetic anhydride}}{CH_3\overset{O}{\overset{\|}{C}}O\overset{O}{\overset{\|}{C}}CH_3} + H_2O \longrightarrow \underset{\text{acetic acid}}{2CH_3\overset{O}{\overset{\|}{C}}OH}$$

Of the chemicals used in part **A**, diethyl ether is not considered toxic to aquatic organisms and does not persist for long in either air or water; bromobenzene is toxic to aquatic organisms and should not be released into the environment; and benzophenone is harmful to aquatic organisms. In water, acetic anhydride hydrolyzes to acetic acid, which readily breaks down to form carbon dioxide and water. Little information is available about the environmental effects of fluoboric acid, but it is likely to be toxic to aquatic organisms.

Reactions and Properties

A

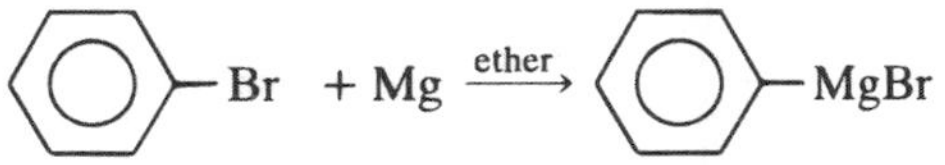

bromobenzene phenylmagnesium bromide

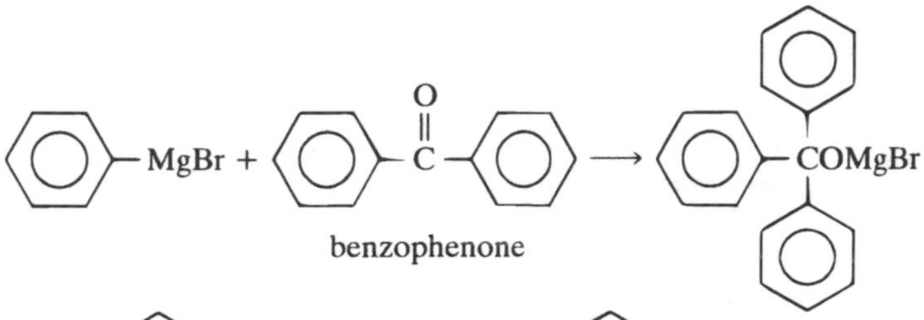

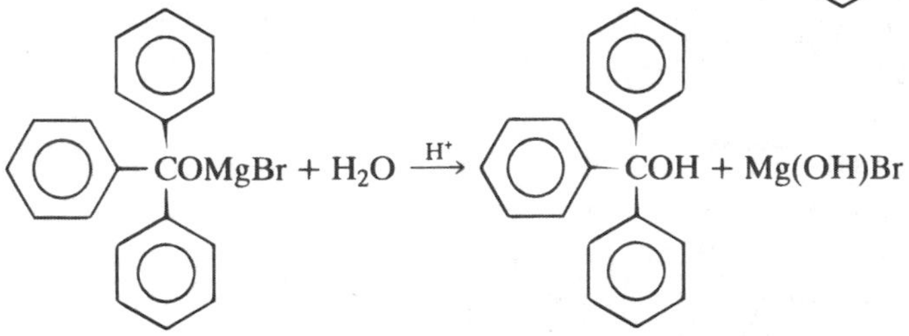

triphenylmethanol

B

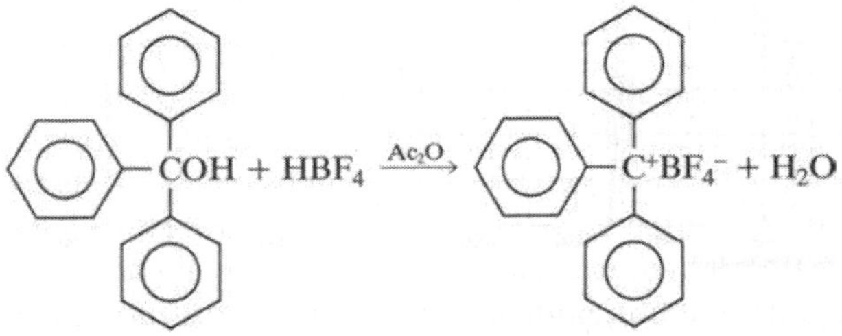

trityl fluoborate

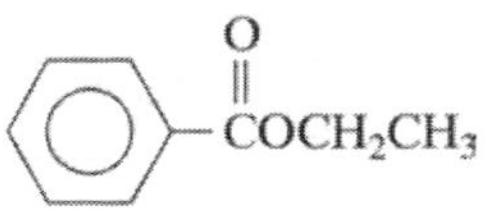

O
‖
⬡—COCH₂CH₃

ethyl benzoate

4. (a) Calculate the atom economy and reaction efficiency of your synthesis. (b) Describe some green features of your synthesis, and any that aren't so green.

5. Following the format in Appendix V, construct a flow diagram for the synthesis of triphenylmethanol (part A).

6. The reaction of phenylmagnesium bromide with benzophenone to form the salt of triphenylmethanol is an example of nucleophilic addition; its reaction with ethyl benzoate to yield the same product involves nucleophilic substitution followed by a nucleophilic addition step. Write reasonable mechanisms for both reactions.

7. Outline a synthetic pathway for preparing each of the following compounds, using the Grignard reaction and starting with benzene or toluene: (a) 1,1-diphenylethanol; (b) 1,2-diphenylethanol; (c) 2,2-diphenylethanol; (d) 2,3-diphenyl-2-butanol.

8. Excluding alternative Kekulé structures for the benzene rings, (a) draw all possible resonance structures for the trityl cation; (b) draw all possible resonance structures for Malachite Green.

9. One possible by-product from the triphenylmethanol synthesis is ethoxytriphenylmethane. Tell how and when it might form, and give an equation and a mechanism for the reaction.

Other Things You Can Do

(Starred items require your instructor's permission.)

*1. Record the ultraviolet–visible spectrum (200–600 nm) of trityl fluoborate in dry acetone.

*2. Dissolve a small amount of trityl fluoborate in dry methanol, and record your observations. Dissolve about 0.1 g of trityl fluoborate in 1 mL of dry acetone; then add a solution of sodium iodide in dry acetone (0.1 g NaI in 1 mL acetone), drop by drop, until no more changes are observed. Write balanced equations to explain your observations.

*3. Prepare the fluorescent dye fluorescein as described in Minilab 26.

4. Write a research paper about the structures, properties, and applications of Grignard reagents, starting with sources listed in the Bibliography.

An Unexpected Reaction
of 2,3-Dimethyl-2,3-butanediol

EXPERIMENT **31**

Reactions of Hydroxyl Compounds. Carbocations. Reaction Mechanisms.
Structure Determination. Infrared Spectrometry. NMR Spectrometry.

Operations

OP-10   Mixing
OP-24   Washing Liquids
OP-25   Drying Liquids
OP-30   Simple Distillation
OP-34   Boiling Point
OP-39   Infrared Spectrometry
OP-40   Nuclear Magnetic Resonance Spectrometry

Before You Begin

1. Read the experiment, read or review the operations as necessary, and write an experimental plan.
2. Calculate the mass of 60.0 mmol (SS) or 12.0 mmol (μS) of 2,3-dimethyl-2,3-butanediol, and the theoretical yield of the product, $C_6H_{12}O$.

Scenario

Willy Hackett, a graduate student at Miskatonic University, has a reputation for carrying out apparently straightforward reactions and coming up with unexpected results. Now his research mentor has asked Willy to develop a simple synthesis of 2,3-dimethyl-1,3-butadiene, which he should then be able to convert to a rubber-like polymer. Willy is familiar with the acid-catalyzed dehydration of alcohols to alkenes in the presence of a sulfuric acid catalyst, so he thinks it should be possible to convert a suitable diol to the target diene by the same method. The most readily available diol that has the same carbon skeleton as the diene is 2,3-dimethyl-2,3-butanediol, so he heated this reactant with some sulfuric acid, expecting to get the following reaction.

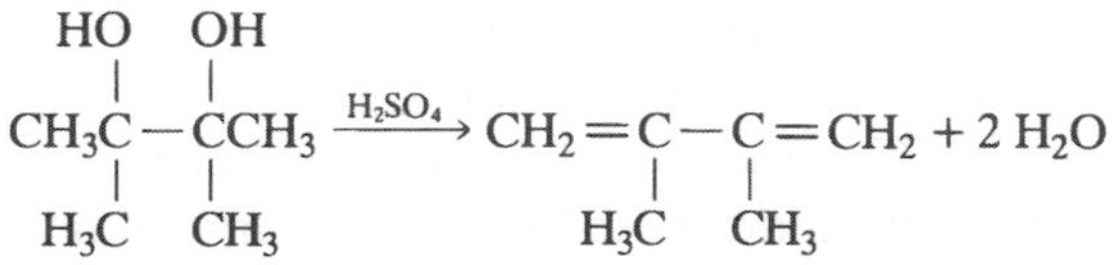

$$CH_3\overset{\overset{\displaystyle HO}{|}}{\underset{\underset{\displaystyle H_3C}{|}}{C}}-\overset{\overset{\displaystyle OH}{|}}{\underset{\underset{\displaystyle CH_3}{|}}{C}}CH_3 \xrightarrow{H_2SO_4} CH_2{=}\overset{}{C}-\overset{\overset{}{|}}{\underset{\underset{\displaystyle H_3C}{}}{C}}{=}\overset{}{\underset{\underset{\displaystyle CH_3}{}}{C}}CH_2 + 2\,H_2O$$

2,3-dimethyl-   2,3-dimethyl-
2,3-butanediol   1,3-butadiene

However, the product he obtained has the chemical formula $C_6H_{12}O$, rather than the expected formula, C_6H_{10}, so it is obviously not the diene he was trying to make. Your assignment, and that of your coworkers, is to carry out the reaction of 2,3-dimethyl-2,3-butanediol with sulfuric acid and deduce the structure of Willy Hackett's unexpected product, with the help of its infrared (IR) and nuclear magnetic resonance (NMR) spectra. You can also attempt to show how the product was formed by writing a reasonable mechanism for the reaction.

5. Following the directions in Appendix V, construct a flow diagram for the synthesis of your product.
6. Give the structure of the product that the BASF chemist (see "Unexpected Outcomes in Chemistry") should have obtained from the reaction of naphthalene with an equivalent amount of sulfuric acid if he hadn't broken his mercury thermometer.
7. (a) Outline a synthesis of 2-3-dimethyl-1,3-butadiene (the product Willy Hackett was trying to make) from 2,3-dimethyl-2-butene. (b) Outline the synthesis of a rubber-like polymer that can be made from this diene.

Other Things You Can Do

(Starred items require your instructor's permission.)

*1. As an alternative to the structure determination method described in this experiment, identify the functional group in the product using one or more chemical tests, and determine its identity by preparing one or more derivatives, as described in Part IV, "Qualitative Organic Analysis."
*2. Prepare a vicinal diol by the photoreduction of benzophenone as described in Minilab 24.
3. Starting with sources listed in the Bibliography, write a research paper about reactions related to the one you carried out in this experiment.

Identification of a Conjugated Diene from Eucalyptus Oil

Reactions of Dienes. Preparation of Bicyclic Compounds. Cycloaddition. Infrared Spectrometry. Qualitative Analysis.

Operations

OP-7   Heating
OP-16   Vacuum Filtration
OP-26   Washing and Drying Solids
OP-28   Recrystallization
OP-33   Melting Point
OP-37   Gas Chromatography
OP-39   Infrared Spectrometry

Before You Begin

1. Read the experiment, read or review the operations as necessary, and write an experimental plan.
2. Be prepared to carry out the calculations described in part **A** of the Directions.
3. If time permits, record the gas chromatogram of the "eucalyptus oil" during a previous experiment.

Scenario

In 1927, Otto Diels and Kurt Alder treated a constituent of one kind of eucalyptus oil with maleic anhydride and obtained a new compound that they described as forming *"grosse glasglänzende Krystalle von ungewöhnlicher Schönheit"* (large, lustrous crystals of unusual beauty). The reaction Diels and Alder used for this preparation was eventually named for them, and the lustrous crystals belonged to the Diels–Alder adduct of a natural diene. Gondwana Natural Products, Ltd. (GNP), which obtains and markets useful products from Australian flora, is investigating the commercial possibilities of an essential oil from *Eucalyptus dives* that has been used to treat colds, as well as malaria and other fevers. The ultraviolet–visible spectrum of the eucalyptus oil suggests that it contains the same diene that Diels and Alder studied—one of the natural dienes described next. GNP wants your institute to identify the diene from a sample of the eucalyptus oil they have provided. Because only conjugated dienes undergo the Diels–Alder reaction, this reaction can be used to separate the diene from the eucalyptus oil, as well as to identify it.

maleic anhydride

aspirin and on aspirin that has been in use for some time. (Try to find some old aspirin that has a "vinegar" odor.) Test them for starch (often used as a binder) by boiling 2 mg of a ground-up tablet in 2 mL of water and adding a drop of a solution of iodine in potassium iodide. Starch forms a blue-violet complex with iodine.

3. Starting with sources listed in the Bibliography, write a research paper on some commercial uses for acetic anhydride other than in aspirin production.

Directive Effects in the Bromination of Vanillin

EXPERIMENT **35**

Reactions of Aromatic Compounds. Preparation of Aryl Bromides. Electrophilic Aromatic Substitution. Directive Effects.

Operations

OP-10   Mixing
OP-16   Vacuum Filtration
OP-26   Washing and Drying Solids
OP-28   Recrystallization
OP-33   Melting Point

Before You Begin

1. Read the experiment, read or review the operations as necessary, and write an experimental plan.
2. Calculate the mass of 10.0 mmol (SS) or 2.00 mmol (μS) of vanillin, and the theoretical yield of bromovanillin from this amount of vanillin.

Scenario

Pulpchem Inc., a subsidiary of a large paper company, produces useful chemicals from lignin and other by-products of paper production. Chemical treatment of lignin can yield vanillin, a white solid that is responsible for the characteristic aroma of vanilla extract. The product development manager of Pulpchem, Woody Aspin, wants to develop new products from vanillin that might be marketed commercially. He has heard of a new way to brominate aromatic compounds on the benzene ring using hydrobromic acid and potassium bromate rather than hazardous liquid bromine, but he doesn't know what products to expect from the reaction. If the *ortho-para* directing methoxyl group of vanillin controls product formation, the product could be 2-bromovanillin, 6-bromovanillin, or a mixture of the two. But, if the hydroxyl group and the *meta*-directing aldehyde group win out, the product should be 5-bromovanillin.

vanillin   2-bromovanillin   5-bromovanillin   6-bromovanillin

Your assignment, and that of your coworkers, is to carry out the bromination of vanillin and identify the product.

Applying Scientific Methodology

Your working hypothesis should involve a prediction of the product (or products) you think the bromination of vanillin should yield. You will test your hypothesis by measuring the melting point of the product.

The Flavor of Vanilla

Most good cooks have a bottle labeled "pure vanilla extract" in the cupboard. It contains a brown liquid with the delightful scent and flavor that we associate with vanilla ice cream, vanilla pudding, cream soda, and many baked goods. Although cheaper forms of vanilla may consist mainly of vanillin synthesized from guaiacol or wood pulp, the real thing comes from the seedpod of a tropical orchid. One of these pods—often called a vanilla bean—looks much like a long (12–15 cm) green bean and has virtually no odor. The characteristic vanilla odor develops during a curing process in which sugar derivatives called glycosides are broken down into vanillin and other flavorful substances. Cured vanilla beans typically contain more than 400 such components. Vanilla extract is made by shredding the beans into small pieces, typically in a machine that works like a giant blender, and soaking the pieces in successive quantities of hot 65–70% ethanol.

Vanilla orchids were probably first discovered and used in southeastern Mexico more than 1000 years ago. By the time Spanish conquistadores discovered Mexico's Aztec Empire in the 1500s, Aztecs were flavoring a cocoa-containing beverage called *xocolatl* (*chocolatl* in Spanish) with honey and vanilla. Vanilla has long had a reputation as an aphrodisiac; the Aztec emperor Montezuma drank xocolatl from a golden goblet before visiting his wives, and in Europe newly married men were once advised to drink beverages flavored with vanilla. There is some scientific support for such practices; recent tests at the Institute for Smell and Taste in Chicago showed that the aroma of vanilla is a powerful stimulant to men.

Today, about half of the world's vanilla is grown in the tropical forests of Madagascar, with smaller amounts from Indonesia, Mexico, Tahiti, and the Comoro Islands. Bourbon vanilla, which is usually considered to be the world's finest, is grown in Madagascar, the Comoros, and the nearby island of Reunion, which was once ruled by the Bourbon kings of France. In addition to vanillin, Bourbon vanilla contains the flavor ingredient bourbonal, an ethyl homolog of vanillin.

Although vanilla's dominant flavor ingredient is vanillin, its other components contribute to the rich, complex flavor of a natural vanilla extract. Many so-called vanilla extracts are actually blends of natural vanilla extract and synthetic vanillin. Because natural vanilla extract costs more than $500 a kilogram, the cheaper products are mostly synthetic vanillin, and the blend labeled "imitation vanilla" is made entirely from synthetic substances. Carbon-13 nuclear magnetic resonance (see OP-40b) can be used to determine the origin of vanillin by measuring the intensities of the ^{13}C signals for each of its eight carbon atoms and calculating their $^{13}C/^{12}C$ ratios. This method can reveal any attempt to fraudulently substitute cheap synthetic vanillin for the natural substance.

bourbonal

The essay in Experiment 29 describes several ways of synthesizing vanillin.

Understanding the Experiment

Aromatic compounds can be brominated on the ring by elemental bromine (Br_2) in the presence of a Lewis acid catalyst such as iron(III) bromide, $FeBr_3$. But liquid bromine, with its toxic red fumes, is dangerous to inhale and can cause severe burns. Paul F. Schatz of the University of Wisconsin–Madison discovered that a mixture of potassium bromate and hydrobromic acid in acetic acid is an efficient reagent for aromatic bromination. This combination generates bromine in the reaction mixture rather than requiring its direct addition.

$$5HBr + KBrO_3 + CH_3COOH \rightarrow 3Br_2 + CH_3COOK + 3H_2O$$

The bromine generated could cause bromination at either the 2, 5, or 6 position of vanillin's benzene ring. Both the methoxyl ($-OCH_3$) and hydroxyl ($-OH$) substituents are *ortho-para* directing, while the aldehyde functional group ($-CHO$) is *meta* directing. Thus, the $-OCH_3$ group can direct electrophiles to both the #2 position, which is *ortho* to it, and the #6 position, which is *para* to it, but electrophiles tend to attack less crowded ring sites. As a result, one of these positions is more likely to be attacked than the other. (**Stop and Think:** Which position is it?) The OH group would tend to direct incoming electrophiles to the #5 position, which is the only open position that is *ortho* or *para* to it. The *meta*-directing $-CHO$ also directs to the #5 position, but *meta*-directors are more weakly directing than *ortho-para* directors, so having two substituents directing to the same position doesn't necessarily mean the electrophile will end up in that position—a strong *ortho-para* director could overpower both.

The procedure isn't difficult and involves only operations that you should have performed before. Because your conclusion will depend on the melting point of your product, it is important to make sure that the product is dry and to measure it melting point accurately.

This is a relatively green experiment because it requires no organic solvents but acetic acid, which occurs naturally in living organisms and readily breaks down to carbon dioxide and water in the environment. Little information is available about the environmental fate and toxicity of hydrobromic acid and potassium bromate.

Key Concept: Electron-donating substituents such as $-OCH_3$ tend to make the ortho *and* para *positions of a benzene ring more inviting to incoming electrophiles than the meta position. Electron-withdrawing substituents such as $-CHO$ tend to make the* ortho *and* para *positions less inviting than the* meta *position.*

Reactions and Properties

vanillin   ?-bromovanillin

Table 35.1 Physical properties

	mol wt	mp	d
vanillin	152.15	81–83	
2-bromovanillin	231.0	155	
5-bromovanillin	231.0	166	
6-bromovanillin	231.0	178	
acetic acid	60.05		1.049
potassium bromate	167.0	~350	3.27
48% hydrobromic acid	80.9		1.490

Note: mp is in °C; density is in g/mL.

DIRECTIONS

Safety Notes

> Acetic acid causes chemical burns that can seriously damage skin and eyes; its vapors are highly irritating to the eyes and respiratory tract. Wear gloves, dispense under a hood, avoid contact, and do not breathe its vapors.
> Hydrobromic acid is toxic and very corrosive, and it can cause very serious damage to the skin, eyes, and respiratory tract. Wear gloves, and dispense under a hood. Avoid contact with the acid, and do not inhale its vapors.
> Potassium bromate is toxic; avoid ingestion.

acetic acid   hydrobromic acid   potassium bromate

 Standard Scale

Reaction.   *Under the hood,* dissolve 10.0 mmol of vanillin in 20 mL of acetic acid in a 50-mL Erlenmeyer flask. Add 0.75 g of potassium bromate, followed by 2.0 mL of 48% hydrobromic acid. (**Observe and Note:** What happens?) Stir [OP-10] the reaction mixture at room temperature for 45 minutes. Pour the mixture into an Erlenmeyer flask containing 150 mL of ice-cold water, and continue to stir for 15 to 20 minutes. If the liquid is an orange color, add 30% sodium thiosulfate solution, drop by drop with stirring, until it turns yellow.

Take Care! Wear gloves, avoid contact with hydrobromic acid, and do not breathe its vapors.

Separation.   Collect the product by vacuum filtration [OP-16], washing it on the filter [OP-26a] with ice-cold water.

Purification and Analysis.   Recrystallize [OP-28] the product from 50% ethanol/water. Dry [OP-26b] the product thoroughly in a desiccator until the next lab period. Measure its mass and melting point [OP-33], and name it.

Waste Disposal: Unless your instructor directs otherwise, all filtrates can be washed down the drain.

 Microscale

Reaction.   *Under the hood,* dissolve 2.00 mmol of vanillin in 4.0 mL of acetic acid in a 10-mL Erlenmeyer flask. Add 0.15 g of potassium bromate, followed by 0.40 mL of 48% hydrobromic acid. (**Observe and Note:** What happens?) Stir [OP-10] the reaction mixture at room temperature for 45 minutes. Pour the mixture into an Erlenmeyer flask containing 30 mL of ice-cold water, and continue to stir for 15 to 20 minutes. If the liquid is an orange color, add 30% sodium thiosulfate solution, drop by drop with stirring, until it turns yellow.

Take Care! Wear gloves, avoid contact with hydrobromic acid, and do not breathe its vapors

Separation.   Collect the product by vacuum filtration [OP-16], washing it on the filter [OP-26a] with ice-cold water. Use a small Buchner funnel, if one is available.

Purification and Analysis.   Recrystallize [OP-28] the product from 50% ethanol/water. Dry [OP-26b] the product thoroughly in a desiccator until the next lab period. Measure its mass and melting point [OP-33], and name it.

Waste Disposal: Unless your in-structor directs otherwise, all filtrates can be washed down the drain.

Exercises

1. Explain why the major product of the reaction was the one you obtained, rather than either of the other two possible products.
2. What did you observe immediately after you added hydrobromic acid to the reaction mixture? Write a chemical equation that explains this result.
3. Describe and explain the possible effect on your results of the following experimental errors or variations. (a) The lab assistant set out a bottle of potassium bromide rather than potassium bromate. (b) You used anisaldehyde (4-methoxybenzaldehyde) rather than vanillin.
4. (a) Calculate the atom economy and reaction efficiency of your synthesis. (b) Describe some green features of your synthesis, and any that aren't so green.
5. Following the format in Appendix V, construct a flow diagram for the experiment.
6. Write a complete mechanism for the reaction you carried out.
7. Show how vanillin is synthesized commercially from guaiacol.

guaiacol

Other Things You Can Do

(Starred items require your instructor's permission.)

*1. Use a different kind of bromination reaction to determine the relative stabilities of free radicals in Minilab 21.
2. Record a ^{13}C NMR spectrum of vanillin, and identify as many of the signals as you can.
3. Starting with sources listed in the Bibliography, write a research paper about artificial flavorings and their constituents.

of the *ortho* product. Use this estimate to calculate a more accurate value of your *ortho/para* nitration ratio for *t*-butylbenzene. (b) Propose a mechanism for the isomerization reaction, which is apparently promoted by the HBF_4 formed during the reaction.

4. Describe and explain the possible effect on your results of the following experimental errors or variations. (a) You rinsed your reaction tubes with water and didn't dry them completely. (b) You added toluene rather than *t*-butylbenzene to the second centrifuge tube. (c) When analyzing the gas chromatogram from the *t*-butylbenzene nitration, you misidentified the *t*-butylbenzene peak as the peak for the *ortho* product and assumed that the next two peaks were for the *meta* and *para* products.

5. (a) Calculate the atom economy of the nitration of mesitylene. (b) Describe some green features of the experiment, and any that aren't so green.

6. Following the format in Appendix V, construct a flow diagram for the nitration of *t*-butylbenzene.

7. In a solution of bromine in acetic acid, mesitylene is brominated nearly 300 million times faster than benzene. Do you think a sigma complex or a pi complex is formed in the rate-determining step of this reaction? Explain.

8. Predict the major product or products of the mononitration of (a) ethyl benzoate, (b) phenyl acetate, (c) phenyl benzoate, (d) *m*-nitrotoluene, and (e) *p*-methoxybenzaldehyde.

Other Things You Can Do

(Starred items require your instructor's permission.)

*1. Carry out the mixed-acid nitration of naphthalene by the procedure in Minilab 30.

2. Read the paper by George A. Olah and his coworkers that describes the nitration of arenes with nitronium fluoborate (*J. Am. Chem. Soc.* **1961**, *83*, 4571), and compare their results and conclusions with your own.

Friedel–Crafts
Acylation of Anisole

Reactions of Aromatic Ethers. Preparation of Carbonyl Compounds.
Electrophilic Aromatic Substitution. Infrared Spectrometry.

Operations

OP-7   Heating
OP-10   Mixing
OP-11   Addition of Reactants
OP-12   Excluding Water from Reaction Mixtures
OP-14   Trapping Gases (optional)
OP-16   Vacuum Filtration
OP-19   Evaporation (μS)
OP-24   Washing Liquids
OP-25   Drying Liquids
OP-26   Washing and Drying Solids
OP-30   Simple Distillation (SS)
OP-33   Melting Point
OP-39   Infrared Spectrometry

Before You Begin

1. Read the experiment, read or review the operations as necessary, and write an experimental plan.
2. Calculate the mass and volume of 10.0 mmol (SS) or 2.50 mmol (μS) of anisole, and the theoretical yield of methoxyacetophenone.

Scenario

The purchasing agent for the Olfactory Factory mistakenly ordered 500 kilograms of anisole rather than 500 pounds, so the company needs to find some way to use up the excess anisole by converting it to perfume ingredients. One possibility is to prepare 4-methoxyacetophenone, also known as crataegon, which occurs naturally in hawthorn blossoms (*Crataegus* spp.). The company's chemical technicians think it should be possible to synthesize 4-methoxyacetophenone from anisole by a Friedel–Crafts reaction, but they are concerned that the reaction may yield the wrong isomer or a mixture of isomers that will be difficult to separate. According to their business manager, the Olfactory Factory cannot sell the product at a competitive price if they have to invest in expensive separation equipment. Your assignment is to see whether or not the Friedel–Crafts acetylation of anisole yields mainly 4-methoxyacetophenone, another isomer, or a mixture of isomers.

Applying Scientific Methodology

After reading the experiment, you should be able to develop a working hypothesis related to the problem, which you will test by obtaining the melting point and infrared (IR) spectrum of the product.

hawthorn blossom

crataegon

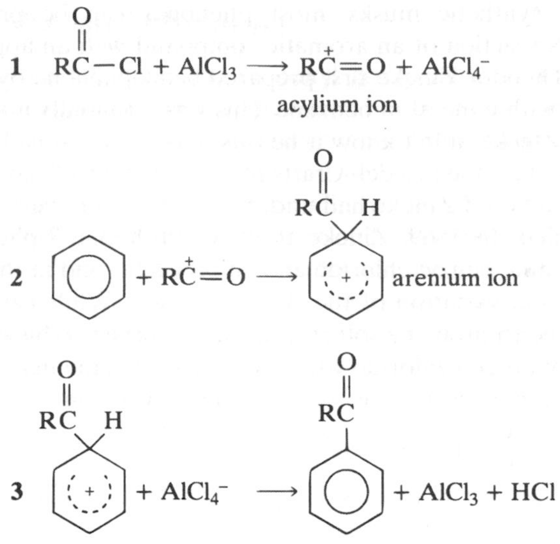

$$1 \quad \underset{\overset{\displaystyle \|}{\text{O}}}{\text{R}\overset{\displaystyle\|}{\text{C}}}\text{—Cl} + \text{AlCl}_3 \longrightarrow \text{R}\overset{+}{\text{C}}\!\!=\!\!\text{O} + \text{AlCl}_4^-$$

acylium ion

$$2 \quad \text{⬡} + \text{R}\overset{+}{\text{C}}\!\!=\!\!\text{O} \longrightarrow \text{arenium ion}$$

$$3 \quad + \text{AlCl}_4^- \longrightarrow + \text{AlCl}_3 + \text{HCl}$$

Figure 37.1 Mechanism of the Friedel-Crafts acylation of benzene

Aluminum chloride complex with acyl compound

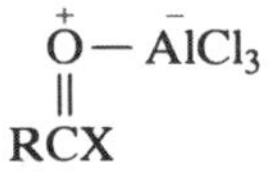

$$\overset{\overset{+}{\text{O}}—\overset{-}{\text{AlCl}_3}}{\underset{\text{RCX}}{\|}}$$

A Greener Way: In the microscale procedure, you can recover the dichloromethane by evaporating it under vacuum using a cold trap.

Table 37.1 Frequencies of C—H out-of-plane bending bands in aromatic hydrocarbons

No. of adjacent hydrogens	Frequency range, cm^{-1}
1	900–860 (weak)
2	840–810
3	810–750
4	770–735
5	770–730

When the acyl group is acetyl (CH$_3$CO), acetic anhydride is often used as the acylating agent rather than acetyl chloride. The anhydride is safer to work with, and it usually provides better yields and a simpler workup. More catalyst is needed with acetic anhydride, however, because some of the aluminum chloride forms complexes with the acetic acid produced during the reaction, making it ineffective as a catalyst. As a rule, 2–3 moles of AlCl$_3$ are used per mole of acetic anhydride.

In this experiment, you will use acetic anhydride as the acylating agent and dichloromethane as the reaction solvent. The reaction is highly exothermic, so it will be carried out by adding acetic anhydride slowly to the other reactants, and then heating under reflux to complete the reaction. Pouring the product into ice water will decompose the aluminum chloride complex of the product and transfer inorganic salts to the aqueous phase. The dichloromethane is removed by evaporation (μS) or distillation (SS) and, in the standard scale procedure, the product is purified by distillation. The infrared spectrum of the product can be obtained by one of the methods described in OP-39.

In principle, acylation of a monosubstituted benzene can yield any or all of three different disubstituted products. From the melting point and IR spectrum of your product, you should be able to determine whether it is predominantly a single compound or a mixture of isomers and, if it is a single compound, to establish its identity. Disubstituted benzenes can be distinguished by the location of their out-of-plane C—H bending bands, which occur at frequencies (expressed in wave numbers) below 850 cm^{-1}. The frequency of such a band decreases with the number of adjacent hydrogens on the ring, as shown in Table 37.1. Thus a *para*-disubstituted benzene, with its two sets of two adjacent hydrogens, should have an absorption band in the 840–810 cm^{-1} region; *meta* compounds, with three adjacent ring hydrogens, absorb in the 810–750 cm^{-1} region; and *ortho* compounds, with four adjacent ring hydrogens, absorb in the 770−735 cm^{-1} region. Absorption by the isolated hydrogen of a *meta* compound is usually very weak, and its frequency may vary. Monosubstituted and *meta*-disubstituted benzenes have an additional band in the 710−680 cm^{-1} region, which arises from a vibration that involves the entire benzene ring.

Possible products from the Friedel−Crafts acylation of anisole

2-methoxyacetophenone   3-methoxyacetophenone

4-methoxyacetophenone

Your product will be an ether as well as a ketone, so its IR spectrum will contain bands characteristic of both functional groups. The carbonyl band of a phenone usually appears in the 1685−1665 cm^{-1} region, and a weak carbonyl overtone band may be observed at twice the frequency of the fundamental band. Aryl alkyl ethers display an asymmetrical C—O—C stretching band at 1275−1200 cm^{-1} and a symmetrical C—O—C band near 1075−1020 cm^{-1}. These ether bands can be seen in the spectrum of anisole in Figure 37.2.

Most Friedel-Crafts syntheses are not very green because they require organic solvents and comparatively hazardous reagents and catalysts. Although this synthesis uses acetic anhydride rather than the more environmentally unfriendly acetyl chloride, the trade-off is the need for more catalyst. Because most Lewis acid catalysts are water sensitive, they are not usually recovered and instead end up as a source of waste. Lanthanide trifluoromethanesulfonates are effective Lewis acid catalysts that are not water sensitive and can therefore be recycled, but they are much more expensive than aluminum chloride and similar Lewis acids. More benign catalysts—such as phosphoric acid—have been used, but most of them give poor yields except with highly reactive aromatic compounds such as ferrocene. Thus, the path to truly green syntheses is often a rocky one and may involve trade-offs that limit their applicability.

In water, acetic anhydride is converted to acetic acid, which readily breaks down into carbon dioxide and water in the environment. Aluminum

For example, pure ytterbium(III) trifluoromethanesulfonate cost about $5 a gram in 2008.

chloride is toxic to aquatic life; it hydrolyzes to aluminum hydroxide and hydrochloric acid in water. The EPA classifies dichloromethane as a priority pollutant and has established an MCL of 5 ppb for its concentration in drinking water.

Reactions and Properties

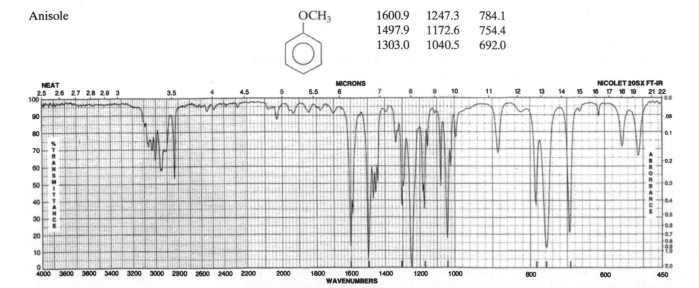

| anisole | acetic anhydride | ?-methoxy-acetophenone |

Table 37.2 Physical properties

	mol wt	mp	bp	d
anisole	108.2	−38	155	0.996
acetic anhydride	102.1	−73	140	1.082
aluminum chloride	133.3	193	subl	
dichloromethane	84.9	−95	40	1.327
2-methoxyacetophenone	150.2		245	1.090
3-methoxyacetophenone	150.2		240	1.034
4-methoxyacetophenone	150.2	39	258	1.082[41]

Note: mp and bp are in °C; density is in g/mL; subl = sublimes.

Anisole

OCH$_3$

1600.9	1247.3	784.1
1497.9	1172.6	754.4
1303.0	1040.5	692.0

Figure 37.2 IR spectrum of anisole

DIRECTIONS

Aluminum chloride reacts with atmospheric moisture and violently with water, generating HCl vapors. It can cause painful burns on moist skin and eyes, and inhaling the dust or vapors can damage the respiratory tract. Weigh it under a hood, wear gloves and safety goggles, avoid contact, do not inhale dust or vapors, and keep it away from water.

Acetic anhydride can cause severe damage to skin and eyes, its vapors are very harmful if inhaled, and it reacts violently with water. Use gloves and a hood; avoid contact with the liquid, do not breathe its vapors, and keep it away from water.

Dichloromethane may be harmful if ingested, inhaled, or absorbed through the skin. There is a possibility that prolonged inhalation of dichloromethane may cause cancer. Minimize contact with the liquid, and do not breathe its vapors.

Safety Notes

aluminum chloride

acetic anhydride

dichloromethane

anisole

 Standard Scale

Reaction.   Wear gloves and eye protection! Work under a hood, if possible. Anhydrous aluminum chloride is deactivated by water, so protect it from atmospheric moisture and be sure that your glassware is thoroughly dried (oven drying is recommended). Assemble an apparatus for addition [OP-11] under reflux using a 25-mL round-bottom flask, and attach a drying tube [OP-12a] containing calcium chloride to the top of the reflux condenser. If you cannot carry out the reaction under a hood, attach a gas trap [OP-14], containing dilute sodium hydroxide to react with any HCl evolved. Clamp the apparatus securely to a ring stand, raising it high enough so that you can remove the boiling flask to add the reactants without disturbing the rest of the apparatus. *Under the hood*, carefully weigh 2.9 g (~22 mmol) of finely powdered anhydrous aluminum chloride into a large, *dry* screw-cap vial (don't let it tip over). Immediately cap the vial and the aluminum chloride container. Weigh 10.0 mmol of anisole, and add it with 10 mL of dichloromethane and a stir bar or boiling chips to the reaction flask. Have a beaker of cold water ready to cool the mixture if it begins to boil, then cautiously add the aluminum chloride in small portions through a dry powder funnel, stirring or shaking [OP-10] the flask after each addition. If necessary, use a Pasteur pipet to wash any adherent aluminum chloride into the flask with a little dichloromethane, and then reassemble the apparatus. *Under the hood*, measure 1.0 mL (~11 mmol) of acetic anhydride into the separatory-addition funnel. Stopper the funnel immediately and put it in place on the reaction apparatus. Add the acetic anhydride slowly (about a drop every 3 seconds), so that the reaction mixture boils gently, while stirring or shaking to mix the reactants. Have a beaker of cold water handy to moderate the reaction, if necessary. When the addition is complete, use a hot-water bath or steam bath to heat the reaction mixture under gentle reflux [OP-7], while stirring or occasionally shaking, for 30 minutes.

Separation and Purification.   Wear gloves and eye protection! Under the hood, pour the warm reaction mixture *slowly,* with vigorous stirring, onto about 10 g of cracked ice in a large beaker. Use a small amount of ice water

Stop and Think: How can HCl be formed during the reaction?

Take Care! Wear gloves and goggles, avoid contact with AlCl₃ and dichloromethane, and do not breathe their vapors.

Take Care! Wear gloves, avoid contact with acetic anhydride, do not breathe its vapors, and keep it away from water.

Take Care! Splattering may occur.

to rinse any residue out of the flask into the beaker. Remove the aqueous layer in a separatory funnel, and wash [OP-24] the dichloromethane layer with 5 mL of 3 M sodium hydroxide followed by 5 mL of saturated aqueous sodium chloride. Dry [OP-25] the dichloromethane layer with anhydrous sodium sulfate or magnesium sulfate.

Assemble a compact apparatus for simple distillation [OP-30], cooling the receiving flask in an ice/water bath. Transfer the dry dichloromethane solution to the flask and, heating gently with a water bath or steam bath, remove the dichloromethane by distillation (it should distill around 40°C). Then remove the cooling bath and use a heating mantle or other heat source to distill the product, collecting everything that distills over about 240°C. If the distillate solidifies in the receiver, melt it with a beaker of hot water. While it is still liquid, transfer the distillate to a watch glass or evaporating dish, and set it aside to crystallize. Wash the product [OP-26a] on a Hirsch funnel [OP-16] with a small amount of cold, low-boiling petroleum ether, and dry it [OP-26b].

Analysis.   Weigh the dry product and measure its melting point [OP-33]. Record its IR spectrum [OP-39] or obtain a spectrum from your instructor. Interpret the spectrum as completely as you can, and turn it in with your report.

Microscale

Reaction.   *Wear gloves and eye protection! Work under a hood, if possible.* Anhydrous aluminum chloride is deactivated by water, so protect it from atmospheric moisture and be sure that all glassware is thoroughly dried (oven drying is recommended). Assemble an apparatus for addition [OP-11] under reflux using a 10-mL round-bottom flask and a water-cooled condenser. Prepare a combination drying tube–gas trap [OP-14] by inserting a cotton plug into a drying tube, adding a layer of pelletized Norit and a layer of anhydrous calcium chloride, and inserting another plug (the Norit can be omitted if the reaction will be carried out under a hood). Attach the drying tube to the top of the condenser and clamp the apparatus securely to a ring stand, raising it high enough so that you can remove the boiling flask to add the reactants without disturbing the rest of the apparatus. *Under the hood,* carefully weigh 0.73 g (~5.5 mmol) of finely powdered anhydrous aluminum chloride into a *dry* screw-cap vial (don't let it tip over). Immediately cap the vial and the aluminum chloride container. Weigh 2.50 mmol of anisole into the reaction flask, and add 2.5 mL of dichloromethane and a stir bar. Have a beaker of cold water ready to cool the mixture if it begins to boil. Start the stirrer [OP-10], then cautiously add the aluminum chloride in small portions from a plastic weighing dish or through a "funnel" made of a square of glazed weighing paper folded into a cone. If necessary, use a Pasteur pipet to wash any adherent aluminum chloride into the flask with a little dichloromethane, and then reassemble the apparatus. *Under the hood,* measure 0.25 mL (~2.6 mmol) of acetic anhydride into a clean, dry syringe. Add the acetic anhydride drop by drop, while stirring, so that the reaction mixture boils gently. When the addition is complete, use a hot-water bath to heat the reaction mixture under gentle reflux [OP-7], while stirring, for 30 minutes. Rinse the syringe with water shortly after using it.

Stop and Think: Which is the dichloromethane layer? What does NaOH remove from the dichloromethane solution?

Waste Disposal: Unless your instructor directs otherwise, wash all aqueous layers down the drain.

Take Care! If distillate begins to solidify in the vacuum adapter drip tube, stop the distillation and melt it with a heat gun or other heating device before you proceed.

Waste Disposal: Place the dichloromethane and petroleum ether in designated solvent recovery containers.

Take Care! Wear gloves and goggles, avoid contact with AlCl₃ and dichloromethane, and do not breathe their vapors.

Take Care! Wear gloves, avoid contact with acetic anhydride, do not breathe its vapors, and keep it away from water.

Separation and Purification.   *Wear gloves and eye protection! Under the hood,* pour the warm reaction mixture *slowly,* with vigorous manual stirring, onto about 3 g of finely cracked ice in a beaker. Use a small amount of ice water to rinse any residue out of the flask into the beaker. Transfer the reaction mixture to a centrifuge tube, add 2 mL of dichloromethane, and stir gently to mix. Transfer the dichloromethane layer to another centrifuge tube, and wash [OP-24] it with 2 mL of 3 *M* sodium hydroxide followed by 2 mL of saturated aqueous sodium chloride. Dry [OP-25] the dichloromethane layer with anhydrous sodium sulfate, and collect it in a 5-mL conical vial. Evaporate [OP-19] the dichloromethane from the vial, and then let it stand. Scratch the vial with a stirring rod and cool it in ice water, if necessary, until the product solidifies. Break up the solid with a flat-bladed microspatula. Then add 1 mL of ice-cold, low-boiling petroleum ether, and triturate (crush and rub) [OP-26a] the product thoroughly in the solvent. Collect the product by vacuum filtration [OP-16] and dry it [OP-26b].

Take Care! Splattering may occur.

Stop and Think: Which is the dichloromethane layer? What does NaOH remove from the dichloromethane solution?

Analysis.   Weigh the dry product and measure its melting point [OP-33]. Record its IR spectrum [OP-39], or obtain a spectrum from your instructor. Interpret the spectrum as completely as you can, and turn it in with your report.

Waste Disposal: Unless your instructor directs otherwise, wash all aqueous layers down the drain. Place the petroleum ether and any recovered dichloromethane in a designated solvent recovery container.

Exercises

1. If your product was a single compound, explain why it was that compound rather than another isomer.
2. Write a mechanism for the Friedel–Crafts reaction of anisole with acetic anhydride.
3. Describe and explain the possible effect on your results of the following experimental errors or variations. (a) You used only 10 mmol (SS) or 2.5 mmol (µS) of aluminum chloride for the reaction. (b) You used acetic acid as the acylating agent. (c) You used acetophenone as the substrate.
4. (a) Calculate the atom economy and reaction efficiency of your synthesis. (b) Describe some green features of your synthesis, and any that aren't so green.
5. (a) Write an equation for the reaction of aluminum chloride with a large excess of water. (b) Write equations for one or more reactions that would account for the production of HCl during the acylation reaction.
6. Following the format in Appendix V, construct a flow diagram for this experiment.
7. Explain why Friedel–Crafts reactions are usually carried out by adding the alkylating or acylating agent *to* the aromatic compound rather than vice versa.
8. 2,5-Dichloro-2,5-dimethylhexane is an important starting material for the aroma chemicals called tetralin musks. Outline a synthesis of the tetralin musk versalide from this starting material and benzene, using any necessary inorganic or organic reagents.

versalide

Other Things You Can Do

(Starred items require your instructor's permission.)

*1. Record the ^{1}H NMR spectrum of the product in deuterochloroform. Interpret it as completely as you can, assigning the signals from protons on the ring as well as those from protons on the side chains.

*2. Carry out some Friedel–Crafts reactions that yield colored products, as described in Minilab 31.

 3. Starting with sources listed in the Bibliography, write a research paper about the Friedel–Crafts reaction, including specific examples and industrial applications.

Determination of the Structure of a Natural Product in Anise Oil

Reactions of Alkenylbenzenes. Preparation of Carboxylic Acids. Side-Chain Oxidation. Structure Determination. Infrared Spectrometry.

Operations

OP-7   Heating
OP-10   Mixing
OP-16   Vacuum Filtration
OP-26   Washing and Drying Solids
OP-28   Recrystallization
OP-33   Melting Point
OP-39   Infrared Spectrometry

Before You Begin

Read the experiment, read or review the operations as necessary, and write an experimental plan.

Scenario

Basil Wormwood, the new-age herbalist with a chemistry degree, has another puzzle for you (see Experiment 18 for his previous puzzles). He obtained some Chinese star anise from an oriental-foods wholesaler, steam-distilled its essential oil, and isolated the major component of the oil. Not knowing its identity, he tentatively named this compound anisene. He sent it off to a chemical analyst for elemental analysis, and from the results found its molecular formula to be $C_{10}H_{12}O$. He also carried out some experiments (described in the "Understanding the Experiment" section) showing that the compound contains a methoxyl group and a three-carbon side chain on a benzene ring, but he doesn't know the identity of the side chain or where it is located with respect to the methoxyl group. He has just shipped a sample of the compound to your supervisor, hoping that your institute's consulting chemists can solve this structure puzzle. Your supervisor thinks that the position of the side chain can be determined by oxidizing it to a COOH group, and that its structure can be determined by infrared (IR) analysis. Your assignment is to determine the complete structure of anisene.

Applying Scientific Methodology

You will have to carry out some experimental work before you can propose a hypothesis about the structure of anisene.

star anise seed clusters

Key Concept: Chemists determine the structures of organic molecules by breaking them down into smaller fragments and identifying the fragments, probing them with different kinds of electromagnetic radiation and interpreting the resulting signals, or both.

The Structure Puzzle—Taking Molecules Apart and Putting Them Back Together

Chinese star anise (*Illicium verum*) is a small evergreen tree of the magnolia family. When its dried, star-shaped seed clusters are ground up and steam distilled, they yield an oily liquid with a strong odor of licorice. Anise oil (from star anise and other spices) or its synthetic equivalent is widely used as a flavoring for licorice, cough drops, chewing gum, and liqueurs such as ouzo and anisette. In this experiment, you will use both classical and modern methods of structural analysis to determine the complete structure of its major component, which we will call "anisene" (not its real name).

Today, when a chemist can run an NMR spectrum or a mass spectrum of an organic compound and often determine its structure in a matter of minutes, it is hard to imagine how much time and effort were once required to determine the structures of even the simpler natural products. In a classical structure determination, the molecular formula of a compound is first obtained by elemental analysis and molecular-weight measurement. Then the compound is degraded (broken down) into smaller structural units that are isolated and, if possible, identified. Finding how the smaller units fit together to form the original molecule is an intellectual challenge that might be compared to putting together a jigsaw puzzle with some pieces missing, others that don't belong, and still others that have been chewed up by the family dog and are no longer recognizable. Finally, when enough information has been gathered to suggest a possible structure, that structure must usually be proven by an independent synthesis in which the compound is built up again, from known compounds, by reactions whose outcomes can be reliably predicted.

In many cases, classical structure determinations involved the efforts of dozens or even hundreds of chemists over many decades, and included the generation of much irrelevant or misleading information and many synthetic dead ends. The advent of modern spectrometric methods has simplified the process enormously by providing detailed structural information that wasn't readily available to the chemists of earlier times.

Understanding the Experiment

In this experiment, you will attempt to determine the structure of the major component of star anise oil, which has the molecular formula $C_{10}H_{12}O$. Most open-chain saturated organic compounds (except those containing nitrogen, phosphorus, or halogen atoms) have $2n + 2$ hydrogen atoms for every n carbon atoms. If anisene were such a compound, it would have $2(10) + 2 = 22$ hydrogen atoms, but since it has only 12, it is said to be "deficient" by 10 hydrogens. Every ring or pi bond in a molecule represents a deficit of two hydrogens. That is, an open-chain compound must lose two hydrogen atoms to form a ring, and a saturated compound must lose two hydrogens to form a pi bond (or a pi-bond equivalent in the Kekulé structure of an aromatic ring). Thus, its deficiency of 10 hydrogens indicates that there must be a total of five rings and pi bonds (or pi-bond equivalents) in an anisene molecule; this is called its *index of hydrogen deficiency* (IHD).

The IHD of a compound that has n carbon atoms and x hydrogen atoms can be calculated using the following formula:

$$\text{IHD} = \frac{(2n + 2) - x}{2}$$

Catalytic hydrogenation of anisene under high pressure yields a saturated compound with the formula $C_{10}H_{20}O$. The gain of eight hydrogens indicates that anisene has four pi bonds, so it must contain only one ring. A high carbon/hydrogen ratio often indicates an aromatic structure, and we can account for the ring and three pi bonds by assuming that anisene contains a benzene ring.

Heating anisene with hydriodic acid yields a phenol with the molecular formula C_9H_9OH and a volatile compound identified as methyl iodide. This reaction is used to test for certain ether functions. Methyl ethers yield methyl iodide, and the formation of a phenol indicates that anisene is an aryl methyl ether, whose formula we write as $C_9H_9OCH_3$ in the following equation for the reaction:

$$C_9H_9OCH_3 + HI \longrightarrow C_9H_9OH + CH_3I$$

At this point, we know that anisene contains a methoxyl ($-OCH_3$) group and a benzene ring, which accounts for seven carbon atoms and three pi bonds. That leaves three more carbons and one pi bond to be accounted for. This remaining fragment could be a three-carbon unsaturated side chain, whose formula can be determined by subtracting the fragments already identified from the molecular formula of anisene:

molecular formula	$C_{10}H_{12}O$
disubstituted benzene ring	$-C_6H_4$
methoxyl group	$-CH_3O$
side chain	C_3H_5

Now we can write a partial structure for anisene, shown in the margin. All that remains is to determine the structure of the unsaturated side chain and its location on the benzene ring.

Potassium permanganate is capable of oxidizing most aliphatic side chains all the way down to the benzylic carbon atom, leaving a COOH group where the side chain was originally located. Oxidizing anisene should yield one of three possible methoxybenzoic acids, whose melting points are given in Table 38.3. By identifying the oxidation product as one of these three, you will establish the position of anisene's side chain.

Although aqueous potassium permanganate is a powerful oxidizing agent, it reacts slowly with water-insoluble organic compounds because $KMnO_4$ is essentially insoluble in the organic phase. In 1974, Herriot and Picker added a quaternary ammonium salt to a stirred heterogeneous mixture of aqueous $KMnO_4$ and benzene, which caused permanganate ions to dissolve in the organic layer and form "purple benzene." The quaternary salt acted as a phase-transfer catalyst, escorting the permanganate ions across the phase boundary into the organic phase (see Experiment 24 for a discussion of phase-transfer catalysis). When an oxidizable organic compound is dissolved in purple benzene, it reacts much more rapidly and under milder conditions than it would with aqueous $KMnO_4$.

Benzene is toxic and can cause leukemia in humans, so you will use a simplified procedure in which anisene and a phase-transfer catalyst

Another possibility, that anisene has two side chains, is explored in Exercise 3.

partial structure of anisene

a methoxybenzoic acid

(tricaprylmethylammonium chloride) are combined directly with aqueous potassium permanganate. Thus, anisene itself will be the organic phase of the two-phase system, and no organic solvent is needed. Because you require only enough product for a melting point, you will start with only a few drops of anisene. Excess potassium permanganate is used because some of it may decompose during the reaction. As the reaction proceeds, permanganate ion is reduced to manganese dioxide, which forms a fine brown precipitate that is difficult to filter and wash. Fortunately, this precipitate can be dissolved during the workup by acidifying the solution and adding sodium bisulfite, which reduces manganese dioxide (and any unreacted permanganate ion) to soluble manganese(II) sulfate.

Removal of manganese dioxide

$$MnO_2 + NaHSO_3 + H^+ \longrightarrow MnSO_4 + H_2O + Na^+$$

The methoxybenzoic acid can then be separated by vacuum filtration and purified by recrystallization from water.

Carbon–carbon double bonds give rise to characteristic $=C-H$ out-of-plane bending bands in the $1000-650$ cm^{-1} region of an IR spectrum. The wave numbers of these bands can reveal the number and location of substituents on the carbon–carbon double bond, as shown in Table 38.1. There are four possible structures for an unsaturated C_3H_5 side chain, corresponding to the four structure types in the table. From the wave number(s) of anisene's $=C-H$ bending band(s), you should be able to deduce the structure of the side chain. First, you must locate the right absorption bands, which is more easily said than done because aromatic $C-H$ bonds give rise to strong bands in the same region (as shown in Table 38.2).

The carbon atom of a vinylic $C-H$ bond is doubly bonded to an adjacent carbon.

Table 38.1 Out-of-plane bending vibrations of vinylic $C-H$ bonds

Structure type	Frequency range, cm^{-1}
$RCH=CH_2$	995–985 and 915–905
$RCH=CHR$ (*cis*)	730–665
$RCH=CHR$ (*trans*)	980–960
$R_2C=CH_2$	895–885

Note: R = alkyl or aryl.

Table 38.2 Out-of-plane bending vibrations of aromatic $C-H$ bonds

Ring substitution	Frequency range, cm^{-1}
ortho	770–735
meta	810–750 and 710–690
para	840–810

Once you learn the position of the side chain on anisene's benzene ring, you should be able to locate any bands due to aromatic $C-H$ bonds in its infrared spectrum, which will help you pick out one or more vinylic $C-H$ bands from the remaining strong bands in the $1000-650$ cm^{-1} region.

This is a relatively green experiment in that no organic solvents are used for the synthesis. Potassium permanganate and manganese dioxide are harmful to aquatic life, but the by-product MnO_2 and any excess $KMnO_4$ are converted to manganese(II) sulfate, which is not known to be a serious environmental contaminant.

Reactions and Properties

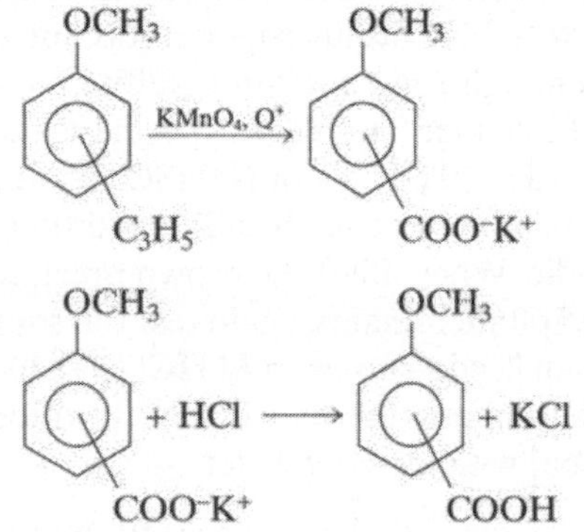

Table 38.3 Physical properties

	mol wt	mp	bp	d
potassium permanganate	158.0			
o-methoxybenzoic acid	152.2	101		
m-methoxybenzoic acid	152.2	110		
p-methoxybenzoic acid	152.2	185		
toluene	92.2	−95	111	0.867

Note: mp and bp are in °C; density is in g/mL.

DIRECTIONS

Potassium permanganate can react violently with oxidizable materials; keep it away from other chemicals and combustibles.
Sodium bisulfite produces harmful vapors when it reacts with acids; do not breathe them.

Safety Notes

potassium
permanganate

  ### Standard Scale and Microscale

Reaction.   Obtain some anisene (or anise oil) from your instructor, or isolate anise oil from anise seeds as described in "Other Things You Can Do." Add 0.50 g of crystalline potassium permanganate and 2 drops of tricaprylmethylammonium chloride (Aliquat 336) to 10 mL of water in a 25-mL

Erlenmeyer flask, and then drop in a stir bar. Heat [OP-7] the mixture in a boiling-water bath, while stirring [OP-10], for 5 minutes or more to dissolve most of the $KMnO_4$. Add 5 drops of anisene or anise oil using a medicine dropper (not a Pasteur pipet), place a watch glass (convex side down) over the mouth of the flask to prevent evaporation, and heat the mixture in a boiling-water bath—with vigorous magnetic stirring—for 15 minutes or more. (Alternatively, the flask can be swirled and shaken vigorously over a steam bath for 15 minutes.)

Separation.   Cool the reaction mixture to room temperature, and transfer it to a small beaker. *Under the hood,* add 1 mL of 6 *M* hydrochloric acid and test the solution with blue litmus paper; if it is not acidic, add more HCl until it is. Add just enough solid sodium bisulfite, in small portions while stirring or swirling, to reduce any excess permanganate and remove the brown manganese dioxide (0.5–1.0 g of $NaHSO_3$ should be sufficient). Test the solution with pH paper after each bisulfite addition, and add 6 *M* HCl as needed to keep it acidic. When all of the brown precipitate has disappeared and only a white precipitate remains, again test the solution with pH paper. If the pH is higher than 2, add enough 6 *M* HCl to reduce it to 2. Collect the product from the reaction mixture by vacuum filtration [OP-16], and wash it on the filter [OP-26a] with ice-cold water.

Purification and Analysis.   Recrystallize [OP-28] the product from boiling water, and dry [OP-26b] it to constant mass. Measure the melting point [OP-33] of the methoxybenzoic acid. Record the IR spectrum [OP-39] of anisene (*not* of the methoxybenzoic acid), or obtain its spectrum from your instructor. Deduce the location and structure of the side chain, and draw the structure of anisene. Turn in the IR spectrum with your report.

Exercises

1. Derive a systematic name for anisene and find its common name in *The Merck Index* or another reference book.
2. (a) Write a balanced equation for the reaction of anisene with potassium permanganate, assuming that the products include manganese dioxide and the potassium salt of acetic acid. (*Note:* The reaction mixture is alkaline.) (b) Assuming that 5 drops of anisene is about 1.0 mmol, calculate the mass of potassium permanganate required to oxidize that much anisene and the percentage in excess that was actually used.
3. (a) The three carbon atoms of anisene's side chain might have formed two separate side chains rather than one. Give the structures of these side chains. (b) Give the structures of all of the dicarboxylic acids that could have resulted from complete side-chain oxidation of anisene had it contained these two side chains.
4. (a) Using a balanced equation for the oxidation reaction (see Exercise 2a), calculate the atom economy and reaction efficiency of your synthesis. (b) Describe some green features of your synthesis, and any that aren't so green.
5. Describe and explain the possible effect on your results of the following experimental errors or variations. (a) You forgot to add the Aliquat 336.

(b) The pH of the reaction mixture was 7 when you filtered it, and you obtained a brown solid. (c) You recorded the IR spectrum of the oxidation product rather than that of anisene itself.

6. Describe the probable role of the phase-transfer catalyst in this reaction, giving equations for the relevant reactions.

7. Following the format in Appendix V, construct a flow diagram for the synthesis of your methoxybenzoic acid.

8. (a) Draw the structure of the compound $C_{10}H_{20}O$ that is obtained by the catalytic hydrogenation of anisene. (b) Draw the structure of the compound C_9H_9OH that is obtained when anisene is treated with hydriodic acid.

9. You could confirm the structure of anisene by synthesizing it from known starting materials. Outline a synthesis of anisene from benzene and alcohols that have four carbon atoms or fewer.

10. The structure shown has been proposed for coniferyl alcohol, which can be obtained by the hydrolysis of coniferin, a natural product found in the sap of conifer trees. Assuming that the structure of coniferyl alcohol had not been reported in the literature, describe how you would go about proving its structure. Indicate what chemical tests and degradations might be carried out, and describe the expected results and conclusions. Summarize the information that could be derived from infrared analysis. Then show how the alcohol could be synthesized from readily available starting materials.

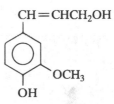

proposed structure for coniferyl alcohol

Other Things You Can Do

(Starred items require your instructor's permission.)

*1. Isolate anise oil from anise seeds (or star anise) as follows. Weigh out 1g (µS) or 10g (SS) of fresh anise seeds and grind them finely, using a spice grinder or a mortar and pestle. Isolate the anise oil by steam distillation and extraction of the distillate with dichloromethane, following the procedure for clove oil given in Experiment 10. (Do *not* extract the dichloromethane layer with NaOH as described in the standard scale procedure.) Dry the dichloromethane solution, and evaporate the solvent completely. You can obtain a gas chromatogram of the oil and estimate the percentage of anisene it contains.

*2. Use air as an oxidizing agent to convert fluorene to fluorenone as described in Minilab 32.

3. Starting with sources listed in the Bibliography, write a research paper on the use of chemical methods for structure determination of natural products. Illustrate it with examples of actual structure determinations.

Identification of an Oxygen-Containing Organic Compound

EXPERIMENT 39

Reactions of Aldehydes and Ketones. Reactions of Alcohols. Infrared Spectrometry. Qualitative Analysis.

Operations

OP-26   Washing and Drying Solids
OP-28   Recrystallization
OP-30   Simple Distillation
OP-33   Melting Point
OP-34   Boiling Point
OP-39   Infrared Spectrometry
OP-40   Nuclear Magnetic Resonance Spectrometry (optional)

Before You Begin

1. Read the experiment, read or review the operations as necessary, and write an experimental plan.
2. Read Part IV, "Qualitative Organic Analysis," except for the sections entitled "Directions."

Scenario

You can find a description of Arkham in the *Dictionary of Imaginary Places* (Harcourt, 2000).

Dr. Keziah Armitage, professor of medieval metaphysics at Miskatonic University in Arkham, Massachusetts, was exploring an abandoned and nearly forgotten room in the basement of the metaphysics building when she came across a grime-encrusted bottle containing an unknown liquid. Its label had long since decomposed to dust, but the liquid in the bottle was clear and colorless. Curious about its origin, she sent the bottle and its contents to your institute for analysis. She thinks it might be a potion used in unmentionable rites practiced by her ancestor, Keziah Mason, a witch whose trial scandalized Arkham in 1692. Your supervisor thinks it is more likely to be an alcohol or carbonyl compound misplaced by an absent-minded alchemy professor and then forgotten. Your assignment is to find out what family the mysterious liquid belongs to and then identify it.

Applying Scientific Methodology

As you carry out the experiment, you should propose provisional hypotheses about the nature and identity of your unknown. You will test—and perhaps reject or revise—your hypotheses as you gather additional experimental evidence. Your conclusion should, if possible, be consistent with all of the experimental evidence you obtain. If any evidence is not consistent with your conclusion, you should attempt to explain why.

The Chemist as Detective

Qualitative organic analysis, the process of identifying unknown organic compounds, can be compared to the approach used by a detective in identifying the perpetrator of a crime. The detective first looks for clues that help to characterize the criminal and indicate the most productive areas of investigation. Once a list of possible suspects has been assembled, the detective can evaluate the evidence already acquired and gather additional evidence to help narrow the list of suspects, focusing the investigation on the most likely suspects. Finally, the detective must evaluate all of the evidence, come to a conclusion regarding the identity of the perpetrator, and organize the facts of the case in such a way as to convince a jury that the accused is, in fact, guilty of the crime.

Key Concept: Identifying an unknown organic compound involves matching the physical and chemical properties of the unknown with those of some known compound.

In carrying out the identification of an organic compound, you, like the detective, should be constantly on the lookout for clues to its identity. Chemical and spectral data should allow you to confine your search to a particular chemical family. Additional physical and chemical evidence will help you narrow down the list of "suspects" and focus your attention on a few of the most probable compounds. Finally, the preparation of one or more derivatives should lead you to a definite conclusion and help you convince the "jury" (your instructor) that the evidence you have gathered justifies your conclusion.

As with any other problem, you must first ask yourself the right questions before you can arrive at the correct solution. Some important questions to be answered regarding an unknown compound are as follows: (1) What are its physical properties? (2) What functional group(s) does it contain? (3) Are there any other significant structural features that might aid in its identification? Each bit of evidence you obtain should, if interpreted correctly, help reveal the answer to one or more of these questions. All of them combined should provide you with an answer to the ultimate question, "What is it?"

A detective trying to solve a case will almost invariably come upon clues that lead nowhere or, even worse, to false conclusions. The same is true in chemical problem solving, so it is important to keep an open mind throughout your investigation and to avoid jumping to conclusions before all the evidence is in. You may formulate tentative assumptions based on your initial observations (for example, "It turns chromic acid reagent green, so it may be an alcohol"), but you should be ready to revise or discard such assumptions if they aren't supported by subsequent observations (for example, "Its IR spectrum has a $C=O$ stretching band but no $O-H$ band, so it may be an aldehyde instead").

Chemical and physical evidence can be misleading for a variety of reasons:

- Some compounds of a given family may undergo an atypical reaction with a given reagent and yield either a false positive or a false negative result.
- Some reagents give positive tests with more than one functional group.
- Impurities may complicate or invalidate a test.
- Spectral bands may occur outside the expected frequency ranges or may be incorrectly assigned.

Because of these and other possible sources of error, it is best not to rely on a single piece of evidence in formulating a conclusion. For example, the classification of an unknown as a secondary alcohol can be convincingly established by a positive chromic acid test, a slow reaction with Lucas' reagent, *and* an infrared (IR) band in the 1100 cm^{-1} region, but not by any one of these alone.

Understanding the Experiment

This section provides a general discussion of most of the procedures you will follow to identify your unknown. See the appropriate sections in Part IV for more detailed information about the interpretation of test results. For information about the interpretation of spectra, see the corresponding operations.

Throughout this experiment, you should have your lab notebook handy to record the data you collect and your observations as you make them. Keeping meticulous records can often mean the difference between the successful identification of a compound and a failure that could prove very costly, insofar as it affects your lab grade.

Because an unknown liquid may be impure, it should be purified by distillation before any chemical tests or spectra are run. The median distillation temperature should also give you a good estimate of its boiling point. Solids can be purified by recrystallization but, unless your instructor indicates otherwise, you can assume that an unknown solid is pure enough to use without purification. It is very important to measure the boiling point or melting point of your unknown as accurately as you can because your list of possibilities will be based on the value you obtain. If your measured boiling point or melting point is inaccurate, your list of possibilities may not even contain the name of your unknown compound, and identifying it correctly may then be impossible.

A preliminary examination of your unknown may provide some clues that will help you identify it. For example, observing that a compound is a liquid at room temperature eliminates most compounds with reported melting points of 30°C or higher. The ignition behavior of a substance can provide clues about its structure; many oxygen-containing compounds burn with a blue flame, but those with a high molecular weight may exhibit a clean yellow flame, and those with aromatic rings a sooty yellow flame. The solubility behavior of your unknown compound in water can also tell you something about its structure. Most alcohols and carbonyl compounds containing up to four carbon atoms are soluble, and most with six carbons or more are relatively insoluble.

To find out what family your compound belongs to, you will carry out several classification tests and record its IR spectrum. To find procedures for the classification tests and directions for their interpretation, see "Classification Tests" in Part IV. The tests you will use include the following:

- The 2,4-dinitrophenylhydrazine (DNPH) test, which is positive for both aldehydes and ketones
- The chromic acid test, which is positive for 1° and 2° alcohols and for aldehydes, but which gives a faster reaction with alcohols
- Tollens' test, which is positive only for aldehydes

A Greener Way: In place of chromic acid, ceric ammonium nitrate can be used to test for alcohols, and Schiff's reagent to test for aldehydes. Your instructor may provide directions for conducting such tests.

IR bands that you should look for include a strong, broad O—H stretching band near 3300 cm^{-1}, a strong carbonyl (C=O) stretching band near 1700 cm^{-1}, and one or two weak-to-moderate bands in the 2700–2850 cm^{-1} region, which arise from C—H stretching vibrations involving the carbonyl carbon of an aldehyde.

Additional structural information can be obtained both from chemical tests and from your infrared spectrum. The iodoform test is positive for methyl carbinols (alcohols having a CH_3 group on the carbon that holds the OH) and methyl ketones. The bromine test can show whether your compound contains any carbon–carbon double or triple bonds. Lucas' test can tell you whether an alcohol is primary, secondary, or tertiary, *if* the alcohol's boiling point is below 150°C (the test is invalid for most alcohols with higher boiling points). The IR spectrum of an alcohol may also help you decide what kind of alcohol it is. The $C-O$ bands of most open-chain primary, secondary, and tertiary alcohols occur near 1050 cm^{-1}, 1110 cm^{-1}, and 1175 cm^{-1}, respectively. The wave number of the $C-O$ band is about $25-50$ cm^{-1} lower (to the right) for cyclic alcohols and alcohols that have aromatic rings or $C=C$ groups on the carbinol carbon. Other structural features that can be detected from IR spectra include aromatic rings and carbon–carbon double or triple bonds. (See OP-39 for more detailed information on the interpretation of IR spectra.)

NMR spectra can provide a great deal of information about the structure of a molecule. If your instructor allows you to obtain an ^1H or ^{13}C NMR spectrum of your unknown, see OP-40 or your textbook for information about NMR spectral interpretation.

After you carry out the classification tests and interpret your spectra, you should be able to prepare a short list of possible compounds. Keep in mind, however, that classification tests and spectral interpretations are subject to error, so later you may want to reconsider some of the compounds you eliminated to arrive at your list. To decide which of the compounds on your list is the correct one, you will need to prepare a derivative. A derivative preparation is a small-scale chemical synthesis in which the unknown compound is converted to a different compound, a solid whose melting point may indicate the identity of the unknown. As for any synthesis, the formation of by-products, incomplete purification, and insufficient drying can lower the melting point of the product. This makes it important to follow the directions carefully and to be certain that the product is completely dry before you measure its melting point. It is also important to select the right derivative. Depending on the reagents available, you can prepare a *p*-nitrobenzoate, 3,5-dinitrobenzoate, α-naphthylurethane, or phenylurethane if you have an alcohol; and a 2,4-dinitrophenylhydrazone, semicarbazone, or oxime if you have an aldehyde or ketone. However, a derivative may be unsuitable because its melting point is too low or is not listed for some of the compounds on your list. Derivatives with melting points of 60° or below are often hard to purify because they tend to melt to an oil in the hot recrystallization solvent. You should also avoid derivatives whose melting points (for the compounds on your list) are too close together. For example, the semicarbazones of 3-methyl-2-butanone and 2-pentanone melt at 113°C and 112°C, whereas their 2,4-dinitrophenylhydrazones melt at 124°C and 143°C, making the second derivative a better choice for distinguishing between these ketones. If you have difficulty preparing a certain derivative, or if the derivative you prepare does not eliminate all of the possibilities but one, you should prepare a second derivative.

When you think you have gathered enough evidence to identify your unknown with some certainty, you are free to write down your conclusion. Keep in mind that your evidence should be sufficient to convince your instructor—and yourself—that your conclusion is correct. Thus, you should go back over the evidence and make sure that it all points to the same conclusion. If some evidence is not consistent with that conclusion—for example, if a chemical test doesn't give the result expected for a compound with the proposed structure—be prepared to either reevaluate your conclusion or explain the inconsistency.

The chromium(VI) in chromic acid reagent is classified as a priority pollutant and is very toxic to aquatic life. Hydrazines (such as 2,4-dinitrophenylhydrazine) and silver nitrate (from Tollens' reagent) are also toxic to aquatic organisms. Some of the unknowns may also be harmful to the environment, so take care to prevent the release of your unknown, the test reagents, or the derivative preparation reagents into the environment.

Reactions and Properties

General equations for classification test reactions are given in the "Classification Tests" section of Part IV. General equations for derivative preparations are given in the "Preparation of Derivatives" section of Part IV. The properties of the different classes of compounds and their derivatives are given in Appendix VI.

DIRECTIONS

Safety Notes

You should consider your unknown compound to be flammable and harmful by inhalation, ingestion, and skin absorption. Minimize your contact with the unknown, and do not breathe its vapors.
Safety information for chemicals used in classification tests and derivative preparations is included with the corresponding procedures in Part IV.

 Standard Scale and Microscale

Take Care! Minimize contact with the unknown, and do not breathe its vapors.

Preliminary Work.   Obtain a numbered vial that contains your unknown compound from your instructor, and record its identification number in your laboratory notebook. If the unknown is a liquid, purify it by simple distillation [OP-30] and record its distillation boiling range and median boiling temperature. Then measure the boiling point [OP-34] of the pure liquid, using a capillary-tube method. If it is a solid, measure its melting point [OP-33]. Describe the physical state, general appearance, and any other notable characteristics of the purified compound in your lab notebook. Carry out an ignition test (see "Ignition Test" in Part IV), and test the solubility of the unknown in water (see "Solubility Tests" in Part IV).

Waste Disposal: Dispose of all wastes as directed by your instructor.

Functional-Class Determination.   Test the unknown with 2,4-dinitrophenylhydrazine reagent (DNPH, classification test C-11), chromic acid reagent (C-9), and Tollens' reagent (C-23), or carry out other classification tests suggested by your instructor. Record the IR spectrum [OP-39] of your unknown. Use it and the results of the classification tests to decide whether your unknown is an alcohol, aldehyde, or ketone.

Detection of Structural Features.   In your lab notebook, list all compounds from the appropriate table in Appendix VI that have melting or boiling points within ±10°C of your observed value, and record their melting or boiling points and the melting points of their derivatives. At your instructor's discretion, show him or her your list; the instructor may approve the list if it includes your unknown, or suggest additional work if it doesn't. Write the structure of every compound on your list and consider whether additional classification tests, such as the bromine test (C-7), iodoform test (C-16), or Lucas' test (C-17), will help you eliminate any compounds from the list. Also look for evidence from your observations and your IR spectrum that suggest specific structural features, such as aromatic rings, conjugation with double bonds, or the structural class (1°, 2°, or 3°) of an alcohol. With your instructor's permission, you can obtain and interpret an ^{1}H or ^{13}C NMR spectrum [OP-40] of your unknown as well. At this point, prepare a short list of compounds by eliminating the least likely possibilities.

Preparation of a Derivative.   Using procedure D-1, D-2, D-3, or D-4 (see "Preparation of Derivatives" in Part IV), prepare a suitable derivative of your unknown. Purify the derivative by recrystallization [OP-28], as described in the appropriate procedure. Dry [OP-26b] it thoroughly, and obtain its melting point [OP-33]. Deduce the identity of your unknown from the derivative melting point and all other relevant evidence.

Waste Disposal: Dispose of all wastes as directed by your instructor. Return any unused unknown to your instructor in its original vial.

Exercises

1. Interpret the spectrum or spectra you obtained as completely as you can.
2. (a) Write balanced equations for the reactions involved in all of the classification tests for which you obtained a positive result. (b) Write balanced equations for the reaction(s) involved in your derivative preparation(s).
3. Describe and explain the possible effect on your results of the following experimental errors or variations. (a) The test tube you used to carry out a DNPH test had just been rinsed with acetone. (b) The watch glass you used for the ignition test had previously been used to weigh sodium sulfate. (c) You performed Lucas' test on a compound that had a boiling point of 175°C. (d) Your derivative formed an oil when you heated it in the recrystallization solvent, but the oil solidified on cooling, so you used it to obtain a melting point.
4. Calculate the atom economy of your derivative preparation(s).
5. Construct a flow diagram showing the process you followed to identify your unknown.
6. The unknown assigned to a student was an aldehyde, but about half of the sample distilled around 65°C, and the rest of it distilled near 155°. (a) What is the name of the aldehyde? (b) What else was in the sample, and why? Write a balanced equation for its formation.
7. An unknown liquid is water soluble and reacts with chromic acid within 2 seconds. It dissolves in Lucas' reagent, but the solution remains clear for 30 minutes. The iodoform test yields a yellow precipitate. Give the name and structure of the unknown.
8. An unknown liquid with a boiling range of 179–181°C is insoluble in water, gives a blue–green suspension with chromic acid, and immediately

forms a separate layer when shaken with Lucas' reagent. Its IR spectrum contains bands at 3060 cm^{-1}, 2805 cm^{-1}, 2730 cm^{-1}, 1705 cm^{-1}, 745 cm^{-1}, and 690 cm^{-1}. Give the name and structure of the unknown.

9. Write mechanisms for the following reactions, which are used in chemical tests and derivative preparations: (a) the reaction of butanal with 2,4-dinitrophenylhydrazine reagent; (b) the preparation of the 3,5-dinitrobenzoate of 1-butanol; (c) the iodoform reaction of 2-butanone; (d) the reaction of 2-methyl-2-butanol with Lucas' reagent.

Other Things You Can Do

(Starred items require your instructor's permission.)

*1. Observe the effect of aqueous potassium permanganate on different classes of alcohols as described in Minilab 25.
*2. Use ^{1}H NMR to identify an unknown arene as described in Minilab 28.
3. Starting with sources listed in the Bibliography, write a research paper about the use of gas chromatography–mass spectrometry (GC–MS) to identify illicit drug samples and trace them back to their sources.

Oxidation of the Insect Repellent "6-12"

Reactions of Diols. Preparation of Carbonyl Compounds. Selective Oxidation. Infrared Spectrometry.

Operations

OP-10 Mixing
OP-11 Addition of Reactants
OP-18 Extraction
OP-19 Evaporation
OP-25 Drying Liquids
OP-30 Simple Distillation
OP-39 Infrared Spectrometry

Before You Begin

1. Read the experiment, read or review the operations as necessary, and write an experimental plan.
2. Calculate the mass and volume of 20.0 mmol (SS) or 3.00 mmol (μS) of 2-ethyl-1,3-hexanediol, and the theoretical yields of each of the possible products.

Scenario

2-Ethyl-1,3-hexanediol, sold under the name "6-12," was used widely as an insect repellent until it was superseded by the more effective repellent *N,N*-dimethyl-*m*-toluamide (deet). That left Skeeters 'n Such, a manufacturer of pest-control chemicals, with a large backlog of unsold 2-ethyl-1,3-hexanediol. They would like to convert this substance to a more useful product, perhaps even a better insect repellent. A simple method of transforming a hydroxyl compound to a potentially useful carbonyl compound is oxidation, which can be carried out using the environmentally friendly oxidizing agent aqueous sodium hypochlorite (NaOCl). But there are three possible products of the oxidation of 2-ethyl-1,3-hexanediol, and because Skeeters 'n Such recently downsized by laying off most of its organic chemists, none of the remaining employees knows which product to expect.

Your assignment, and that of your coworkers, is to carry out the oxidation of 2-ethyl-1,3-hexanediol and record its infrared spectrum so that you can identify it as one of the three possible products shown.

$$
\text{CH}_3\text{CH}_2\text{CH}_2\text{CHCHCH}_2
\quad
\begin{array}{c}\text{OH}\quad\text{OH}\\ | \quad\quad |\end{array}
$$

$$
\underset{\text{2-ethyl-1,3-hexanediol}}{\text{CH}_3\text{CH}_2\text{CH}_2\text{CHCHCH}_2}
\xrightarrow[\text{HOAc}]{\text{NaOCl}}
$$

1
$$
\text{CH}_3\text{CH}_2\text{CH}_2\text{CHCHCH}
\quad \text{CH}_2\text{CH}_3
$$

2
$$
\text{CH}_3\text{CH}_2\text{CH}_2\text{CCHCH}_2
\quad \text{CH}_2\text{CH}_3
$$

3
$$
\text{CH}_3\text{CH}_2\text{CH}_2\text{CCHCH}
\quad \text{CH}_2\text{CH}_3
$$

Applying Scientific Methodology

Unless you have a good knowledge of oxidation reactions, your working hypothesis may be only a guess. To find out whether your hypothesis is correct, you will need to consider how compounds **1**, **2**, and **3** can be distinguished by infrared spectrometry.

Ethylene Glycol and Other Diols

Beginning in October 1937, 107 people—most of them children—died after taking a newly developed version of the "wonder drug" of that era, sulfanilamide. At that time, new drugs were not required to be tested for safety or approved by the U.S. federal government. Because children had a hard time swallowing sulfanilamide pills, the drug's manufacturer used ethylene glycol to dissolve the sulfanilamide, and marketed the resulting liquid as an easy-to-swallow form of the drug—without testing it first. The glycol was later shown to be responsible for the deaths. This tragedy led to passage of the 1938 Food, Drug, and Cosmetic Act, which required that drugs be cleared for safety before going on the market.

Ethylene glycol, $HOCH_2CH_2OH$, is the simplest common diol, where a *diol* is an alcohol that contains two hydroxyl ($-OH$) groups. It is the most widely used antifreeze for motor vehicles, and it is used to de-ice aircraft and airport runways as well. Methanol is a better antifreeze for some purposes (for example, in windshield washer fluids) because it lowers water's freezing point nearly twice as much as an equal mass of ethylene glycol does; however, it tends to boil away much faster. Like methanol, ethylene glycol is quite toxic. Unfortunately, its sweet taste makes it attractive to children as well as to dogs and other pets, who may die after lapping up spilled antifreeze.

Another important use of ethylene glycol is in the manufacture of plastics and fibers. One of the most widely used plastics, polyethylene terephthalate (PET), is manufactured by combining ethylene glycol with terephthalic acid.

Key Concept: Impurities lower the freezing point of any liquid. The magnitude of the freezing-point depression is proportional to the number of molecules of the impurity present, so low–molecular-weight compounds cause a larger freezing-point depression than those with higher molecular weights.

$$
n\text{HOCH}_2\text{CH}_2\text{OH} + n\text{HOC}-\!\!\bigcirc\!\!-\text{COH} \longrightarrow \left[\text{OCH}_2\text{CH}_2\text{OC}-\!\!\bigcirc\!\!-\text{C}\right]_n + n\text{H}_2\text{O}
$$

ethylene glycol   terephthalic acid   polyethylene terephthalate

Polyethylene terephthalate is used to manufacture plastic bottles, packaging materials, and films. Ethylene glycol can be converted to di- and triethylene glycols, as well as higher homologs, by reactions with ethylene oxide.

$$HOCH_2CH_2OH \xrightarrow{\triangle} HOCH_2CH_2OCH_2CH_2OH \xrightarrow{\triangle} HOCH_2CH_2OCH_2CH_2OCH_2CH_2OH$$

ethylene glycol   diethylene glycol   triethylene glycol

A mixture of these three substances has been used in some kinds of hydraulic brake fluids. Triethylene glycol is very *hygroscopic,* meaning that it absorbs water vapor from the atmosphere, so it is used as a drying agent to prevent condensation in natural gas pipelines.

2-Ethyl-1,3 hexanediol, formerly used in the insect repellent 6-12, is manufactured by an aldol condensation reaction of butanal (butyraldehyde) followed by reduction.

$$2CH_3CH_2CH_2\overset{O}{\overset{\|}{C}}H \xrightarrow{NaOH} CH_3CH_2CH_2\underset{CH_2CH_3}{\overset{OH}{\underset{|}{C}}H}\overset{O}{\overset{\|}{C}}H \xrightarrow[Ni]{H_2} CH_3CH_2CH_2\underset{CH_2CH_3}{\overset{OH}{\underset{|}{C}}H}\overset{OH}{\underset{|}{C}}H$$

butanal   2-ethyl-1,3-hexanediol

In 1991, Union Carbide, the sole manufacturer of the insect repellant, filed a report with the Environmental Protection Agency (EPA) on possible adverse developmental effects of 2-ethyl-1,3-hexanediol in laboratory animals. The EPA subsequently asked retailers to remove from their shelves all products that contained it, and advised women of childbearing age not to use such products. At this time, the only really effective insect repellents on the market are those that contain *N,N*-diethyl-*m*-toluamide (deet), which you will prepare if you do Experiment 46. Repellents that contain citronella and other ingredients appear to be much less effective than those that contain deet.

Some diols are found in nature, such as 1,18-octadecanediol, $HOCH_2(CH_2)_{16}CH_2OH$, which has been isolated from the plant Spanish broom (*Spartium junceum*). A natural diol with the intriguing common name sirenin (after the sirens of Greek mythology) is a sperm attractant for a water mold, *Allomyces javanicus.*

sirenin

Understanding the Experiment

You will use a commercial chlorine bleach such as Clorox or Javex to oxidize 2-ethyl-1,3-hexanediol. Most chlorine bleaches are 5.25% aqueous sodium hypochlorite (NaOCl), but new "Ultra" Clorox is 6.0% NaOCl; either form can be used, but a smaller volume of the 6.0% bleach is needed. Because the actual NaOCl concentration of the bleach tends to decrease with age, it may be necessary to use more than the amount given in the directions. Acetic acid is added to the reaction mixture to convert some of the NaOCl to hypochlorous acid, HOCl, which is probably the actual oxidant.

The bleach should be unscented, and there should be no ingredient other than sodium hypochlorite listed on the label.

You can find out whether hypochlorite is present in the reaction mixture by periodically testing it with starch–iodide test paper, which turns a blue–black color in the presence of excess NaOCl. If the test is negative at any time, you will need to add more bleach. Because the reaction mixture is heterogeneous—having separate organic and aqueous layers—it is important to stir the reactants vigorously to keep the layers well mixed. Inadequate stirring will result in a low yield. At the end of the reaction, any unreacted NaOCl can be converted to common table salt, NaCl, by adding a little sodium bisulfite ($NaHSO_3$).

$$NaOCl + NaHSO_3 \longrightarrow NaCl + NaHSO_4$$

You will then extract the product from the reaction mixture with diethyl ether, evaporate the ether, and purify the product by simple distillation.

A Greener Way: You can recover the diethyl ether by evaporating it under vacuum using a cold trap.

Infrared spectrometry is a good method for identifying functional groups, and it may provide additional structural information as well. From an infrared spectrum, it is relatively easy to distinguish an alcohol's OH group from the carbonyl ($C=O$) group of an aldehyde or ketone, and to distinguish an aldehyde from a ketone. It may also be possible to distinguish a primary from a secondary alcohol. Read "Interpretation of Infrared Spectra" in OP-39 to find out how.

The respectable atom economy of the reaction, the use of acetic acid as a catalyst, the use of hypochlorite bleach as the oxidant (rather than environmentally harmful reagents such as chromic acid), and the harmless nature of the by-products make this a green synthesis. Sodium hypochlorite is often used to disinfect drinking water, and the EPA has concluded that such uses present no unreasonable adverse effects to the environment. Acetic acid occurs naturally in living organisms and readily breaks down to carbon dioxide and water in the environment. Sodium hydroxide may be harmful to the environment, especially with respect to aqueous organisms, but it is used to neutralize excess acetic acid and is itself neutralized in this experiment.

Reactions and Properties

$$
\underset{\substack{|\\ CH_2CH_3}}{CH_3CH_2CH_2\overset{\overset{\displaystyle OH}{|}}{C}H\overset{\overset{\displaystyle OH}{|}}{C}HCH_2} + NaOCl \xrightarrow{CH_3COOH} \mathbf{1} \text{ or } \mathbf{2} + NaCl + H_2O
$$

or

$$
\underset{\substack{|\\ CH_2CH_3}}{CH_3CH_2CH_2\overset{\overset{\displaystyle OH}{|}}{C}H\overset{\overset{\displaystyle OH}{|}}{C}HCH_2} + 2NaOCl \xrightarrow{CH_3COOH} \mathbf{3} + 2NaCl + 2H_2O
$$

2-ethyl-1,3-hexanediol

Table 40.1 Physical properties

	mol wt	mp	bp	d
2-ethyl-1,3-hexanediol	146.2	−40	244	0.942
acetic acid	60.05	16	118	1.049
sodium hypochlorite	74.4			

Note: mp and bp are in °C; density is in g/mL.

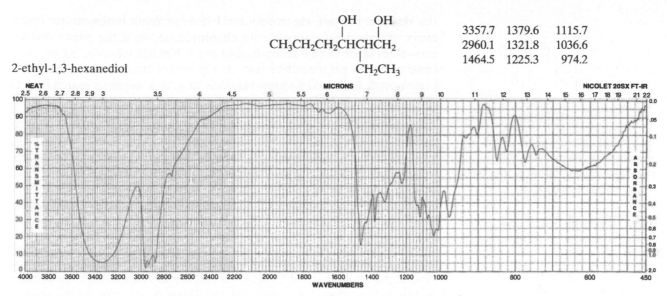

2-ethyl-1,3-hexanediol

$$\underset{\underset{\displaystyle CH_2CH_3}{|}}{CH_3CH_2CH_2\overset{\overset{\displaystyle OH}{|}}{C}H\overset{\overset{\displaystyle OH}{|}}{C}HCH_2}$$

3357.7	1379.6	1115.7
2960.1	1321.8	1036.6
1464.5	1225.3	974.2

Figure 40.1 IR spectrum of 2-ethyl-1,3-hexanediol

DIRECTIONS

Acetic acid causes chemical burns that can seriously damage skin and eyes; its vapors are highly irritating to the eyes and respiratory tract. Wear gloves, and dispense under a hood. Avoid contact, and do not breathe its vapors.

2-Ethyl-1,3-hexanediol is moderately irritating to the eyes and mucous membranes but not to the skin.

Aqueous sodium hypochlorite can irritate the skin, eyes, and respiratory tract. Avoid contact, and do not breathe its vapors.

Sodium hydroxide is toxic and corrosive, causing severe damage to skin, eyes, and mucous membranes. Wear gloves, and avoid contact with the NaOH solution.

Safety Notes

acetic acid

sodium hypochlorite

sodium hydroxide

Standard Scale

Reaction. Weigh 20.0 mmol of 2-ethyl-1,3-hexanediol into a 125-mL Erlenmeyer flask. Add 3.0 mL of glacial acetic acid and a stir bar, and cool the reaction mixture in an ice/water bath. While stirring [OP-10], use a separatory-addition funnel to add [OP-11] 30 mL of 6.0% (or 34 mL of 5.25%) aqueous sodium hypochlorite (NaOCl), drop by drop, during a period of 4 to 5 minutes. Remove the flask from the cold bath and stir

Take Care! Wear gloves, avoid contact with acetic acid and aqueous sodium hypochlorite, and do not breathe their vapors.

the reaction mixture vigorously for 1 hour at room temperature. Test it every 10 minutes or so with starch–iodide paper; if the paper doesn't turn blue–black in few seconds, add more NaOCl solution, ~1 mL at a time, until you get a positive test. At the end of the reaction period, add just enough saturated sodium bisulfite to give a negative starch–iodide test, unless the solution already tests negative.

Separation.   Add 3 *M* sodium hydroxide to the stirred reaction mixture, about 1 mL at a time, until it tests basic to red litmus paper. Transfer the reaction mixture to a separatory funnel, add 6 g of sodium chloride, and stopper and shake to dissolve the NaCl. Extract [OP-18] the product from this solution, using two 20-mL portions of diethyl ether. Dry [OP-25] the combined ether layers with anhydrous sodium sulfate or magnesium sulfate. Evaporate [OP-19] the ether from the solution.

Purification and Analysis.   At your instructor's request, purify the product by simple distillation [OP-30] using a compact distillation apparatus. Collect the liquid that distills between 200°C and 210°C. Weigh the product and record its infrared spectrum [OP-39]. Draw the structure of the product and give its IUPAC name.

Microscale

Reaction.   Weigh 3.00 mmol of 2-ethyl-1,3-hexanediol into a 10-mL round-bottom flask. Add 0.40 mL of glacial acetic acid and a stir bar, attach an air condenser, and cool the reaction mixture in an ice/water bath. While stirring [OP-10], use a Pasteur pipet to add [OP-11] 4.5 mL of 6.0% (or 5.0 mL of 5.25%) aqueous sodium hypochlorite (NaOCl), drop by drop, during a period of 2 to 3 minutes. Remove the flask from the cold bath and stir the reaction mixture vigorously for 1 hour at room temperature. Test it every 10 minutes or so with starch–iodide paper; if the paper doesn't turn blue–black in a few seconds, add more NaOCl solution, ~5 drops at a time, until you get a positive test. At the end of the reaction period, add just enough saturated sodium bisulfite to give a negative starch–iodide test, unless the solution already tests negative.

Separation.   Add 3 *M* sodium hydroxide to the stirred reaction mixture, drop by drop, until it tests basic to red litmus paper. Transfer the reaction mixture to a 12-mL centrifuge tube, add 1.0 g of sodium chloride, and stopper and shake to dissolve the NaCl. Extract [OP-18] the product from this solution using two 3-mL portions of diethyl ether. Dry [OP-25] the combined ether layers with anhydrous sodium sulfate. Evaporate [OP-19] the ether from the solution, in two portions if necessary.

Purification and Analysis.   At your instructor's request, purify the product by simple distillation [OP-30] using an air condenser. Collect the liquid that distills between 200°C and 210°C. You will need to insulate the neck of the Hickman still and use a high heat setting for your hot plate-stirrer. Weigh the product and record its infrared spectrum [OP-39]. Draw the structure of the product and give its IUPAC name.

Take Care! Wear gloves, and avoid contact with 3 *M* NaOH.

Stop and Think: What is the purpose of adding NaCl?

Waste Disposal: Place any recovered diethyl ether in an appropriate waste container.

Take Care! Wear gloves, avoid contact with acetic acid and aqueous sodium hypochlorite, and do not breathe their vapors.

Take Care! Wear gloves, and avoid contact with 3 *M* NaOH.

Stop and Think: What is the purpose of adding NaCl?

Waste Disposal: Place any recovered diethyl ether in an appropriate waste container.

Exercises

1. Tell how you arrived at the structure of your product from its infrared spectrum.
2. What was the purpose of adding sodium chloride during the separation step?
3. Describe how each of the following experimental errors or variations might affect your results. (a) The lab assistant didn't know what glacial acetic acid is, so she put out 1 *M* acetic acid instead. (b) You mixed up the vials of test paper and used red litmus paper when you should have used starch–iodide paper. (c) You used Clorox that was purchased several years ago.
4. (a) Calculate the atom economy and reaction efficiency of your synthesis. (b) Describe some green features of your synthesis, and any that aren't so green.
5. Following the directions in Appendix V, construct a flow diagram for the synthesis of your product.
6. The diol 1,4-cyclohexanedimethanol reacts with terephthalic acid to form the polyester known as PCT. Draw the structure of a repeating unit of this polyester.
7. Outline a synthesis of dioxane starting with ethylene glycol.

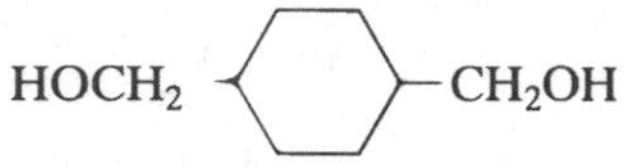

1,4-cyclohexanedimethanol

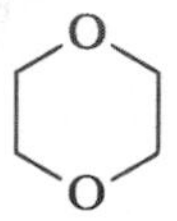

dioxane

Other Things You Can Do

(Starred items require your instructor's permission.)

*1. Prepare 2.0 mL of a 1% solution of borax (sodium tetraborate), and add enough phenolphthalein indicator solution to yield a definite pink color. Add 2 drops of each of the following to 0.5 mL of the solution: (a) 2-ethyl-1,3-hexanediol; (b) 2-butanol; (c) ethylene glycol. Decide what structural feature is necessary to yield a positive test.
*2. Obtain a sample of a suitable alcohol from your instructor, develop a procedure for oxidizing it to a carbonyl compound using sodium hypochlorite and acetic acid, and have your procedure approved by your instructor. Then carry out the oxidation reaction and turn in your product, along with its infrared spectrum and a laboratory report (see Appendix III).
3. Starting with sources listed in the Bibliography, write a research paper about commercial processes for manufacturing ethylene glycol and some of its commercial uses.

EXPERIMENT 41

Isomerization of a Cyclic Ketone

Isomerization. Reactions of Alkenes. Reactions of Carbonyl Compounds. Infrared Spectrometry.

Operations

OP-7   Heating
OP-8   Cooling
OP-10 Mixing
OP-18 Extraction
OP-19 Evaporation
OP-24 Washing Liquids
OP-25 Drying Liquids
OP-39 Infrared Spectrometry
OP-40 Nuclear Magnetic Resonance Spectrometry (optional)

Before You Begin

1. Read the experiment, read or review the operations as necessary, and write an experimental plan.
2. Calculate the mass and volume of 10.0 mmol (SS) or 2.00 mmol (μS) of carvone, and the theoretical yield of the product.

Scenario

New-age herbalist Basil Wormwood (see Experiment 18) often steam distills chopped-up spearmint leaves to isolate their essential oil, whose main component is (*R*)-carvone. This time he decided to *digest* the leaves in aqueous sulfuric acid before distillation to reduce their volume and make it possible to process a larger batch each time. He was surprised to find that the resulting oil smelled more like thyme than spearmint. Curious about this outcome, he carried out the same procedure with ground caraway seeds, which he knew to contain (*S*)-carvone (the enantiomer of spearmint's carvone), and obtained the same thyme-scented product. Despite its odor, the unexpected product isn't thymol—but, like thymol, it is mildly acidic.

In chemistry, to digest *something is to soften or disintegrate it by means of moisture, heat, or a chemical reaction.*

Thymol is an isomer of carvone and the main component of thyme's essential oil.

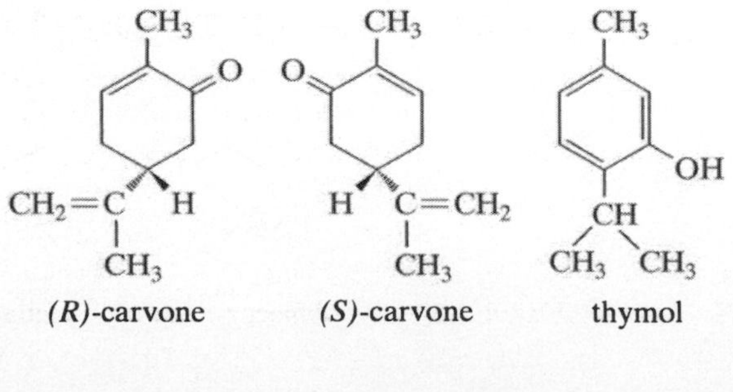

(*R*)-carvone   (*S*)-carvone   thymol

Your assignment is to carry out the reaction of either *(R)*- or *(S)*-carvone with sulfuric acid and identify the product. Your supervisor has already had the product analyzed and found its molecular formula to be $C_{10}H_{14}O$, the same as that of carvone, so Basil must have carried out an acid catalyzed *isomerization* reaction—one in which a compound is converted to one of its possible isomers.

Applying Scientific Methodology

There should be enough clues in the Scenario and elsewhere to help you formulate a reasonable working hypothesis about the structure of the product, based on the structure of the reactant and your knowledge of the chemistry of $C=C$ and $C=O$ double bonds. You will test your hypothesis using spectral analysis.

Chemicals from Herbs and Spices

The carvones that are found in spearmint leaves and caraway seeds also occur in other herbs and spices, such as dill seed, which contains *(S)*-carvone. An *herb* is a flowering plant that has a non-woody stem, or parts of such a plant, such as thyme leaves. A *spice* is a pungent or aromatic plant product used as a seasoning, often a dried fruit or seed or even the bark of a tree, such as cloves and cinnamon. Spices are at their best when bought whole and ground just before use because powdered spices lose their volatile flavor components rapidly. A good cook will have dozens of herbs and spices in the cupboard to add flavor to foods and to make teas and other beverages.

Many of the flavorful chemicals found in herbs and spices, including carvone, are terpenes. For example, coriander seeds contain linalool, camphor, α-pinene, and a host of other terpenes.

See Experiment 33 for a discussion of terpenes.

linalool   camphor α-pinene

Aromatic compounds—some of which are also terpenes—are major flavor constituents of many herbs and spices. These include aromatic aldehydes, ketones, and ethers, such as cuminaldehyde from cumin seed, cinnamaldehyde from cinnamon, zingerone from ginger, eugenol from cloves, and anethole from fennel seeds.

cuminaldehyde   cinnamaldehyde   zingerone   eugenol   anethole

Experiment 29 describes some other vanilloids.

Turmeric, a major ingredient of curry powder, is used widely in East Indian and other Asian cooking, and has also been used as a food coloring for mustard and other food products. Its main constituent is a yellow pigment, curcumin, which appears to be effective for treating digestive disorders, osteoarthritis, and cancer; and for preventing the buildup of plaque in arteries. Curcumin is easily oxidized to vanillin, the main flavor ingredient of vanilla. In fact, curcumin—along with zingerone and eugenol—contains the same 4-hydroxy-3-methoxy combination found in vanillin. These substances are therefore classified as *vanilloids*.

curcumin   vanillin

Several of the previous compounds are *phenols*—compounds having one or more OH groups on an aromatic ring. Phenols are abundant in the plant kingdom. They include simple phenols such as thymol, the main flavor ingredient of thyme, and carvacrol, which occurs in both winter savory and summer savory. Apigenin, which occurs in parsley, is one member of a chemical family called the *flavones*. Flavones and similar multi-ring phenolics, which are lumped under the term *flavonoids,* are widely distributed in the plant world. Flavonoids are potent antioxidants that contribute to the health benefits of plant-based foods. The Mediterranean diet is particularly high in flavonoids. For example, Greeks consume unusually large quantities of apigenin from parsley, which is an essential ingredient of the grain salad tabouli.

thymol   carvacrol   apigenin

Pungent herbs and spices such as garlic, horseradish, and mustard usually contain sulfur compounds. A sulfoxide called alliin is an important constituent of garlic. When garlic cloves are crushed or otherwise damaged, the cell membranes are ruptured so that alliin comes into contact with an enzyme, alliinase, which catalyzes a reaction that forms allicin. Allicin is actually a chemical defense agent for the garlic plant, protecting it from insects and fungi. It is also partly responsible for the characteristic "garlicky" odor that many people enjoy but others find offensive. Allicin is quite unstable and rapidly decomposes into other substances such as diallyl disulfide, so the flavor of garlic changes with cooking or standing.

$$CH_2\!=\!CHCH_2SCH_2\underset{\underset{NH_2}{|}}{CH}COH \xrightarrow{\text{alliinase}} CH_2\!=\!CHCH_2S\!-\!SCH_2CH\!=\!CH_2$$

alliin   allicin

$$\longrightarrow CH_2\!=\!CHCH_2S\!-\!SCH_2CH\!=\!CH_2$$

diallyl disulfide

Horseradish roots contain sinigrin and the enzyme myrosinase, which combine when the root is grated, forming some very pungent sulfur compounds that include allyl isothiocyanate. Most store-bought horseradish is not very potent, but when the root is fresh it generates enough of this volatile substance to cause a nose-clearing burst of stinging vapors that can bring tears to your eyes.

$$CH_2\!=\!CHCH_2\underset{\underset{S-C_6H_{11}O_5}{|}}{C}\!=\!NOSO_3K \xrightarrow{\text{myrosinase}} CH_2\!=\!CHCH_2N\!=\!C\!=\!S \text{ etc.}$$

sinigrin   allyl isothiocyanate

Sinigrin is also a constituent of the black mustard plant; white mustard contains a related compound, sinalbin, which yields a different isothiocyanate after an enzyme-catalyzed reaction analogous to that of sinigrin. Such isothiocyanates produce the "heat" of prepared mustards, which usually contain both black and white mustard seeds. The Japanese use a relative of horseradish called wasabi to flavor sashimi (raw fish), sushi, and noodles. Like horseradish and mustard, wasabi produces pungent isothiocyanates by an enzyme-catalyzed reaction. True wasabi is very expensive and, when fresh, loses its flavor within 15 minutes, so most of the "wasabi" that makes its way to North America is a paste or dry powder that consists mainly of artificially colored European horseradish and may contain less than 0.1% real wasabi.

Understanding the Experiment

The isomerization of carvone is catalyzed by aqueous mineral acids, so you will heat your carvone under reflux with 6 M sulfuric acid. The reaction mixture has a tendency to boil up rather violently; therefore, it is important to use vigorous magnetic stirring or a sufficient number of boiling chips to prevent bumping. You will separate the unknown product from the reaction mixture by extraction with low-boiling petroleum ether, which is not a true ether but a mixture of low-boiling hydrocarbons. Because of its low boiling range (usually ~35–60°C), this solvent can be removed easily by evaporation. The product is somewhat corrosive, so you should clean your glassware thoroughly after use. It also darkens over

Key Concept: The first step in an acid-catalyzed reaction of an unsaturated compound is usually addition of a proton to one or more double bonds.

A Greener Way: You can recover the petroleum ether by evaporating it under vacuum using a cold trap.

time, so it is best to record its infrared (IR) spectrum on the same day that you prepare it.

From the IR spectrum of your product, you should be able to identify its functional group(s) and determine what family or families of organic compounds it belongs to. That will help you check (and perhaps modify) your working hypothesis and come up with a reasonable structure for the product, which you may be able to verify by comparing your IR spectrum to standard spectra in *The Aldrich Library of FT-IR Spectra* or some other collection of IR spectra listed in the Bibliography. At your instructor's discretion, you can also obtain the ^{1}H NMR spectrum of the product and use it to confirm your structure or figure out a better one.

This is a relatively green experiment; it has a high atom economy, and the organic solvent used for extraction can be recovered and recycled. Sulfuric acid is harmful to aquatic organisms, so it should not be released into the environment.

Reactions and Properties

Table 41.1 Physical properties

	mol wt	bp	d
carvone	150.2	230	0.965
sulfuric acid	98.1	290	1.84

Note: bp is in °C; density is in g/mL.

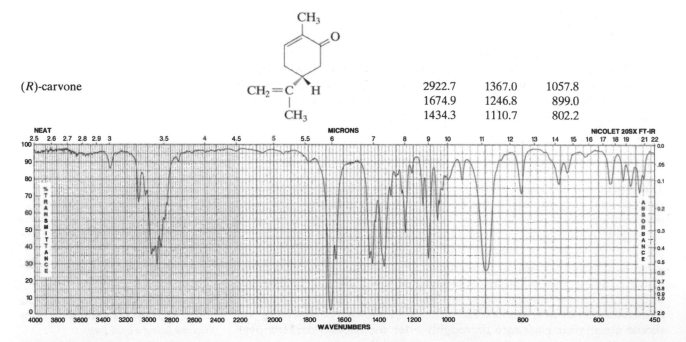

Figure 41.1 IR spectrum of (R)-carvone

DIRECTIONS

At the instructor's discretion, students can use different enantiomers of carvone and compare their results.

> **Sulfuric acid causes chemical burns that can seriously damage skin and eyes. Wear gloves and avoid contact.**
> **The product can cause chemical burns to skin and eyes. Wear gloves and avoid contact.**

Safety Notes

sulfuric acid

 Standard Scale

Reaction.   Combine 10.0 mmol of *(R)*- or *(S)*-carvone with 15 mL of 6.0 *M* sulfuric acid in a 50-mL round-bottom flask. Add several small boiling chips (preferably microporous chips) or a stir bar, and attach a condenser. Start the stirrer [OP-10] (if you are using one), and heat the reaction mixture under gentle reflux [OP-7] for 35 minutes. Cool [OP-8] the reaction mixture in an ice/water bath, and then disassemble the apparatus. Use acetone to rinse (into a waste container) any glassware that comes in contact with the product.

Take Care! Wear gloves, and avoid contact with sulfuric acid.

If severe bumping occurs, cool the reaction mixture and add more boiling chips (if you are using them). Raise the flask just enough so that it doesn't contact the heating manual, and resume heating.

Separation.   *Under a fume hood,* transfer the reaction mixture to a separatory funnel, and use two 10-mL portions of low-boiling petroleum ether to extract [OP-18] the product from the reaction mixture (wear gloves during the extraction). Wash [OP-24] the combined petroleum ether layers with 5% aqueous sodium bicarbonate; this process releases CO_2 gas, so stir and shake gently at first. Dry [OP-25] the organic layer over anhydrous sodium sulfate or magnesium sulfate, and then evaporate [OP-19] the solvent.

Analysis.   Weigh the product and record its infrared spectrum [OP-39]. If requested, record its ^{1}H NMR spectrum [OP-40] or obtain one from your instructor. Then deduce the structure or your product.

Waste Disposal: Put the aqueous layers and any recovered solvent in appropriate waste containers.

 Microscale

Reaction.   Combine 2.00 mmol of *(R)*- or *(S)*-carvone with 3.0 mL of 6.0 *M* sulfuric acid in a 10-mL round-bottom flask. Equip the flask with a water-cooled condenser and a stir bar. Heat the reaction mixture gently under reflux [OP-7], with vigorous stirring [OP-10], for 35 minutes. Cool [OP-8] the reaction mixture in an ice/water bath, and then disassemble the apparatus. Use acetone to rinse—into a waste container—any glassware that comes in contact with the product.

Take Care! Wear gloves, and avoid contact with sulfuric acid.

Separation.   *Under a fume hood,* transfer the reaction mixture to a conical centrifuge tube, and use two 2-mL portions of low-boiling petroleum ether to extract [OP-18] the product from the reaction mixture (wear gloves during the extraction). Wash [OP-24] the combined petroleum ether layers with 5% aqueous sodium bicarbonate; this process releases CO_2 gas, so stir and shake gently at first. Dry [OP-25] the organic layer over anhydrous sodium sulfate, and then evaporate [OP-19] the solvent.

Analysis.   Weigh the product and record its infrared spectrum [OP-39]. If requested, record its ^{1}H NMR spectrum [OP-40] or obtain one from your instructor. Then deduce the structure or your product.

Waste Disposal: Put the aqueous layers and any recovered solvents in appropriate containers.

Exercises

1. Write a reasonable mechanism for the isomerization of carvone in the presence of sulfuric acid.
2. (a) Derive the IUPAC name of your product, and give its common name. (b) List several herbs that contain the product as a major component.
3. Describe and explain the possible effect on your results of the following experimental errors or variations. (a) You used high-boiling petroleum ether for the extraction. (b) You used 5% sodium bisulfate rather than 5% sodium bicarbonate to wash the petroleum ether solution. (c) After adding 5% sodium bicarbonate to the petroleum ether solution, you immediately capped the separatory funnel (or centrifuge tube, for microscale work) and shook the mixture vigorously.
4. (a) Calculate the atom economy and reaction efficiency of your synthesis. (b) Describe some green features of your synthesis, and any that aren't so green.
5. Following the directions in Appendix V, construct a flow diagram for the synthesis of your product.
6. Identify the terpenes (see Experiment 33), excluding the compounds identified as such, whose structures are shown in "Chemicals from Herbs and Spices."
7. Outline a synthesis of vanillin from curcumin.

Other Things You Can Do

(Starred items require your instructor's permission.)

*1. Following the procedure for solubility tests in Part IV, test your product for solubility in 5% NaOH and 5% NaHCO₃, and explain your results.
*2. Carry out the isomerization reaction of dimethyl maleate described in Experiment 17, and use a spectrometric method to show that the expected isomerization has taken place.
3. Starting with sources listed in the Bibliography, write a research paper about the components and therapeutic applications of some culinary herbs.

A Wittig Reaction of *trans*-Cinnamaldehyde

Reactions of Carbonyl Compounds. Preparation of Dienes. Nucleophilic Addition. Wittig Reaction. Ylides.

Operations

OP-7   Heating
OP-10 Mixing
OP-16 Vacuum Filtration
OP-18 Extraction
OP-19 Evaporation
OP-25 Drying Liquids
OP-26 Washing and Drying Solids
OP-28 Recrystallization
OP-33 Melting Point

Before You Begin

1. Read the experiment, read or review the operations as necessary, and write an experimental plan.
2. Calculate the mass and volume of 10.0 mmol (SS) or 1.00 mmol (µS) of *trans*-cinnamaldehyde, and the theoretical yield of 1,4-diphenyl-1,3-butadiene.

Scenario

Marvelous Molecules Incorporated (MMI) has experienced a lower than expected demand for its product line of aldehydes, so it has a large inventory of cinnamaldehyde that it would like to reduce. Penny Wise, MMI's peripatetic marketing executive, has learned that there is some demand for novel dienes such as 1,4-diphenyl-1,3-butadiene, which can be converted to interesting products such as *p*-terphenyl by means of Diels–Alder reactions.

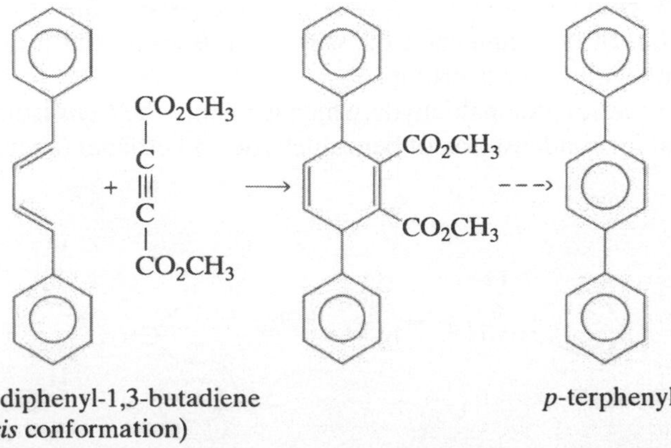

(*E,E*)-1,4-diphenyl-1,3-butadiene
(*s-cis* conformation)   *p*-terphenyl

A staff chemist has informed her that it should be possible to prepare 1,4-diphenyl-1,3-butadiene from cinnamaldehyde by a procedure known as the Wittig synthesis, but its value as a Diels–Alder diene will depend on its stereochemistry. The (*E,E*) diene can easily attain the *s-cis* conformation needed to form a Diels–Alder adduct, but the (*E,Z*) diene is less likely to do so. Your assignment is to find out whether or not you can prepare 1,4-diphenyl-1,3-butadiene from *trans*-cinnamaldehyde and whether or not the major product has the desired (*E,E*) stereochemistry.

Applying Scientific Methodology

The scientific problems in this experiment are implicit in the Scenario. After reading the experiment, you should be able to develop a working hypothesis for the second problem, which you will test by obtaining the melting point of the major product.

Bark Spices and Cinnamaldehyde

Despite claims by wild foods advocate Euell Gibbons that the inner bark of the slippery elm and other trees is edible and nutritious, tree bark is not, as a rule, a popular source of food products. The most notable exceptions to the rule are certain trees of the genus *Cinnamomum,* which provide the spices cinnamon and cassia. True cinnamon is obtained from *Cinnamomum zeylanicum,* a tree that grows in Sri Lanka (formerly Ceylon) and southern India. Cinnamon is obtained by peeling the bark from the cut branches of the cinnamon tree and then scraping off any wood and the outer layers of bark. The thin strips of inner bark are dried in the sun, forming rolled-up "quills" that extend up to a meter in length. The quills are generally cut into shorter lengths to produce cinnamon sticks, or ground up to make powdered cinnamon. Cinnamon bark from Sri Lanka contains 1–2% of an aldehyde-rich essential oil, of which about 70% is cinnamaldehyde (3-phenyl-2-propenal). Other components of cinnamon oil include benzaldehyde, *p*-isopropylbenzaldehyde, 3-phenylpropanal, nonanal, and 2-furaldehyde, along with such nonaldehyde ingredients as 2-heptanone, caryophyllene, and various other flavor components. Cinnamon leaves, surprisingly, contain no cinnamaldehyde but are rich in eugenol, the main flavor component of cloves.

Nearly all of the "cinnamon" consumed in the United States is actually cassia, which is obtained from the Chinese cassia tree, *Cinnamomum cassia,* and several related species grown in southeast Asia. Chinese cassia oil is 80–95% cinnamaldehyde, but its strong, spicy-sweet flavor is quite different from that of true cinnamon oil, which is less sweet but more complex and fragrant, with citrus overtones.

Synthetic cinnamaldehyde, which is mainly the *trans* isomer, is prepared by an aldol condensation of benzaldehyde and ethanal (acetaldehyde).

cinnamon stick

Cinnamaldehyde, as well as natural cinnamon and cassia oils, is used to flavor candies, chewing gum, and baked goods, and as an ingredient in perfumes.

Understanding the Experiment

The German chemist Georg Wittig developed the Wittig reaction in 1954, but 25 years passed before he received full recognition for originating one of the most synthetically useful reactions in organic chemistry. In 1979, Wittig shared the Nobel Prize in chemistry with another well-known synthetic organic chemist, Herbert C. Brown of the United States.

Like the aldol condensation (discussed in Experiment 43), the Wittig reaction is used to construct larger molecules from smaller ones, connecting the components of the smaller molecules with carbon–carbon double bonds. Both reactions involve the attack of a nucleophilic carbon atom (stabilized by a neighboring electron-withdrawing group) on the carbonyl carbon atom of an aldehyde or ketone, as shown by the following examples.

aldol condensation

$$RC(=O)\cdots \overset{-}{:}CH_2CH(=O) \longrightarrow R\overset{\overset{\overset{-}{\ddot{O}}:}{|}}{\underset{H}{C}}-CH_2CH(=O) \xrightarrow{H^+} R\overset{\overset{OH}{|}}{\underset{H}{C}}-CH_2CH(=O)$$

an enolate ion

Wittig reaction

$$RC(=O)\cdots \overset{-}{:}CH_2-\overset{+}{P}Ph_3 \longrightarrow R\overset{\overset{\overset{-}{\ddot{O}}:}{|}}{\underset{H}{C}}-CH_2-\overset{+}{P}Ph_3$$

a phosphorus ylide

In the aldol condensation, the nucleophile is an enolate ion, which is stabilized by resonance involving the carbonyl group. In the Wittig reaction, the nucleophile is a phosphorus ylide, which is stabilized by resonance involving a triphenylphosphonium group. In both reactions, the carbon–carbon double bond then forms by elimination (in several steps) of a molecular species: H_2O in the case of the aldol condensation, and $Ph_3P=O$ in the case of the Wittig reaction.

Key Concept: Carbon is ordinarily not nucleophilic because it has no unshared electron pair, but a nucleophilic carbon atom can be formed by transfer of a proton from a C—H bond to a strong base. This transfer is facilitated by the presence of some group that can stabilize the resulting species.

aldol condensation

$$R\overset{\overset{HO}{|}}{\underset{H}{C}}-\overset{\overset{H}{|}}{C}H\overset{O}{\overset{||}{C}}H \xrightarrow{-H_2O} RCH=CHCH(=O)$$

Wittig reaction

$$R\overset{\overset{\overset{-}{\ddot{O}}:}{|}\ \overset{+}{P}Ph_3}{\underset{H}{C}}-CH_2 \xrightarrow{-Ph_3P=O} RCH=CH_2$$

During a Wittig reaction, the Ph_3P group needed to stabilize the nucleophilic carbon atom is lost along with the carbonyl oxygen. Thus, the Wittig reaction, unlike the aldol condensation, can be used for the synthesis of unsaturated hydrocarbons that have no additional functional groups.

See your lecture textbook for a more complete description and mechanism of the Wittig reaction.

Table 43.1 Physical properties

	mol wt	mp	bp	d
furfural	96.1	−39	162	1.159
cyclopentanone	84.1	−51	131	0.949
2-butanone	72.1	−86	80	0.805
tricaprylmethylammonium chloride	404.2			0.884
product **A**	162.2	60.5	154[15]	
product **B**	240.3	162		

Note: mp and bp are in °C; superscripts indicate pressure in torr; density is in g/mL.

Cyclopentanone

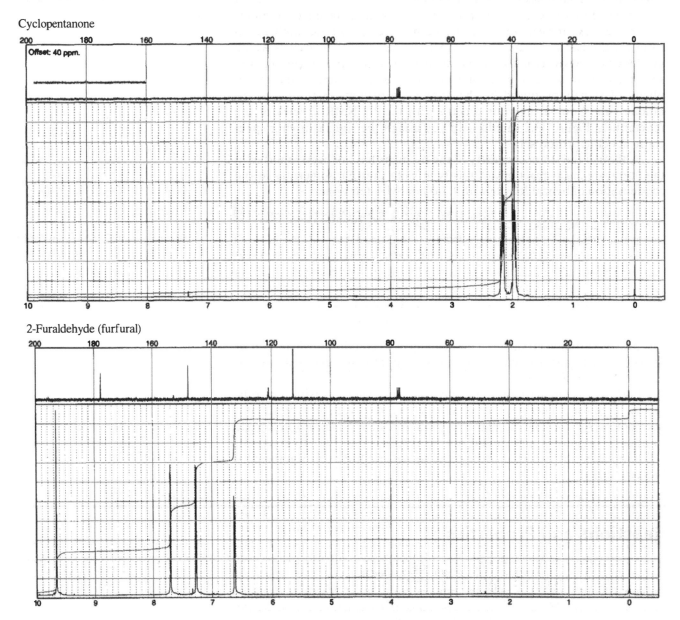

2-Furaldehyde (furfural)

Figure 43.2 NMR spectra of the starting materials

DIRECTIONS

A. *Claisen–Schmidt Reaction of Cyclopentanone and Furfural*

Cyclopentanone is a skin irritant and a severe eye irritant; avoid contact. Diethyl ether is extremely flammable and may be harmful if inhaled. Do not breathe its vapors, and keep it away from flames and hot surfaces. Furfural irritates the skin, eyes, and respiratory tract, and it may cause allergic skin or respiratory reactions. Wear gloves while handling furfural and the reaction mixture (which will stain your hands yellow), and do not breathe their vapors.

A vacuum-distillation apparatus may implode if any of its components are cracked or otherwise damaged. Inspect the parts for damage, and have your instructor check your apparatus. Protect yourself with a safety shield or hood sash while the apparatus is under vacuum.

Deuterochloroform is harmful if inhaled or absorbed through the skin, and it is a suspected human carcinogen. Avoid contact with the liquid, and do not breathe its vapors.

Safety Notes

furfural   cyclopentanone

diethyl ether

Standard Scale

Reaction. In a 125-mL Erlenmeyer flask, dissolve 50.0 mmol of cyclopentanone in 25 mL of solvent-grade diethyl ether. Add 45 mL of 0.10 *M* aqueous sodium hydroxide and a magnetic stir bar. Cool [OP-8] the mixture to 5°C in an ice/water bath, and add 50.0 mmol of freshly distilled furfural while stirring. Seal the flask with Parafilm, and stir [OP-10] the reaction mixture vigorously in a cold water bath (10–15°C) for 45 minutes. Parafilm dissolves in ether, so don't let it contact the reaction mixture. Replace any ether that evaporates during the reaction.

Separation. Using a clean filter flask, filter the reaction mixture by vacuum filtration [OP-16] and save the filtrate, which contains product **A**. Turn off the vacuum immediately after filtration to keep the ether from evaporating. Wash any solid on the filter with 10 mL of diethyl ether, and combine the wash liquid with the filtrate. If your instructor assigned Exercise 2, save this solid and weigh it when it is dry. If any solid remains in the filtrate, it will be removed during subsequent operations.

Place the filtrate in a separatory funnel and separate the layers, saving both layers. Extract [OP-18] the aqueous layer with 15 mL of ethyl ether, and combine the ether extract with the initial ether layer. Wash [OP-24] this solution with two separate portions of saturated aqueous sodium chloride. Dry [OP-25] it over anhydrous sodium sulfate or magnesium sulfate, and evaporate [OP-19] the ether under vacuum until the volume of the liquid residue remains essentially constant.

Purification and Analysis. Assemble an apparatus for vacuum distillation [OP-31], using the compact apparatus shown in Figure E9 of OP-27, and have your instructor approve it. Make sure that a safety shield or hood sash is between you and the apparatus, and then purify the residue by vacuum distillation using *no* cooling bath. Monitor the distillation carefully; if any solid begins to form in the outlet tube, melt it with a heat gun or

Take Care! Keep diethyl ether away from ignition sources, and do not breathe its vapors. Wear gloves, avoid contact with furfural, and do not breathe its vapors.

Observe and Note: What happens during the reaction period?

Stop and Think: What could this solid be?

Waste Disposal: Place any recovered ether in a solvent recovery container. Unless your instructor directs otherwise, wash all aqueous layers down the drain.

Take Care! A vacuum-distillation apparatus may implode if any of its components are cracked or otherwise damaged. Follow the precautions described in OP-31 and the Safety Notes.

Observe and Note: Compare your observations during this reaction with your observations during the first reaction.

Waste Disposal: Place the filtrate in a designated solvent recovery container.

Take Care! Do not breathe the vapors of 2-butanone, and keep it away from ignition sources.

Take Care! Avoid contact with CDCl₃, and do not breathe its vapors.

0.50 mL of freshly distilled furfural while stirring [OP-10]. Seal the flask with Parafilm, and stir it vigorously at room temperature for 15 minutes, occasionally swirling it in the ice/water bath to reduce pressure buildup from vaporizing ether. (Parafilm dissolves in ether, so don't let it contact the reaction mixture.) Then let the reaction mixture stand at room temperature, with continued stirring, for 10 minutes.

Separation.   Collect the product by vacuum filtration [OP-16], wash it [OP-26a] with two portions of diethyl ether, and air-dry it on the filter.

Purification and Analysis.   Recrystallize [OP-28] product **B** from 2-butanone, using about 6 mL or less of the solvent. Wash the product on the filter [OP-26a] with diethyl ether, dry it [OP-26b], and weigh it. (**Waste Disposal:** Place the filtrate in a designated solvent recovery container.) Measure the melting point [OP-33] of product **B**. Record its ¹H NMR spectrum [OP-40] in deuterochloroform, or obtain a spectrum from your instructor. Interpret the NMR spectrum as completely as you can, deduce the structure of product **B**, and name it.

Exercises

1. Discuss the effect of reaction conditions on the outcome of the Claisen–Schmidt reaction, telling what reaction conditions promote the formation of each product, and why.
2. (a) What is the probable identity of the solid that was filtered from the reaction mixture in part **A**? How could you have confirmed its identity? (b) What percentage of the cyclopentanone that you started with in part **A** was converted to condensation products? (This is not the same as the percentage yield of **A**.)
3. Write balanced equations and detailed mechanisms for the formation of both products, **A** and **B**.
4. (a) Using balanced equations (see Exercise 3) for the reactions you carried out, calculate the atom economy and reaction efficiency of each synthesis. (b) Describe some green features of your syntheses, and any that aren't so green.
5. Describe and explain the possible effect on your results of the following experimental errors or variations. (a) You used 10 *M* NaOH rather than 0.10 *M* NaOH in part **A**. (b) In part **A**, you rinsed the reaction flask with acetone and didn't dry it completely. (c) You left out the tricaprylmethylammonium chloride in part **B**. (d) You used 50 mmol (SS) or 10 mmol (µS) of cyclopentanone in part **B** as well as in part **A**.
6. Diagram a possible phase-transfer process for the formation of product **B**, using the format illustrated in Experiment 24.
7. (a) Following the format in Appendix V, construct a flow diagram for the synthesis in part **A**. (b) Construct a flow diagram for the synthesis in part **B**.
8. From your ¹H NMR spectra, is it more likely that your products are (*Z*) or (*E*) stereoisomers? Explain your answer.
9. An error-prone student, Mel A. Droyt, forgot to add the furfural in part **A**, but he recovered a small amount of liquid that distilled at 139–142°C at 20 torr and didn't solidify on cooling. The ¹H NMR spectrum of the liquid showed no signals from vinylic or hydroxylic protons. Propose a structure for this product, and write a mechanism for its formation.

Other Things You Can Do

(Starred items require your instructor's permission.)

*1. As a group project, carry out part **B** using different phase-transfer catalysts and compare the crude yields to find out which catalysts are most effective. Suggested catalysts are tetrabutylammonium bromide, tetrabutylphosphonium bromide, cetyltrimethylammonium bromide, and 1-hexadecylpyridinium chloride.

*2. Prepare some other aldol condensation products as described in Minilab 34.

3. Starting with sources listed in the Bibliography, write a research paper about the production and uses of furan, furfural, and some derivatives of these compounds.

Electronic Effect
of a *para*-Iodo Substituent

EXPERIMENT **44**

Reactions of Aromatic Amines. Preparation of Aryl Halides. Aromatic Nucleophilic Substitution. Carboxylic Acids. Diazonium Salts. Linear Free-Energy Relationships.

Operations

OP-7 Heating
OP-8 Cooling
OP-10 Mixing
OP-16 Vacuum Filtration
OP-26 Washing and Drying Solids
OP-28 Recrystallization

Before You Begin

1. Read the experiment, read or review the operations as necessary, and write an experimental plan.
2. Calculate the masses of 10.0 mmol (SS) or 2.00 mmol (μS) of *p*-aminobenzoic acid, 10.0 mmol (SS) or 2.00 mmol (μS) of sodium nitrite, and 15 mmol (SS) or 3.0 mmol (μS) of potassium iodide. Calculate the theoretical yield of *p*-iodobenzoic acid.
3. For each acid listed in Table 44.1, calculate the mass of 0.80 mmol (SS) or 0.20 mmol (μS) of the acid.

Scenario

Si Starr, an energetic professor of metaphysical chemistry at Miskatonic University, is using molecular orbital theory to predict the electronic effects of various substituents on such reactions as the ionization of aromatic carboxylic acids. Substituent effects can be expressed quantitatively by empirical parameters called sigma values. To test the validity of his results, Professor Starr wants to compare his calculated sigma values with experimentally measured sigma values. Sigma values have been determined for most of the common substituents, but Starr has been unable to locate reliable sigma values for the iodo substituent ($-$I) on a benzene ring. Your assignment is to prepare *p*-iodobenzoic acid, measure its pK_a value, and use that to determine the sigma value for a *para*-iodo substituent.

Applying Scientific Methodology

After reading the experiment, you can propose a hypothesis about the electronic effect of a *p*-iodo substituent. The sigma value you obtain will show whether or not your hypothesis is correct.

Linear Free-Energy Relationships

In general chemistry, you learned that electrons in a covalent bond tend to migrate toward the more electronegative atom, building up its electron density at the expense of the less electronegative atom. The situation is not always so simple in conjugated organic compounds, where the electrons of unshared pairs or in pi bonds sometimes migrate *away* from a more electronegative atom into the "electron sink" of a delocalized pi-electron system. For example, lone-pair electrons from an oxygen-containing substituent such as methoxyl ($-OCH_3$) tend to migrate toward and overlap with the pi-electron cloud of a benzene ring, as illustrated for anisole (methoxybenzene). The net electronic effect of a substituent is indicated by an empirical (experimentally measured) parameter called its *sigma value*. Electron-withdrawing groups have positive sigma values, and electron-donating groups have negative ones. For example, the measured sigma value of $-OCH_3$ is -0.27, indicating that it has a net electron-donating effect at the *para* position of a benzene ring, even though oxygen is considerably more electronegative than carbon.

Consider a general substituent Z at the *para* position of a substituted benzoic acid. If Z is more electronegative than carbon, it will tend to withdraw electrons through the sigma-bond framework of the benzene ring by an *inductive effect,* and this should increase the strength of the acid by stabilizing its conjugate base. Conversely, a substituent that is more electropositive than carbon can donate electrons inductively and weaken an acid. But inductive effects decrease rapidly with distance, and because a *para* substituent is remote from the reaction site (the COOH group), its inductive effect may be quite small.

Substituents that have unpaired electrons and are adjacent to a conjugated system tend to donate electrons by a *resonance effect*. Electron donation by resonance can cause a buildup of electron density at locations within the ring and on conjugated substituents, as illustrated by the following resonance structures for the conjugate base of a substituted benzoic acid:

Overlap of lone-pair electrons with pi system in anisole

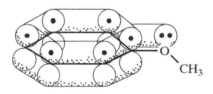

Conjugate base is stabilized by inductive electron withdrawal.

Z—⟨O⟩— COOH

‖

Z⟵⟨O⟩— COO⁻ + H⁺

Conjugate base is destabilized by electron donation
transmitted through the pi-electron system.

In this example, the conjugate base is destabilized by a concentration of negative charge near the reaction site. Destabilization of the conjugate base shifts the ionization equilibrium to the left and reduces the strength of the acid. Resonance effects are transmitted freely throughout a conjugated system and do not decrease significantly with distance. They are most important when the substituent is *ortho* or *para* to the ring carbon nearest the

Key Concept: Stabilization of the conjugate base of an acid strengthens the acid; destabilization of its conjugate base weakens the acid.

Such a microburet can be constructed from a 10-mL graduated pipet as described in J. Chem. Educ. **1991,** *68,* A125.

measured its equivalent weight and melting point. For the microscale titration, a 10-mL microburet can be used if desired. With your instructor's permission, you can obtain the IR or ^{1}H NMR spectrum of the acid to help confirm its identity.

In the environment, maleic anhydride hydrolyzes to maleic acid, which is toxic to aquatic organisms. Hydrochloric acid is expected to be toxic to aquatic life.

Properties

Table 45.1 Physical properties

	mol wt	mp	bp
maleic anhydride	98.1	53	202
zinc	65.4	419	907d

Note: mp and bp are in °C; density is in g/mL; d = decomposes.

DIRECTIONS

Safety Notes

maleic anhydride   hydrochloric acid

Maleic anhydride is corrosive and toxic and can cause severe damage to the eyes, skin, and upper respiratory tract. Wear gloves, avoid contact, and do not breathe its dust. If you must powder maleic anhydride briquettes, do it under the hood and wear safety goggles and protective clothing.

Concentrated hydrochloric acid is poisonous and corrosive. Contact or inhalation can cause severe damage to the eyes, skin, and respiratory tract. Wear gloves, and dispense under a hood. Avoid contact, and do not breathe its vapors.

The reaction of zinc with hydrochloric acid produces hydrogen gas, which is highly flammable. Keep the reaction mixture away from flames.

The product may irritate the eyes, skin, or respiratory tract. Avoid contact, and do not breathe its dust.

Take Care! Avoid contact with maleic anhydride, and do not breathe its dust.

Observe and Note: What evidence is there that a reaction is occurring?

Take Care! Wear gloves, avoid contact with concentrated HCl, and do not breathe its vapors.

 ### Standard Scale

Reaction.   Dissolve 25.0 mmol of maleic anhydride in 15 mL of water in a 50-mL Erlenmeyer flask by heating the water just to boiling, but don't let any water boil away. Remove the flask from the heat source and immediately add 28 mmol of 40-mesh zinc in three or four portions, stirring or swirling [OP-10] after each addition. Let the flask stand for 15 minutes, with magnetic stirring or occasional swirling. *Under the hood,* slowly add 5.0 mL of concentrated HCl, with stirring or swirling.

Separation.   When the zinc (or most of it) has dissolved, heat the mixture to boiling under the hood. Any white solid that formed during the reaction should dissolve. Filter [OP-15] the hot solution through fluted filter paper. Boil the filtrate under the hood until the solution becomes *just* cloudy at the boiling point. Cover the beaker with a watch glass, and set it aside to cool to room temperature. Then cool the beaker in an ice/water bath until crystallization is complete. Collect the product by vacuum filtration [OP-16], and wash it on the filter [OP-26a] with cold acetone. Air-dry the product on the filter for a few minutes; then dry [OP-26b] it to constant mass.

Analysis.   Measure the mass and melting point [OP-33] of the thoroughly dried product. Weigh about 0.20 g of the product to the nearest milligram, and dissolve it in 25 mL of water in a 125-mL Erlenmeyer flask. Add 2 drops of phenolphthalein indicator, and titrate with a standardized ~0.2 M NaOH solution to the light pink end point. Calculate the equivalent weight of your unknown acid, and identify it by referring to Table 7 of Appendix VI. Write the structure of the product and a balanced equation for its formation, and give its systematic and common names.

Microscale

Reaction.   Dissolve 5.00 mmol of maleic anhydride in 3.0 mL of water in a 10-mL Erlenmeyer flask by heating the water just to boiling, but don't let any water boil away. Remove the flask from the heat source and immediately add 5.5 mmol of 40-mesh zinc, with swirling. Let the flask stand for 15 minutes, with magnetic stirring [OP-10] or occasional swirling. *Under the hood*, slowly add 1.0 mL of concentrated HCl, with stirring or swirling.

Separation.   When the zinc (or most of it) has dissolved, heat the mixture to boiling under the hood. Any white solid that formed during the reaction should dissolve. Rapidly filter [OP-15] the hot solution through a preheated filtering pipet into a small beaker. Rinse the filter with 0.5 mL of hot water, and collect the water in the beaker. Boil the filtrate gently under the hood until the solution becomes *just* cloudy at the boiling point. Cover the beaker with a watch glass, and set it aside to cool to room temperature. Then cool the beaker in an ice/water bath until crystallization is complete. Collect the product by vacuum filtration [OP-16], and wash it on the filter [OP-26a] with cold acetone. Air-dry the product on the filter for a few minutes; then dry [OP-26b] it to constant mass.

Analysis.   Measure the mass and melting point [OP-33] of the thoroughly dried product. Weigh about 0.10 g of the product to the nearest milligram, and dissolve it in 10 mL of water in a 25-mL Erlenmeyer flask. Add a drop of phenolphthalein indicator and a magnetic stir bar, and titrate with a standardized ~0.1 *M* NaOH solution to the light pink end point. Calculate the equivalent weight of your unknown acid, and identify it by referring to Table 7 of Appendix VI. Write the structure of the product and a balanced equation for its formation, and give its systematic and common names.

Waste Disposal: Unless your instructor directs otherwise, wash the filtrate down the drain.

Observe and Note: Record the exact concentration of the NaOH solution in your lab notebook.

Take Care! Avoid contact with maleic anhydride, and do not breathe its dust.

Observe and Note: What evidence is there that a reaction is occurring?

Take Care! Wear gloves, avoid contact with concentrated HCl, and do not breathe its vapors.

Waste Disposal: Unless your instructor directs otherwise, wash the filtrate down the drain.

Observe and Note: Record the exact concentration of the NaOH solution in your lab notebook.

Exercises

1. Estimate the amount of product that was lost in the filtrate, assuming that the volume of the reaction mixture was 5.0 mL (SS) or 1.0 mL (μS) when you collected the product by vacuum filtration. Compare this with the amount of product you would have lost if you had not boiled off most of the water. The solubility of the product is 6.8 g/100 mL at 20°C.
2. (a) What was wrong with the graduate student's idea (see the Scenario) that the reaction of maleic acid with zinc and aqueous HCl would yield

tetrahydrofuran? (b) The actual synthesis that you carried out involves two separate reaction steps. Write a balanced equation for each step.

3. Describe and explain the possible effect on your results of the following experimental errors or variations. (a) You used phthalic anhydride (1,2-benzenedioic anhydride) instead of maleic anhydride. (b) After filtering the hot solution in the separation step, you forgot to boil down the filtrate. (c) For the standard scale titration, you didn't record the concentration of the NaOH solution (which was 0.255 M), but assumed a concentration of exactly 0.2 M. (d) For the microscale titration, you didn't record the concentration of the NaOH solution (which was 0.127 M), but assumed a concentration of exactly 0.1 M.

4. (a) Calculate the atom economy and reaction efficiency of your synthesis. (b) Describe some green features of your synthesis, and any that aren't so green.

5. Following the format in Appendix V, construct a flow diagram for the synthesis you carried out in this experiment.

6. Propose structures for the products you would obtain by treating fumaric acid, cinnamic acid, and butynedioic acid with excess zinc and HCl. Write balanced equations for the reactions.

7. Suppose that 0.196 g of an unknown carboxylic acid is titrated using 19.3 mL of 0.196 M aqueous NaOH. What is the probable identity of the unknown if its melting point is 132±5°C? (Use Table 7 in Appendix VI.)

8. Sketch the ^{1}H NMR spectrum you would expect from the product of this experiment, giving peak areas, multiplicities, and approximate chemical shifts for all signals.

9. Write balanced equations for the reactions of maleic anhydride with water, cyclohexanol, aniline, and isoprene (2-methyl-1,3-butadiene).

Other Things You Can Do

(Starred items require your instructor's permission.)

*1. Record the infrared spectrum of the product, and compare it with the spectrum of the starting material in Figure 32.1 (Experiment 32). Interpret both spectra as completely as you can.

*2. After you predict the ^{1}H NMR spectrum you would expect from the product (see Exercise 8), record its spectrum in DMSO-d$_6$ or another suitable solvent and see how accurate your prediction was.

*3. Observe the relative hydrolysis rates of some esters in Minilab 37.

4. Starting with sources listed in the Bibliography, write a research paper about the manufacture and uses of maleic anhydride, maleic acid, and fumaric acid.

Preparation of the Insect Repellent *N,N*-Diethyl-*meta*-toluamide

Reactions of Carboxylic Acids. Preparation of Amides. Nucleophilic Acyl Substitution. Acid Chlorides. Infrared Spectrometry.

Operations

OP-7   Heating
OP-8   Cooling
OP-10   Mixing
OP-11   Addition of Reactants
OP-14   Trapping Gases
OP-18   Extraction
OP-19   Evaporation
OP-21   Column Chromatography
OP-24   Washing Liquids
OP-25   Drying Liquids
OP-37   Gas Chromatography
OP-39   Infrared Spectrometry
OP-40   Nuclear Magnetic Resonance Spectrometry (optional)

Before You Begin

1. Read the experiment, read or review the operations as necessary, and write an experimental plan.
2. Calculate the mass of 30 mmol (SS) or 3.0 mmol (μS) of *m*-toluic acid, the mass of 25.0 mmol (SS) or 2.50 mmol (μS) of diethylamine hydrochloride, and the theoretical yield of *N,N*-diethyl-*m*-toluamide.

Scenario

Skeeters 'n Such manufactures insect repellents such as *Skeedaddle,* whose main active ingredient is *N,N*-diethyl-*m*-toluamide, better known as deet. Its current process for the manufacture of deet requires the use of diethyl ether as a solvent and a 2:1 molar ratio of nucleophile (diethylamine) to substrate. To reduce production costs, Skeeters 'n Such wants your institute to develop a synthetic method that uses a cheaper and more environmentally friendly solvent, such as water, and a 1:1 or lower nucleophile:substrate ratio. Your supervisor thinks a procedural variation called the Schotten–Baumann reaction may accomplish both of these objectives but is not sure whether the product will be pure enough to meet specifications. Your assignment is to determine whether or not deet can be synthesized in at least 95% purity using the Schotten–Baumann procedure.

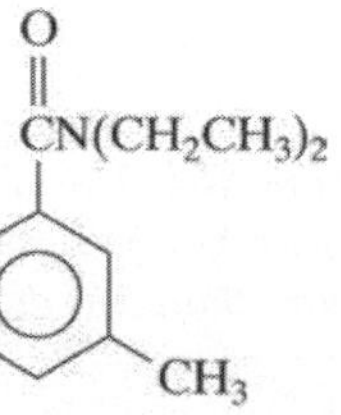

deet
(*N,N*-diethyl-*m*-toluamide)

a hungry mosquito

Applying Scientific Methodology

You should develop a working hypothesis, based on the Scenario, which will be tested when you analyze the product by gas chromatography and infrared spectrometry.

Chemical Mosquito Evasion

Is there anyone on Earth who hasn't cringed upon hearing the high-pitched whine of a hungry mosquito? Besides their capacity to torment us, these bloodthirsty insects have a well-earned reputation for spreading diseases, including malaria, yellow fever, West Nile disease, and viral encephalitis. Numerous methods of controlling mosquitoes have been developed, but the hardy creatures can withstand a variety of adverse conditions. Mosquitoes have been known to breed in the hot alkaline volcanic pools of Uganda, and even in a tank of hydrochloric acid in India! Because we aren't likely to eradicate mosquitoes from the Earth anytime soon, we must resign ourselves to living with them. This fate is made more tolerable by the availability of effective insect repellents. Among the best of these is deet, which is the major ingredient of most commercial mosquito repellents manufactured in North America.

Mosquito "repellents" don't really repel mosquitoes in the same way that a disagreeable odor might repel a human from its source. Instead, they appear to jam the insect's sensors so that it can't find its victim. Warm objects generate convection currents in the air around them; warm living objects also emit carbon dioxide, which alerts a mosquito to the presence of a blood source and starts it on its flight. This flight is initially random, but when the insect encounters a warm, moist stream of air, it moves toward the source, which is generally a living object. Unless the object takes rapid evasive action, the mosquito follows the convection current until it makes contact — unless it gets squashed first.

When you (the intended victim) are protected by an effective insect repellent, the mosquito still knows you're around but is unable to find you. This is because the repellent prevents the insect's moisture sensors from responding normally to the high humidity of your convection current. Ordinarily, when a mosquito passes from warm, moist air into drier air, its moisture sensors send fewer signals to its central nervous system, causing it to turn back into the air stream. By blocking these sensors, the repellent reduces the signal frequency and convinces the mosquito that it is heading into drier rather than moister air, so it turns away before landing. Individual variations in diet, skin chemistry, or other factors — such as the color of one's clothing (dark colors attract mosquitoes) — may help explain why some unlucky individuals are eaten alive by mosquitoes and others escape unscathed. For example, thiamine (Vitamin B_1) taken orally is excreted through the skin, where it acts as an insect repellent. On the other hand, lactic acid and many other chemicals that emanate from human skin attract mosquitoes.

The molecular features that make a compound a good insect repellent are not well understood at this time. Repellents occur in nearly every chemical family and exhibit a large variety of molecular shapes, as shown in Figure 46.1. A number of *N,N*-disubstituted amides similar to deet are represented, including the diethylamide of thujic acid, a constituent of the western red cedar that may be partly responsible for that tree's resistance to insect attack. Other effective repellents include esters such as dimethyl phthalate and diols such as 2-ethyl-1,3-hexanediol (also known as 6–12; see Experiment 40).

Scientists from the U.S. Department of Agriculture's research station have identified more than 340 different skin chemicals.

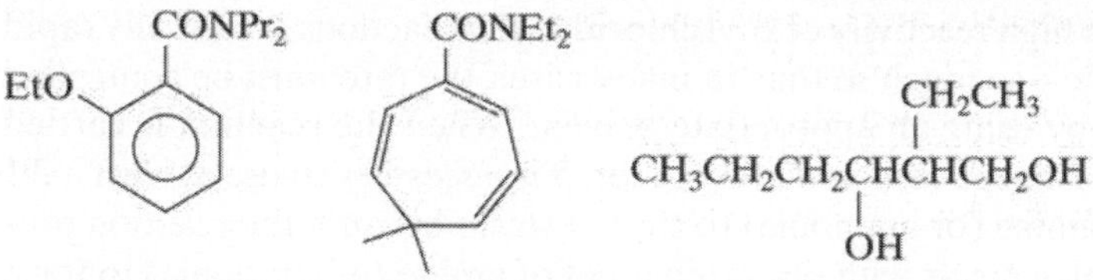

N,N-dipropyl-2-
ethoxybenzamide

thujic acid
diethylamide

2-ethyl-1,3-hexanediol

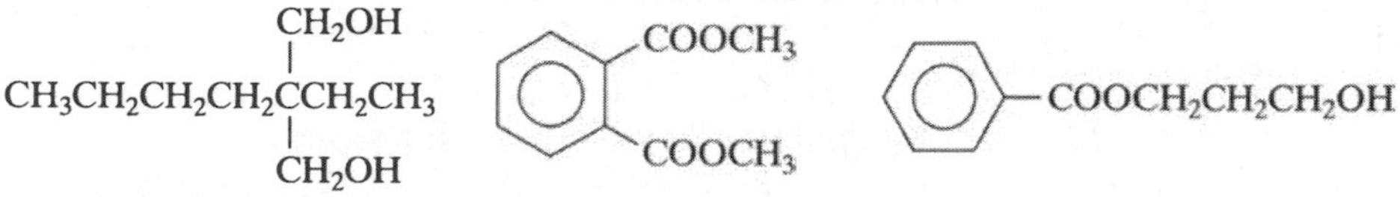

2-butyl-2-ethyl-1,3-
propanediol

dimethyl
phthalate

1,3-propanediol
monobenzoate

Et = CH_3CH_2- Pr = $CH_3CH_2CH_2-$

Figure 46.1 Some typical insect repellents

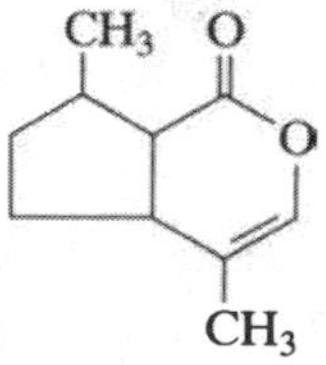

Recent lab tests with catnip oil, which contains two nepetalactone stereoisomers, have shown it to be 10 times more effective than deet as a mosquito repellent. Further tests are needed (perhaps with both mosquitoes and cats) to see whether the oil can be used safely and effectively by humans. When more is learned about the structural features that make a substance act as an insect repellent, it should be possible to develop even more effective and convenient repellents for long-term protection against insect bites.

nepetalactone

Understanding the Experiment

Amides are usually prepared by treating a carboxylic acid derivative with ammonia or with a primary or secondary amine. This is a nucleophilic acyl substitution reaction, in which ammonia or the amine acts as the nucleophile. Acid anhydrides and esters are sometimes used as the acid derivative, but acyl chlorides are the most useful for preparing the widest variety of amides.

General reactions for preparing amides

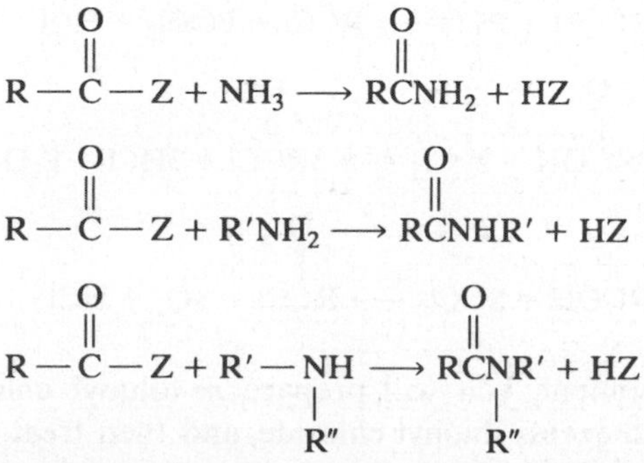

$$R-\overset{\overset{\text{O}}{\|}}{C}-Z + NH_3 \longrightarrow R\overset{\overset{\text{O}}{\|}}{C}NH_2 + HZ$$

$$R-\overset{\overset{\text{O}}{\|}}{C}-Z + R'NH_2 \longrightarrow R\overset{\overset{\text{O}}{\|}}{C}NHR' + HZ$$

$$R-\overset{\overset{\text{O}}{\|}}{C}-Z + R'-\underset{\underset{R''}{|}}{N}H \longrightarrow R\overset{\overset{\text{O}}{\|}}{C}N\underset{\underset{R''}{|}}{R'} + HZ$$

Z = Cl, OR, OCOR, etc.

Because of the high reactivity of acyl chlorides, the reactions are usually rapid and exothermic—so much so that, in many cases, the rate must be controlled by cooling or by using an appropriate solvent. When the reaction is carried out in an inert solvent such as diethyl ether, it is necessary to use at least a 2:1 mole ratio of amine (or ammonia) to the substrate because the reaction produces HCl, which reacts with one equivalent of amine (or ammonia) to form an ammonium salt. The salt is not nucleophilic, so it can't react with the acyl compound; it may also be difficult to separate from the product.

Key Concept: A nucleophile is usually basic enough to accept a proton from an acid. A protonated nucleophile, having donated a lone pair, is either a much weaker nucleophile or is not nucleophilic at all.

Example of reaction in inert solvent

$$\underset{\text{O}}{\overset{\parallel}{\text{R}}}\text{CCl} + 2\text{R}'\text{NH}_2 \longrightarrow \underset{\text{O}}{\overset{\parallel}{\text{R}}}\text{CNHR}' + \text{R}'\text{NH}_3{}^+\text{Cl}^-$$

The Schotten–Baumann reaction is a synthetic method that uses aqueous sodium hydroxide (or potassium hydroxide) as a solvent for the reactions of certain acyl chlorides. Some of the sodium hydroxide (NaOH) neutralizes the HCl produced during the reaction, making it unnecessary to add excess amine for that purpose. Some acyl chlorides, particularly low–molecular-weight aliphatic ones, hydrolyze rapidly in water to form carboxylic acids and thus are unsuitable candidates for the Schotten–Baumann reaction. However, aromatic and long-chain aliphatic acyl chlorides are nearly insoluble in water and therefore hydrolyze much more slowly. The small amount of acyl chloride lost by hydrolysis can be compensated for by using an excess of this reactant. The presence of aqueous NaOH in the reaction mixture also makes it possible to use an amine hydrochloride in place of the free amine, since the amine hydrochloride reacts with base to liberate the amine *in situ*. Because many amines are volatile, corrosive, and quite unpleasant to handle, the use of the comparatively well-behaved amine salt is a definite advantage.

Schotten-Baumann method for preparing amides

$$\underset{\text{O}}{\overset{\parallel}{\text{R}}}\text{CCl} + \text{R}'\text{NH}_2 + \text{NaOH} \longrightarrow$$

$$\underset{\text{O}}{\overset{\parallel}{\text{R}}}\text{CNHR}' + \text{NaCl} + \text{H}_2\text{O}$$

Reaction of an amine hydrochloride with a base

$$\text{RNH}_3{}^+\text{Cl}^- + \text{NaOH} \longrightarrow$$

$$\text{RNH}_2 + \text{NaCl} + \text{H}_2\text{O}$$

The acyl chlorides used for preparing amides are usually made from the corresponding carboxylic acids. Several reagents can be used for this transformation, each with its advantages and disadvantages. Thionyl chloride (SOCl_2) is usually the reagent of choice because its inorganic reaction products (HCl and SO_2) are gases that can easily be removed from the acyl chloride, which can thus be used for further reactions without purification.

Methods for preparing acyl chlorides

$$\underset{\text{O}}{\overset{\parallel}{\text{R}}}\text{COH} + \text{PCl}_5 \longrightarrow \underset{\text{O}}{\overset{\parallel}{\text{R}}}\text{CCl} + \text{POCl}_3 + \text{HCl}$$

$$3\underset{\text{O}}{\overset{\parallel}{\text{R}}}\text{COH} + 2\text{PCl}_3 \longrightarrow 3\underset{\text{O}}{\overset{\parallel}{\text{R}}}\text{CCl} + 3\text{HCl} + \text{P}_2\text{O}_3$$

$$\underset{\text{O}}{\overset{\parallel}{\text{R}}}\text{COH} + \text{SOCl}_2 \longrightarrow \underset{\text{O}}{\overset{\parallel}{\text{R}}}\text{CCl} + \text{SO}_2 + \text{HCl}$$

In this experiment, you will prepare *m*-toluoyl chloride by heating *m*-toluic acid with excess thionyl chloride, and then treat the acid chloride with diethylamine (from the hydrochloride) in aqueous NaOH to obtain

N,N-diethyl-*m*-toluamide. The excess thionyl chloride from the first step is used up by reacting with sodium hydroxide in the second. Because corrosive gases are released, you will need to carry out the reaction under a fume hood or with a gas trap to keep them out of the atmosphere. Since the acid chloride is relatively insoluble in the aqueous reaction mixture, efficient mixing is necessary to provide adequate contact between the phases. The detergent sodium lauryl sulfate helps disperse the acyl chloride into smaller droplets, increasing the area of contact between phases and thus increasing the reaction rate.

After the product has been isolated by extraction with diethyl ether and evaporation of the ether, it will be purified by column chromatography and then analyzed by gas chromatography to assess its purity. By comparing the infrared spectrum of your product with those of the starting materials in Figure 46.2, you should find evidence indicating whether or not the expected reaction has taken place.

When released into moist soil or water, thionyl chloride hydrolyzes to yield hydrochloric acid and sulfur dioxide, which are expected to be toxic to aquatic life. Diethylamine is not expected to be toxic to aquatic life. Diethyl ether is not considered toxic to aquatic organisms and does not persist for long in either air or water. Deet is slightly toxic to birds, fish, and aquatic invertebrates, but it has very low toxicity potential in mammals.

*A **Greener Way:** You can recover the diethyl ether by evaporating it under vacuum using a cold trap (see OP-16) and placing it in an appropriate waste container.*

Reactions and Properties

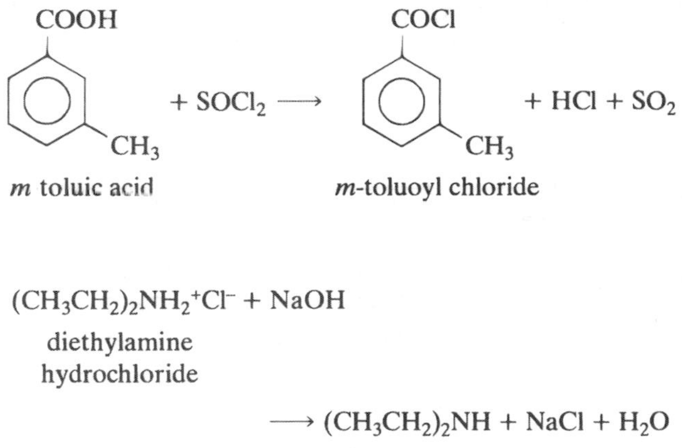

m toluic acid $+ SOCl_2 \longrightarrow$ *m*-toluoyl chloride $+ HCl + SO_2$

$(CH_3CH_2)_2NH_2{}^+Cl^- + NaOH$
   diethylamine
   hydrochloride

$\longrightarrow (CH_3CH_2)_2NH + NaCl + H_2O$
   diethylamine

$+ (CH_3CH_2)_2NH + NaOH \longrightarrow$

deet $+ NaCl + H_2O$

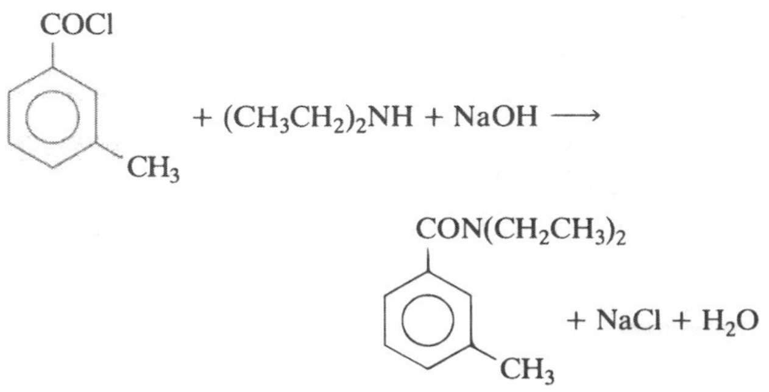

Synthesis of Dimedone and Measurement of Its Tautomeric Equilibrium Constant

EXPERIMENT 47

Reactions of α,β-Unsaturated Carbonyl Compounds. Preparation of Dicarbonyl Compounds. Nucleophilic Addition to Carbon–Carbon Double Bonds. Condensation Reactions. Decarboxylation. Reaction Equilibria. NMR Spectrometry.

Operations

OP-7   Heating
OP-10   Mixing
OP-13   Excluding Air from Reaction Mixtures
OP-16   Vacuum Filtration
OP-19   Evaporation
OP-26   Washing and Drying Solids
OP-28   Recrystallization
OP-33   Melting Point
OP-40   Nuclear Magnetic Resonance Spectrometry

Before You Begin

1. Read the experiment, read or review the operations as necessary, and write an experimental plan.
2. Calculate the mass and volume of 25.0 mmol (SS) or 5.00 mmol (μS) of dimethyl malonate, and the theoretical yield of dimedone.

Scenario

Harry Lingo, a punctilious chemistry editor for the Fulcourt Press, is faced with the dilemma of how to deal with compounds that exist in two tautomeric forms. In a soon-to-be published encyclopedia of organic compounds, he wants to list such a compound under the name corresponding to the major species present. For example, acetylacetone, which goes by the IUPAC name 2,4-pentanedione, contains four times more enol than keto tautomer, so he plans to list this compound under the name 4-hydroxy-3-penten-2-one.

$$
\underset{\text{20\% keto}}{CH_3CCH_2CCH_3} \overset{O\quad O}{\underset{}{\rightleftharpoons}} \underset{\text{80\% enol}}{CH_3CCH=CCH_3}
$$

acetylacetone

The organic compound known by the common name dimedone is represented as a β-diketone in most textbooks of organic chemistry. But many β-diketones contain a substantial amount of enolic tautomer, so Mr. Lingo has asked your institute for help in determining the most appropriate structure and name for dimedone. Your assignment is to prepare dimedone, measure its tautomeric equilibrium constant to determine whether the predominant species present is the β-diketone or the enolic ketone, and give this species an appropriate IUPAC name.

Applying Scientific Methodology

Your working hypothesis should include an "educated guess" about the structure of dimedone. You will test your hypothesis by analyzing its ^{1}H NMR spectrum.

Tautomers and Life

Enols have long been known as unstable intermediates in reactions involving carbonyl compounds, such as the bromination of acetone. Although acetone exists overwhelmingly in the keto form, it is the minute amount of the enolic form present that actually reacts with bromine under acidic conditions. Other enols are considerably more stable than that of acetone. For example, ethyl 3-oxobutanoate (ethyl acetoacetate) contains about 7.5% enol at equilibrium, and 2,4-pentanedione (acetylacetone) contains about 80% enol. Certain natural compounds—such as vitamin C, an enediol—exist almost entirely in the enolic form.

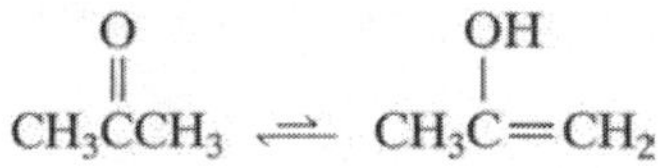

The Kekulé structures of phenols are enol-like, suggesting that some phenols may exist in keto forms as well. For example, phlorglucinol (1,3,5-trihydroxybenzene) forms carbonyl-type derivatives with hydroxylamine and similar derivatizing agents, which indicates that its phenolic form may exist in equilibrium with a triketone.

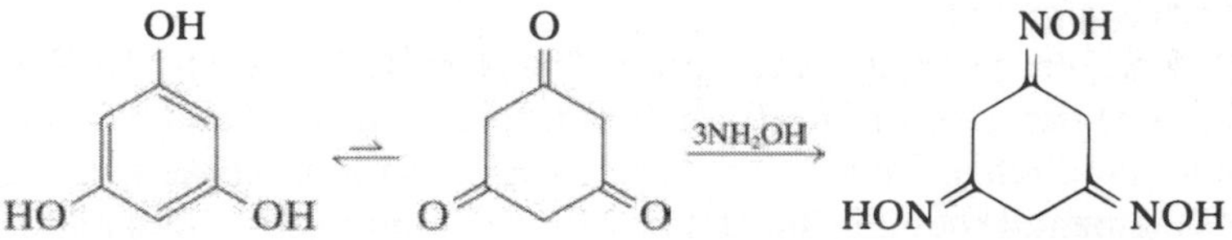

Keto-enol equilibrium for dimedone

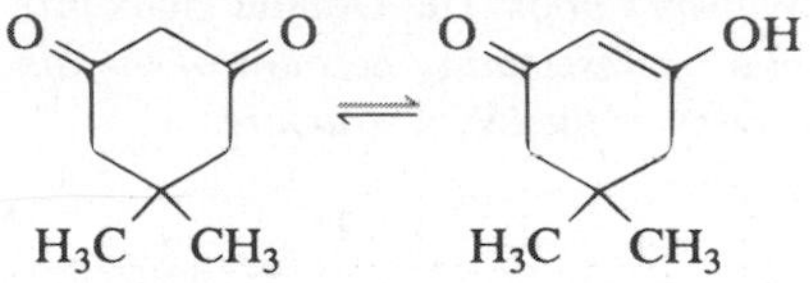

β-diketone   enolic ketone

~100% keto   0.00025% enol

acetone

Key Concept: The enolic form of a β-dicarbonyl compound is stabilized by conjugation of its C=C bond with a carbonyl group and by hydrogen bonding between the enolic OH and the carbonyl oxygen.

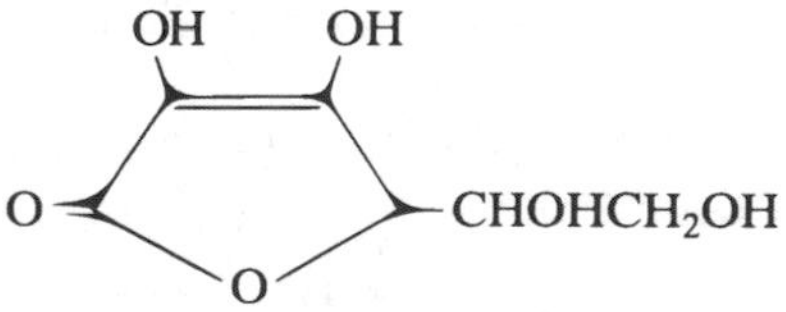

vitamin C
(ascorbic acid)

phlorglucinol   phlorglucinol oxime

A molecule's preference for one of several possible tautomeric structures might appear to be a matter of interest only to a few chemists, but in fact it plays a crucial role in living systems. Ordinarily, the keto form of a phenolic compound is the less stable tautomer by far because its formation is accompanied by a loss of resonance energy. In the early 1950s, however, chemists discovered that certain biological amines (bases) such as guanine and thymine exist mainly in the keto forms at the pH of physiological systems.

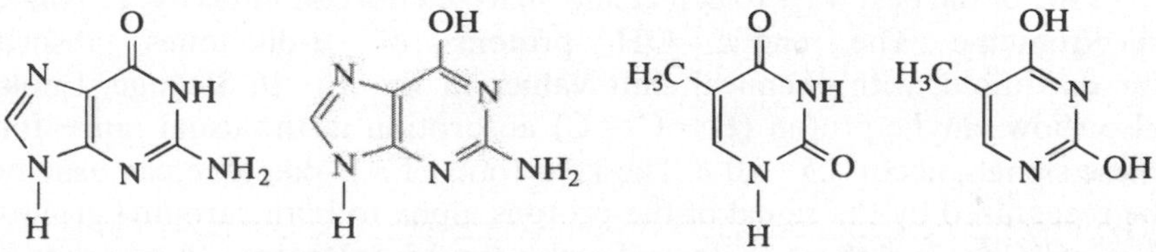

keto   enol   keto   enol

guanine   thymine

Watson's book The Double Helix *provides a fascinating account of the discovery of the DNA structure.*

This discovery provided Francis Crick and James D. Watson with the key to the structure of DNA, and thus to the genetic code. The four bases that are attached to the polyester backbone of a nucleic acid molecule—guanine, thymine, adenine, and cytosine—are responsible for both the transmission of genetic traits (by DNA) and the synthesis of proteins (by RNA) in living beings. Only the keto forms of guanine and thymine allow for the formation of adenine–thymine and guanine–cytosine base pairs, and such base pairing is essential for nucleic acid molecules to function. If these two bases existed only in enolic forms rather than keto forms, life as we know it might be impossible!

Understanding the Experiment

In this experiment, you will synthesize dimedone starting with the α,β-unsaturated ketone 4-methyl-3-penten-2-one, commonly known as mesityl oxide. This synthesis involves four distinct reactions that take place in sequence (see "Reactions and Properties"). The first reaction is a *Michael addition* of dimethyl malonate to mesityl oxide. Combining sodium methoxide with dimethyl malonate generates an enolate ion that undergoes nucleophilic addition to the carbon–carbon double bond of mesityl oxide, yielding a keto diester (**1**). In the presence of sodium methoxide, the methyl group alpha to the keto carbonyl group loses a proton, forming another enolate ion that attacks the carbonyl carbon of one of the ester functions and displaces its methoxyl group. The result of this Claisen-type *cyclization* reaction is a diketo ester (**2**) with a six-membered ring. Both of these reactions occur spontaneously in the same reaction mixture. Subsequent *hydrolysis* of the ester yields a carboxylic acid that, when heated, undergoes *decarboxylation* to form dimedone.

A literature procedure in *Organic Syntheses* [Bibliography, B20] for the synthesis of dimedone requires the *in situ* preparation of sodium ethoxide by adding sodium metal to absolute ethanol. Because any operation that involves elemental sodium can be hazardous, commercial sodium methoxide in methanol will be used instead. The enolate ion of dimethyl malonate, $[CH(COOCH_3)_2]^-$, forms immediately when sodium methoxide is added to dimethyl malonate. This species reacts rapidly and exothermically with mesityl oxide, which should therefore be added slowly to prevent side reactions. The Michael addition and the subsequent cyclization reaction should go virtually to completion during a 1-hour reflux period. After this reaction you will evaporate most of the methanol, hydrolyze the cyclic ester with 3 M NaOH, and acidify the solution to form the carboxylic acid, which loses carbon dioxide on heating. You will then isolate the resulting dimedone by vacuum filtration and recrystallize it from aqueous acetone.

A Greener Way: You can recover the methanol by evaporating it under vacuum using a cold trap.

One of the best ways to detect and analyze enol content is by ^{1}H NMR spectrometry. The enolic OH protons of β-diketones absorb far downfield, with chemical shift values in the 10–16 δ range. Enols also show vinylic proton (H—C=C) absorption in the usual range for these signals, about 4.5–6.0 δ. The keto form of a β-diketone can usually be recognized by the signal of the protons alpha to both carbonyl groups $[H—C(C=O)_2]$; these protons absorb near 3.5 δ. Because there are two such protons for every enolic vinyl proton in the enolic form of dimedone, the equilibrium constant for dimedone's keto–enol equilibrium can be determined from the integrated areas of these two signals using the following formula:

$$K = \frac{[\text{enol}]}{[\text{keto}]} = \frac{2 \times \text{area of the H}-\text{C}=\text{C signal}}{\text{area of the H}-\text{C(C}=\text{O})_2 \text{ signal}}$$

Enols are stabilized by hydrogen-bonding interactions with other polar species, so the equilibrium constant might vary depending on the solvent used. The "Other Things You Can Do" section describes some additional studies you can carry out with your product.

Methanol is slightly toxic to aquatic organisms but biodegrades readily in water and soil. Mesityl oxide is not expected to be toxic to aquatic life. Deuterochloroform, like chloroform, is toxic to aquatic organisms and should not be released into the environment. Although acetone is slightly toxic to aquatic life, it does not bioaccumulate and is not considered a serious environmental contaminant.

Reactions and Properties

Note: All of the cyclohexanedione derivatives shown can also be represented by enolic forms.

Table 47.1 Physical properties

	mol wt	mp	bp	d
mesityl oxide	98.2	−52	129	0.858
dimethyl malonate	132.1	−62	181	1.154
sodium methoxide	54.0			
methanol	32.0	−94	65	0.791
dimedone	140.2	151		

Note: mp and bp are in °C; density is in g/mL. A 25% solution of sodium methoxide in methanol has a density of 0.945 g/mL.

Other Things You Can Do

(Starred items require your instructor's permission.)

*1. Record ^{1}H NMR spectra of dimedone in solvents other than deuterochloroform, such as DMSO-d_6, and compare the keto–enol equilibrium constants for the different solvents. Try to explain any differences.

*2. Record the infrared spectrum [OP-39] of dimedone using a KBr disc or Nujol mull and then using a chloroform solution. Look for absorption bands arising from the enolic form and the diketo form in both spectra, and compare the relative amounts of enol. Try to explain any differences.

*3. Use your product to prepare dimedone derivatives of benzaldehyde as described in Minilab 39.

4. Like the synthesis of dimedone from mesityl oxide, a Robinson annulation sequence involves a Michael addition followed by a ring-forming condensation reaction. Starting with sources listed in the Bibliography, write a research paper about the Robinson annulation, describing some of its applications in the synthesis of terpenoids and steroids.

Preparation of Para Red and Related Azo Dyes

Reactions of Amines. Reactions of Diazonium Salts. Preparation of Azo Compounds. Electrophilic Aromatic Substitution.

Operations

OP-8   Cooling
OP-10 Mixing
OP-16 Vacuum Filtration
OP-26 Washing and Drying Solids

Before You Begin

1. Read the experiment, read or review the operations as necessary, and write an experimental plan.
2. Calculate the mass of 10.0 mmol (SS) or 2.00 mmol (μS) of *p*-nitroaniline, the mass of 10.0 mmol (SS) or 2.00 mmol (μS) of 2-naphthol, and the theoretical yield of Para Red. Be prepared to calculate the mass of 10.0 mmol (SS) or 2.00 mmol (μS) of any other coupling component or diazo component, and the theoretical yield of any other azo dye.

Scenario

The despotic king of the somewhat backward kingdom of Erewhon has just been overthrown in a coup led by Sergeant Obmar, a soldier of fortune from California. In the sergeant's honor, the provisional government has authorized a new flag, consisting of a navel orange on a field of blue. But the first flags they ordered were sent back because the orange was the wrong color—it looked more like a pink grapefruit. Acting president Gib Retsim has asked your institute to come up with a dye that will produce just the right shade of orange. Your supervisor knows how to make "American Flag Red," an orange-red dye the color of the stripes in the U.S. flag, and thinks that by tinkering with its molecular structure, your project team should be able to come up with a suitable orange dye for the new flag.

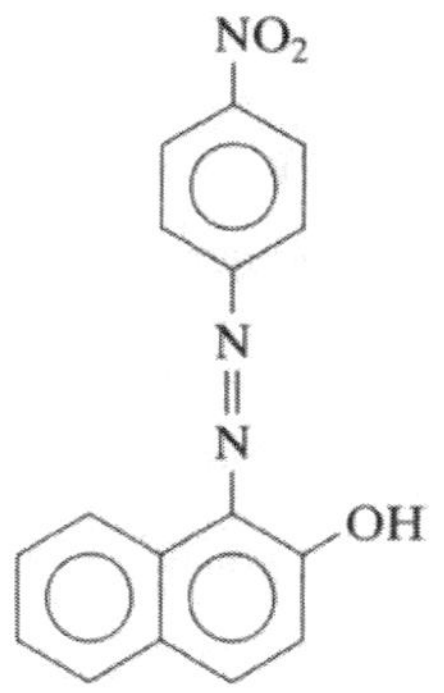

"American Flag Red"
(Para Red)

Applying Scientific Methodology

Based on the information in the experiment, you should develop a hypothesis regarding a pair of reactants from Table 48.1 that you think might produce a dye the color of a navel orange. Alternatively, members of your project group can get together and select a different reactant pair for each member to work on.

Dyes and Serendipity

In the Persian fairy tale *The Three Princes of Serendip,* the title characters were forever discovering things they weren't looking for at the time. Thus,

B. *Dyeing a Cloth by the Ingrain Process*

  Standard Scale and Microscale

Mix 40 mL (SS) or 8 mL (μS) of water into coupling component solution **c2**, and soak a piece of clean, white cloth in it for 2–3 minutes. Remove the cloth with forceps or a pair of stirring rods, blot it between paper towels to remove most of the water, and hang it up to dry. Mix 40 mL (SS) or 8 mL (μS) of ice-cold water into diazonium salt solution **d2**, insert the dry cloth, and agitate the solution with a stirring rod long enough to dye the cloth uniformly. If your coupling component was an aromatic amine, dip the cloth briefly into a small amount of 3 *M* sodium carbonate solution. Remove the cloth and dry it as before. If there is a navel orange handy, compare its color to that of your dyed cloth. Prepare a table describing the colors of the cloths dyed by the azo dyes prepared by your group or lab section.

Stop and Think: What is happening on the cloth to account for your observations?

Exercises

1. Discuss the effects of structural features (such as substituents and chromophore size) on the colors of the dyes prepared by your group.
2. Write a mechanism for the coupling reaction of *p*-nitrobenzenediazonium chloride with 2-naphthol.
3. Describe and explain the possible effect on your results of the following experimental errors or variations. (a) You forgot to cool the solution of your diazo component before adding aqueous sodium nitrite. (b) Your coupling component was a phenol, but you followed the procedure in *2b* to couple it. (c) You tried to dye a cloth by dipping it into a solution of 2-naphthol in 1 *M* NaOH, drying it, and then dipping it into a solution of aniline in 1 *M* HCl.
4. (a) Calculate the atom economy and reaction efficiency of your synthesis of Para Red. (b) Describe some green features of your synthesis, and any that aren't so green.
5. Following the format in Appendix V, construct a flow diagram for your synthesis of Para Red in part **A**.
6. Mel A. Droyt was trying to prepare *p*-dimethylaminoazobenzene (Butter Yellow) by coupling 2.0 mmol of *N,N*-dimethylaniline with an equimolar amount of aniline. He first added 4.0 mL of 1 *M* sodium nitrite to the diazo component. Mixing this solution with the coupling component yielded some Butter Yellow, along with a pale yellow oil. (a) What did he do wrong, and what was the yellow oil? (b) Write a balanced equation for its formation.
7. Bea Wilder was attempting to prepare chrysoidine by coupling 2.0 mmol of *m*-phenylenediamine with 2.0 mmol of aniline. To her surprise, she had to add 4.0 mL of 1 *M* sodium nitrite in the diazotization step before the solution turned starch–iodide paper blue. After pouring the diazonium salt solution into the solution of the other component, she recovered a dark-colored precipitate that was not chrysoidine. The following

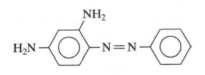

chrysoidine

day, the filtrate contained another precipitate that she identified as resorcinol. (a) What did she do wrong, and what was the structure of the azo dye she synthesized? (b) Write balanced equations for its synthesis and for the reaction that formed resorcinol.

8. Why is it important to keep the temperature low during diazotization and coupling? Give the structure of the product that might form if the reaction mixture is heated during the diazotization of p-nitroaniline, and write an equation for its formation.

9. Explain why coupling of p-nitrobenzenediazonium chloride occurs mainly *para* to the $-N(CH_3)_2$ group of N,N-dimethylaniline but *ortho* to the $-OH$ group of 2-naphthol.

Other Things You Can Do

(Starred items require your instructor's permission.)

*1. Use your dye for direct dyeing by suspending 0.5 g of the dye in 100 mL of hot water and acidifying the mixture with a few drops of concentrated sulfuric acid. Immerse pieces of wool or cotton cloth in the mixture for 5 minutes or more. Remove the cloth, rinse it with water, and let it dry. Adjusting the pH of the dyeing mixture with dilute HCl or NaOH may give better results in some cases. All quantities may be divided by 5 for a microscale lab.

Take Care! Wear gloves, and avoid contact with H_2SO_4.

*2. Use your dye for disperse dyeing by suspending 0.5 g of the dye in 100 mL of hot water and stirring in 0.1 g of biphenyl (the carrier) and 2–3 drops of liquid detergent. Then immerse a piece of cloth made of Dacron or another polyester in the mixture, and heat the solution on a steam bath or boiling-water bath for 15–20 minutes. Remove the cloth and let it dry. Quantities may be divided by 5 for a microscale lab; use one small drop of the liquid detergent.

*3. Dissolve 3–5 mg of an azo dye in 10 mL of 95% ethanol. If any solid remains undissolved, filter the solution. Record the ultraviolet–visible spectrum [OP-41] of the dye over the tungsten lamp range (~800–350 nm), diluting the solution with more ethanol if necessary. Compare the λ_{max} values of different dyes, and try to explain some of the differences you observe. Note that such comparisons are meaningful only if the bands you are comparing arise from the same kind of electronic transition; such bands should be similar in appearance and intensity.

*4. In Minilab 40, see what happens when you diazotize anthranilic acid and heat the resulting solution.

5. Starting with sources listed in the Bibliography, write a research paper about the chemistry and uses of food colorings. Outline syntheses for some azo dyes that have been used as food colorings, and discuss the controversy surrounding such dyes as FD&C Red No. 2.

precipitate to filter. Explain what went wrong, and write an equation for the reaction that caused the problem. (b) How could she have recovered the product and salvaged the experiment?

3. Describe and explain the possible effect (if any) on your results of the following experimental errors or variations. (a) The phthalimide wasn't dried completely and was allowed to sit for a week before it was used in the reaction. (b) The laundry bleach came from an old bottle, and its NaOCl concentration was about 4%. (c) The lab assistant put out a bottle of Clorox 2 Ultra bleach rather than standard Clorox (check the labels at a local store). (d) You used 3.0 M acetic acid rather than glacial acetic acid, and there was no foaming after you added the specified amount of it.

4. (a) Calculate the atom economy and reaction efficiency of your synthesis. (b) Describe some green features of your synthesis, and any that aren't so green.

5. Following the format in Appendix V, construct a flow diagram for this experiment (excluding the preparation of phthalimide).

6. (a) When 35 mg of the product from this experiment was mixed with 0.46 g of camphor, the melting point of the mixture was found to be 157°C. Calculate the approximate molecular weight of the product if the melting point of pure camphor is 179°C and its freezing-point depression constant (K_f) is 40°C $\cdot$ kg $\cdot$ mol^{-1}. (b) Show how the molecular formula $C_7H_7NO_2$ can be derived using this result and data from the Scenario.

7. When 9-fluorenone hydrazone is treated with sodium nitrite in aqueous sulfuric acid, it rearranges to form phenanthridone. Propose a detailed mechanism that explains this reaction, showing the transition state for the rearrangement step. (*Hint*: What happens to amino groups in an acidified solution of sodium nitrite?)

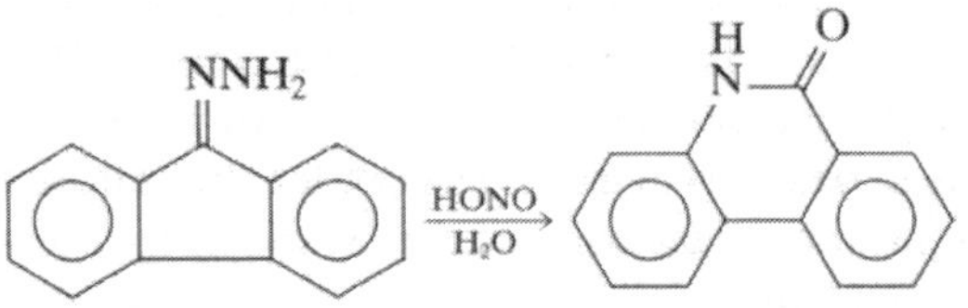

9-fluorenone   phenanthridone
hydrazone

8. (a) When a certain German chemist warmed a solution of N-bromoacetamide in base, he recognized an unmistakable pungent odor that slowly faded and was replaced by the strong ammonia-like odor of an escaping gas. What were the two substances that his nose told him were there? Write a mechanism explaining the formation of both. (b) Who was the chemist, and what reaction had he discovered?

Other Things You Can Do

(Starred items require your instructor's permission.)

*1. Record the infrared spectrum [OP-39] of the product, and use it to assist you in identifying the product. Compare its spectrum with that of phthalimide in Figure 49.2, and interpret it as completely as you can.

*2. Carry out a molecular rearrangement of benzophenone oxime as described in Minilab 41.

3. Starting with sources listed in the Bibliography, write a research paper about the use of potassium phthalimide in the synthesis of amines and amino acids. Include a discussion of the phthalimidomalonic ester method and the Gabriel synthesis, and illustrate synthetic routes to specific products using each method.

EXPERIMENT **50**

Identification
of an Unknown Amine

Reactions of Amines. Infrared Spectrometry. Qualitative Analysis.

Operations

OP-26 Washing and Drying Solids
OP-28 Recrystallization
OP-30 Simple Distillation
OP-33 Melting Point
OP-34 Boiling Point
OP-39 Infrared Spectrometry

Before You Begin

1. Read the experiment, read or review the operations as necessary, and write an experimental plan.
2. Read or review Part IV, "Qualitative Organic Analysis," except for the sections entitled "Directions."

Scenario

The city health department of Arkham, Massachusetts, has been deluged with reports of bad-tasting city water, which may have been responsible for several reported cases of illness. Arkham's municipal water supply comes from the Miskatonic River, which winds through the town. A routine water analysis indicates the presence of a basic, nitrogen-containing compound, apparently an amine. The three most likely sources of the pollution, all up-stream of the town, are:

- A dye factory that uses aniline and other aromatic amines as raw materials
- A chemical specialties company that synthesizes aliphatic amines for the manufacture of surfactants, corrosion inhibitors, and antioxidants
- An abandoned graveyard on Hangman's Hill, overlooking the river

With some help from the alchemy faculty at nearby Miskatonic University, health department personnel have obtained a sample of the unknown amine, and the Arkham town council has now asked your institute for help in identifying the source of this water contaminant. Your assignment is to identify the unknown amine and determine its probable source.

Applying Scientific Methodology

As you carry out the experiment, you should develop provisional hypothe-ses about the nature and identity of the unknown amine, which you will test—and perhaps reject or revise—as you gather additional experimental evidence. Your conclusion should, if possible, be consistent with all of the experimental evidence you obtain. Once you have identified the unknown, you should be able to deduce its probable source.

Biological Amines

Certain families of organic compounds, such as aldehydes and esters, tend to be associated with the pleasant aromas of fruits and perfumes. Amines, on the other hand, are more often associated with the unpleasant smells of body wastes, not-so-fresh fish, and decaying flesh. The amine family includes deadly poisons such as coniine, a component of the poison hemlock that killed Socrates, and dangerous drugs such as LSD, heroin, and methamphetamine. But the same family also includes some highly beneficial members that we couldn't get along without.

Some amines are produced by the enzyme-catalyzed breakdown of proteins and their component amino acids in decaying plant or animal material. For example, bacteria containing the enzymes called amino acid decarboxylases bring about the degradation of the amino acids ornithine and lysine to putrescine (1,4-butanediamine) and cadaverine (1,5-pentanediamine), respectively.

$$\underset{\text{ornithine}}{^+\!H_3NCH_2CH_2CH_2\underset{\underset{NH_2}{|}}{CH}CO^-} \xrightarrow[-CO_2]{\text{enzyme}} \underset{\text{putrescine}}{H_2NCH_2CH_2CH_2CH_2NH_2}$$

$$\underset{\text{lysine}}{^+\!H_3NCH_2CH_2CH_2CH_2\underset{\underset{NH_2}{|}}{CH}CO^-} \xrightarrow[-CO_2]{\text{enzyme}} \underset{\text{cadaverine}}{H_2NCH_2CH_2CH_2CH_2CH_2NH_2}$$

As their common names suggest, these amines are responsible for much of the objectionable odor of decaying flesh. The next homolog in this family of diamines, 1,6-hexanediamine, is more often associated with hosiery, camping gear, and outdoor clothing. Along with hexanedioic acid (adipic acid), it is a monomer used in the preparation of nylon 6,6, a commercially important polyamide.

$$n\underset{\text{1,6-hexanediamine}}{H_2NCH_2CH_2CH_2CH_2CH_2CH_2NH_2} + n\underset{\text{hexanedioic acid}}{HO\overset{\overset{O}{\|}}{C}CH_2CH_2CH_2CH_2\overset{\overset{O}{\|}}{C}OH} \xrightarrow[-H_2O]{\Delta}$$

$$-\underset{\text{nylon 6,6}}{[HNCH_2CH_2CH_2CH_2CH_2CH_2NH - \overset{\overset{O}{\|}}{C}CH_2CH_2CH_2CH_2\overset{\overset{O}{\|}}{C}]_n} -$$

The family of amines called *phenethylamines,* whose parent compound is 2-phenylethylamine ($C_6H_5CH_2CH_2NH_2$), has many biologically active members, including body regulators such as epinephrine (adrenaline), useful drugs such as pseudoephedrine, and dangerous street drugs such as

IR wave numbers are not infallible indicators of molecular structure, so it may be necessary later to reconsider some of the compounds that you eliminated from your short list.

Preparation of a Derivative. Refer to the section "Preparation of Derivatives" in Part IV for procedures. Select the derivative that should best differentiate the compounds on your short list. If your amine is primary or secondary, you can prepare one or more of the following derivatives for which reagents are available: benzamide (derivative D-8), *p*-toluenesulfonamide (D-9), phenylthiourea (D-10), or picrate (D-12). If your amine is tertiary, you can prepare a methiodide (D-11) or picrate (D-12). Purify the derivative by recrystallization [OP-28] as described in the appropriate procedure, dry [OP-26b] it thoroughly, and measure its melting point [OP-33]. Deduce the identity of your unknown from the derivative melting point and all other relevant evidence, and justify your conclusion based on the evidence. Then deduce the probable source of the amine based on information given in this experiment.

Waste Disposal: Dispose of all wastes as directed by your instructor. Return any unused unknown to your instructor in its original vial.

Exercises

1. Interpret the infrared spectrum you obtained as completely as you can.
2. (a) Write balanced equations for the reactions involved in all of the classification tests for which you obtained a positive result. (b) Write balanced equations for the reaction(s) involved in your derivative preparation(s).
3. Describe and explain the possible effect on your results of the following experimental errors or variations. (a) When you carried out Hinsberg's test, you inadvertently used 3 *M* HCl in place of 3 *M* NaOH. (b) You mistakenly classified a tertiary amine as secondary and tried to prepare a *p*-toluenesulfonate derivative. (c) While performing the basicity test on a water-insoluble unknown, you inadvertently used a sodium acetate solution rather than the acetate–acetic acid buffer.
4. Calculate the atom economy of your derivative preparation.
5. Construct a flow diagram showing the process you followed to identify your unknown.
6. The basicity test differentiates aromatic and aliphatic amines based on their solubility in a pH 5.5 buffer. Given that K_b for aniline is 4.2×10^{-10} and K_b for cyclohexylamine is 5.0×10^{-4}, calculate the ratio of amine salt to dissolved amine for both compounds in such a buffer, and explain the difference in their solubility behavior.
7. An unknown liquid boiling around $185 \pm 5°C$ dissolves in 5% HCl but is insoluble in water and in a pH 5.5 buffer. Shaking the unknown with *p*-toluenesulfonyl chloride in aqueous NaOH produces a clear solution that, when acidified, yields a white precipitate. Assuming that the unknown is listed in Appendix VI, give its name and draw its structure.
8. An unknown liquid boiling around $185 \pm 5°C$ dissolves in 5% HCl and in a pH 5.5 buffer but is insoluble in water. Shaking the unknown with *p*-toluenesulfonyl chloride in aqueous NaOH produces a white precipitate that doesn't dissolve in dilute HCl. Assuming that the unknown is listed in Appendix VI, give its name and draw its structure.

9. Write mechanisms for the following reactions, which are used in chemical tests and derivative preparations: (a) the reaction of aniline with benzoyl chloride in aqueous NaOH; (b) the formation of the methiodide of triethylamine; (c) the reaction of diethylamine with benzenesulfonyl chloride in aqueous NaOH.

Other Things You Can Do

(Starred items require your instructor's permission.)

*1. Obtain and interpret an ^{1}H or ^{13}C NMR spectrum [OP-40] of your unknown.

2. Starting with sources listed in the Bibliography, write a research paper describing the structures, biological functions, and therapeutic uses (if any) of some phenethylamines.

Table 52.1 Nucleophilic constants for various nucleophiles

Nucleophile	n
CH_3OH	0.00
F^-	2.7
Cl^-	4.37
pyridine	5.23
NH_3	5.50
aniline	5.70
Br^-	5.79
CH_3O^-	6.29
$(CH_3CH_2)_3N$	6.66
$(CH_3CH_2)_2NH$	7.0
pyrrolidine	7.23
piperidine	7.30
I^-	7.42

Note: n values are measured relative to methanol, with methyl iodide as the substrate.

is called the *Swain-Scott equation,* relates a reaction rate to the strength of the nucleophile (n) and the sensitivity of the substrate to nucleophilic substitution (s).

$$\log\frac{k}{k_0} = ns \tag{1}$$

It has been applied widely to nucleophilic substitution reactions with aliphatic substrates, and some values of the nucleophilic constant n for reactions of various nucleophiles with methyl iodide are given in Table 52.1.

Attempts to use such correlations for S_NAr reactions have met with less success because changing the substrate or the solvent often changes the order of nucleophilic strength. However, an equation similar to Equation **1** can be useful in comparing the nucleophilic strengths of various reactants with reference to the same class of substrates. For this experiment, we define a nucleophilic constant (n_{Ar}) for the S_NAr reaction as follows:

$$n_{Ar} = \frac{1}{s}\log\frac{k}{k_0} \tag{2}$$

The reaction of 2,4-dinitrochlorobenzene with ammonia in absolute ethanol, for which the rate constant (k_0) is 4.0×10^{-6} L mol^{-1} s^{-1} at 25°C, is used as the reference reaction for Equation **2**. For this substrate and nucleophile, s is 1 and n_{Ar} is zero by definition. The rate constant k is for a reaction involving the nucleophile whose n_{Ar} value is being determined.

Understanding the Experiment

In this experiment, you and your coworkers will measure the rates of the reactions of piperidine and morpholine with 2,4-dinitrochlorobenzene and use the rate constants to calculate their nucleophilic constants, as defined by Equation **2**. The reaction of 2,4-dinitrochlorobenzene with an amine is second order in both substrate and nucleophile, and follows the general rate equation

$$\frac{dx}{dt} = k(S_0 - x)(N_0 - 2x) \tag{3}$$

where x is the concentration of the product at time t, and S_0 and N_0 are the initial concentrations of substrate and nucleophile, respectively. The computations can be simplified considerably if the experiment is carried out with the initial concentration of nucleophile being just twice that of 2,4-dinitrochlorobenzene. Equation **3** then becomes $dx/dt = 2k(S_0 - x)^2$, and the integrated rate equation is

$$\frac{1}{(S_0 - x)} = 2kt + \frac{1}{S_0} \tag{4}$$

By measuring the concentration of the product, x, at regular intervals during the reaction, you can calculate the term on the left side of Equation **4**. Graphing this expression versus time should then yield a straight line with slope $2k$.

The products of the S_NAr reactions are yellow–orange and absorb strongly in the visible region around 380 nm, so the concentration of each product will be determined indirectly by measuring the absorbance of 380-nm light by aliquots that are removed from the reaction mixture at various times. Because the absorbances are determined at a single wavelength, you can use a nonrecording spectrophotometer (colorimeter). Each aliquot must first be *quenched* by adding dilute acid to stop the reaction; this is done so that the product concentration will remain constant until you are ready to take the absorbance readings. The concentration term in Equation 4, $S_0 - x$, is proportional to $A_\infty - A$, where A_∞ is the absorbance when the reaction is 100% complete, and A is the absorbance at time t. Therefore,

$$\frac{1}{(S_0 - x)} = \frac{q}{(A_\infty - A)} \tag{5}$$

where q is a proportionality constant. The "infinity" value of the absorbance A_∞ will be obtained by warming the reaction mixture to complete the reaction and measuring the absorbance of the resulting solution. The value of q can then be calculated from the relationship $q = A_\infty / S_0$. Note that S_0 is the initial substrate concentration in the *reaction mixture,* not in the stock solution you will use to prepare the reaction mixtures.

Because of their different reaction rates, the amines will be used in different initial concentrations so that both reactions will be about half complete after 30 minutes. The absorbance values of the quenched products are too high to measure, so you will have to dilute these solutions to obtain readings in a convenient range.

Morpholine and piperidine may be harmful to aquatic life; 2,4-dinitrochlorobenzene may also be harmful to aquatic organisms.

Reaction and Properties

2,4-dinitrochlorobenzene   piperidine ($Y = CH_2$) or morpholine ($Y = O$)   dinitrophenylated amine

The extra mole of amine combines with the HCl liberated during the reaction.

Table 52.2 Physical properties

	mol wt	mp	bp	d
2,4-dinitrochlorobenzene	202.6	53	315	
morpholine	87.1	−5	128	1.000
piperidine	85.2	−9	106	0.861

Note: mp and bp are in °C; density is in g/mL.

Ketohexoses dehydrate more rapidly than aldohexoses, making it possible to differentiate them using Seliwanoff's reagent, a solution of resorcinol in dilute HCl.

Reduction of a monosaccharide with sodium borohydride converts it to an alditol by reducing its carbonyl group. D-Glucose is converted to the alditol D-glucitol, which has no symmetry plane and is therefore optically active.

$$
\begin{array}{ccc}
\text{CH}=\text{O} & & \text{CH}_2\text{OH} \\
\text{H}-\text{OH} & & \text{H}-\text{OH} \\
\text{HO}-\text{H} & \xrightarrow{\text{NaBH}_4} & \text{HO}-\text{H} \\
\text{H}-\text{OH} & & \text{H}-\text{OH} \\
\text{H}-\text{OH} & & \text{H}-\text{OH} \\
\text{CH}_2\text{OH} & & \text{CH}_2\text{OH}
\end{array}
$$

D-glucose   D-glucitol

Key Concept: *Compounds that have a symmetry plane are* achiral, *meaning that they cannot exist in unique "left-handed" and "right-handed" forms. Achiral compounds do not rotate plane-polarized light, so they are optically inactive.*

D-Allose is converted to D-allitol, which has a symmetry plane and is therefore optically inactive.

$$
\begin{array}{ccc}
\text{CH}=\text{O} & & \text{CH}_2\text{OH} \\
\text{H}-\text{OH} & & \text{H}-\text{OH} \\
\text{H}-\text{OH} & \xrightarrow{\text{NaBH}_4} & \text{H}-\text{OH} \\
\text{H}-\text{OH} & & \text{H}-\text{OH} \\
\text{H}-\text{OH} & & \text{H}-\text{OH} \\
\text{CH}_2\text{OH} & & \text{CH}_2\text{OH}
\end{array}
$$

symmetry plane

D-allose   D-allitol

Thus, the optical activity or inactivity of the alditol formed from reduction of a monosaccharide can yield structural information about the monosaccharide itself, thereby narrowing down the number of possible structures.

Converting monosaccharides to their phenylosazones in effect destroys any differences at the #1 and #2 carbon atoms of their molecules by changing both —CHOH—CHO and —CO—CH$_2$OH to the same structural unit:

$$
\begin{array}{ccccc}
\text{CH}=\text{O} & & \text{CH}=\text{NNHPh} & & \text{CH}_2\text{OH} \\
| & \longrightarrow & | & \longleftarrow & | \\
\text{CHOH} & & \text{C}=\text{NNHPh} & & \text{C}=\text{O} \\
| & & | & & |
\end{array}
$$

For example, D-glucose, its epimer D-mannose, and D-fructose are all converted to the same phenylosazone by phenylhydrazine.

```
     CH=O                    CH=NNHPh                 CH₂OH
  H ─┼─ OH                 C=NNHPh                  C=O
 HO ─┼─ H      PhNHNH₂   HO ─┼─ H     PhNHNH₂    HO ─┼─ H
  H ─┼─ OH    ────────►    H ─┼─ OH    ◄────────    H ─┼─ OH
  H ─┼─ OH                  H ─┼─ OH                 H ─┼─ OH
     CH₂OH                    CH₂OH                   CH₂OH
   D-glucose              D-glucosazone             D-fructose
```

↑ PhNHNH₂

```
     CH=O
 HO ─┼─ H
 HO ─┼─ H
  H ─┼─ OH
  H ─┼─ OH
     CH₂OH
   D-mannose
```

Only compounds that differ in structure from carbon #3 and on down the chain will yield different phenylosazones. Among the D-hexoses, there are four C-3 to C-6 structural units that yield different phenylosazones; these are illustrated in Figure 53.2 using Rosanoff symbols.

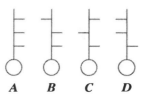

A   B   C   D

Figure 53.2 C-3 to C-6 structural units of D-hexoses

Rosanoff symbols for functional groups

△ = CHO   ◿ = COOH

○ = CH₂OH   ─┤ or ├─ = OH

```
Example:  △              CHO
         ─┤    =    HO ─┼─ H
          ├─         H ─┼─ OH
          ○             CH₂OH
```

Thus, D-glucose, D-mannose, and D-fructose yield the same phenylosazone because they all contain the same C-3 to C-6 structural unit, **B**.

In part **A** of this experiment, you will reduce your unknown D-hexose to an alditol by adding an excess of sodium borohydride in aqueous NaOH to an aqueous solution of the unknown. Like many sugars, the alditol tends to form supersaturated solutions and crystallizes slowly from solution. If your alditol refuses to crystallize after you cool the reaction mixture in ice water and rub the inside surface of its container with a stirring rod, you may be able to obtain a seed crystal from your instructor to help induce crystallization.

4. (a) Calculate the atom economy for the reaction of tristearin by the procedure used in this experiment. (b) Describe some green features of your synthesis, and any that aren't so green.

5. (a) Following the format in Appendix V, construct a flow diagram for this experiment. (b) Explain why there was no glycerol peak on the gas chromatogram of the methyl ester mixture, even though glycerol was a product of the hydrolysis.

6. Why was the Lewis acid boron trifluoride, rather than hydrochloric acid, used to catalyze the transesterification reaction?

7. Calculate the (MFA + PFA)/SFA ratio for palm oil, whose fatty acid content is approximately 9% linoleic, 2% myristic, 40% oleic, 45% palmitic, and 4% stearic acid.

8. (a) Neat's-foot oil consists almost entirely of the triglycerides of oleic and palmitic acids. How many different triglycerides of these two acids can it contain? (b) Draw structures for the triglycerides that contain two oleic acid units and one palmitic acid unit.

9. Outline a synthesis of the detergent sodium lauryl sulfate from glyceryl trilaurate (trilaurin).

$$CH_3(CH_2)_{10}CH_2OSO_2O^-Na^+$$

sodium lauryl sulfate

Other Things You Can Do

(Starred items require your instructor's permission.)

*1. Record an infrared spectrum [OP-39] of your methyl ester mixture and compare it with the spectra of the 18-carbon methyl esters in Figure 54.2. Try to account for significant similarities and differences in the spectra, and point out any bands that show evidence of unsaturation.

*2. Extract the fat trimyristin from nutmeg as described in Minilab 44.

*3. Make some soap using a phase-transfer catalyst as described in Minilab 45.

4. Starting with sources listed in the Bibliography, write a research paper about the health implications of various types of fats and oils. Include a description of the HDL and LDL forms of cholesterol and a discussion of the role they play in heart disease.

Structure of an Unknown Dipeptide

*Reactions of Peptides. Nucleophilic Aromatic Substitution. Amino Acids.
Structure Determination.*

Operations

OP-23 Paper Chromatography
OP-3   Using Glass Rod and Tubing
OP-18   Extraction
OP-19   Evaporation
OP-22   Thin-Layer Chromatography
OP-24   Washing Liquids

Before You Begin

Read the experiment and operation OP-23, read or review the other
operations as necessary, and write an experimental plan.

Scenario

Snake venoms have been used in medicine as anticoagulants, which help
dissolve blood clots or prevent their formation. Natural Nostrums, a pharmaceutical company that manufactures drugs based on natural substances,
anticipates some medical uses for the venom of the black boomslang, a
deadly African tree snake. Their native snake hunter recently had an unfortunate accident, so the supply of natural boomslang venom has dried up.
Before they can prepare a synthetic version of the venom, which is a
polypeptide, they need to determine the sequence of amino acids in its
polypeptide chain. Ferdie Lance, the company's snake-venom expert, has
used an enzyme called cathepsin C to break down the boomslang venom
into dipeptide units. Now each dipeptide unit has to be identified so that
Dr. Lance can reconstruct the amino acid sequence in the polypeptide. Your
project group's assignment is to determine the structures of the unknown
dipeptides.

Applying Scientific Methodology

After you analyze the hydrolysis mixture from your assigned dipeptide
using paper chromatography, you can formulate a tentative hypothesis
about the structure of the dipeptide. Your hypothesis will be tested by thin-
layer chromatography (TLC) analysis of a hydrolysis mixture from the dinitrophenylated dipeptide.

$$^+H_3N - CH - COO^-$$
$$|$$
$$CH_2CH_2CH_2CH_2NH_2$$

lysine

$$^+H_3N - CH - COO^-$$
$$|$$
$$CH_2$$

OH

tyrosine

6. When you extracted the DNP–dipeptide hydrolysate with diethyl ether, why wasn't your *C*-terminal amino acid extracted along with your DNP–amino acid? Write equations explaining your answer.

7. (a) Propose a detailed mechanism for the reaction of 2,4-dinitrofluorobenzene with the dipeptide you identified. (b) With reference to the mechanism, explain why the reaction would not take place at low pH.

8. Will Bobble accidentally added aqueous sodium bisulfate instead of sodium bicarbonate to the dinitrophenylation reaction mixture just before the first ether extraction. His DNP–dipeptide hydrolysate produced no spots when analyzed by TLC. What happened to his product, and why?

9. Bea Wilder decided to save time by adding a large excess of sodium bicarbonate at the beginning of the dinitrophenylation reaction instead of adding smaller amounts during the reaction. When she developed her TLC plate with a solvent system containing butanol and ammonia, a large yellow spot showed up that didn't match any of the DNP–amino acid standards. What compound formed the yellow spot? Write an equation for its formation.

10. (a) Some amino acids, such as lysine and tyrosine, yield dinitrophenylated derivatives even when they are not at the end of a peptide chain. Explain, giving structures for the DNP derivatives. (b) Such derivatives do not usually interfere with the identification of the *N*-terminal DNP–amino acids because they are not extracted from the aqueous hydrolysis mixture at pH 1 by diethyl ether. Explain.

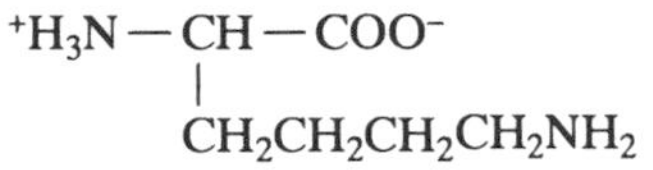

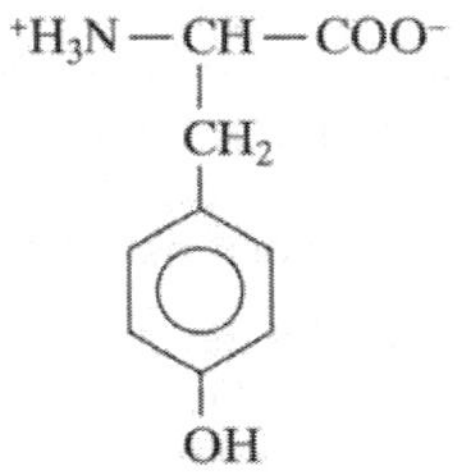

Other Things You Can Do

(Starred items require your instructor's permission.)

*1. To confirm the identity of the *C*-terminal amino acid, evaporate the reserved aqueous layer from the DNP–dipeptide hydrolysate, add a drop of water to the residue, and identify the *C*-terminal amino acid by paper chromatography as described in the Directions.

*2. Isolate the protein casein from milk as described in Minilab 46.

3. Starting with sources listed in the Bibliography, write a research paper about primary structure determination of polypeptides and proteins, describing the applications of such reagents and enzymes as phenyl isothiocyanate, dansyl chloride, trypsin, chymotrypsin, cathepsin C, and cyanogen bromide.

Multistep Synthesis of Benzilic Acid from Benzaldehyde

Reactions of Carbonyl Compounds. Preparation of Carboxylic Acids. Nucleophilic Addition. Oxidation. Molecular Rearrangements.

Operations

OP-7   Heating
OP-10   Mixing
OP-15   Gravity Filtration
OP-16   Vacuum Filtration
OP-26   Washing and Drying Solids
OP-28   Recrystallization
OP-33   Melting Point
OP-39   Infrared Spectrometry

Before You Begin

1. Read the experiment, read or review the operations as necessary, and write an experimental plan.
2. Calculate the mass and volume of 150 mmol (SS) or 15.0 mmol (μS) of benzaldehyde, and the theoretical yields of benzoin, benzil, and benzilic acid expected from that much benzaldehyde.

Scenario

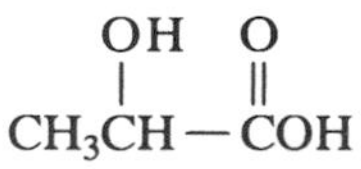

The α-hydroxy acids (AHAs) include lactic acid, which forms in milk as it sours and is also produced in muscles and blood after vigorous physical activity. Certain AHAs, such as glycolic acid ($HOCH_2COOH$), are used in anti-aging "wrinkle creams" that soften the skin and smooth out fine wrinkles and roughness. Golden Age Sundries is an organization that develops and markets various consumer goods for older people, and the success of AHAs in combating some effects of aging has led them to support research exploring the possible anti-aging benefits of other α-hydroxy acids. Your supervisor has just received a grant from them to investigate one of the AHAs, benzilic acid.

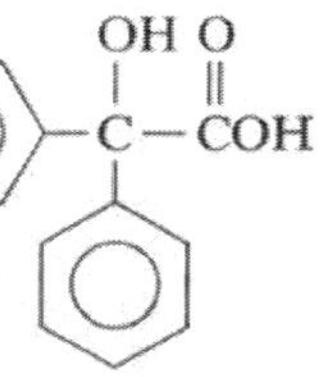

Benzilic acid can be prepared from an inexpensive starting material, benzaldehyde, by a three-step synthesis that involves a reaction called the benzoin condensation, an oxidation step, and a molecular rearrangement (see the "Reactions and Properties" section for the equations). The benzoin condensation has traditionally been carried out using cyanide ion as a catalyst, but because of the toxicity of cyanide, your supervisor has decided to use vitamin B_1 instead. Your assignment is to find out whether or not the vitamin is a suitable catalyst for the benzoin condensation and, if it is, to convert the benzoin you obtain to benzilic acid.

lactic acid

benzilic acid

PART III

Minilabs

The minilabs are short, self-contained experiments that ordinarily take no more than an hour or two to complete. They can be used to supplement the experiments in Parts I and II, and to fill in gaps that can occur when there is a long reaction time or when an experiment is completed well before the end of the lab period. Minilabs require only small amounts of chemicals and can be performed with equipment provided in both standard scale and microscale lab lockers, so separate standard scale and microscale procedures are not given here. When they differ, standard scale (SS) and microscale (μS) quantities or equipment are designated by the usual abbreviations in parentheses. You should submit a report for each minilab that includes your data, the percent yield (when appropriate), and any other information specified in the minilab or by your instructor.

Making Useful Laboratory Items

Before You Begin: Read OP-3, "Using Glass Rod and Tubing."

A flat-bottomed stirring rod can come in handy when you are trying to dissolve lumps of a solid, pulverize crystals for a melting-point measurement, wash a solid on a Buchner funnel, or stir a solution manually. You will need a boiling tube to carry out a semi-microscale boiling-point determination [OP-34b]; in preparing one, you will learn how to seal and fire-polish glass tubing. You can get some practice bending glass tubing by preparing a filter trap (also used as a solvent trap), which is used to prevent water from backing up into a filter flask from an aspirator and to recover volatile solvents that are being evaporated under vacuum.

DIRECTIONS

Safety Notes

> Be careful not to burn or cut yourself while working with glass rods and tubing. See OP-3 for safe glassworking procedures.

Your instructor should demonstrate the correct glassworking techniques [OP-3]. Prepare as many of the following items as requested, and have your instructor inspect and approve the items when you are finished.

Making an acceptable flat-bottomed stirring rod may take practice. You can develop your technique using scrap pieces of glass rod.

Take Care! Don't burn yourself on the hot glass.

Flat-Bottomed Stirring Rod. Cut a 20–25-cm length of soft glass rod that has a diameter of 5–6 mm (SS) or 3–4 mm (μS). Flatten one end by rotating that end in a burner flame until it is soft and incandescent; without delay, hold the rod vertically and firmly press its hot end onto the metal base of a ring stand. The flat end should flare out to a diameter approximately twice that of the rod itself. Be sure to heat the rod only at its tip, as heating it farther up will cause it to bend rather than flatten. When the flat end has cooled, round off the other end in a burner flame.

Boiling Tube. (This part can be omitted if you will not be using the semi-microscale boiling-point determination method described in OP-34b.) Obtain a piece of 4–5-mm o.d. (outer diameter) soft glass tubing, and carefully seal it at one end. When it has cooled, cut it to a length of 8–10 cm and fire-polish the open end. Test the tube as described in OP-3 to make sure it is sealed. Save it for use in Experiment 8 and later experiments.

Filter Trap. Using a 125–250-mL thick-walled bottle, 6–8-mm o.d. soft glass tubing, and a rubber stopper to fit, construct a filter trap like the one shown in Figure C4 of OP-16. One length of glass tubing should be about 10–15 cm long, and the other should be about half that long. First, fire-polish both ends of each tube. Using a flame spreader, bend both pieces of tubing smoothly so that the shorter arm on each is approximately 3 cm long. Bore two holes of appropriate diameter in the rubber stopper (or use a 2-hole stopper provided), and insert the longer arm of each tube through each hole, using glycerol as a lubricant. When this assembly is inserted in the bottle, the lower end of the long tube should be 5 cm or so from the

Take Care! Hold the glass close to the stopper and protect your hands.

bottom; the short tube has only to extend through the stopper. Wrap the bottle with heavy-duty transparent plastic tape to prevent possible injury from implosion.

Extraction of Iodine by Dichloromethane

MINILAB **2**

Before You Begin: Read the directions for liquid–liquid extraction in OP-18a.

Many extractions involve colorless solutions, making it impossible to observe the transfer of a solute from one layer to the other. In this mini-lab, the solute (iodine) is colored so you will be able to see and describe what is going on as the solute is extracted from an aqueous solution by an organic solvent. Iodine is nearly insoluble in water, so potassium iodide is added to the aqueous solution to increase its solubility. Because iodide ions combine chemically with I_2 in water, the iodine color in the aqueous and organic layers will be different (brown in one and violet in the other). You should interpret such a color in either layer as indicating the presence of iodine in that layer.

DIRECTIONS

Record your observations carefully in your laboratory notebook because you will have to explain them in your report.

Safety Notes

> Dichloromethane may be harmful if ingested, inhaled, or absorbed through the skin. There is a possibility that prolonged inhalation of dichloromethane may cause cancer. Minimize contact with the liquid, and do not breathe its vapors.

Add 2 mL of 0.50 M iodine–potassium iodide solution to a conical centrifuge tube. Tilt the container at an angle, and use a Pasteur pipet to add 2 mL of dichloromethane down its side. The dichloromethane layer should slide underneath the colored aqueous layer with a minimum of mixing. Record the color of each layer and the intensity of the color (dark, very light, etc.). Cap the tube or vial and shake it vigorously, with occasional venting, until the color of the aqueous layer does not change with further shaking. Again record the color of each layer and the intensity of the color. Let the mixture stand until there is a sharp interface (dividing line) between the liquid layers. Use a Pasteur pipet to transfer [OP-6] all of the dichloromethane layer to a small Erlenmeyer flask. Now add a fresh 2-mL portion of dichloromethane to the aqueous solution, shake the capped container as before, and record your observations.

Stop and Think: What happened that caused the color changes you observed?

Waste Disposal: Place the combined dichloromethane layers in a chlorinated solvents waste container. Unless your instructor directs otherwise, wash the aqueous layer down the drain.

Describe the colors of the two liquid phases before mixing, and after each extraction. Account for the color changes and for any differences in the color intensity of the layers after the first and second extractions.

MINILAB 3

Purification of an Unknown Compound by Recrystallization

Before You Begin: Read OP-28c, "Choosing a Recrystallization Solvent," and read or review the other operations as necessary.

When you are purifying a solid substance by recrystallization, the solid must be soluble in the boiling solvent but quite insoluble in the same solvent when it is cold. In this minilab, you will have to select a suitable solvent for the recrystallization of the unknown solid by carrying out some preliminary solubility tests in different solvents.

DIRECTIONS

Safety Notes

The solvents and the unknown solid may be harmful if ingested, inhaled, or absorbed through the skin. Avoid contact with them, and do not breathe their vapors.

Waste Disposal: Place the filtrate in an appropriate solvent recovery container. With your instructor's permission, water and ethanol filtrates can be washed down the drain.

Obtain an unknown solid from your instructor. Following the directions in OP-28c, "Choosing a Recrystallization Solvent," select a suitable recrystallization solvent by testing the unknown's solubility in hot and cold water, ethanol, hexane, 2-butanone, and any other solvents suggested by your instructor. Accurately weigh [OP-4] 1–2 g (SS) or 0.2–0.4 g (µS) of the unknown solid, and recrystallize [OP-28] it from the solvent you selected. Dry [OP-26b] the purified solid to constant mass and weigh it. Measure the melting points [OP-33] of the impure and purified solids. Calculate the percent recovery, and report your results in tabular form.

MINILAB 4

Developing and Testing a Hypothesis

Before You Begin: Read or review the "Scientific Methodology" section in the Introduction.

In this minilab, you will observe and attempt to explain the effect of a ferric chloride ($FeCl_3$) solution on solutions of seven organic compounds. Record your observations carefully, and think about their significance. After noting what happens to the first three solutions, you will develop a hypothesis to account for your observations. You will then test your hypothesis by adding $FeCl_3$ to two more solutions, modify your original hypothesis as necessary to account for your observations, and repeat this procedure with two more solutions until you arrive at a hypothesis that accounts for all of your observations.

DIRECTIONS

> Methyl salicylate irritates the skin and eyes; avoid contact.

Safety Notes

Use a 1-mL measuring pipet or a calibrated Pasteur pipet [OP-5] to add 0.5 mL of water and 0.5 mL of 95% ethanol to each of eight clean, numbered test tubes. Add one drop of (1) methyl salicylate to test tube #1, about 10 mg each of (2) salicylic acid, (3) aspirin, (4) acetaminophen, (5) phenacetin, and (6) menthol to test tubes #2 through #6, and one drop of (7) benzyl alcohol to test tube #7. Add two drops of (8) 2.5% ferric chloride solution to test tube #8, which will serve as a control.

methyl salicylate   salicylic acid   aspirin

acetaminophen   phenacetin   menthol   benzyl alcohol

Add two drops of 2.5% $FeCl_3$ to each of the first *three* test tubes; then **stop** and record your observations, comparing the contents of these test tubes to the control. Based on the structures of the compounds in these test tubes, formulate a hypothesis to account for your results.

Add two drops of 2.5% $FeCl_3$ to each of the next two test tubes, #4 and #5, then **stop** and record your observations without delay. Do the results support your original hypothesis? If not, formulate a new hypothesis or revise your original one to explain them.

Add two drops of 2.5% $FeCl_3$ to each of the next two test tubes, #6 and #7. Do the results support your current hypothesis? If not, formulate a new hypothesis or revise your current one to explain them.

Observe and Note: Which of the test tubes show evidence of a reaction?

Waste Disposal: Dispose of the solutions as directed by your instructor.

Report your observations in a table. Write down your hypothesis from each stage of the procedure, telling why it changed from one step to the next (if it did), and state your final conclusion.

MINILAB 5   # Preparation of Acetate Esters

Before You Begin: Read or review the operations as necessary.

The pleasant aromas of many esters make them popular ingredients of flavorings and perfumes. In this minilab, you will prepare some acetate esters by treating the corresponding alcohols with acetyl chloride, and then compare their odors.

$$CH_3\overset{\overset{\displaystyle O}{\|}}{C}-Cl + ROH \longrightarrow CH_3\overset{\overset{\displaystyle O}{\|}}{C}-OR + HCl$$
      acetyl chloride   acetate ester

Alternatively, your instructor may give you an unknown alcohol whose ester you will analyze by mass spectrometry as described in Minilab 29.

DIRECTIONS

This minilab can be performed as a group project with each student responsible for preparing one ester.

Safety Notes

> Acetyl chloride is very corrosive, and its vapors are irritating and toxic. It reacts violently with water and some alcohols. Use gloves and a hood, avoid contact, do not breathe its vapors, and keep it away from water.

Take Care! Violent reactions are possible. Wear gloves, avoid contact with acetyl chloride, and do not breathe its vapors.

Waste Disposal: Unless your instructor directs otherwise, wash the aqueous layers down the drain. Place the esters in a designated waste container.

Obtain as many clean, *dry* centrifuge tubes or 13 × 100-mm test tubes as there are alcohols, and number them consecutively. Add 10 drops or 0.3 mL of one of the following alcohols (or any other alcohols specified by your instructor) to each tube: ethanol, 1-propanol, 3-methyl-1-butanol, 1-octanol, benzyl alcohol. *Under the hood, slowly* add 10 drops or 0.3 mL of acetyl chloride to each of these reaction tubes (use of an automatic pipet is recommended). Let the solutions stand for 3 minutes or more. Carefully add 2 mL of water to each tube, and shake gently to mix. Extract [OP-18] the contents of each tube by adding 2 mL of diethyl ether, shaking the capped tube thoroughly, and removing the lower, aqueous layer with a Pasteur pipet. *Under the hood,* evaporate [OP-19] the ether from each tube. Do not apply heat or evaporate the contents to dryness. Transfer a drop of each ester to a spot plate, and cautiously observe the odor of each ester. (Note whether the odor changes with time; if it does, the ether may not have evaporated completely.)

Describe and compare the odors of the esters as best you can. You may be able to associate an ester's odor with the odor of something familiar, such as a nail-polish remover or a kind of fruit. Write the formula and give the name of each ester you prepared.

Gas Chromatographic Analysis of Commercial Xylene

MINILAB 6

Before You Begin: Read or review OP-37, "Gas Chromatography."

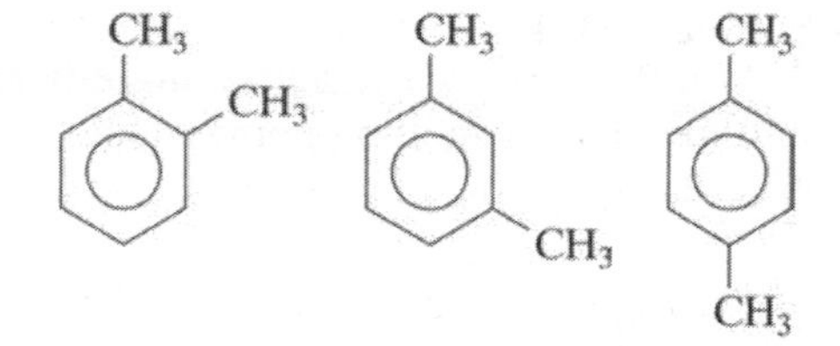

ortho-xylene   *meta*-xylene   *para*-xylene

Commercial xylene, sometimes called xylol, is actually a mixture of three isomeric xylenes (dimethylbenzenes). You may find some in your local hardware store, where it is sold for use as a solvent and thinner for oil-based paints and coatings, such as porch and deck enamels. It is also used for microscopy and in the manufacture of starting materials for the preparation of polyester fibers. You will be analyzing a commercial xylene mixture to determine the percentages of *ortho*-, *meta*-, and *para*-xylene it contains.

DIRECTIONS

Safety Notes

Xylenes are flammable, toxic by inhalation and ingestion, and irritating to skin and eyes. Minimize contact with the xylene mixtures, and do not breathe their vapors.

A standard mixture containing *ortho*-, *meta*-, and *para*-xylene will be provided. Record the percentage of each component from the label on the bottle. Obtain gas chromatograms [OP-37] of (1) the standard mixture and (2) a commercial xylene mixture as directed by your instructor. From the relative retention times and peak areas in the gas chromatogram of the standard mixture, identify the component corresponding to each peak and calculate its detector response factor. Identify each peak, and measure all peak areas on the gas chromatogram of the commercial xylene. Then calculate the mass percentage of each component in the commercial xylene.

Report your results in a table showing the retention time, peak area, detector response factor, and mass percentage of each component. Show your calculations, and include your gas chromatograms with your report.

Waste Disposal: Place any unused xylene mixture in the appropriate waste container.

Isolation of an Expectorant from Cough Capsules

MINILAB 7

OH
|
OCH₂CHCH₂OH

(structural diagram of guaifenesin: benzene ring with OCH₂CHCH₂OH and OH substituents and OCH₃)

OCH₃

guaifenesin

Before You Begin: Read or review the operations as necessary.

Guaifenesin is an expectorant that is used to thin and loosen bronchial secretions, thereby helping a cold sufferer cough them up. It is an ingredient in many cough syrups, such as Robitussin, but recent scientific studies have shown that the amount of guaifenesin in such remedies is too low to be effective. It is also marketed in some cough tablets and capsules, which usually contain 200 mg of guaifenesin per tablet. This is about twice the amount in a dose of cough syrup.

In this minilab, you will isolate the active ingredient from a cough-medicine capsule and measure its melting point to find out whether or not it is guaifenesin, which has a melting point of 79°C.

DIRECTIONS

Safety Notes

The mixed hexanes solvent is highly flammable, so keep it away from flames and hot surfaces.
Ethyl acetate is flammable and may be harmful if inhaled or absorbed through the skin. Avoid contact, do not breathe its vapors, and keep it away from flames.

Take apart a cough-medicine capsule provided by your instructor and transfer the ingredients to a 25-mL Erlenmeyer flask. Extract [OP-18c] the active component by adding 5 mL of ethyl acetate, and manually or magnetically stirring [OP-10] the suspension at room temperature for 10 minutes. Filter the mixture by gravity [OP-15], save the filtrate, and discard the solids. Add 10 mL of hexanes to the filtrate in 2-mL portions, swirling the flask for half a minute or so after each addition. Let the mixture stand until a significant amount of precipitate forms. (You can work on another experiment or minilab while you're waiting.)

Cool the mixture [OP-8] in an ice-water bath for 10 minutes or more. Collect the precipitate by vacuum filtration [OP-16]. Wash the solid with 2.5 mL of ice-cold hexanes, and air-dry it on the filter for 10 minutes or more. When it is completely dry, measure its mass [OP-4] and melting point [OP-33].

Waste Disposal: Place the filtrate in a designated waste container.

State whether or not your results suggest that the active ingredient in the cough-medicine capsule is guaifenesin. Assuming that the capsule contained 200 mg of the active ingredient (or another amount specified by your instructor), calculate your percent recovery.

A Missing-Label Puzzle

Before You Begin: After reading the minilab, devise a method for distinguishing the two dry-cleaning solvents.

Most dry-cleaning solvents are hydrocarbon mixtures or chlorinated hydrocarbons that, because of their low polarity, dissolve greasy stains in clothing. Many chlorinated solvents that were once used for dry cleaning, such as carbon tetrachloride, are no longer allowed because of their toxicity. Tetrachloroethene ($Cl_2C=CCl_2$), sold under such trade names as Perclene, is less toxic than most other chlorinated solvents. Mineral spirits, a mixture of petroleum hydrocarbons, is also used widely in dry cleaning.

For this minilab, you will assume that the labels have fallen off a bottle of tetrachloroethene and a bottle of mineral spirits, and you will devise a method of telling the solvents apart. Your method cannot be based on odor differences. Instruments such as balances or refractometers are not allowed. You can use only the equipment in your locker and basic lab utilities, plus reference books and anything else your instructor is willing to provide (check in advance if you're not sure what will be available). The simplest method may be the best— a few minutes of thought can often save hours of experimental work.

DIRECTIONS

Safety Notes

> Tetrachloroethene is an eye and skin irritant, and it may be harmful by inhalation. It is also a suspected carcinogen. Avoid contact, and do not breathe its vapors.
> Mineral spirits is very flammable, and inhalation may be harmful. Do not breathe its vapors, and keep flames away.

In the laboratory, you will find two containers of "dry-cleaning solvent," labeled **A** and **B**. One of the solvents is tetrachloroethene, and the other is mineral spirits. Assuming that the hydrocarbons in mineral spirits have properties similar to those of the alkanes in Experiment 8 (except for their boiling points), devise an experiment to find out which solvent is in which container. Then carry out your experiment, report the identities of **A** and **B**, and tell how you arrived at your conclusion. Don't reveal your method or results to others—let them think for themselves, as you did.

Waste Disposal: Place any leftover solvents in designated waste containers.

Paper Chromatography of Dyes in Commercial Drink Mixes

Before You Begin: Read OP-23, "Paper Chromatography."

Many foods, drugs, and cosmetics are colored with FD&C dyes to give them eye appeal or, in the case of foods, to give them the color we associate with the food in question. For example, the artificial flavors used to prepare a grape drink may be completely colorless, so dyes are added to give the drink a purple "grape" color. A number of former FD&C dyes have been removed from the market because they were found to be toxic or were suspected of causing cancer or birth defects. For example, FD&C Red No. 2, which was once the most widely used food dye, was banned in 1976 because it is a suspected carcinogen. At present, only nine FD&C dyes are allowed for food use in the U.S., four of the most popular being Blue No. 1, Red No. 40, Yellow No. 5, and Yellow No. 6. In this minilab, you will analyze some powdered drink mixes (such as Kool-Aid) using paper chromatography to see which FD&C dyes they contain. The four dyes mentioned can be identified by their colors and R_f values. Some foods also contain FD&C Green No. 3, which can be identified by the sea green color of its spot.

Table M1 Colors and approximate R_f values for FD&C dyes

FD&C dye	Color	R_f
Yellow #5 (Tartrazine)	bright yellow	0.31
Yellow #6 (Sunset Yellow)	orange	0.58
Red #40 (Allura Red)	bright red	0.62
Blue #1 (Brilliant Blue)	turquoise blue	0.67

Note: R_f values are for the solvent mixture 95% ethanol/ 1-butanol/2.0 M ammonia (1:1:1).

DIRECTIONS

Safety Notes

> **Ethanol and 1-butanol are flammable, and 1-butanol may cause eye or skin irritation. Ammonia can cause severe skin and eye irritation. Avoid contact with the developing solvent, do not breathe its vapors, and keep flames away.**

Take Care! Avoid contact with the developing solvent, and do not breathe its vapors.

You will be provided with a selection of sugar-free drink mix flavors, each containing one or more of the food dyes listed in Table M1. *Under the hood*, place enough developing solvent (a 1:1:1 mixture of 95% ethanol, 1-butanol, and 2.0 M aqueous ammonia) in a suitable developing chamber (such as a 600-mL beaker) to cover its bottom to a depth of about 1 cm. Cover it with a lid or plastic wrap, swirl it to agitate the liquid, and let it sit to equilibrate. Label the wells of a spot plate to correspond to the drink mix flavors, using a one- or two-letter code. Place 0.2–0.3 g of each drink mix powder in a well of the spot plate; then add room-temperature water—drop by drop, with stirring—to each well until the powder dissolves. Rinse your stirring rod before going on to the next spot plate.

Stop and Think: Why not use a pen?

Obtain an approximately 11 × 22-cm rectangle of Whatman #1 chromatography paper [OP-23], and use a pencil to draw a starting line along one of its long sides, about 1.5 cm from that side. Using a different end of a capillary micropipet (or toothpick) for each spot, spot the solutions 1.5–2.0 cm apart along the starting line. If space permits, apply two or three spots of varying concentration for each solution. Make each spot 2–3 mm in diameter, and write its code letter underneath it with a pencil. Wait for the spots to dry completely. Develop the chromatogram in the developing chamber, and let it air-dry (don't forget to mark the solvent front).

Prepare a table showing the color and your experimental R_f value for each spot in the chromatogram of each drink mix. Using information from Table M1, identify as many dyes in each drink mix as you can. Turn in your paper chromatogram with your report.

Gas Chromatographic Analysis of an Essential Oil from Orange Peel

MINILAB **10**

Before You Begin: Read OP-18c, "Liquid–Solid Extraction," and read or review the other operations as necessary.

The orange tree originated in China and was first cultivated in the United States by Franciscan monks, in the part of Spanish North America that is now California. Orange oil is used medicinally and also to flavor foods, drinks, and confections. It is colored by β-carotene and contains a number of minor components, but its major component is limonene. Limonene is a ubiquitous terpene that occurs in a multitude of other essential oils, including the oils of lemon, caraway, and dill. Limonene exists in two enantiomeric (mirror image) forms, (R)-$(+)$-limonene and (S)-$(-)$-limonene, which have different odors.

In this minilab, you will isolate orange oil by extraction of grated orange peel with hexanes (a mixture of isomeric six-carbon alkanes) and analyze it by gas chromatography (GC) to determine the approximate percentage of limonene it contains. If your instructor has samples of (R)-$(+)$-limonene and (S)-$(-)$-limonene available, you can compare their odors to that of your extract to find out which enantiomer you have. Some people are unable to distinguish the enantiomers by odor; if you are one of them, ask a coworker for help. If a suitable preparative GC column is available, you can also isolate pure limonene and record its infrared spectrum as described in *J. Chem. Educ.* **1994**, *71*, A146.

limonene

DIRECTIONS

The hexanes mixture is flammable, and its vapors may be harmful. Avoid inhalation, and keep flames away.

Safety Notes

On a piece of wax paper or aluminum foil, grate the rind of an orange until you have about 1 g. Measure the mass of the grated orange rind, and transfer it to a small Erlenmeyer flask. Extract [OP-18c] the orange oil with two successive 4-mL portions of hexanes, each time using a flat-bottomed stirring rod to mix and crush the peel with the hexanes for 3 minutes or more. Then dry [OP-25] the combined extracts through a drying column that contains 0.5 g of anhydrous sodium sulfate. Use about 0.5 mL of hexanes to rinse the drying column, and combine it with the extracts. *Under the hood,* remove the solvent by evaporation [OP-19]. Weigh the orange oil and, if necessary, resume evaporating until its mass is constant between weighings. Compare the odor of the orange oil to those of authentic samples of (R)-$(+)$-limonene and (S)-$(-)$-limonene, if available. Record a gas chromatogram [OP-37] of the orange oil.

Estimate the percentage of limonene in the orange oil by assuming the same detector response factor for all components, and calculate the percentage recovery of limonene from orange peel. If you can, identify the limonene in orange peel as (R)-$(+)$-limonene or (S)-$(-)$-limonene, and draw a structural formula showing its stereochemistry.

MINILAB 11

Identification of an Unknown Felt-Tip Pen Ink by TLC

Before You Begin: Read or review OP-22, "Thin-Layer Chromatography."

Unlike food colorings, which are made from a very limited selection of approved dyes (see Minilab 9), pen inks are made from a wide variety of dyes, and the dye mixtures in pen inks from different manufacturers can vary greatly. These dyes can be separated by thin-layer chromatography (TLC), producing chromatograms with characteristic patterns of colored spots. For this reason, forensic scientists often use TLC to identify pen inks from documents associated with a criminal or civil case. For example, matching the ink from a pen in the suspect's possession with ink in the signature on a forged document provides evidence that may result in the suspect's conviction.

In this minilab, you will attempt to identify the ink from an unknown felt-tip pen by comparing its TLC pattern with those of known pen inks. The pens will have fine points, so they can be used to spot the TLC plate directly. You will develop the chromatogram using a 1-butanol/water/ethanol/acetic acid (120:40:20:1) mixed solvent or another suitable developing solvent.

DIRECTIONS

Safety Notes

> **The developing solvent is flammable and harmful by inhalation, ingestion, and skin absorption. Avoid contact, do not breathe its vapors, and keep flames away.**

Under the hood, prepare a developing chamber using a 1-L beaker or another suitable container as described in OP-22, and add enough developing solvent to cover the bottom to a depth of about 5 mm. Cover the developing chamber with a lid or plastic food wrap, swirl it to agitate the liquid, and let it sit to equilibrate while you prepare the TLC sheet [OP-22]. Obtain a 10×10-cm silica gel TLC sheet, and mark the starting line in pencil. Using the known and unknown felt-tip pens provided, carefully apply spots about 1.5 cm from each edge and 1 cm or more apart, labeling them in pencil. Spot the unknown in at least two places, applying the spots between known spots to make the inks easier to compare. Each spot should be no more than 2 mm in diameter, so practice your spotting technique on a scrap piece of

TLC sheet first. Develop the TLC sheet in the pre-equilibrated developing chamber, and let it air-dry (don't forget to mark the solvent front).

For each pen ink, including the unknown, describe the pattern of colored spots you observed. Then identify the unknown pen ink by matching its pattern with that from one of the known pen inks. Turn in your chromatogram with your report.

Waste Disposal: Place the used developing solvent in an appropriate solvent recovery container.

Optical Rotation of Turpentine   MINILAB **12**

Before You Begin: Read or review OP-36, "Optical Rotation."

North American turpentine contains $(+)$-α-pinene and $(-)$-β-pinene (see Experiment 12). In this minilab, you will measure the optical rotation of a commercial turpentine (or a simulated turpentine) to estimate the percentages of $(+)$-α- and $(-)$-β-pinene it contains.

DIRECTIONS

> Turpentine and its components are flammable and irritate the skin and eyes; inhalation of their vapors may be harmful. Minimize contact with the turpentine, and do not breathe its vapors.

Safety Notes

Using a 25-mL volumetric flask, prepare a solution that contains about 2.5 g (accurately weighed) of turpentine in absolute ethanol, and fill a 2-dm sample cell with the solution. (For microscale work, you can use 1.0 g of turpentine, a 10-mL volumetric flask, and a 1-dm sample cell.) Measure the optical rotation of the solution and of an absolute ethanol blank, using an accurate polarimeter [OP-36]. Prepare solutions of $(+)$-α-pinene and $(-)$-β-pinene in the same way, and measure their optical rotations.

Calculate the specific rotation of each solution. Assuming that it contains only $(+)$-α-pinene and $(-)$-β-pinene, calculate the percentage of each constituent in the turpentine.

Waste Disposal: Place the ethanol solutions in an appropriate solvent recovery container.

Stop and Think: What equation in OP-36 can you use to do this?

The Structures of Organic Molecules   MINILAB **13**

Before You Begin: Familiarize yourself with the different kinds of formulas used to represent organic compounds, and know how to name organic compounds by the IUPAC system.

In this minilab, you will study some molecular models to help you (1) better understand the structure and geometry of organic molecules and (2) learn how to write and interpret the different kinds of formulas that are used to represent them.

DIRECTIONS

When you arrive, you will find numbered molecular models of representative organic compounds distributed around your organic chemistry laboratory. Start at one of the models, and proceed around the laboratory until you have studied all of them. Unless your instructor indicates differently, assume that atoms are represented by balls of the following colors: carbon—black; hydrogen—white or yellow; oxygen—red; nitrogen—blue; chlorine—green; bromine—orange or brown; sulfur—yellow. The type of covalent bond connecting two atoms is indicated by the number of connectors: one for a single bond, two for a double bond, and three for a triple bond. For each model, write the following in your lab notebook, along with the number of the model:

- IUPAC name (the name may be provided in some cases)
- Empirical formula
- Molecular formula
- Condensed structural formula
- Expanded structural formula (Kekulé structure)
- Bond-line formula

Examples of these types of formulas are shown for 2-methylpropane.

C_2H_5
empirical formula

C_4H_{10}
molecular formula

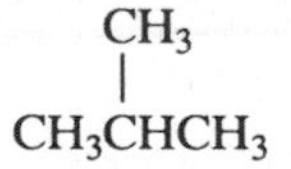

CH_3CHCH_3
condensed structural formula

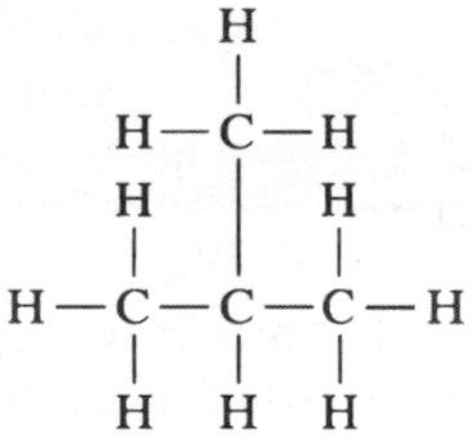

$$\begin{array}{c} H \\ | \\ H-C-H \\ H \quad | \quad H \\ | \quad | \quad | \\ H-C-C-C-H \\ | \quad | \quad | \\ H \quad H \quad H \end{array}$$
expanded structural formula

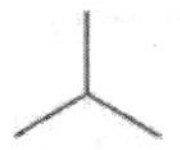

bond-line formula

formulas for 2-methylpropane

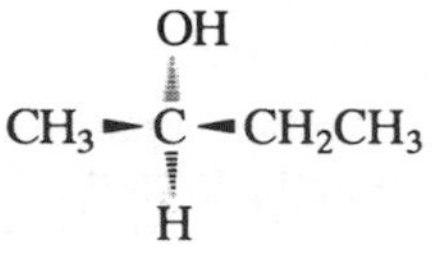

$$\begin{array}{c} OH \\ | \\ CH_3-C-CH_2CH_3 \\ | \\ H \end{array}$$
stereochemical formula

If molecular models of chiral compounds are provided, write their stereochemical formulas as well, using either flying wedge, ball-and-stick, or Fischer projections. A flying wedge projection is illustrated in the margin for (R)-2-butanol. Include the (R) or (S) designation of any chiral compound in its name. Your instructor may request special formulas in some cases, such as chair-ring formulas for substituted cyclohexanes.

MINILAB **14**   Who Else Has My Compound?

Before You Begin: Develop an experimental plan based on the equipment and chemicals available to you, and read or review the appropriate operations as necessary.

Few, if any, scientists perform their work in isolation. Successful science requires cooperation and collaboration among scientists, who exchange information, ideas, and even materials. For example, suppose you isolated a natural product that was not previously reported in the chemical literature, but shortly afterward a Japanese chemist reported a natural product (isolated from a different source) whose spectra and properties appear to be the same as yours. You might then exchange data and samples with the Japanese chemist to establish whether your compounds were, in fact, the same.

In this minilab, you will receive an unknown organic compound, knowing that at least one other student in your laboratory has the same compound. You will be expected to learn enough about your compound that, by sharing your findings with other students, you can find another unknown that appears to match your own. You and the student who has that unknown should then confirm that your compounds are identical by, for example, having student **A** obtain data for his or her unknown that student **B** has already obtained for the other unknown, and vice versa. If more than two students share the same unknown, you may eventually identify yourself as part of a larger group of students. Because the outcome of the experiment depends on the efforts of all of the participants, your individual contribution is important for the success of the group.

Your instructor may advise you about the techniques you should use, or you may be asked to plan your own experimental strategy, given the chemicals and equipment available.

DIRECTIONS

Safety Notes

> Assume that the unknown compound may be flammable and harmful by inhalation, ingestion, and skin absorption. Avoid contact, do not breathe its vapors, and keep it away from flames and hot surfaces.

You will be issued an unknown compound with an identification number. Obtain as much information about your compound as you think is necessary to characterize it, given the equipment and chemicals available. Then approach other students with your findings (they may approach you first) to locate another student who appears to have the same compound you do. When you find one or more such students, perform any additional work necessary to confirm that your compounds are, in fact, identical.

Waste Disposal: Return any unused unknown to your instructor it its original vial.

Report the names and unknown numbers of other students whose unknowns are identical to your own, and tell how you arrived at your conclusion. Report all of your findings in an appropriate format, and turn in any spectra or chromatograms you obtained.

Isomers and Molecular Structure   **MINILAB 15**

Before You Begin: As necessary, review material from your lecture textbook about structural (constitutional) isomers and stereoisomers.

Just as zoology is the study of animals and botany the study of plants, organic chemistry can be regarded as the study of carbon-containing molecules.

An instrument called a scanning tunneling microscope can generate fuzzy images of molecules on surfaces, but whether this is equivalent to "seeing" the molecules is debatable.

Certain plants and animals are familiar to everyone because we see them all around us, but molecules are not. We can't *see* a molecule—the best we can do is to imagine what one looks like, and molecular models can help us do that. All models have their limitations. A plastic model of a Sopwith Camel is a far cry from the real thing, but it can show us what that WWI biplane looked like in three dimensions. A real molecule is obviously not made of colored balls, but a good molecular model can show the three-dimensional structure of a molecule far better than any drawing. In this minilab, you will use molecular models to help you visualize—in three dimensions—the structural and geometric differences between isomers.

Isomers are different compounds that share the same molecular formula. This means that the same set of atoms can be combined in different ways to form molecules with different structures. For this minilab, you will apply a hands-on approach to the study of isomers and molecular structure. You will be issued a set of atoms and bonds from a molecular-model kit, and you will be expected to construct molecular models for as many isomers as you can in the time allowed. The most popular molecular models are the ball-and-stick type, in which balls of different colors represent different kinds of atoms, and rigid or flexible connectors represent the bonds that hold the atoms together in molecules. Each ball is ordinarily drilled with a number of holes equal to the *normal covalence* of the corresponding atom—the number of covalent bonds formed by the neutral atom. Thus balls representing carbon atoms—colored black—are drilled with four holes arranged tetrahedrally, whereas those representing oxygen atoms have two holes, and those representing hydrogen atoms have one. Building models of all the isomers that have a given molecular formula is thus a matter of putting the appropriate colored balls together in all possible combinations, using just enough connectors to fill the holes. Often, a large number of isomers will share the same molecular formula, and it may take a considerable amount of ingenuity to find them all!

In some molecular model kits the nitrogen (blue) atoms have four holes to allow construction of ammonium salt models. If yours do, use only three of them.

DIRECTIONS

This minilab can be done individually or in groups. Your instructor will issue you or your group a set of atoms and will provide connectors, including flexible connectors for constructing strained and multiple bonds. Unless he or she indicates differently, assume that atoms are represented by balls of the colors given in Table M2.

Table M2 Colors of model-kit balls and normal covalences of atoms

Atom	Color of ball	Normal covalence
bromine	orange or brown	1
carbon	black	4
chlorine	green	1
hydrogen	white or yellow	1
nitrogen	blue	3
oxygen	red	2
sulfur	yellow	2

Construct molecular models for as many isomers as you can, based on the normal covalences in Table M2. In your lab notebook, neatly draw the structural formulas for the molecular models you constructed. Some of your molecular models may exhibit stereoisomerism; in that case, you can count each geometric (*cis-trans*) isomer or enantiomer as a different compound. Designate any geometric isomers as (*Z*) or (*E*) and any enantiomers as (*R*) or (*S*), and show their stereochemistry clearly. If your instructor requests, obtain another set of atoms and connectors, and use it to prepare isomers as well.

Reactivities of Alkyl Halides in Nucleophilic Substitution Reactions

MINILAB **16**

Before You Begin: Draw the structures of all substrates you will be using in this reaction, and classify them as 1°, 2°, 3°, aryl, benzylic, or some combination of these (such as 1° benzylic). Identify the nucleophile, substrate, and leaving group in the general equations for reactions **1** and **2**.

In this minilab, you will compare the relative reactivities of different alkyl halides with two different reagents: sodium iodide in acetone and silver nitrate in ethanol. General equations for their reactions are

1. $RX + NaI \xrightarrow{\text{acetone}} RI + NaX$ (X= Cl or Br)

2. $RX + AgNO_3 + EtOH \longrightarrow ROEt + AgX + HNO_3$

(Additional organic products, such as alkenes, may be formed in reaction **2**.) For each reagent, the occurrence of a reaction is indicated by the formation of a precipitate: sodium chloride or sodium bromide (which are insoluble in acetone) in reaction **1**, and silver chloride or silver bromide in reaction **2**. Your initial objective is to discover what kind of mechanism (S_N1 or S_N2) is involved in the reactions of each reagent. Based on your conclusions, you will predict the relative reactivities of other substrates with the reagents and test your predictions. In order to accomplish these objectives, you will have to think about the significance of your observations as you make them, so that your results from one set of reactivity measurements can lead to predictions about another set of measurements.

DIRECTIONS

All of the alkyl bromides are toxic and have harmful vapors, and some of them are suspected carcinogens. Avoid contact, and do not breathe their vapors.
Silver nitrate is toxic, causes skin irritation, and stains the skin black. Avoid contact with the silver nitrate reagent.

Safety Notes

A. *Reactions in Sodium Iodide/Acetone*
Directions for conducting reaction **1** follow. Be sure to label the reaction tubes so you know which substrate each contains.

1. Carry out reaction **1** using the following substrates: 2-bromobutane, 2-bromo-2-methylpropane, 1-bromobutane. Based on your results, decide whether the reaction in NaI/acetone is S_N1 or S_N2.
2. Predict the reactivities of the following substrates in NaI/acetone relative to the substrates in step 1: bromocyclohexane, 1-bromoadamantane. Then carry out reaction **1** using these substrates.

Stop and Think: Are your results as you predicted? If not, how can you explain them?

Reaction 1.   Obtain as many clean, dry 13 × 100-mm test tubes as there are alkyl halides to test. Measure 1 mL of 15% sodium iodide in acetone into each test tube. Add 2 drops of a different alkyl halide to each test tube, and stopper and shake the test tubes. (For a solid halide, use 0.1 g dissolved in a minimal volume of acetone). Observe them closely, and record the time needed for any precipitate to form. After 5 minutes, put any test tubes that do *not* contain a precipitate into a 50°C water bath, and leave them there for 6 minutes (loosen their stoppers first). Then cool the test tubes to room temperature, and note the formation of any precipitate.

Waste Disposal: Place the sodium iodide test solutions in a designated waste container.

B. *Reactions in Silver Nitrate/Ethanol*
Directions for conducting reaction **2** follow. Be sure to label the reaction tubes so you know which substrate each contains.

1. Carry out reaction **2** using the following substrates: 2-bromobutane, 2-bromo-2-methylpropane, 1-bromobutane. Based on your results, decide whether the reaction in $AgNO_3$/ethanol is S_N1 or S_N2.
2. Predict the reactivities of the following substrates in $AgNO_3$/ethanol relative to the substrates in step 1: α-bromotoluene, bromobenzene, 1-bromoadamantane. Then carry out reaction **2** using these substrates.

Stop and Think: Are your results as you predicted? If not, how can you explain them?

Reaction 2.   Obtain as many clean, dry 13 × 100-mm test tubes as there are alkyl halides to test. Measure 2 mL of a 0.10 *M* solution of silver nitrate in ethanol into each test tube. Add one drop of a different alkyl halide to each test tube, and stopper and shake the test tubes. (For a solid halide, use 50 mg dissolved in a minimal volume of ethanol.) Observe them closely, and record the time needed for any cloudiness or precipitate to form. After 5 minutes, use a hot-water bath or steam bath to gently boil for 2–3 minutes any solutions that do *not* contain a precipitate. Note the formation of any precipitate.

Waste Disposal: Place the silver nitrate test solutions in a designated waste container.

In your report, write balanced equations for the reactions undergone by each halide, and write mechanisms for both of the reactions undergone by 2-bromobutane. Arrange the alkyl bromides in order of reactivity in each reaction, tell whether each reaction is S_N1 or S_N2, and explain your reasoning. If either reaction is S_N1, use your results to predict the relative stabilities of the carbocations formed by each substrate. If any substrates in the S_N1 reaction appear to be equally reactive (or unreactive), show their carbocations as being of approximately equal stability, and try to learn their actual relative stabilities from your lecture textbook or elsewhere.

An S$_N$1 Reaction of Bromotriphenylmethane

Before You Begin: Read or review the operations as necessary.

The traditional Williamson synthesis of ethers involves the reaction of an alkyl halide with the sodium salt of an alcohol or phenol.

$$RX + R'ONa \longrightarrow ROR' + NaX$$

An alkoxide ion (R'O$^-$) is strongly nucleophilic and displaces halide ion by an S$_N$2 mechanism. Because an alkoxide is also a strong base, most *tertiary* alkyl halides tend to undergo E2 elimination under these conditions, producing alkenes rather than ethers. Using a less nucleophilic alcohol (R'OH) in place of the corresponding alkoxide prevents E2 elimination, but E1 elimination may then compete with S$_N$1 substitution to yield by-product alkenes along with the desired ether. Both E2 and E1 elimination are impossible for bromotriphenylmethane (trityl bromide), and the triphenyl-methyl (trityl) carbocation is very stable, so this tertiary halide reacts readily with alcohols to form ethers but no by-product alkenes. In this minilab, you will heat bromotriphenylmethane with ethanol to form an ether, ethoxy-triphenylmethane, by an S$_N$1 reaction.

Stop and Think: Why are these elimination reactions impossible?

Reaction of bromotriphenylmethane with ethanol

bromotriphenylmethane
(trityl bromide)

ethoxytriphenylmethane
(trityl ethyl ether)

DIRECTIONS

Bromotriphenylmethane is harmful if inhaled or absorbed through the skin. Avoid contact, and do not breathe its dust.
Since the reaction generates some gaseous hydrogen bromide, carry it out under a hood. Avoid contact with the reaction mixture, and do not breathe its vapors.

Safety Notes

You can use purified bromotriphenylmethane from Experiment 25 in this minilab, scaling down the quantities if necessary. *Under the hood,* mix 0.50 g (SS) or 0.10 g (µS) of bromotriphenylmethane with 5.0 mL (SS) or 1.0 mL (µS) of absolute ethanol in a test tube (SS) or Craig tube (µS). Add a boiling chip, and boil the mixture gently over a steam bath or in a hot-water bath

[OP-7] until no more HBr is evolved (test by holding moist blue litmus paper over the mouth of the tube). Replace any ethanol that evaporates. Remove the boiling chip, let the reaction mixture cool to room temperature, induce crystallization (if necessary), and cool [OP-8] it further using an ice/water bath. Then collect the ethoxytriphenylmethane by vacuum filtration [OP-16] on a Hirsch funnel (SS) or by centrifugation (µS) [OP-17]. Dry [OP-26b] the product, and measure its mass and melting point [OP-33].

Write a detailed mechanism for the reaction, and explain why E1 elimination, which often competes with S_N1 substitution, does not occur during this reaction.

MINILAB 18

Preparation and Properties of a Gaseous Alkene

Before You Begin: Predict the structure of the gaseous alkene that you will be preparing.

OH
|
CH_3CCH_3
|
CH_3
2-methyl-2-propanol

Alkenes can be prepared by elimination reactions in which a molecule of hydrogen halide (HX), halogen (X_2), or water is removed from a substrate. In this minilab, you will be carrying out an acid-catalyzed elimination reaction of 2-methyl-2-propanol to form a gaseous alkene with the molecular formula C_4H_8. You should be able to predict the structure of this alkene knowing the structure of the substrate. You will test your alkene with bromine in dichloromethane (CH_2Cl_2 is the solvent) and with aqueous $KMnO_4$, and look for evidence of a reaction in each case. You will also test its flammability to see whether it reacts with atmospheric oxygen. You should then be able to explain your observations and write equations for the reactions involved. (You may have to consult your lecture textbook for help in some cases.)

DIRECTIONS

With your instructor's permission, you can work in pairs. If your microscale lab kit doesn't have a gas delivery tube, use apparatus A in Figure M1.

Safety Notes

Sulfuric acid causes chemical burns that can seriously damage skin and eyes. Wear gloves and avoid contact.
Keep the gas you collect away from flames, except when you are testing its flammability.

Fill four 15-cm test tubes with water, stopper them tightly, and invert them in a pneumatic trough or a 1 L beaker that is about three-quarters filled with water. Remove the stoppers under water, so that no water flows out of the test tubes, and leave them inverted in the beaker or trough. Measure 1.0 mL of 2-methyl-2-propanol (*t*-butyl alcohol) into a 15-cm Pyrex test tube (SS) or a 3-mL conical vial (µS), add 5 drops of concentrated sulfuric acid, swirl to mix, and drop in a

Take Care! Wear gloves and avoid contact with H_2SO_4.

boiling chip. (If necessary, warm the bottle of 2-methyl-2-propanol over a steam bath or in a hot-water bath until the alcohol flows freely.)

Construct a gas generator as illustrated in Figure M1. If you are using the standard scale apparatus, clamp the reaction tube to a ring stand and position the free end of the gas delivery tube under water in the trough or beaker. If you are using the microscale apparatus, attach a plastic gas delivery tube (from your lab kit) to the conical vial with a compression cap, making sure that the O-ring is undamaged and the cap is screwed on securely, and clamp the vial to a ring stand. Then secure the free end of the tube under water in the beaker or trough (you can hold it in place with a forceps or another gripping device). Move one of the water-filled test tubes so that its mouth is over the outlet of the gas delivery tube. Heat [OP-7] the reaction tube or vial gently with a steam bath or a hot-water bath until a steady stream of gas bubbles emerges from the delivery tube and fills the test tube. As each test tube fills with gas, quickly remove it, stopper it, and replace it with a water-filled test tube. Repeat this until all of the test tubes are filled. Remove the gas delivery tube from the water, and then remove the heat source and cool the reaction vessel in cold water to stop the generation of gas.

Take Care! Keep flames away.

Don't stop heating until you have collected all of the gas samples and removed the gas delivery tube from the water. Otherwise, water will back up into the reaction vessel.

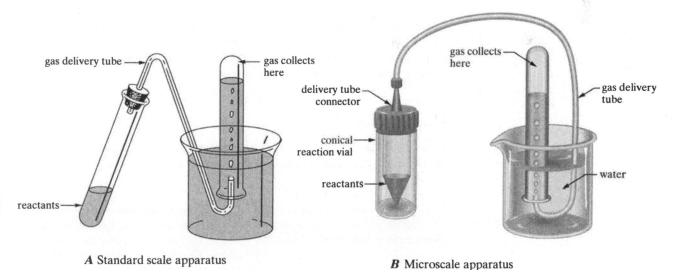

A Standard scale apparatus   *B* Microscale apparatus

Figure M1 Apparatus for gas generation

Discard the gas in the first test tube, which contains air. Add 5 drops of 0.10 *M* potassium permanganate to the second tube, then stopper and shake it. Add 5 drops of 1.0 *M* bromine in dichloromethane to the third tube, then stopper and shake it. Light one end of a wood splint with a match or a burner flame, and carefully lower the burning end into the fourth tube.

Write the structure of the gas and a balanced equation for its synthesis from 2-methyl-2-propanol. At your instructor's request, write a detailed mechanism for this reaction. Describe and explain your observations during the tests, and write a balanced equation for the chemical reaction that occurred in each of them.

Observe and Note: What happens?

Waste Disposal: Dispose of the contents of the test tubes as directed by your instructor.

MINILAB 19   Addition of Iodine to α-Pinene

α-pinene   cyclohexene

Before You Begin: Review material in your lecture textbook about ring strain and carbocation rearrangements.

In *All Creatures Great and Small,* the author, James Herriot, describes how veterinarians once disinfected wounds of cows, horses, and other large animals. The veterinarian would pack the wound with iodine, splash some turpentine on it, and stand back. The result was a violent reaction that forced gaseous iodine into the wound amid a cloud of purple vapor—accompanied by an equally violent reaction from the startled animal!

The major component of turpentine is α-pinene, an alkene having a carbon–carbon double bond in a six-membered ring and adjacent to the highly strained four-membered ring highlighted here. Although alkenes readily undergo addition reactions with chlorine and bromine, most of them are unreactive with iodine. If α-pinene is responsible for the reaction of turpentine with iodine, it must possess some special structural feature that makes it more reactive than most other alkenes. You will investigate the effect of treating α-pinene with iodine, and compare it to the effect of treating a control compound, cyclohexene, with iodine. Then you will attempt to explain your observations by proposing a mechanism for any reaction and predicting its products.

DIRECTIONS

Quantities may be cut in half for the microscale lab. Alternatively, the reaction may be carried out by your instructor, as a demonstration.

Safety Notes

> α-Pinene is flammable and irritates the skin and eyes; inhalation of its vapors may be harmful. Minimize contact, and do not breathe its vapors. The reaction with iodine may be violent. Conduct it under a fume hood; wear safety goggles and adequate protective clothing.

Take Care! Wear safety goggles and protective clothing.

Observe and Note: What happened?

Waste Disposal: Dispose of the mixture in both test tubes as directed by your instructor.

Weigh 0.50 g of iodine into each of two test tubes. *Under the hood,* add 1.0 mL of cyclohexene to the first test tube in one portion. Then add 1.0 mL of α-pinene to the second test tube in one portion, and step back quickly. Record your observations in your lab notebook.

Write a mechanism that explains the exothermicity of the α-pinene reaction, assuming a carbocation as the initial intermediate. Write an equation for this reaction showing two likely products (neither is a vicinal diiodide). Tell how your mechanism explains your experimental observations.

Unsaturation in Commercial Products

Before You Begin: For as many of the commercial products as you can, try to predict whether or not the product should be unsaturated or contain unsaturated components.

A substance is *unsaturated* if it contains fewer hydrogen atoms than are possible based on its molecular structure. Compounds that have carbon–carbon double bonds are unsaturated because they can add more hydrogen.

$$-C=C- + H_2 \xrightarrow{\text{catalyst}} -\overset{\displaystyle H}{\underset{\displaystyle |}{C}}-\overset{\displaystyle H}{\underset{\displaystyle |}{C}}-$$

Because bromine also adds to most double (and triple) bonds, a solution of bromine in carbon tetrachloride has often been used to test for unsaturation. If the compound tested is unsaturated, the red–brown color of the bromine fades as the bromine is consumed.

$$\underset{\text{red–brown}}{-C=C- + Br_2} \longrightarrow \underset{\text{colorless}}{-\overset{\displaystyle Br}{\underset{\displaystyle |}{C}}-\overset{\displaystyle Br}{\underset{\displaystyle |}{C}}-}$$

Carbon tetrachloride is toxic and carcinogenic, so you will use a saturated solution of bromine in water instead. When this solution is shaken with a solution of an unsaturated compound dissolved in dichloromethane, bromine migrates to the dichloromethane layer, where it can react. Thus, decolorization of the lower dichloromethane layer upon shaking indicates unsaturation, and the amount of bromine water it takes to produce a color in the lower layer is a measure of the degree of unsaturation.

DIRECTIONS

Dichloromethane may be harmful if inhaled or absorbed through the skin, and it is a suspected carcinogen. Avoid contact, and do not breathe its vapors.
Bromine is toxic and corrosive, and its vapors are very harmful. Avoid contact with the saturated bromine water, and do not breathe its vapors.

Safety Notes

Test as many of the following commercial products as possible (your instructor may add or remove some):

butter	canola oil
corn oil	dry-cleaning solvent
linseed oil	margarine
mineral oil	olive oil
paint thinner (mineral spirits)	rubber cement
rubbing alcohol	safflower oil
turpentine	vegetable shortening (Crisco, etc.)

Have ready enough clean 13 × 100-mm test tubes (with stoppers) to test each commercial product provided, and label each test tube appropriately. Dissolve 1 drop of each commercial product (or about 30 mg of a solid) in 0.5 mL of dichloromethane. You can use a calibrated Pasteur pipet [OP-5] to measure the solvent and a clean medicine dropper to measure the liquid commercial products. *Under the hood,* use a clean, calibrated Pasteur pipet to add 0.5 mL of saturated bromine water to each test tube. Stopper each test tube, and shake it vigorously for 10 seconds. Record the volume of bromine water added during this and all future additions. If the dichloromethane layer in a given test tube has a red–orange color, classify the commercial product it contains as saturated and set it aside. Add another 0.5 mL portion of bromine water to each of the remaining test tubes, stopper them, and shake as before. Repeat this process with any test tube whose dichloromethane layer is colorless after shaking, until the dichloromethane layer of every test tube is a red–orange color. Record the total volume of bromine water you added to each test tube.

In your report, classify each commercial product as saturated or unsaturated, and compare your results with your predictions. Considering the volume of bromine water you added to each test tube as a rough measure of the unsaturation of its contents, arrange the commercial products in order of degree of unsaturation. Note that there may be several compounds with about the same degree of unsaturation. Using sources such as those cited in the Bibliography, find out what kinds of unsaturated compounds may be present in each of the unsaturated commercial products. Draw structural formulas for representative components when you can.

Take Care! Avoid contact with dichloromethane and bromine water, and do not breathe their vapors.

Waste Disposal: Place the dichloromethane layers in a designated solvent recovery container.

MINILAB 21   Free-Radical Stability

Before You Begin: Try to predict the structures and relative stabilities of the free-radical intermediates that will form when each of the arenes (aromatic hydrocarbons) reacts with bromine; from that, predict the relative reactivities of the arenes.

The side chain of an arene such as toluene can undergo free-radical halogenation in the presence of light, as illustrated for the bromination of toluene. The rate of such a reaction depends on the stability of the intermediate free radical. As a rule, the more stable a free radical is, the faster it will form. In this minilab, you will determine the relative stabilities of the intermediates by measuring the relative reactivities of the corresponding substrates.

DIRECTIONS

Quantities may be cut in half for the microscale lab.

> Dichloromethane may be harmful if inhaled or absorbed through the skin, and it is a suspected carcinogen. Minimize contact with the liquid, and do not breathe its vapors.
>
> Bromine is toxic and corrosive, and its vapors are very harmful. Avoid contact with the bromine solution, and do not breathe its vapors.
>
> Toluene and the other aromatic hydrocarbons are flammable and have harmful vapors. Do not inhale their vapors.

Safety Notes

Add 2.0 mL of dichloromethane to each of four clean, dry, labeled 13 × 100-mm test tubes. To each test tube, add 0.5 mL of a different aromatic hydrocarbon—toluene, ethylbenzene, isopropylbenzene, or *t*-butylbenzene—and swirl to mix. *Under the hood,* carefully add 0.5 mL of *freshly prepared* 1.0 *M* bromine in dichloromethane to each test tube, then stopper and shake it. Record the time of bromine addition to the nearest minute. Set the test tubes in a well-lighted location, such as a windowsill, and record the approximate time it takes for each solution to become colorless. Observe the solutions closely for the first 5 minutes or so, and then at intervals during the lab period. If two or more solutions are not completely colorless by the end of the lab period, describe the relative intensity of their colors at that time.

Take Care! Avoid contact with dichloromethane, the aromatic hydrocarbons, and the bromine solution; do not breathe their vapors.

Arrange the four hydrocarbons in order of their reactivity toward bromine, most reactive first, and compare your results with your predictions. Write a balanced equation for each reaction (assuming monobromination), and give the structure of the free-radical intermediate. Arrange the free radicals in order of stability, and explain their relative stabilities. Write a complete mechanism for the bromination of toluene.

Waste Disposal: Place the bromine/dichloromethane solutions in a designated solvent recovery container.

The Nylon Rope Trick   MINILAB **22**

Before You Begin: Review the reactions of acyl chlorides with amines in your lecture textbook.

In a chemical magic show, the "magician" will sometimes combine two immiscible solutions in a beaker and draw out a seemingly endless rope of nylon. This "nylon rope trick" is based on the fact that reactive molecules in two immiscible liquid layers can come together and form a product at the interface between the liquids. If the product is a polymer that—like nylon—forms strong fibers, it can be pulled from the interface like a rope. If the rope is drawn out slowly enough, the nylon that is removed is continually replenished at the interface until one of the reactants is used up.

In this minilab, the reactants are 1,6-hexanediamine (hexamethylenedi-amine) and decanedioyl chloride (sebacoyl chloride). The product, because it is made from a 6-carbon diamine and a 10-carbon acyl dichloride, is called nylon 6,10.

$$n\text{H} - \underset{\overset{|}{\text{H}}}{\text{N}}(\text{CH}_2)_6\underset{\overset{|}{\text{H}}}{\text{N}} - \text{H} + n\text{Cl} - \overset{\overset{\text{O}}{\|}}{\text{C}}(\text{CH}_2)_8\overset{\overset{\text{O}}{\|}}{\text{C}} - \text{Cl} \longrightarrow$$

1,6-hexanediamine   decanedioyl chloride

$$-[\text{NH}(\text{CH}_2)_6\text{NH} - \overset{\overset{\text{O}}{\|}}{\text{C}}(\text{CH}_2)_8\overset{\overset{\text{O}}{\|}}{\text{C}}]_n^- + n\text{HCl}$$

nylon 6,10

DIRECTIONS

Quantities may be cut in half and beaker sizes reduced for the microscale lab.

Safety Notes

> **Acid chlorides are corrosive and harmful by inhalation and skin absorption. Avoid contact with decanedioyl chloride, and do not breathe its vapors.**
> **1,6-Hexanediamine is corrosive and harmful by inhalation. Avoid contact, and do not breathe its vapors.**
> **Dichloromethane may be harmful if inhaled or absorbed through the skin, and it is a suspected carcinogen. Minimize contact with the liquid, and do not breathe its vapors.**
> **Wear protective gloves throughout this experiment. Avoid touching the wet polymer with your hands; if you do, wash them immediately with soap and warm water.**

Take Care! Wear gloves and avoid contact with decanedioyl chloride, dichloromethane, and 1,6-hexane-diamine; do not breathe their vapors.

Mix 20 mL of 95% ethanol with 20 mL of water in a 100-mL beaker, and set it aside. *Under the hood*, dissolve 0.40 mL of pure decanedioyl chloride in 20 mL of dichloromethane in a 50-mL beaker. Combine 4.0 mL of 1.0 M sodium hydroxide with 8 mL of water in a small beaker, and then stir in 0.22 g of pure 1,6-hexanediamine until it dissolves. Tilt the beaker that contains the dichloromethane solution and slowly pour the 1,6-hexanediamine solution down its side, taking care not to mix the layers. Use a small spatula to free the polymer film from the side of the beaker, if necessary; then use a piece of copper wire, bent at one end like a fishhook, to hook the film at its center. Wearing protective gloves, pull the film up slowly and continuously to form a strand of nylon, loop it around a cardboard tube (such as the core of a paper towel or toilet tissue roll), and rotate the tube to wind it out of the solution until no more nylon rope can be drawn out. Unwind the nylon into the aqueous ethanol in the 100-mL beaker, and stir gently to wash it. Then decant the wash solvent, lay the polymer on a paper towel to dry (blotting it between two towels will reduce the drying time), and weigh it when it is dry.

Waste Disposal: Place the liquids from the *reaction* beaker in a designated solvent recovery container. Unless your instructor directs otherwise, flush the wash solvent down the drain.

Nucleophilic Substitution Rates of Alcohols

MINILAB 23

Before You Begin: Classify each alcohol as primary, secondary, or tertiary, and try to predict their relative reactivities with the HCl–ZnCl$_2$ reagent.

In acidic solutions, alcohols can react with various nucleophiles by either an S_N1 or S_N2 mechanism. The S_N1 mechanism involves loss of water from the protonated alcohol to form a carbocation, which then combines with the nucleophile. The S_N2 reaction involves nucleophilic attack on the protonated alcohol to yield the product directly.

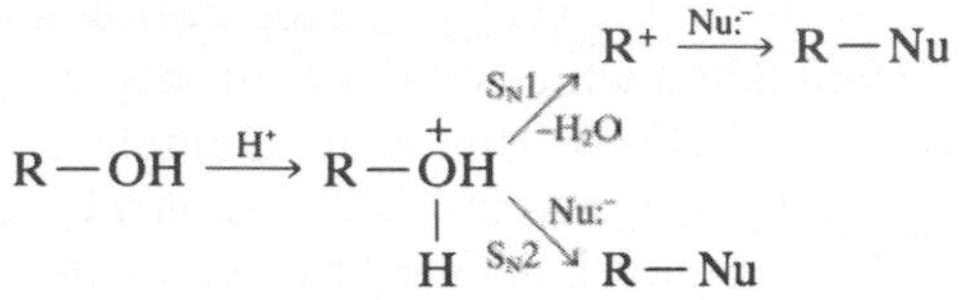

$$R-OH \xrightarrow{H^+} R-\overset{+}{\underset{\underset{H}{|}}{O}}H \begin{array}{c} \overset{S_N1}{\nearrow} \quad R^+ \xrightarrow{Nu:^-} R-Nu \\ {\scriptstyle -H_2O} \\ \underset{S_N2}{\searrow} \quad R-Nu \\ {\scriptstyle Nu:^-} \end{array}$$

In this minilab, you will carry out the reaction of an alcohol with hydrochloric acid in the presence of zinc chloride, a Lewis acid catalyst.

$$R-OH + HCl \xrightarrow{ZnCl_2} R-Cl + H_2O$$

The ZnCl$_2$ apparently coordinates with the oxygen atom of the alcohol, converting its $-OH$ (a very poor leaving group) to a better leaving group.

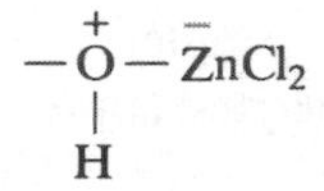

$$-\overset{+}{\underset{\underset{H}{|}}{O}}-\overset{-}{Zn}Cl_2$$

You will use your results to decide whether the reaction appears to proceed by an S_N1 or S_N2 mechanism.

DIRECTIONS

Safety Notes

Label and number three clean, dry 13 × 100-mm test tubes. Measure 10 drops of (1) 1-butanol, (2) 2-butanol, and (3) 2-methyl-2-propanol into the corresponding test tubes. *Under the hood,* add 2.0 mL of the HCl–ZnCl$_2$ reagent to each test tube, stopper and shake each tube vigorously for 5 seconds, and then let them stand at room temperature. Look for any evidence of a reaction, recording your observations during the first 15 minutes or so and at intervals throughout the lab period.

Take Care! Wear gloves, avoid contact with the HCl–ZnCl$_2$ solution, and do not breathe its vapors.

Waste Disposal: Put the contents of your test tubes in a designated waste container.

Compare your results with your predictions. Assuming that all of the alcohols react by the same mechanism, if they react, decide whether the reaction occurs by an S_N1 or S_N2 mechanism and explain how you arrived at your conclusion. Write balanced equations and mechanisms for any reactions for which you saw evidence.

MINILAB 24   Photoreduction of Benzophenone

Before You Begin: Read or review the operations as necessary, and propose a hypothesis regarding the outcome of the reaction.

Around 1900, an Italian scientist mixed benzophenone with isopropyl alcohol and left the mixture on a sunny rooftop in Bologna, Italy. When he returned, he discovered that a white solid had formed as a result of the action of sunlight on the reactants. This is an example of a *photochemical reaction*—a reaction that is initiated by visible or ultraviolet radiation.

When a benzophenone molecule absorbs light of an appropriate wavelength, one of two paired ground-state electrons on its oxygen atom jumps to an antibonding pi orbital without changing its spin state. This puts the molecule into a *singlet* excited state, in which both electrons have opposite spins. The singlet-state molecule can undergo another transition to a *triplet* excited state, in which both electrons have the same spin.

$$\underset{\substack{\text{ground}\\\text{state}}}{\underline{\uparrow\downarrow}} \quad \xrightarrow{\;h\nu\;} \quad \underset{\substack{\text{singlet}\\\text{excited state}}}{\overset{\downarrow}{\underline{}}\;\uparrow} \quad \longrightarrow \quad \underset{\substack{\text{triplet}\\\text{excited state}}}{\overset{\uparrow}{\underline{}}\;\uparrow}$$

A triplet-state benzophenone molecule is very reactive and behaves like a diradical. It can even strip a hydrogen atom from a molecule of 2-propanol (a very unlikely reducing agent), which then loses a second hydrogen atom to ground-state benzophenone and is converted to a molecule of acetone.

$$\underset{\substack{\text{benzophenone}\\(* = \text{triplet state})}}{\underset{\text{Ph}}{\overset{O^*}{\underset{|}{\overset{||}{PhC}}}} + \underset{\text{Ph}}{\overset{O}{\underset{|}{\overset{||}{PhC}}}} + \underset{}{\overset{OH}{\underset{|}{CH_3CHCH_3}}}} \longrightarrow 2\underset{\text{Ph}}{\overset{OH}{\underset{|}{PhC\cdot}}} + \underset{}{\overset{O}{\underset{}{\overset{||}{CH_3CCH_3}}}}$$

This leaves two identical diphenylhydroxymethyl radicals that might combine to yield a molecule of benzopinacol.

$$2\underset{\text{Ph}}{\overset{OH}{\underset{|}{PhC\cdot}}} \longrightarrow \underset{\substack{\\\text{benzopinacol}}}{\underset{\text{Ph}}{\overset{OH}{\underset{|}{PhC}}}\!-\!\underset{\text{Ph}}{\overset{OH}{\underset{|}{CPh}}}}$$

Bases can catalyze cleavage of this product, so a drop of acetic acid is added to neutralize any base present in the reaction mixture. Another possible product of the reaction is benzhydrol, which can form if a diphenylhydroxymethyl radical abstracts a hydrogen atom from 2-propanol.

$$
\underset{\text{benzhydrol}}{\overset{\displaystyle\overset{\text{OH}}{|}}{\text{PhCPh}} + \overset{\displaystyle\overset{\text{OH}}{|}}{\text{CH}_3\text{CHCH}_3} \longrightarrow \overset{\displaystyle\overset{\text{OH}}{|}}{\text{PhCHPh}} + \overset{\displaystyle\overset{\text{OH}}{|}}{\text{CH}_3\text{CCH}_3}}
$$

In this minilab, you will find out whether benzophenone will react with isopropyl alcohol in the presence of light and, if so, whether the product is benzhydrol or benzopinacol.

DIRECTIONS

Quantities may be cut in half for the microscale lab. Use a Pasteur pipet to deliver a drop of acetic acid.

> Acetic acid causes chemical burns, and its vapors are highly irritating to the eyes and respiratory tract. Dispense under a hood, avoid contact, and do not breathe its vapors.

Combine 1.0 g of benzophenone with 5.0 mL of 2-propanol (isopropyl alcohol) in a test tube, and warm [OP-7] the mixture gently with manual stirring to dissolve the benzophenone. *Under the hood,* add a drop of glacial acetic acid with a medicine dropper, then stopper the test tube tightly and shake it. Place it on a windowsill where it will receive direct sunlight, if possible; otherwise, place it close to a strong artificial light source. After a week or more, collect any precipitate by vacuum filtration [OP-16], washing it on the filter [OP-26a] with cold ethanol. Dry [OP-26b] the product, and measure its melting point [OP-33]. Leave the filtrate in sunlight for another week or so to see if any additional product forms. If it does, collect and dry it also; then weigh the combined product.

Decide whether the solid you obtained is benzopinacol, benzhydrol, or unreacted benzophenone by looking up these compounds in *The Merck Index.* Write a balanced equation for the reaction.

Safety Notes

Take Care! Avoid contact with acetic acid, and do not breathe its vapors.

If the laboratory is very cold, some benzophenone may precipitate before it reacts.

Waste Disposal: Place the filtrate in a designated solvent recovery container.

Oxidation of Alcohols by Potassium Permanganate

MINILAB 25

Before You Begin: Classify the alcohols as primary, secondary, and tertiary. Review the reactions of alcohols in your lecture textbook.

Primary and secondary alcohols can be converted to aldehydes and ketones by certain oxidizing agents. Tertiary alcohols are not converted directly to carbonyl compounds by oxidizing agents because such a reaction would require cleavage of a carbon–carbon bond. In this minilab, you will

$$
-\underset{|}{\overset{|}{\text{C}}}-\text{H} \xrightarrow[-2\text{H}]{\text{oxidizing agent}} -\underset{|}{\overset{\|}{\text{C}}}
$$

treat several alcohols with neutral potassium permanganate, then with potassium permanganate acidified with HCl, and compare their reactivities. You will also observe the effect of adding sulfuric acid to any reaction mixture containing an alcohol that has not yet reacted.

DIRECTIONS

Quantities may be cut in half for the microscale lab.

Safety Notes

> **Sulfuric acid causes chemical burns that can seriously damage skin and eyes; avoid contact.**

Stop and Think: What is the solid that forms?

Clean and number five small test tubes. Add 2.0 mL of aqueous 0.05% potassium permanganate to each test tube. Use test tube #1 as a control, and add two drops of each of the following alcohols to the other test tubes: #2, methanol; #3, ethanol; #4, 2-propanol; #5, 2-methyl-2-propanol. Stopper and shake each test tube for 10 seconds; record your observations immediately after shaking, then after standing for 5 and 10 minutes, respectively. If any solution shows little or no evidence of reaction (compared to the control) after 10 minutes, add 4 drops of 3.0 M HCl, shake, and observe at the same intervals as before. If any solution shows little or no evidence of reaction 10 minutes after the HCl addition, add 2 drops of concentrated sulfuric acid, shake, and observe at the same intervals as before.

Take Care! Avoid contact with H_2SO_4.

Waste Disposal: Place the potassium permanganate test solutions in a designated waste container.

Arrange the alcohols in order of reactivity toward $KMnO_4$, and describe the effect of substrate structure on reactivity. Based on alcohol reactions you have studied, explain any reaction of a tertiary alcohol for which you saw evidence. Draw the structure of the organic product of each reaction. Write a balanced equation for the reaction of methanol with acidic $KMnO_4$ (you can balance it using the half-reaction method you learned in general chemistry).

MINILAB 26

Preparation of a Fluorescent Dye

Before You Begin: Calculate the molar amounts of resorcinol and phthalic anhydride, decide which one is the limiting reactant, and calculate the theoretical yield of fluorescein.

Certain dyes and indicators, such as phenolphthalein and fluorescein, resemble the triphenylmethane dyes (see Experiment 30) in that their molecules contain three benzene rings attached to a central carbon atom. In this minilab, you will prepare fluorescein by a Lewis-acid catalyzed reaction of resorcinol (1,3-dihydroxybenzene) with phthalic anhydride.

You will convert the fluorescein to its basic form, disodium fluorescein, by dissolving it in dilute NaOH. Then you will irradiate the resulting solution with ultraviolet light at different pH values and record your observations.

DIRECTIONS

If "shortie" thermometers are available in your microscale lab, the quantities can be cut in half.

Safety Notes

Zinc chloride is toxic and corrosive, with harmful fumes. Resorcinol and phthalic anhydride are severe skin and eye irritants. Wear gloves and use a hood during this experiment. Avoid contact with zinc chloride, resorcinol, and phthalic anhydride, and do not breathe their fumes or dust. Before you light a burner, make sure that no flammable solvents are nearby.

Under the hood, measure 0.32 g of anhydrous zinc chloride into a 13 × 100-mm test tube. Heat [OP-7] it over a burner flame or (preferably) in a heating block until the zinc chloride melts and no more bubbles of vapor are evolved. When you remove the test tube from the heat source, tilt and rotate it so that the zinc chloride coats its sides as it cools. Add 0.44 g of phthalic anhydride and 0.72 g of resorcinol, and heat the test tube cautiously until the temperature of the melt is 180°C. Use a mercury-free thermometer to measure the temperature. Keep it near that temperature, stirring continuously with a stirring rod, until no more bubbles are evolved. Let the mixture cool for a minute or so; then add 5 mL of 2.0 *M* hydrochloric acid and heat the mixture to boiling, with constant stirring. Continue to stir it at the boiling point for 2–3 minutes to dissolve zinc salts and unreacted starting materials, using the stirring rod (as needed) to break up the solid

Take Care! Wear gloves, avoid contact with anhydrous zinc chloride, and do not breathe its fumes.

Take Care! Avoid contact with phthalic acid and resorcinol. Do not use your thermometer as a stirring rod.

Fluorescein stains are very hard to remove, so keep it off your skin and clothing.

Waste Disposal: Unless your instructor directs otherwise, wash the filtrates down the drain.

Take Care! Do not look directly at the UV light source.

Waste Disposal: Place the solution in a designated waste container.

mass. Cool the mixture in an ice/water bath, and collect the crude product by vacuum filtration [OP-16]. Transfer the air-dried solid to a 13×100-mm test tube and use a sturdy stirring rod, as needed, to crush any lumps and grind it to a powder (be careful not to break the test tube). Add another 5-mL portion of 2.0 M HCl and boil the mixture, with stirring, as before. Cool it in an ice/water bath, and collect the fluorescein by vacuum filtration. Dry [OP-26b] the fluorescein and weigh it.

Dissolve about 10 mg (0.010 g) of fluorescein in 10 mL of 0.10 M sodium hydroxide. Irradiate the solution with an ultraviolet lamp in a darkened room. Add 2.0 M hydrochloric acid, drop by drop, until the appearance of the solution under the UV lamp changes markedly, and record your observations. Describe and explain your observations, and explain why the color of a fluorescein solution is different at high and low pH.

Diels–Alter Reaction of Maleic Anhydride and Furan

MINILAB 27

Before You Begin: Read or review the operations as necessary. Referring to Experiment 32, propose a hypothesis regarding the stereochemistry of the adduct.

furan　　resonance structure
for furan

Some aromatic compounds behave like conjugated dienes when reacting with certain dienophiles. Furan is an aromatic heterocyclic compound that undergoes Diels–Alder reactions as if it existed as the diene shown in the margin (this is one of several resonance structures for furan). Furan forms a bicyclic adduct with maleic anhydride that can have either an *endo* or an *exo* stereochemistry.

furan　　maleic　　*endo* adduct　　*exo* adduct
anyhdride

The transition state leading to an *endo* adduct is stabilized by pi-electron overlap, causing the *endo* adduct to form faster. When a Diels–Alder reaction is under *kinetic control*, meaning that the product that forms faster is favored, the *endo* adduct is the major or sole product. However, most *endo* adducts are less stable than the corresponding *exo* adducts, so when a Diels–Alder reaction is under *thermodynamic control*—meaning that the more stable product is favored—the *exo* adduct should be the major or sole product.

In this minilab, you will prepare the Diels–Alder adduct of maleic anhydride and furan, measure its melting point, and decide whether the reaction is under kinetic or thermodynamic control. Because the reaction takes several days, you should prepare the reaction mixture during a lab period prior to the one in which you plan to isolate and analyze the product. The melting point of the *endo* adduct is 81°C, and the melting point of the *exo* adduct is 114°C. The adduct tends to decompose near its melting point, so measure an approximate melting point (T_1) at a rapid rate, and then obtain a more accurate melting point by raising the temperature slowly and inserting a melting-point capillary when it reaches T_1.

Stop and Think: What products do you think the adduct forms when it decomposes?

DIRECTIONS

The quantities may be divided by 5 for the microscale lab.

Maleic anhydride is corrosive and toxic, and it can cause severe damage to the eyes, skin, and upper respiratory tract. Wear gloves, avoid contact, and do not breathe its dust. If you must powder maleic anhydride briquettes, do it under the hood, and wear safety goggles and protective clothing.
Diethyl ether and hexanes are extremely flammable and may be harmful if inhaled. Do not breathe their vapors, and keep them away from flames and hot surfaces.
Furan is flammable and harmful by inhalation, ingestion, and skin contact. Avoid contact, do not breathe its vapors, and keep it away from flames and hot surfaces.

Safety Notes

Dissolve 1.20 g of finely divided maleic anhydride in 10 mL of anhydrous diethyl ether in a conical centrifuge tube or a test tube by warming the mixture gently on a steam bath or in a hot-water bath [OP-7]. Replace any ether that evaporates. When the solution is cool, add 1.00 mL of furan (accurately measured). Using a square of Parafilm to prevent evaporation of ether, cap or stopper the reaction tube and leave it in a designated location for several days or until the next lab period. Collect the crystallized adduct by vacuum filtration [OP-16], and air-dry it on the funnel. Recrystallize [OP-28] the adduct from hexanes/ethyl acetate by heating it *just* to boiling in 5 mL of hexanes, and then adding enough warm ethyl acetate (~1–3 mL) to the mixture, with stirring, to dissolve the solid. After you collect the product by vacuum filtration, wash it on the filter [OP-26a] with cold hexanes. Dry [OP-26b] the adduct, and measure its mass and melting point [OP-33].

Take Care! Wear gloves, avoid contact with maleic anhydride and furan, and do not breathe their dust or vapor. Keep flames away from diethyl ether.

Tell whether the adduct is *endo* or *exo*, and propose an explanation for your result; write equations for any relevant reactions. (*Hint:* Why do you think this adduct decomposes at its melting point while most other maleic anhydride adducts do not?)

Take Care! Keep flames away from the solvents.

Waste Disposal: Place all filtrates in appropriate solvent recovery containers.

Stop and Think: Was your hypothesis correct?

Identification of an Unknown
Arene by NMR Spectrometry

MINILAB **28**

Before You Begin: Read or review OP-40, "Nuclear Magnetic Resonance Spectrometry." Be sure you understand how to interpret nuclear magnetic resonance (NMR) spectra by reading the appropriate sections in OP-40 and, if necessary, relevant sections from your lecture textbook.

NMR spectrometry is one of the most valuable tools at the disposal of an organic chemist. A chemist skilled in spectral interpretation can often derive the molecular structure of a complex organic compound from its ^1H and ^{13}C NMR spectra alone. In this minilab, you will record the ^1H NMR spectrum of a relatively simple aromatic hydrocarbon (arene) or another type of compound selected by your instructor. At your instructor's discretion, you may also record its ^{13}C NMR spectrum. You will then use your spectrum (or spectra) to deduce the molecular structure of the unknown compound.

DIRECTIONS

Your instructor may elect to assign you a compound with a different molecular formula than the one specified here.

Safety Notes

> The aromatic hydrocarbons are flammable and have harmful vapors. Do not inhale their vapors.
>
> Deuterochloroform is harmful if inhaled or absorbed through the skin, and it is a suspected human carcinogen. Avoid contact with the liquid, and do not breathe its vapors.

Take Care! Avoid contact with CDCl$_3$, and do not breathe its vapors.

Waste Disposal: Place the deuterochloroform solution in a designated solvent recovery container. Place any remaining unknown in a designated waste container.

You will be issued a small amount of an unknown arene that has the molecular formula $C_{10}H_{14}$. As directed by your instructor, record an integrated ^1H NMR spectrum [OP-40] of the compound in deuterochloroform (CDCl$_3$), using tetramethylsilane (TMS) as a reference compound. If requested, record its ^{13}C NMR spectrum as well, or obtain the spectrum from your instructor.

Letter the signals (a, b, c, etc.) from right to left, and construct a table listing the chemical shift (δ), signal area, and multiplicity for each signal. For each signal, determine the number of protons giving rise to the signal, the number of neighboring protons (except for Ar—H signals), and the proton type (aromatic, benzylic, etc.); include this information in your table. Use this information to deduce the structure of your unknown compound and explain, in detail, how you arrived at it. Turn in your table and NMR spectrum (or spectra) with your report.

MINILAB 29   Interpretation of a Mass Spectrum

Before You Begin: Read OP-42, "Mass Spectrometry." If you are to analyze an acetate ester of an unknown alcohol, also read the spectral interpretation rules provided by your instructor.

When an organic compound is injected into a mass spectrometer, its molecules are bombarded by a stream of high-energy electrons. When such an electron encounters a molecule, it can dislodge one of the molecule's electrons, producing a charged *molecular ion*, $M^{\cdot+}$. Each molecular ion can then fragment in a variety of ways, giving rise to an array of *daughter ions*. A mass spectrum of a compound is a record of all of the molecular ions and daughter ions arising from the fragmentation of its molecules. Each peak on a mass spectrum corresponds (usually) to one kind of ion; its location gives the mass/charge ratio of the ion (usually equal to its mass), and its intensity indicates the relative abundance of the ion.

In this minilab, you will obtain the mass spectrum of the major component of an unknown liquid using a gas chromatograph–mass spectrometer (GC–MS) or the mass spectrum of a pure liquid using a mass spectrometer. Following your instructor's directions and the procedure described here, you will then interpret your mass spectrum as completely as you can.

DIRECTIONS

This minilab may be performed by teams of three or more students, each working with a different unknown.

> **Assume that the unknown liquid is flammable and harmful by inhalation, ingestion, and skin absorption. Avoid contact, do not breathe its vapors, and keep flames away.**

Safety Notes

You will receive a liquid in a capped vial for analysis. Alternatively, you can use an acetate ester of an unknown alcohol prepared as described in Minilab 5. Your instructor will show you how to operate the mass spectrometer or GC–MS instrument [OP-42], or will operate it for you. Unless directed otherwise, inject a $2-3$-μL headspace sample into the injection port and obtain a printout of the compound's mass spectrum.

Identify the base peak and molecular ion peak, and determine the molecular weight of your compound. Analyze as many peaks as you can by assigning structures for the species that may be responsible for them, including (for example) species arising from α-cleavage and McLafferty rearrangements. At your instructor's request, determine the molecular formula of the compound and attempt to derive its structure, working with the other members of your team. Summarize your spectral data and interpretations in a table, and report and justify your conclusions. Write mechanisms for the formation of as many species as you can.

Waste Disposal: Return any unused unknown to your instructor in the original vial.

Nitration of Naphthalene   MINILAB **30**

Before You Begin: Read or review the operations as necessary. Review the mechanisms of electrophilic aromatic substitution reactions, as needed, and then predict the major product of the reaction.

Polynuclear aromatic hydrocarbons such as naphthalene can be nitrated by the same methods as benzene derivatives, including the well-known "mixed acid" method that utilizes a mixture of nitric acid and sulfuric acid. The electrophile is the nitronium ion, NO_2^+, which is formed at low concentration by a reaction of the two acids. The mononitration of naphthalene could lead to either one of two products, 1-nitronaphthalene or 2-nitronaphthalene.

1-nitronaphthalene
m.p. 61°C

2-nitronaphthalene
m.p. 79°C

The major product of the reaction you will carry out is the one that forms from the more stable carbocation intermediate (also called an arenium ion). By drawing all possible resonance structures for the carbocation intermediates leading to these products, you should be able to predict the major product. You will then carry out the nitration of naphthalene, identify the product from its melting point, and find out whether your prediction was correct. Because it is difficult to purify the product completely, your melting point may be somewhat lower than the listed value.

DIRECTIONS

Quantities may be cut in half for the microscale lab

Safety Notes

Sulfuric acid and nitric acid can cause very serious burns, and they react violently with water and other chemicals. Nitric acid produces toxic nitrogen dioxide fumes during the reaction. Use gloves and a hood, avoid contact with the acids, and do not breathe their vapors.
The nitronaphthalene is a suspected carcinogen; avoid contact.
The mixture of hexanes is very flammable; keep flames away.

If the mixed-acid nitrating solution has not been prepared, make it under the hood (wear gloves) by measuring 1.0 mL of concentrated nitric acid into a conical centrifuge tube or test tube, cooling it in ice, and cautiously mixing in 1.0 mL of concentrated sulfuric acid.

Take Care! Wear gloves while handling mixed acid, avoid contact, and do not breathe its vapors. Do not use your thermometer as a stirring rod.

Waste Disposal: Dispose of the liquid as directed by your instructor.

Waste Disposal: Unless your instructor directs otherwise, wash the filtrate down the drain.

Take Care! Keep flames away from hexanes.

Waste Disposal: Place the filtrate and any remaining oil in a designated solvent recovery container.

Measure 2.0 mL of the mixed acid (1:1 sulfuric acid and nitric acid) into a small test tube or a conical vial. In small portions, add 1.0 g of finely divided naphthalene to the mixed acid, stirring or shaking [OP-10] after each addition and cooling [OP-8] as necessary to keep the temperature around 45–50°C. Then stir or shake the reaction mixture in a 60°C water bath for 20 minutes. After the reaction mixture cools to room temperature, transfer it to a beaker containing 50 mL of ice-cold water, with stirring. Wait for the yellow product to solidify, and then decant the liquid (see OP-15), leaving the solid behind. *Under the hood,* boil the solid with 15 mL of fresh water for 10 minutes or more. Cool the mixture in ice, and collect the product by vacuum filtration [OP-16]. Recrystallize [OP-28] about 0.2 g of the crude product by heating it under reflux [OP-7] for 5 minutes or more with 10 mL of hexanes and filtering [OP-15] the hot solution (leave any undissolved oil behind) with a preheated filtering pipet or a powder funnel. When crystallization is complete, collect the product by vacuum filtration. Dry [OP-26a] it and the unpurified product. Measure the total mass of the nitronaphthalene and the melting point [OP-33] of the purified product.

Deduce the structure of the product. Write a mechanism for the reaction, showing all resonance structures for the intermediate, and explain its orientation.

Preparation of Carbocations
by the Friedel–Crafts Reaction   MINILAB **31**

Before You Begin: Review the mechanism of Friedel–Crafts alkylation in your lecture textbook.

A simple chemical test for aromatic hydrocarbons can be carried out by pipetting a solution of the unknown compound in trichloromethane (chloroform) over some freshly sublimed aluminum chloride. If the unknown is aromatic, a characteristic color (other than light yellow) will appear. The test is based on the Friedel–Crafts reaction of the aromatic hydrocarbon with trichloromethane, which, because it has three chlorine atoms, reacts with three molecules of the aromatic hydrocarbon to form a triarylmethane. The triarylmethane then loses a hydride ion to one of several different carbocation intermediates, yielding a colored triarylmethyl carbocation that is structurally related to the triphenylmethane dyes discussed in Experiment 30.

$$3ArH + CHCl_3 \xrightarrow{AlCl_3} Ar_3CH + 3HCl$$

$$Ar_3CH + R^+ \longrightarrow Ar_3C^+ + RH \quad (R^+ = Ar_2CH^+, \text{ etc.})$$

In this minilab, you will carry out the Friedel–Crafts reaction on a test-tube scale with several aromatic hydrocarbons and observe the colors of the products. You will use only a few drops of trichloromethane for each reaction, but because it is a suspected carcinogen, you must wear gloves and work under a hood.

DIRECTIONS

At your instructor's discretion, this minilab can be carried out by teams of two or more students. Your instructor may add or remove some test compounds.

Safety Notes

> Aluminum chloride reacts violently with water; skin and eye contact can cause painful burns, and inhaling its dust or vapors is harmful. Wear gloves, avoid contact, do not inhale dust or vapors, and keep it away from water.
>
> Trichloromethane is harmful if inhaled, ingested, or absorbed through the skin, and it is a suspected human carcinogen. Wear gloves, and work under a hood. Avoid contact with the liquid, and do not breathe its vapors.
>
> The aromatic hydrocarbons have harmful vapors; avoid inhalation.

Label five or more clean, *dry*, test tubes, and add a drop of one of the following compounds (or about 20 mg, if it is a solid) to each test tube: toluene, limonene, naphthalene, anthracene, biphenyl. *Under the hood,* add 8 drops of trichloromethane to each test tube. *Under the hood,* carefully measure about 0.10 g of anhydrous aluminum chloride into a clean, *dry* 13 × 100-mm test tube. Heat the test tube gently over a burner flame [OP-7] until the aluminum chloride forms a thin layer of sublimed solid up the sides of the tube. When it is cool, pipet the toluene solution down one

Take Care! Wear gloves, avoid contact with trichloromethane and aluminum chloride, and do not breathe their vapors.

Take Care! Be sure that there are no flammable solvents in the vicinity.

Observe and Note: What happened? Describe your observations.

Waste Disposal: Rinse the test tubes that contain the trichloromethane solutions into a designated waste container.

Stop and Think: Which of the test compounds are aromatic?

MINILAB 32

side that is coated with the white solid. Repeat the test, applying the remaining solutions to fresh areas of the sublimed solid. You should be able to use the same $AlCl_3$ layer to test several compounds; if necessary, prepare a fresh layer on another clean, dry test tube. Tabulate and explain your observations. Write equations and a detailed mechanism for the reaction of toluene with trichloromethane, assuming *para* substitution.

Air Oxidation of Fluorene to 9-Fluorenone

Before You Begin: Read or review the operations as necessary.

Oxidizing the side chain of an arene usually requires a powerful oxidizing agent such as potassium permanganate or chromium(III) oxide in acetic anhydride, as illustrated for the following reactions of toluene:

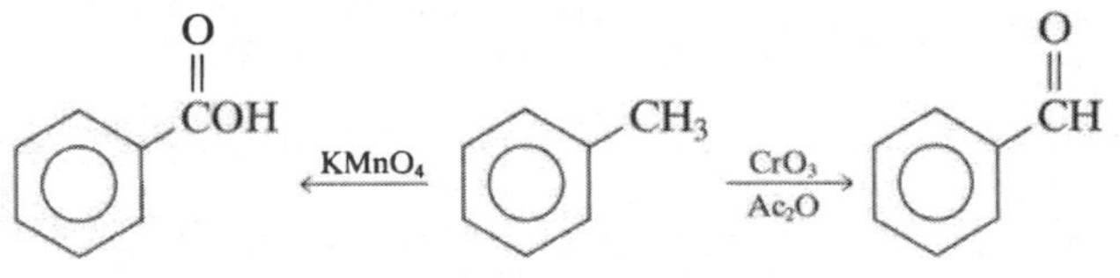

toluene

The methylene side chain of fluorene, however, can be oxidized to a carbonyl group by a much milder oxidizing agent, air.

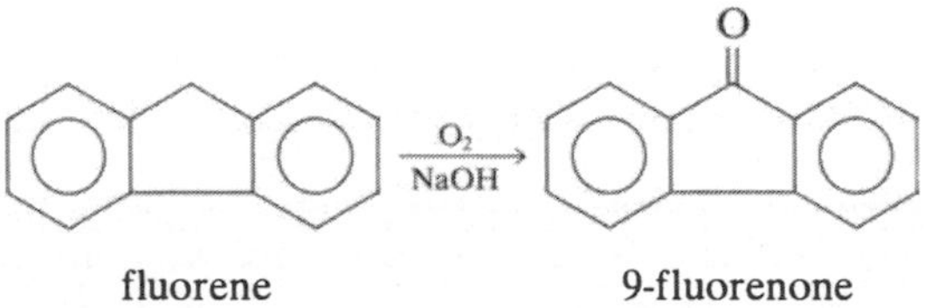

fluorene   9-fluorenone

This reaction, which yields the aromatic ketone 9-fluorenone, is ordinarily quite slow, but with vigorous stirring and a phase-transfer catalyst, it can be carried out in about an hour.

DIRECTIONS

Quantities may be cut in half and a 12-mm stir bar used for the microscale lab.

Safety Notes

Sodium hydroxide is toxic and corrosive, causing severe damage to skin, eyes, and mucous membranes. Wear gloves, and avoid contact with the NaOH solution.

Take Care! Keep flames away from heptane. Wear gloves, and avoid contact with the NaOH solution.

Mix 0.80 g of fluorene with 8.0 mL of heptane in a 50-mL Erlenmeyer flask. Add 4 mL of 10 M (~30%) aqueous sodium hydroxide. Then add 10 drops of tricaprylmethylammonium chloride (Aliquat 336) and stir [OP-10] the mixture vigorously for an hour or more, using a 1-inch or larger magnetic stir bar. The stirring rate should be high enough to produce a froth on the surface of the reaction mixture. Transfer the reaction mixture to a 15-mL conical centrifuge tube or a large test tube, cool it [OP-8] in an ice/water bath, and carefully remove the aqueous (lower) layer with a Pasteur pipet. Collect the crude fluorenone by vacuum filtration [OP-16], washing it on the filter with a small amount of 1.0 *M* HCl, and then with water. Dry [OP-26] it at room temperature or in an oven at 60°C. Recrystallize [OP-28] the 9-fluorenone from cyclohexane, and measure its mass and melting point [OP-33].

Explain why fluorene is oxidized by O_2 much more rapidly than is toluene, given that oxidation by O_2 involves free-radical intermediates.

Take Care! Keep flames away from cyclohexane.

Waste Disposal: Place the filtrates containing heptane and cyclohexane in a designated waste container.

A Nucleophilic Addition–Elimination Reaction of Benzil

MINILAB 33

Before You Begin: Read or review the operations as necessary. Review the reactions of carbonyl compounds with ammonia derivatives in your lecture textbook.

Like the Wittig reaction (see Experiment 42), the reaction of an ammonia derivative with a carbonyl compound involves a nucleophilic addition step, followed by an elimination step that yields a double bond.

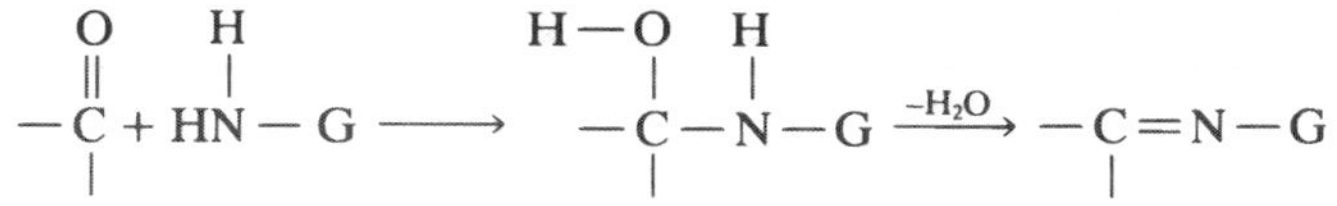

nucleophilic addition   elimination

G = R, Ar, NHAr, OH, etc.

Benzil has two carbonyl groups, so it can react with certain ammonia derivatives that have two NH_2 groups to form cyclic compounds. In this minilab, you will carry out the reaction of benzil with 1,2-benzenediamine (*o*-phenylenediamine) to prepare the heterocyclic amine 2,3-diphenylquinoxaline.

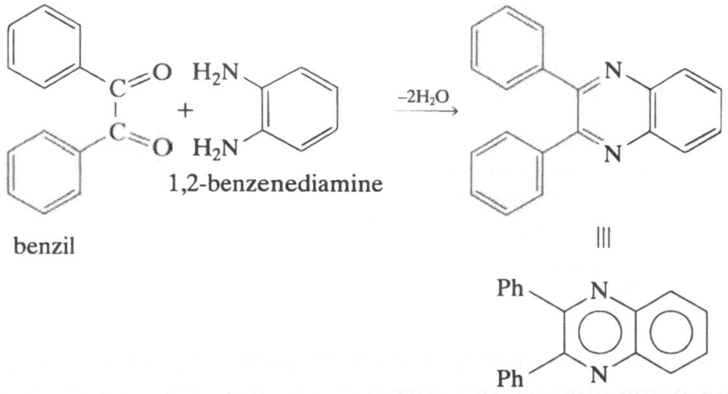

benzil   1,2-benzenediamine   III

2,3-diphenylquinoxaline

PART IV

Qualitative Organic Analysis

Part IV describes how to classify and identify unknown organic compounds using chemical and spectrometric methods. Qualitative organic analysis procedures require only small amounts of chemicals and can be performed with equipment provided in both standard scale and microscale lab lockers, so separate standard scale and microscale procedures are not given here. All students will follow the same directions, but microscale options will be described for some procedures.

on shaking, but should soon escape) for suspended liquid droplets. If the mixture looks cloudy or shows suspended droplets when shaken, or if a separate layer is visible above or below the water layer after standing, shake it again for a short while, and then observe it. If the cloudiness, droplets, or separate layer disappear on shaking, classify it as *soluble;* otherwise, classify it as *insoluble.*

If the unknown is a solid, weigh out approximately 90 mg of the solid and grind it to a fine powder on a watch glass using a flat-bottomed stirring rod or a flat-bladed microspatula. Mix the solid with 3.0 mL of water in a 13×100-mm test tube; stopper and shake the test tube vigorously for about 30 seconds or until the solid dissolves. If some of the solid remains undissolved, grind it against the bottom or sides of the test tube with your stirring rod and continue to shake and stir at intervals until the solid dissolves, or until it is apparent that it will not completely dissolve. (It may take several minutes to dissolve some solids.) If the solid dissolves completely, classify it as *soluble;* if it doesn't dissolve completely, even after extensive shaking and grinding, classify it as *insoluble.*

If the unknown is *soluble* in water, test its aqueous solution with red and blue litmus paper. If there is no reaction to litmus but you suspect that the unknown may be an aromatic amine or a phenol, dissolve a small amount of the unknown in 5% HCl (for an amine) or 5% NaOH (for a phenol) and see if its odor disappears. Amines and phenols generally have strong odors, but their salts are odorless. Decide whether the unknown should be in class S_n, S_a, or S_b, and go on to the classification tests.

If the unknown is *insoluble* in water, test its solubility (using 0.10 mL of a liquid or 90 mg of a solid) in 3.0 mL of 5% HCl by the same procedure as described for water. If it appears to dissolve partially but not completely in 5% HCl, transfer [OP-6] most of the solution to another test tube and carefully neutralize it to red litmus with a dilute NaOH solution. If a precipitate, a separate liquid phase, or a cloudy solution occurs upon neutralization, consider the unknown soluble. If it is *soluble* in 5% HCl, place it in class **B** and go on to the classification tests.

If the unknown is *insoluble* in 5% HCl, test its solubility (using 0.10 mL of a liquid or 90 mg of a solid) in 3.0 mL of 5% NaOH and in 3.0 mL of 5% NaHCO$_3$ by the same procedure as before. When testing with NaOH, notice whether the mixture foams on shaking, which could indicate a long-chain carboxylic acid. If the unknown appears to dissolve partially but not completely, transfer most of the solution to another test tube and carefully neutralize it to blue litmus with a dilute HCl solution. If a precipitate, a separate liquid phase, or a cloudy solution occurs upon neutralization, consider the unknown soluble. If the unknown is *soluble* in 5% NaOH or in both solvents, decide whether it should be in class A_1 or A_2, and go on to the classification tests.

If the unknown is *insoluble* in all of the foregoing solutions, carefully test its solubility in 3.0 mL of cold (room temperature or below), concentrated sulfuric acid. Shake this mixture vigorously and look for any evidence of a reaction, such as the generation of heat, a distinct change in color, the formation of a precipitate, or the evolution of a gas. Solubility or a definite reaction is considered a positive test. The nature of any reaction that takes place may provide some clues to the identity of the unknown. Based on the results of this test, place the unknown into class **N** or **X**.

Waste Disposal: Dispose of the solutions as directed by your instructor.

Take Care! Don't use your thumb as a stopper.

Take Care! Wear gloves, and avoid contact with H$_2$SO$_4$.

Classification Tests

The results of the solubility tests should reduce the number of families to which your compound may belong, limiting the number of classification tests that are needed to classify it into one of the remaining families. You should choose the tests carefully so that they will provide the information you need in a minimum number of steps. The tests used to detect functional groups are listed in Table Q1. Within families, functional-class tests are listed in approximate order of simplicity and utility. It may be necessary to perform two (or more) tests for the same functional group in case the first test is inconclusive, or to use an infrared spectrum for confirmation.

You may be able to obtain additional information about your unknown using one or more of the classification tests listed in Table Q2. Some of these tests are used to further classify alcohols, amines, and alkyl halides. Others can distinguish aromatic compounds from aliphatic compounds in the same family, detect unsaturation, and detect certain groups of atoms, such as $-COCH_3$ in methyl ketones.

Tertiary amines are listed separately from primary and secondary amines in Appendix VI, so if you have an amine, you should classify it before you prepare your list of possibilities. If you have any other kind of compound, you can prepare your list first, and then decide which of the tests in Table Q2 will help you shorten it.

Table Q1 Functional-class tests

Family	No.	Test	Comments
alcohols	C-9	chromic acid	negative for 3° alcohols
	C-17	Lucas' test	negative for 1° and high mol wt alcohols
	C-1	acetyl chloride	useful if other tests are inconclusive
aldehydes	C-9	chromic acid	reacts more slowly than alcohols
	C-23	Tollens' test	
aldehydes and ketones	C-11	2,4-dinitrophenyl-hydrazine	ketones react with C-11, not with C-9 or C-23
amides	C-2	alkaline hydrolysis	best for amides of ammonia or low mol wt amines
amines	C-12	solubility tests elemental analysis	soluble in 5% HCl detects N; use to confirm solubility test results
aromatic hydrocarbons	C-3	aluminum chloride/ chloroform	should be confirmed by tests indicating absence of functional groups (such as halogens)
carboxylic acids		solubility tests	soluble in 5% NaOH and 5% $NaHCO_3$
esters	C-14	ferric hydroxamate	
	C-2	alkaline hydrolysis	also used to prepare derivatives
halogenated hydrocarbons	C-5	Beilstein's test	simple, but not always reliable
	C-21	silver nitrate/ethanol	negative for vinyl and aryl halides
	C-10	density test	negative for monochloroalkanes
	C-12	elemental analysis	can distinguish Cl, Br, and I
phenols	C-13	ferric chloride	positive for most (but not all) phenols
	C-8	bromine water	aromatic amines also react

Table Q2 Chemical tests that provide structural information

Family or structural feature	No.	Test	Application
alcohols	C-17	Lucas' test	to classify alcohols as 1°, 2°, 3°, etc.
	C-16	iodoform test	to detect $-CH(OH)CH_3$ groupings
aldehydes	C-6	Benedict's test	to distinguish aliphatic from aromatic aldehydes
ketones	C-16	iodoform test	to detect $-COCH_3$ groupings
amines	C-15	Hinsberg's test	to classify amines as 1°, 2°, or 3°
	C-4	basicity test	to distinguish alkylamines from arylamines
	C-20	quinhydrone	complements C-15
carboxylic acids	C-18	neutralization equivalent	to determine the equivalent weight of an acid
halogenated hydrocarbons	C-10	density test	to distinguish chlorides, bromides, and iodides; also aliphatic and aromatic halides
	C-22	sodium iodide/ acetone	to classify halides as 1°, 2°, 3°, etc.
	C-21	silver nitrate/ ethanol	complements C-22
unsaturation	C-7	bromine test	to detect $C\!=\!C$ and $C\!\equiv\!C$ bonds
	C-19	potassium permanganate	complements C-7

DIRECTIONS

Directions for performing all classification tests are given in this section by test numbers that are preceded by **C**. Unless otherwise indicated, solutions used for the classification tests are aqueous.

When each test is performed for the first time, it is advisable to run a *control* and a *blank* at the same time. Only by doing so will you know what to look for in deciding whether the test with the unknown is positive or negative. A control is a known compound that is expected to give a predictable result with the test reagent. A blank is run by combining all reagents as in the actual test, but omitting the unknown. Unless otherwise indicated, all compounds suggested as controls in the following procedures should give a positive test.

Most of the tests are carried out in test tubes, whose sizes are usually specified. If you don't have a test tube of the specified size (e.g., 10 × 75-mm), use the next size larger (e.g., 13 × 100-mm). In the procedures, the volumes of most liquid reactants are given in drops of the size delivered by a medicine dropper. For microscale work, you can measure drops using Pasteur pipets, reducing the amount of unknown needed by about half; note that you must then divide the quantities of all reagents *not* measured with Pasteur pipets in half. Always use different dropping devices for the reagent and the unknown, and clean your own droppers thoroughly after using them. Never insert your own droppers into reagent bottles, as you may contaminate the reagents.

Select the tests you want to perform, and then turn to the appropriate procedures. Always read any Safety Notes before starting a test.

Waste Disposal: For each classification test, dispose of any wastes or unused reagents as directed by your instructor.

C-1 *Acetyl Chloride*

If you think your unknown is a tertiary alcohol, try method **B**; otherwise, use method **A**. Quantities for part **A** may be cut in half in the microscale lab.

> Acetyl chloride is very corrosive, and its vapors are irritating and toxic. It reacts violently with water and some alcohols. Use gloves and a hood, avoid contact, do not breathe vapors, and keep it away from water. *N,N*-Dimethylaniline and ammonia (procedure B) are harmful if inhaled or allowed to contact the skin. Use gloves and a hood, avoid contact, and do not breathe vapors.

Reaction: $CH_3COCl + ROH \longrightarrow CH_3COOR + HCl$

Control: 1-butanol

A. *Under the hood,* cautiously add 10 drops of acetyl chloride to 10 drops of the unknown (or 0.40 g, if it is a solid) in a 10×75-mm test tube. Observe any evolution of heat; carefully exhale over the mouth of the test tube to see if a cloud of HCl gas is revealed by the moisture in your breath. After a minute or two, pour the mixture into about 2 mL of water, stopper and shake it, and note any phase separation. Carefully smell the mixture for evidence of an ester aroma, which is usually pleasant and fruity.

Take Care! A violent reaction is possible. Wear gloves, and avoid contact with and inhalation of acetyl chloride.

Interpretation: Evidence of reaction (heat, HCl gas), especially if accompanied by phase separation and an ester-like odor, indicates a primary or secondary alcohol. Amines and phenols also react, but amines don't yield pleasant odors. Tertiary alcohols do not form esters by this procedure, but they should by method **B**.

B. *Under the hood,* mix 5 drops of acetyl chloride with 10 drops of *N,N*-dimethylaniline. Cautiously add 5 drops of the unknown (or 0.20 g, if it is a solid). Warm the mixture in a 50° water bath for 15 minutes; then cool the mixture to room temperature. *Under the hood,* carefully add 1.0 g of ice and 1.0 mL of concentrated aqueous ammonia, mix, and let the mixture stand. If an organic layer forms, separate it from the aqueous layer and test it for ester using the ferric hydroxamate test (**C-14**).

Take Care! Wear gloves, and avoid contact with and inhalation of the reactants.

C-2 *Alkaline Hydrolysis*

Use procedure **A** if your unknown may be an amide, or procedure **B** if it may be an ester. Esters with boiling points higher than 200°C may be unreactive in aqueous NaOH. For microscale work, quantities for part **B** may be reduced to one-fifth of those indicated.

> Sodium hydroxide is toxic and corrosive, causing severe damage to skin, eyes, and mucous membranes. Wear gloves, and avoid contact with the NaOH solution.

A. *Amides*

Reactions: $RCONR'_2 + NaOH \longrightarrow RCOONa + R'_2NH$

$RCOONa + H^+ \longrightarrow RCOOH + Na^+$

$R' = H$, alkyl, or aryl

Take Care! Wear gloves, and avoid contact with the NaOH solution.

Control: benzamide

Stir 0.10 g of the unknown (or 3 drops, if it is a liquid) with 4.0 mL of 6 *M* sodium hydroxide in an 18 × 150-mm test tube. Secure a small piece of filter paper over the top of the tube, and moisten it with 2 drops of 10% copper(II) sulfate. Boil the mixture gently for a minute or two, and note any color change on the filter paper. Remove the paper, and cautiously note the odor of the vapors while the solution is boiling. Acidify the solution with 6 *M* HCl; if a carboxylic acid precipitate forms, collect it by vacuum filtration and use it as a derivative (see **D-6**).

Interpretation: An intense blue color on the filter paper, accompanied by an ammonia or amine-like odor, indicates an amide. Amides of higher amines that don't turn the paper blue may nevertheless give an amine-like odor. Some amides will yield a precipitate or a separate liquid phase (the carboxylic acid) when the hydrolysis mixture is acidified. The characteristic odor of a carboxylic acid may also be observed. If the test is inconclusive, try increasing the reaction time or repeating the reaction at 200°C using 20% KOH in glycerine.

B. *Esters*

Reactions: $RCOOR' + NaOH \longrightarrow RCOONa + R'OH$
$$RCOONa + H^+ \longrightarrow RCOOH + Na^+$$

Take Care! Wear gloves, and avoid contact with the NaOH solution.

Control: butyl acetate

Mix 1.0 mL of the unknown (or 1.0 g, if it is a solid) with 10 mL of 6 *M* sodium hydroxide and heat the mixture under reflux for 30 minutes, or until the solution is homogeneous. Note whether the odor of the unknown is gone and (if the unknown was water insoluble) whether the organic layer has disappeared. If a separate organic layer or residue remains, heat the mixture longer, until it disappears or it becomes apparent that no reaction is taking place. Most esters with boiling points below 110°C will hydrolyze in 30 minutes; higher-boiling esters may take several hours. Cool the reaction mixture, remove the organic layer (if there is one), and acidify the aqueous solution with 6 *M* sulfuric acid. If a carboxylic acid precipitates on acidification, collect it by vacuum filtration and use it as a derivative (see **D-16**). If acidification does not yield a solid carboxylic acid, carefully note the odor of the acidified reaction mixture. Then make the solution basic with 6 *M* NaOH, and saturate it with potassium carbonate to see if an organic layer (the alcohol) separates. Note the odor of this layer also.

Interpretation: Evidence for an ester is indicated by the disappearance of the organic layer (if any) and of the odor of the unknown during the reflux period, and by the appearance of a precipitate or the odor of a carboxylic acid upon acidification. If an organic layer (presumably an alcohol) separates after the addition of potassium carbonate, an odor different from that of the original unknown suggests that the unknown was an ester.

C-3 *Aluminum Chloride and Chloroform*

Safety Notes

Reaction: $\text{ArH} \xrightarrow{\text{CHCl}_3, \text{AlCl}_3} \text{Ar}_3\text{C}^+$

Controls: toluene, biphenyl

Under the hood, prepare a solution that contains 3 drops of a solubility class **X** unknown (or 0.10 g, if it is a solid) in 2.0 mL of dry chloroform (trichloromethane). Place 0.20 g of anhydrous aluminum chloride in a dry 13×100-mm test tube and heat it over a flame, angling the test tube so that the AlCl_3 sublimes onto the inner wall of the tube. Allow the tube to cool until it can be held comfortably in the hand, and then pipet a few drops of the solution down the side of the tube so that it contacts the aluminum chloride. Note any color change at the point of contact.

Take Care! Wear gloves, and avoid contact with and inhalation of chloroform and aluminum chloride.

Interpretation: An intense color, such as yellow–orange, red, blue, green, or purple, indicates an aromatic compound. A light yellow color is inconclusive or negative.

C-4 *Basicity Test*

Reaction:

$\text{RNH}_2 + \text{H}^+ \xrightarrow{\text{pH 5.5}} \text{RNH}_3^+$ (and similar reactions for 2° and 3° amines)

Controls: *p*-toluidine, dibutylamine

If the unknown is water soluble, dissolve 4 drops (or 0.10 g, if it is a solid) in 3.0 mL of water in a 13×100-mm test tube, and measure the pH of the solution using pH paper or a universal indicator. If the unknown is insoluble in water, add 4 drops (or 0.10 g, if it is a solid) to 3.0 mL of a pH 5.5 acetate–acetic acid buffer in a 13×100-mm test tube, and then stopper and shake the test tube.

Interpretation: Most water-soluble aliphatic amines give pH values above 11, and water-insoluble aliphatic amines should dissolve in the buffer. Most water-soluble aromatic amines give pH values below 10, and water-insoluble aromatic amines don't dissolve in the buffer. Test **C-8** can also be used to test for aromatic amines.

C-5 *Beilstein's Test*

Control: chlorobenzene

Make a small loop in the end of a length of copper wire (10 cm or longer), and heat the loop to redness in a flame. Let the wire cool; then dip the loop into the unknown and heat it in the nonluminous (blue) flame of a burner, near the lower edge.

Interpretation: A distinct green or blue–green flame indicates a halogen compound.

C-6 *Benedict's Test*

Reaction: $RCHO + 2Cu^{2+} + 4OH^- \longrightarrow RCOOH + Cu_2O + 2H_2O$

Control: butanal (butyraldehyde)

Benedict's reagent contains copper(II) sulfate, sodium citrate, and sodium carbonate.

Add 2 drops of the unknown (or 80 mg, if it is a solid) to 2.0 mL of water in a 13 × 100-mm test tube, and mix in 2.0 mL of Benedict's reagent. Heat the mixture to boiling. Observe whether a precipitate forms, and, if one forms, record its color.

Interpretation: Aliphatic aldehydes generally produce a yellow to orange suspension or precipitate of copper(I) oxide; it may appear greenish in the blue solution. Most ketones and aromatic aldehydes do not react.

C-7 *Bromine Test*

Safety Notes

> **Dichloromethane may be harmful if inhaled or absorbed through the skin, and it is a suspected carcinogen. Avoid contact, and do not breathe its vapors.**
> **Bromine is toxic and corrosive, and its vapors are very harmful. Avoid contact with the bromine solution, and do not breathe its vapors.**

Reaction:

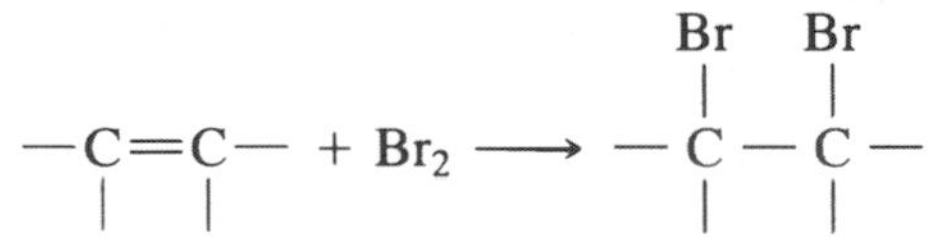

$$\underset{\vert\quad\vert}{-C=C-} + Br_2 \longrightarrow \overset{\quad Br\quad Br}{\underset{\vert\quad\vert}{-\underset{\vert}{C}-\underset{\vert}{C}-}}$$

Control: cyclohexene

Take Care! Avoid contact with and inhalation of dichloromethane and the bromine solution.

Under the hood, dissolve 1 drop of the unknown (or 40 mg, if it is a solid) in 0.50 mL of dichloromethane in a 10 × 75-mm test tube. Add freshly prepared 1.0 *M* bromine in dichloromethane, drop by drop, with shaking. Continue adding until the red–orange color of bromine persists *or* until about 20 drops have been added. Immediately after the addition, carefully exhale over the mouth of the test tube and observe whether a cloud of HBr gas appears.

Interpretation: Decolorization of more than 1 drop of the bromine solution, without the evolution of HBr, indicates unsaturation (C=C or C≡C bonds). Aldehydes, ketones, amines, and phenols react by substitution to evolve HBr.

C-8 *Bromine Water*

Safety Notes

> **Bromine is toxic and corrosive, and its vapors are very harmful. Avoid contact with the bromine water, and do not breathe its vapors.**

Reaction:

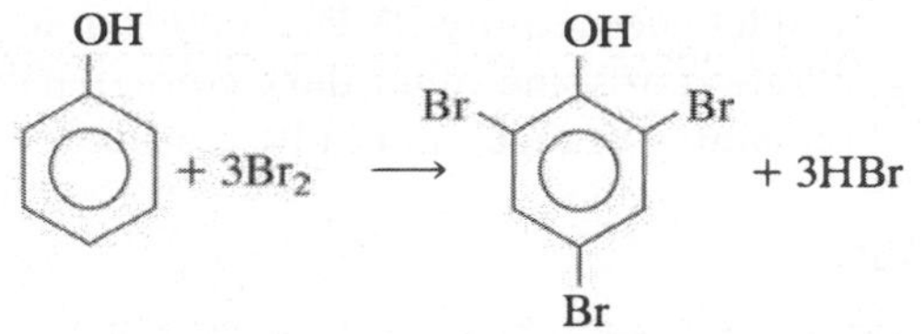

Reaction is for phenol; aromatic amines and substituted phenols undergo similar reactions.

Control: phenol

Dissolve 3 drops of the unknown (or 0.10 g, if it is a solid) in 10 mL of water in an 18 × 150-mm test tube. If it is insoluble in water, add just enough ethanol to bring it into solution. Measure the pH of the solution with pH paper. *Under the hood,* add saturated bromine water, drop by drop, until the bromine color persists. Watch for evidence of a precipitate.

Take Care! Avoid contact with and inhalation of the bromine solution.

Interpretation: Decolorization of the bromine, accompanied by formation of a white (or nearly white) precipitate, indicates a phenol or aromatic amine. If the unknown is a phenol, the pH of the initial solution should be less than 7.

C-9 *Chromic Acid*

The chromic acid reagent is very corrosive and may be carcinogenic. Avoid contact.

Safety Notes

Reactions:

1°Alcohol:
$$3RCH_2OH + 4CrO_3 + 6H_2SO_4 \longrightarrow 3RCOOH + 2Cr_2(SO_4)_3 + 9H_2O$$

2°Alcohol:
$$3R_2CHOH + 2CrO_3 + 3H_2SO_4 \longrightarrow 3R_2CO + Cr_2(SO_4)_3 + 6H_2O$$

Aldehyde:
$$3RCHO + 2CrO_3 + 3H_2SO_4 \longrightarrow 3RCOOH + Cr_2(SO_4)_3 + 3H_2O$$

Controls: 1-butanol, butanal

Dissolve 1 drop of the unknown (or 40 mg, if it is a solid) in 1.0 mL of reagent-grade acetone in a 10 × 75-mm test tube. (If there is any doubt about the purity of the acetone, test it with a drop of the reagent beforehand.) Add 1 drop of the chromic acid reagent and swirl, noting the time required for a positive test.

Take Care! Avoid contact with the chromic acid reagent.

The chromic acid reagent contains chromium(VI) oxide and concentrated sulfuric acid.

Interpretation: Formation of an opaque blue–green suspension within 2–3 seconds, accompanied by disappearance of the orange color of the reagent, indicates a primary or secondary alcohol. Aldehydes give the same result but react more slowly. With aliphatic aldehydes, the solution turns cloudy in about 5 seconds, and the blue–green suspension forms within 30 seconds; aromatic aldehydes require 30–90 seconds or longer to form the suspension. The generation of some other dark color, particularly with the color of the liquid remaining orange, should be considered a negative test.

C-10 *Density Test*

Controls: 1-chlorobutane, 1-bromobutane

Add 5 drops of a liquid solubility class **X** unknown to 1.0 mL of deionized water in a 10 × 75-mm test tube, stir gently, and note whether the unknown floats or sinks. If it sinks, determine its density by accurately measuring 0.10 mL of the unknown liquid (use an automatic pipet or measuring pipet) into a tared vial and weighing the liquid on an accurate balance.

Interpretation: Of the compounds that are insoluble in cold, concentrated sulfuric acid, most aromatic hydrocarbons and monochloroalkanes will float, whereas aryl chlorides, polychloroalkanes, and all bromides and iodides will sink. Density ranges for some classes of organic halides are listed here.

Approximate density ranges for halogenated hydrocarbons

Halide type	Density range
alkyl chloride (mono)	0.85–1.0
alkyl bromide (mono)	1.1–1.5
alkyl iodide (mono)	>1.4
alkyl chloride (poly)	1.1–1.7
alkyl bromide (poly)	1.5–3.0
aryl chloride	1.1–1.3
aryl bromide	1.3–2.0
aryl iodide	>1.8

Note: Density is in g/mL.

C-11 *2,4-Dinitrophenylhydrazine*

Safety Notes

2,4-Dinitrophenylhydrazine (DNPH) is harmful if absorbed through the skin, and it will dye your hands yellow. Wear gloves, avoid contact with the DNPH reagent, and wash your hands after using it.

Reaction:

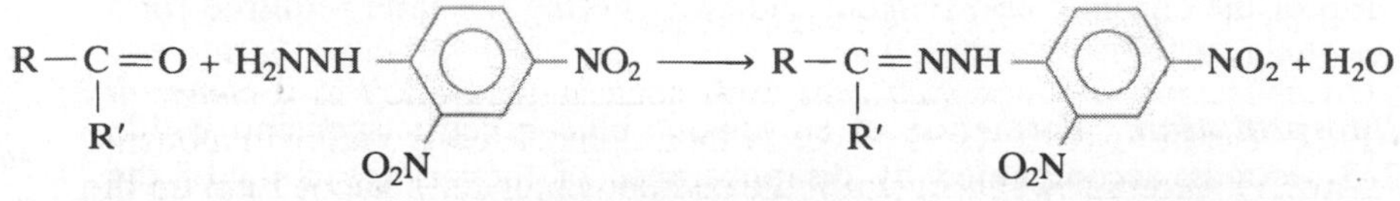

R, R′ = alkyl, aryl, or H

Controls: cyclohexanone, benzaldehyde

Dissolve 1 drop of the unknown (or 40 mg, if it is a solid) in 1.0 mL of 95% ethanol; use more ethanol, if necessary. Add this solution to 2.0 mL of the DNPH reagent in a 10 × 75-mm test tube. Stopper and shake the test tube, and let the mixture stand for 15 minutes or until a precipitate forms. If no precipitate has formed after 15 minutes, scratch the inside of the test tube with a glass stirring rod.

Take Care! Wear gloves, and avoid contact with the DNPH reagent.

Interpretation: Formation of a crystalline yellow or orange–red precipitate indicates an aldehyde or ketone. Some carbonyl compounds initially form oils that may or may not become crystalline; a few may require *gentle* heating, but overheating can cause oxidation of allylic or other reactive alcohols, resulting in a false-positive test. Some aromatic compounds (hydrocarbons, halides, phenols, and phenyl esters) may form slightly soluble complexes with the reagent, and some alcohols may be contaminated with small amounts of the corresponding aldehyde or ketone. In such cases, the amount of precipitate should be quite small, and comparison with a control should show the difference between a positive test and a doubtful one. The color of the precipitate may give a clue to the structure of the carbonyl compound; unconjugated aliphatic aldehydes and ketones usually yield yellow precipitates, whereas aromatic and α,β-unsaturated aldehydes and ketones yield orange–red precipitates.

Rinsing the reaction tube with acetone and not drying it thoroughly may also result in a false-positive test.

C-12 *Elemental Analysis*

Safety Notes

> Sodium can cause serious burns, and the sodium–lead alloy may react violently with some substances. Wear gloves, avoid contact, and keep Na(Pb) away from other chemicals. *Do not use this procedure with sodium metal*; it will react violently when water is added.
> The PNB reagent is harmful if inhaled or allowed to contact the skin. Wear gloves, avoid contact, and do not breathe its vapors.

Reactions:

Nitrogen: $[C, N] \xrightarrow{Na(Pb)} NaCN \xrightarrow{PNB}$ purple color

Halogens: RX, ArX $\xrightarrow{Na(Pb)} NaX \xrightarrow{AgNO_3}$ **AgX** (X = Cl, Br, I)

Chlorine: $AgCl + 2NH_3 \longrightarrow Ag(NH_3)_2Cl$

Bromine: $2HBr + Cl_2 \longrightarrow 2HCl + Br_2$ (red-orange)

Iodine: $2HI + Cl_2 \longrightarrow 2HCl + I_2$ (purple)

Controls: acetamide (N), bromobenzene (Br)

Under the hood, place 0.25 g of 10% sodium–lead alloy in a *clean, dry* 10 × 75-mm test tube held vertically by a clamp. Melt the alloy in a burner flame, and continue heating until the sodium vapor rises about 1 cm up the inside of the test tube. Add 2 drops of the unknown from a Pasteur pipet

Take Care! Wear gloves, and avoid contact with the sodium–lead alloy.

(or add 10 mg, if it is a solid) directly onto the molten alloy so that it doesn't touch the sides of the tube. Heat gently to start the reaction, remove the flame until the reaction subsides, and then heat the tube strongly for a minute or two, keeping the bottom a dull red color. Let the tube cool to room temperature. Add 1.5 mL of water and heat gently for a minute or so, until the excess sodium has decomposed and gas evolution ceases. Filter the solution through a filtering pipet (see OP-15) containing a cotton plug, wash the cotton with 1 mL of water, and combine the wash water with the filtrate. The filtrate should be colorless or just slightly yellow. If it is darker, repeat the fusion with stronger heating or more of the alloy.

To test for *nitrogen,* put 5 drops of the sodium fusion solution into a 10 × 75-mm test tube; add enough solid sodium bicarbonate, with stirring, to saturate it (a small amount of excess solid should be present). Add 1 drop of this solution to another 10 × 75-mm test tube containing 10 drops of PNB reagent (*p*-nitrobenzaldehyde in dimethyl sulfoxide), and note any color change.

Take Care! Wear gloves, and avoid contact with and inhalation of the PNB reagent.

To test for *halogens,* transfer 10 drops of the sodium fusion solution to a 10 × 75-mm test tube, and acidify it with dilute nitric acid. Then boil it gently *under the hood* for a few minutes, add a drop or two of 0.30 *M* silver nitrate, and note the color and volume of any precipitate that forms. If a voluminous precipitate forms, remove the liquid with a filter-tip pipet (see OP-6). Then add 2.0 mL of 3 *M* aqueous ammonia to the solid, shake vigorously, and note your observations. To test further for bromine and iodine, acidify 1 mL of the original sodium fusion solution with 1 *M* sulfuric acid in a 10 × 75-mm test tube, boil gently for a few minutes, and then add 0.50 mL of dichloromethane and a drop of freshly prepared chlorine water. Shake, and look for a color in the dichloromethane layer.

Interpretation: In the PNB test, a purple color indicates the presence of nitrogen (green indicates sulfur). In the halogen tests, formation of a voluminous precipitate on addition of silver nitrate indicates that a halogen is present, and the color of the precipitate (a silver halide) may suggest which halogen: white for chloride, pale yellow for bromide, and yellow for iodide. If only a faint turbidity is produced, it may be caused by traces of impurities or by incomplete sodium fusion. If the precipitate is silver chloride, it will dissolve in aqueous ammonia; silver bromide is only slightly soluble, and silver iodide is insoluble. In the chlorine water test, a red–orange color is due to elemental bromine, and a violet color to elemental iodine.

C-13 *Ferric Chloride*

Control: phenol

In a 10 × 75-mm test tube, dissolve 1 drop of the unknown (or 40 mg, if it is a solid) in 1.0 mL of water, or in a water/alcohol mixture if it doesn't dissolve in water. Add two drops of 2.5% ferric chloride solution.

Interpretation: Formation of an intense red, green, blue, or purple color suggests a phenol or an easily enolizable compound. A few phenols don't react under these conditions. Many aromatic carboxylic acids form tan precipitates; aliphatic hydroxy acids yield yellow solutions.

C-14 *Ferric Hydroxamate Test*

Hydroxylamine hydrochloride is toxic and mutagenic, and it can cause a form of anemia. Avoid contact with its solution.
Sodium hydroxide is toxic and corrosive, causing severe damage to skin, eyes, and mucous membranes. Wear gloves, and avoid contact with the NaOH solution.

Safety Notes

Reactions:

$$RC(=O)-OR' + H_2NOH \longrightarrow RC(=O)-NHOH + R'OH$$

$$3RCONHOH + FeCl_3 \longrightarrow \underset{\text{ferric hydroxamate}}{(RCONHO)_3Fe} + 3HCl$$

Control: butyl acetate

Before you carry out the ferric hydroxamate test, perform the following preliminary test. Dissolve 1 drop of the unknown (or 40 mg, if it is a solid) in 1.0 mL of 95% ethanol in a 10 × 75-mm test tube. Add 1.0 mL of 1 *M* hydrochloric acid; then add two drops of 2.5% ferric chloride. If a definite color other than yellow results, the ferric hydroxamate test cannot be used. This test eliminates those phenols and enols that yield colors with ferric chloride in acidic solution and that would therefore give an inconclusive result in the ferric hydroxamate test.

Mix 1.0 mL of 0.50 *M* ethanolic hydroxylamine hydrochloride with 5 drops of 6 *M* sodium hydroxide in a 13 × 100-mm test tube. Add 1 drop of the unknown (or 40 mg, if it is a solid), and heat the solution to boiling. Allow it to cool slightly, and add 2.0 mL of 1 *M* hydrochloric acid. If the solution is cloudy at this point, add enough 95% ethanol to clarify it. Add 5 drops of 2.5% ferric chloride solution, and observe any color produced. If the color doesn't persist, continue to add the ferric chloride solution until the color becomes permanent.

Take Care! Avoid contact with the hydroxylamine hydrochloride and NaOH solutions.

Interpretation: A burgundy or magenta color that is distinctly different from the color obtained in the preliminary test indicates an ester.

C-15 *Hinsberg's Test*

Record all observations carefully during this test.

***p*-Toluenesulfonyl chloride is toxic and corrosive. Use gloves and a hood, avoid contact, and do not breathe its vapors.**

Safety Notes

Reactions:

1° Amine:

$$RNH_2 + ArSO_2Cl + 2NaOH \longrightarrow ArSO_2NR^-Na^+ + NaCl + 2H_2O$$
$$ArSO_2NR^-Na^+ + HCl \longrightarrow \mathbf{ArSO_2NHR} + NaCl$$

2° Amine:

$$R_2NH + ArSO_2Cl + NaOH \longrightarrow \mathbf{ArSO_2NR_2} + NaCl + H_2O$$

3° Amine:

$$R_3N + ArSO_2Cl \longrightarrow \text{no reaction}$$
$$R_3N + HCl \longrightarrow R_3NH^+Cl^-$$

Controls: butylamine, dibutylamine, tributylamine

Take Care! Wear gloves, and avoid contact with and inhalation of *p*-toluenesulfonyl chloride.

Benzenesulfonyl chloride (6 drops) can be used in place of p-*toluenesulfonyl chloride, but it is more hazardous and it tends to form oils.*

Under the hood, mix 3 drops of the unknown (or 0.10 g, if it is a solid) with 5.0 mL of 3 *M* sodium hydroxide in an 18 × 150-mm test tube; then add 0.20 g of *p*-toluenesulfonyl chloride. Stopper the test tube, and shake it intermittently for 3–5 minutes. Remove the stopper and heat the solution in a boiling-water bath, with shaking, for 1 minute. The solution should be basic at this point (if not, add more NaOH). If there is a solid or liquid residue in the test tube, separate it from the solution by vacuum filtration [OP-16], if it is a solid, or with a Pasteur pipet, if it is a liquid. Test the solubility of the residue in water; if it is insoluble in water, separate it as before and test its solubility in 5% hydrochloric acid. Acidify the original solution with 6 *M* hydrochloric acid and, if no precipitate forms immediately, scratch the sides of the test tube and cool. If you obtain a solid either from the original reaction mixture or after addition of 6 *M* HCl, save it for possible use as a *p*-toluenesulfonate derivative (see **D-9**).

Interpretation: Formation of a white precipitate (a *p*-toluenesulfonamide) when the reaction mixture is acidified indicates a *primary amine.* Most primary amines yield a clear solution after the initial reaction, but some form sodium salts or disulfonyl derivatives that precipitate during the reaction. The sodium salts should be soluble in water, and amines that form disulfonyl derivatives should yield additional precipitate when the reaction mixture is acidified.

Most *secondary amines* yield a white solid that doesn't dissolve in water or 5% HCl. A liquid residue that is more dense than water and insoluble in 5% HCl may be a secondary amine's arenesulfonamide that has failed to crystallize.

Tertiary amines do not react; any residue will be the original liquid or solid amine, which should dissolve in dilute HCl. Water-soluble tertiary amines yield a clear solution that doesn't form a separate phase on acidification.

C-16 *Iodoform Test*

Reactions: Methyl carbinols

$$\underset{\overset{|}{RCH}}{OH} - CH_3 + 4I_2 + 5NaOH \longrightarrow \overset{O}{\overset{||}{RC}} - CI_3 + 5NaI + 5H_2O$$

$$\overset{O}{\overset{||}{RC}} - CI_3 + NaOH \longrightarrow \overset{O}{\overset{||}{RC}} - ONa + CHI_3$$
(iodoform)

Methyl ketones and acetaldehyde

$$\overset{O}{\overset{||}{RC}} - CH_3 + 3I_2 + 3NaOH \longrightarrow \overset{O}{\overset{||}{RC}} - CI_3 + 3NaI + 3H_2O$$

$$\overset{O}{\overset{||}{RC}} - CI_3 + NaOH \longrightarrow \overset{O}{\overset{||}{RC}} - ONa + CHI_3$$

R = alkyl, aryl, or H

Control: 2-butanone

Dissolve 3 drops of the unknown (or 0.10 g, if it is a solid) in 2.0 mL of water in a 25 × 150-mm test tube. (If the unknown is insoluble in water, dissolve it in 2.0 mL or more of methanol instead.) Add 1.0 mL of 3 M sodium hydroxide solution; then add 0.50 M iodine–potassium iodide reagent, drop by drop, until the brown iodine color persists after shaking. If no yellow precipitate appears, place the test tube in a 60°C water bath and add more iodine–potassium iodide solution, as necessary, until the brown color remains after at least 2 minutes of heating. Then add 3 M NaOH, drop by drop, until the brown color just disappears (a light yellow color may remain). Remove the test tube from the water bath, add 10 mL of cold water, and let it stand for 15 minutes.

Interpretation: Formation of a yellow precipitate with the characteristic medicinal odor of iodoform is a positive test. If there is any doubt about the identity of the precipitate, its melting point (121°C) can be measured. The test is positive for acetaldehyde, methyl ketones, and methyl carbinols— alcohols that contain a —CH(OH)CH$_3$ grouping. Other compounds that may yield iodoform in this test include certain conjugated aldehydes, such as acrolein and furfural, and some 1,3-dicarbonyl or dihydroxy compounds.

C-17   *Lucas' Test*

This test is not applicable to most alcohols with boiling points higher than 140–150°C, or to solid alcohols.

The Lucas reagent (ZnCl$_2$ in concentrated HCl) can cause serious burns, and inhaling the vapors is harmful. Use gloves and a hood, avoid contact, and do not breathe its vapors.

Safety Notes

Reaction: $\text{ROH} + \text{HCl} \xrightarrow{\text{ZnCl}_2} \text{RCl} + \text{H}_2\text{O}$

Controls: 1-butanol (no reaction), 2-butanol, 2-methyl-2-propanol

Under the hood, place 2.0 mL of the Lucas reagent in a 10 × 75-mm test tube. Add 4 drops of the liquid unknown, stopper the test tube immediately, and shake vigorously, taking note of any cloudiness or layer separation. Allow the mixture to stand for 15 minutes or more, observing it periodically for evidence of reaction. If the alcohol appears to be secondary or tertiary, repeat the test using concentrated HCl in place of the Lucas reagent.

Take Care! Wear gloves, and avoid contact with and inhalation of Lucas' reagent.

Take Care! Wear gloves, and avoid contact with and inhalation of HCl.

Interpretation: *Tertiary alcohols* that are soluble in the Lucas reagent should turn the reagent cloudy almost immediately and soon form a separate layer of alkyl chloride. *Secondary alcohols* usually turn the clear solution cloudy in 3–5 minutes and form a distinct layer within 15 minutes. *Primary alcohols* do not react under these conditions. Most allylic and benzylic alcohols give the same result as tertiary alcohols, except that the chloride formed from allyl alcohol is itself soluble in the reagent and separates only upon addition of ice water. High-boiling alcohols that are insoluble in the Lucas reagent cannot be tested, because they will form a separate layer immediately. When tested with concentrated HCl, a tertiary alcohol should react within minutes, and a secondary alcohol should not react.

C-18 *Neutralization Equivalent*

Quantities may be cut in half for the microscale lab.

Reaction: RCOOH + NaOH $\longrightarrow$ RCOONa + H$_2$O

Control: hexanedioic acid (adipic acid)

Accurately weigh (to three decimal places) about 0.20 g of an unknown carboxylic acid, transfer it to an Erlenmeyer flask, and dissolve it in 50 mL of water, ethanol, or a mixture of the two, depending on its solubility. (If necessary, you can use more solvent to dissolve it.) Add a drop of phenolphthalein indicator (or bromothymol blue indicator, if the solvent is ethanol), and titrate this solution with a standardized solution of ~0.1 *M* sodium hydroxide. Record the exact concentration of the NaOH solution from its label. Calculate the neutralization equivalent (N.E.) of the acid using this formula:

$$\text{N.E.} = \frac{\text{mass of sample (g)} \times 1000}{\text{volume of NaOH (mL)} \times \text{concentration of NaOH}}$$

Interpretation: The neutralization equivalent (equivalent weight) of a carboxylic acid is equal to its molecular weight divided by the number of carboxyl groups it has. For instance, the N.E. of adipic acid [HOOC(CH$_2$)$_4$COOH: mol wt = 146] is 73. A solid carboxylic acid that has an unusually low neutralization equivalent for its melting point probably contains more than one carboxyl group.

C-19 *Potassium Permanganate*

Reaction: 3 $-$ C $=$ C $-$ + 2KMnO$_4$ + 4H$_2$O $\longrightarrow$

$$3 - \underset{\underset{\text{HO}}{|}}{\text{C}} - \underset{\underset{\text{OH}}{|}}{\text{C}} - + 2MnO_2 + 2KOH$$

Control: cyclohexene

Dissolve 1 drop of the unknown (or 40 mg, if it is a solid) in 2.0 mL of water or 95% ethanol in a 10 × 75-mm test tube. (If ethanol is the solvent, perform the test with a blank as well.) Add 0.10 *M* potassium permanganate, drop by drop, until the purple color of the permanganate persists or until about 20 drops have been added. If a reaction doesn't take place immediately, shake the mixture and let it stand for up to 5 minutes. Disregard any decolorization that takes place after 5 minutes have elapsed.

Interpretation: Decolorization of more than one drop of the purple permanganate solution, accompanied by the formation of a brown precipitate (or reddish–brown suspension) of manganese dioxide, suggests unsaturation. The test is positive for most compounds containing double and triple bonds, except for conjugated alkadienes. Easily oxidizable compounds, such as aldehydes, aromatic amines, phenols, formic acid, and formate esters, also give positive tests. Most pure alcohols will not react in less than 5 minutes, but alcohols that contain oxidizable impurities may react slightly, so decolorization of only the first drop of potassium permanganate shouldn't be considered a positive test.

C-20 *Quinhydrone*

This test is not applicable to diaminobenzenes or nitro-substituted aromatic amines.

Controls: butylamine, dibutylamine, tributylamine, aniline, *N*-methylaniline, *N,N*-dimethylaniline

This test should be run in conjunction with Test **C-4** or with an infrared spectrum that shows whether the amine is aliphatic or aromatic. Controls should be run for comparison because the colors are difficult to describe accurately. Shake 1 drop of an unknown alkylamine (use 30 mg, if it is a solid) or 6 drops of an unknown arylamine (use 0.20 g, if it is a solid) with 6.0 mL of water in an 18 × 150-mm test tube. If the amine dissolves, add 6.0 mL more of water; if not, add 6.0 mL of ethanol. Shake the mixture, add 1 drop of 2.5% quinhydrone in methanol, and let it stand for 2 minutes or more. Compare the color of this solution with those of the controls.

Take Care! Avoid contact with the quinhydrone solution.

Interpretation: Most amines from the following classes give the colors indicated.

   1° aliphatic: violet
   2° aliphatic: rose
   3° aliphatic: yellow
   1° aromatic: rose
   2° aromatic: amber
   3° aromatic: yellow

It is best to use this test in conjunction with the Hinsberg test or an IR spectrum for confirmation.

C-21 *Silver Nitrate in Ethanol*

Reaction: $RX + AgNO_3 + EtOH \longrightarrow ROEt + \mathbf{AgX} + HNO_3$
(Organic products other than ROEt are also formed.)

Controls: 1-chlorobutane, 2-chloro-2-methylpropane, 1-bromobutane, iodoethane

Add 1 drop of the unknown (or 50 mg, dissolved in a small amount of ethanol, if it is a solid) to 2.0 mL of 0.10 M ethanolic silver nitrate in a 13 × 100-mm test tube. Shake the mixture, and let it stand. If no precipitate forms within 5 minutes, heat the solution to boiling and boil it gently for 30 seconds. If a precipitate forms, note its color and see if it dissolves when the mixture is shaken with 2 drops of 1 M nitric acid.

Take Care! Avoid contact with the silver nitrate solution.

Halides that react with silver nitrate at room temperature:

   Chlorides: 3°, allyl, benzyl

   Bromides: 1°, 2°, and 3° alkyl (except gem-di- and tribromides); allyl, benzyl, CBr₄

   Iodides: All aliphatic and alicyclic, except vinyl

Interpretation: The reaction of a halide with silver nitrate occurs by an S_N1 mechanism, so the reactivity of a halide varies considerably with its structure. Alkyl iodides react faster than the corresponding bromides, which are more reactive than alkyl chlorides. For the same halogen, tertiary, allylic, and benzylic halides react fastest, followed by secondary and primary halides. Most

Halides that react upon heating:

    Chlorides: 1° and 2° alkyl

    *Bromides: alkyl gem-di-
and tribromides*

    *Some activated aryl halides, such
as 2,4-dinitrohalobenzenes*

Halides that do not react:

    *Chlorides: alkyl gem-di- and
trichlorides, CCl₄*

    Most aryl and vinyl halides

aryl and vinyl halides are unreactive, except for aryl halides activated by two or more nitro groups. Most *geminal* alkyl halides, which have two or more halogen atoms on the same carbon, are less reactive than the corresponding monohaloalkanes. The types of compounds that react at room temperature, react after boiling the solution, or don't react at all are listed in the margin.

The color of the precipitate formed may indicate the type of halide responsible. Silver chloride is white, silver bromide is pale yellow or cream colored, and silver iodide is yellow. These salts will not dissolve when the mixture is acidified. Some carboxylic acids and alkynes yield silver salts, but these salts should dissolve in the acidic solution.

C-22 *Sodium Iodide in Acetone*

Reactions:
$$RCl + NaI \xrightarrow{\text{acetone}} RI + \textbf{NaCl}$$

$$RBr + NaI \xrightarrow{\text{acetone}} RI + \textbf{NaBr}$$

Controls: 1-chlorobutane, 2-chloro-2-methylpropane (no reaction), 1-bromobutane

*Halides that react with sodium iodide at
room temperature:*

    1° alkyl bromides

    benzyl and allyl halides

    vic-dihalides*; CBr₄*

    α-haloketones, -esters, and -amides

Halides that react at 50°C:

    1° and 2° alkyl chlorides

    2° and 3° alkyl bromides

    gem-di- and tribromides*

Halides that do not react:

    3° alkyl chlorides

    aryl and vinyl halides

    *cyclopropyl, cyclobutyl, and cyclo-
hexyl halides*

    *gem-polychloro compounds
(except benzyl and allyl)*

* Turns the solution red-brown

Place 1.0 mL of the sodium iodide/acetone reagent into a 13 × 100-mm test tube. Add 2 drops of a liquid halogen compound (or 0.10 g, dissolved in the minimum volume of acetone, if it is a solid). Shake the mixture, allow it to stand for 3 minutes, and note whether a precipitate or color forms. Disregard any precipitate that forms upon mixing but then dissolves. If there is no precipitate at the end of this time, place the test tube in a 50°C water bath (replenish the acetone if some evaporates), and leave it there for an additional 6 minutes; then cool the mixture to room temperature and record your observations.

Interpretation: Certain alkyl chlorides and bromides react to precipitate sodium chloride or sodium bromide, which are insoluble in acetone. Bromides react faster than comparable chlorides, and the test is not applicable to iodides. Because the reaction involves an S_N2 displacement by iodide ion, halides of the same halogen react in the order methyl > primary > secondary > tertiary > aryl, vinyl. Cycloalkyl halides tend to react more slowly than the corresponding open-chain compounds and may give no precipitate even after heating. *Vicinal* dihalides (with two halogen atoms on adjacent carbon atoms) and some *geminal* halides (with two or more halogen atoms on the same carbon atom) undergo oxidation–reduction reactions to liberate iodine—which is red–brown in acetone—while precipitating the sodium halide. A summary of the results with various halides is given in the margin.

C-23 *Tollens' Test*

Safety Notes

> **Silver nitrate is corrosive and toxic and it stains the skin black. Avoid contact with its solutions.**
> **The Tollens reagent and the test solution must never be stored—explosive silver salts form on standing.**

Reaction:

$$RCHO + 2Ag(NH_3)_2OH \longrightarrow 2\textbf{Ag} + RCOONH_4 + H_2O + 3NH_3$$

Control: benzaldehyde

Prepare the reagent immediately before use as follows: Measure 2.0 mL of 0.30 *M* silver nitrate into a *thoroughly cleaned* 13 × 100-mm test tube and add 1 drop of 3 *M* sodium hydroxide. Then add 2 *M* aqueous ammonia drop by drop, with shaking, until the resulting precipitate of silver oxide just dissolves (avoid an excess of ammonia). Add 1 drop of the unknown (or 40 mg, if it is a solid) to this solution, shake the mixture, and let it stand for 10 minutes. If no reaction has occurred by this time, heat the mixture in a 35°C water bath for 5 minutes.

Interpretation: Formation of a silver mirror on the inside of the test tube is a positive test for an aldehyde. If the tube isn't sufficiently clean, a black precipitate or a suspension of metallic silver may form instead. Certain cyclic ketones (such as cyclopentanone), aromatic amines, phenols, and α-alkoxy- or α-dialkylaminoketones may also give positive tests.

Take Care! Avoid contact with the silver nitrate solution.

Waste Disposal: Shortly after the test is completed, dissolve any residue in dilute nitric acid and place the solution in a designated waste container (*important!*).

Spectral Analysis

Infrared Spectra

To anyone proficient in spectral interpretation, an infrared (IR) spectrum provides so much information that it is equivalent to many classification tests. Because infrared absorption bands arise from the vibrational motions of specific chemical bonds, it is usually possible to identify or confirm the functional group(s) present in an organic compound from its IR spectrum. For example, a compound whose IR spectrum has a C=O stretching band at 1715 cm^{-1}, a C—O stretching band at 1240 cm^{-1}, and a very broad O—H stretching band centered at 3000 cm^{-1} is almost certainly a carboxylic acid. Characteristic infrared bands of the most common families of organic compounds are described in the section "Interpretation of Infrared Spectra" in OP-39.

Structural features other than functional groups can be detected from IR spectra. If your unknown compound is an alcohol, amide, or amine, you should be able to classify it as primary, secondary, or tertiary by reading about the IR spectra of these families in OP-39. If your unknown may have a benzene ring or a carbon–carbon double bond, you can confirm this and perhaps determine the kind of substitution on the ring or the C=C bond by reading about the IR spectra of aromatic hydrocarbons and alkenes. You can also find out whether the C=O group of an aldehyde, ketone, ester, or carboxylic acid is conjugated with an aromatic ring or a carbon–carbon double bond.

The best way to become proficient in the interpretation of infrared spectra is to read about and interpret actual spectra. Before attempting to interpret your IR spectrum, you should read "Interpretation of Infrared Spectra" in OP-39 and examine the sample spectra provided there.

DIRECTIONS

Obtain an infrared spectrum [OP-39] of the unknown as directed by your instructor. Interpret the spectrum as completely as you can (see OP-39). Use it to confirm any functional group suggested by the classification tests and to detect any additional functional groups and other structural features.

NMR Spectra

Like infrared spectra, nuclear magnetic resonance (NMR) spectra can be used to detect certain functional groups, but they are more often used to provide detailed structural information about organic molecules. With practice, an organic chemist can deduce the structural units present in an organic compound, or even its entire molecular structure, from an NMR spectrum. See the section "Interpretation of ^{1}H NMR Spectra" in OP-40 for help.

DIRECTIONS

Safety Notes

Assume that the NMR solvent is flammable and harmful by inhalation, ingestion, and skin absorption. Some NMR solvents, such as deuterochloroform, are also carcinogenic. Avoid contact, and do not breathe their vapors.

With your instructor's permission and guidance, record an integrated ^{1}H NMR spectrum [OP-40] of your unknown in deuterochloroform or another suitable solvent, using a tetramethylsilane (TMS) reference standard. Measure and tabulate the NMR parameters (chemical shift, signal area, signal multiplicity, and coupling constant). Then use them to reconstruct as much of the molecular structure of your unknown as you can.

Waste Disposal: Dispose of NMR solutions as directed by your instructor.

Identification

After you learn what chemical family your unknown belongs to, you are ready to begin the identification phase of your analysis by preparing a list of possible compounds. This phase will be completed when you have obtained sufficient evidence to eliminate all of the possibilities but one.

List of Possibilities

At your instructor's discretion, you may use either the tables of selected organic compounds provided in Appendix VI of this book or consult a more complete listing, such as the *CRC Handbook of Tables for Organic Compound Identification* [Bibliography, G5]. Most tables of this kind separate the compounds into liquids and solids, listing the liquids in order of increasing boiling point and the solids in order of increasing melting point.

Your initial list of possibilities should include all compounds that boil or melt within about ±10° of your measured value (your instructor may suggest a different range). The list should be prepared in the form of a table that shows, for each compound,

• Its name and structural formula
• Its boiling point or melting point
• The listed melting points of its derivatives

If necessary, you can look up some of the structural formulas in *The Merck Index* [Bibliography, A11], *Lange's Handbook of Chemistry* [Bibliography, A6], the *CRC Handbook of Chemistry and Physics* [Bibliography, A15], or another appropriate reference book. If the chemicals for some derivatives aren't available in your laboratory, their melting points can be omitted from your list. Some derivative melting points may not be given in published tables, either because the compound doesn't form that derivative or because the derivative's melting point has not been reported in the literature. Additional properties (such as the densities of organic halides) obtained from reference books can be included in your table as well.

DIRECTIONS

Referring to the appropriate table in Appendix VI (or another source recommended by your instructor), prepare a table that lists each compound whose boiling point or melting point is within the designated range. Give the boiling point or melting point of each compound, its molecular structure, any other useful data or information you can find, and the melting points of possible derivatives. If requested, submit your list to your instructor, who may (or may not) tell you if your unknown compound is on the list.

Additional Tests and Data

Once you have prepared your list of possibilities, you should be able to decide which compounds can be eliminated on the basis of spectral data and tests already performed, and what physical properties, chemical tests, or spectral bands will help you shorten the list further. If your list is already a short one, you may decide to prepare a derivative immediately. Otherwise, you may need to shorten it before you can decide on the most suitable derivative. Some ways of shortening your list are described in the following "Directions" section. Don't try to do them all; just do the ones that should be the most useful and that can be performed with the chemicals and equipment available in your laboratory.

Waste Disposal: Dispose of any wastes as directed by your instructor.

DIRECTIONS

To arrive at your short list, carry out one or more of the following procedures. Use only those that are permitted by your instructor (many instructors will not allow the use of NMR to identify qual organic unknowns).

1. Refer to Table Q2 in the section "Classification Tests," and decide which classification test or tests will help you shorten your list. Then carry out the tests according to the directions provided.
2. Reexamine your infrared spectrum, looking for bands that may indicate the presence or absence of a subsidiary functional group or a structural feature that is present in some of the compounds on your list but absent in others.
3. Record an ^1H NMR spectrum of your unknown, if you haven't already. Try to predict the kinds of NMR spectra that would be produced by the compounds on your list, and compare the predicted spectra with the actual one.
4. Measure the refractive index [OP-35] of an unknown liquid at 20°C, or correct it to that temperature. Compare it with literature values for the refractive indexes of the compounds on your list. If the unknown is very pure, a refractometer that measures to the fourth decimal place can be used to eliminate most compounds whose refractive index values deviate by more than ±0.001 or so from the observed value.

5. Determine the density of an unknown liquid by accurately weighing a precisely measured volume [OP-5] (0.20 mL or more) of the unknown. Compare it with literature values for the densities of the compounds on your list. Density cannot be measured as accurately as refractive index, but it is useful for distinguishing among compounds that have different structural features. For example, most aromatic compounds are more dense than aliphatic compounds of the same family, and density varies among halogenated hydrocarbons as described in Test **C-10**.

Preparation of Derivatives

In qualitative organic analysis, a *derivative* is a crystalline solid that can be prepared from nearly any compound in a particular family by using a standardized procedure, and that, after purification, should give an accurate melting point that can be used to identify the compound from which it was prepared. For example, an unknown carboxylic acid can be converted to an amide by treating it with thionyl chloride, followed by ammonia.

$$\underset{\overset{\displaystyle \|}{O}}{RC}-OH \xrightarrow{SOCl_2} \underset{\overset{\displaystyle \|}{O}}{RC}-Cl \xrightarrow{NH_3} \underset{\overset{\displaystyle \|}{O}}{RC}-NH_2$$

If the unknown acid is hexanoic acid (b.p. = 205°C), its amide (hexanamide) should melt near 101°C, as shown in Table 7 of Appendix VI. The only other carboxylic acid listed that boils near 205°C is 2-bromopropanoic acid, but its amide melts at 123°C, making it easy to distinguish these compounds by means of their derivative melting points.

You will need to prepare at least one derivative to confirm the identity of your unknown. In some cases, it may be necessary to prepare two or more derivatives to be certain of your identification. A suitable derivative should have a melting point between about 60°C and 250°C because solids that melt below 60°C are not easily purified by recrystallization, and melting points higher than 250°C are hard to measure accurately. Its melting point should not be close to the melting point of the unknown itself because it would then be hard to tell whether the compound obtained from a reaction is the derivative or the unreacted starting material. For example, preparing the amide of a compound believed to be 2-chlorobenzoic acid would not be a good idea because the amide has the same melting point (140°C) as the acid.

If possible, the derivative should be one whose melting-point value will point to just one compound from your list of possibilities. For example, suppose your compound is a ketone whose boiling point is 168°C, and you have prepared the list of possibilities shown in Table Q3. The oxime would not be a suitable derivative because melting points haven't been reported for two of the possibilities and two of the oximes melt below 60°C. Semicarbazones are reported for all of the ketones, but those for 2,6-dimethyl-4-heptanone and 2-octanone melt within a degree of each other. 2-Octanone might be distinguished by an iodoform test, but that would still leave 2-methyl- and 4-methylcyclohexanone, whose semicarbazones melt within 4°C of each other—a little too close to distinguish them with certainty. (Your derivative might melt at 197°C, for example.)

Table Q3 Derivatives of selected ketones

Compound	bp	Oxime	Semicarbazone	2,4-Dinitro-phenylhydrazone
2-methylcyclohexanone	163	43	195	137
2,6-dimethyl-4-heptanone	168	210	121	92
3-methylcyclohexanone	169	...	180	155
4-methylcyclohexanone	169	37	199	130
2-octanone	172	...	122	58

Note: bp is in °C.

The 2,4-dinitrophenylhydrazone is the preferred derivative because its melting points are well spread out.

The procedures whose page locations are given in Table Q4 are suitable for preparing derivatives of most common organic compounds in the specified class. In some cases, a variation of the procedure (the use of different reaction conditions or recrystallization solvents, etc.) may be required for satisfactory results. If you want to prepare a derivative that is not described in this section, see your instructor for permission and to find out whether the reagents are available. Procedures for additional derivatives, and alternative procedures for some of the derivatives used here, are given in qualitative analysis texts listed under Category G of the Bibliography.

Sometimes the same procedure will be used to prepare two related derivatives, such as the phenylurethane and α-naphthylurethane of an alcohol, and will list two different reagents, such as phenyl isocyanate and α-naphthyl isocyanate. In such cases, select the reagent appropriate for the derivative you wish to prepare. Thus, you would use phenyl isocyanate to prepare a phenylurethane, and α-naphthyl isocyanate to prepare an α-naphthylurethane.

The relative quantities of unknown and reagent are usually not crucial, because any excess reagent is removed during the isolation and purification of the derivative. For cases in which the quantities could affect the results, the quantity of the unknown is given in millimoles so that the required mass can be calculated using an estimate of its molecular weight.

In preparing a derivative, you will be using small quantities of the unknown and reagents, so you should use small-scale or microscale equipment whenever possible. If you are using microscale equipment and the quantity of unknown is limited, you can reduce the quantities of chemicals as specified in the directions for some derivatives. Quantities specified in drops are for medicine-dropper–size drops; if you are using a Pasteur pipet, double the number of drops.

Many of the reactions can be run in test tubes or Craig tubes. If you don't have a test tube of the specified size (e.g., 10 × 75 mm), use the next size larger (e.g., 13 × 100 mm). Some of the reactions require heating under reflux [OP-7c]. If you don't have access to microscale equipment, use a side-arm test tube fitted with a cold-finger condenser, or a West condenser attached to the smallest available round-bottom flask. Vacuum filtration [OP-16], recrystallization [OP-28], and other operations should be carried out with small-scale or microscale equipment, as outlined in the corresponding operation

Table Q4 Location of procedures for preparing derivatives

Family	Page number
alcohols	600
aldehydes and ketones	601
amides	602
primary and secondary amines	604
tertiary amines	606
carboxylic acids	607
esters	609
alkyl halides	611
aryl halides	612
aromatic hydrocarbons	613
phenols	614

For example, use a Hirsch funnel rather than a Buchner funnel for vacuum filtration.

descriptions. Nearly all of the derivatives must be purified by recrystallization from an appropriate solvent or solvent mixture. If the derivative forms an oil when boiled in the solvent specified, you may be able to substitute a lower boiling solvent of the same type, such as methanol for 95% ethanol. (Unless otherwise indicated, "ethanol" refers to 95% ethanol.) When the recrystallization solvent is described as an ethanol/water mixed solvent or some other mixture, use the procedure for recrystallization from mixed solvents described in OP-28b. The derivative should ordinarily be dissolved in the less polar solvent, and the solution saturated by adding the more polar solvent drop by drop. It should be understood that each derivative preparation requires a melting-point determination [OP-33] using the purified product.

Always read the Safety Notes before beginning any derivative preparation, and heed their warnings. Many of the reagents are highly reactive and may react violently with water or other substances. All should be considered toxic, and many of them are corrosive, lachrymatory, or have other unpleasant properties. Wear your safety goggles at all times, and wear protective gloves when directed to do so by the Safety Notes.

In the following Directions section, basic operations such as heating, weighing, and drying are not flagged by "OP" numbers in brackets.

Waste Disposal: For each derivative preparation, dispose of any wastes or unused reagents as directed by your instructor.

DIRECTIONS

Derivatives of Alcohols

D-1 *3,5-Dinitrobenzoates,* p-*Nitrobenzoates*

Safety Notes

The acid chlorides are corrosive and lachrymatory. Use a hood, and avoid contact with and inhalation of vapors.

Reaction: $\text{ArCOCl} + \text{ROH} \longrightarrow \text{ArCOOR} + \text{HCl}$

Under the hood, mix 0.20 g of pure 3,5-dinitrobenzoyl chloride *or* p-nitrobenzoyl chloride with 0.10 g of the unknown alcohol in a 13×100-mm test tube. Heat the mixture carefully in a heating block or over a *small* flame, so that it is just maintained in the liquid state. If you overheat the mixture, it may decompose—turning dark brown or black—and you will have to start over. If the alcohol boils below 160°C, heat the liquid mixture for 5 minutes; otherwise, heat it for 10–15 minutes. Allow the melt to cool and solidify. Break it up with a stirring rod, and stir in 4 mL of 0.2 *M* sodium carbonate. Heat this mixture to 50–60°C with a hot-water bath or steam bath (measure the temperature in the test tube, not in the bath), and stir it at that temperature for 30 seconds. Then cool it, and collect the precipitate by vacuum filtration [OP-16]. Wash the precipitate several times [OP-26a] with cold water, and recrystallize [OP-28] it from ethanol or an ethanol/water mixed solvent. Derivatives of higher boiling or higher melting alcohols require a higher ethanol/water ratio in the recrystallization solvent.

Take Care! Avoid contact with the acid chloride, and do not breathe its vapors.

D-2 α-*Naphthylurethanes, Phenylurethanes*

The alcohol and glassware must be dry, because moisture will cause the formation of either diphenylurea or di-α-naphthylurea, depending on the derivative you are preparing (these compounds melt at 241°C and 297°C, respectively). Tertiary alcohols do not form urethanes readily.

Safety Notes

Reaction:

$$ArN{=}C{=}O + ROH \longrightarrow ArNH\overset{\displaystyle O}{\overset{\displaystyle \|}{C}}{-}OR$$

Dry a 13 × 100-mm test tube or a Craig tube in an oven, then stopper it and let it cool. Unless you are sure that your alcohol is anhydrous, dry it with magnesium sulfate or sodium sulfate. *Under the hood,* mix 0.20 g of the unknown alcohol with 0.20 mL of phenyl isocyanate *or* 0.25 mL of α-naphthyl isocyanate in the reaction tube. If no reaction takes place immediately, heat the mixture in a 60–70°C water bath for 5–15 minutes. Cool the reaction tube in ice; gently scratch its sides with a glass stirring rod, if necessary, to induce crystallization. Collect the precipitate by vacuum filtration [OP-16], or by centrifugation [OP-17] if you used a Craig tube. Recrystallize [OP-28] it from about 5 mL of high-boiling petroleum ether or heptane, filtering the hot solution by gravity [OP-15], if necessary, to remove high-melting impurities.

Take Care! Avoid contact with and inhalation of the isocyanate.

Derivatives of Aldehydes and Ketones

D-3 *2,4-Dinitrophenylhydrazones*

Safety Notes

Reaction:

$$R{-}\underset{R'}{\overset{\displaystyle \|}{C}}{=}O + H_2NNH{-}\!\!\bigcirc\!\!{-}NO_2 \longrightarrow R{-}\underset{R'}{\overset{\displaystyle \|}{C}}{=}NNH{-}\!\!\bigcirc\!\!{-}NO_2 + H_2O$$

$$O_2N \qquad\qquad\qquad\qquad O_2N$$

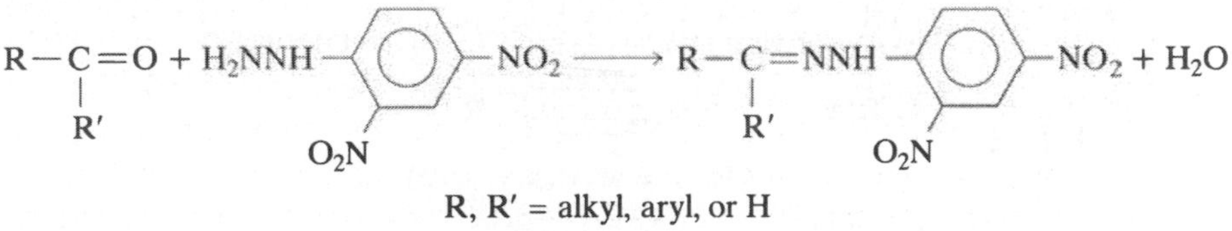

R, R' = alkyl, aryl, or H

Dissolve 0.10 g of the unknown aldehyde or ketone in 4.0 mL of 95% ethanol in an 18 × 150-mm test tube. Add 3.0 mL of the 2,4-dinitrophenyl-hydrazine–sulfuric acid (DNPH) reagent, and allow the solution to stand at room temperature until crystallization is complete. If necessary, warm the solution gently for a minute on a steam bath or in a hot-water bath. If no precipitate appears after 15 minutes, add water—drop by drop—to the warm solution until it just becomes cloudy; heat it until it clears up, and let it cool. Collect the derivative by vacuum filtration [OP-16]. Recrystallize [OP-28] it from 95% ethanol or an ethanol/water mixed solvent. If the derivative

Take Care! Avoid contact with the DNPH reagent.

doesn't dissolve in 6 mL of boiling 95% ethanol, add ethyl acetate—drop by drop—to the boiling mixture until it becomes clear.

D-4 *Semicarbazones*

For microscale work, all quantities may be divided by 2.

Safety Notes

Semicarbazide hydrochloride is a suspected carcinogen. Avoid contact.

Reaction:

$$R-\underset{\underset{R'}{|}}{\overset{\overset{O}{\|}}{C}} + H_2NNHCNH_2 \longrightarrow R-\underset{\underset{R'}{|}}{C}=NNHCNH_2 + H_2O$$

R, R′ = alkyl, aryl, or H

Take Care! Avoid contact with semicarbazide hydrochloride.

Mix together 0.20 g of semicarbazide hydrochloride, 0.30 g of sodium acetate, 2 mL of water, and 2 mL of 95% ethanol in a small test tube (if the unknown is water soluble, omit the ethanol). Add 0.20 g of the unknown aldehyde or ketone, and stir or shake to dissolve. If the mixture is cloudy, add more ethanol until it clears up. Stopper the test tube, and shake the mixture for a minute or two. Then let it stand; cool it in ice, if necessary, to induce crystallization. If no crystals form, place the test tube in a boiling-water bath for a few minutes, and then let it cool. Collect the product by vacuum filtration [OP-16], wash it on the filter [OP-26a] with cold water, and recrystallize [OP-28] it from 95% ethanol or an ethanol/water mixed solvent.

D-5 *Oximes*

Oximes are suitable derivatives for most ketones and for some (though not all) aldehydes.

Safety Notes

Hydroxylamine hydrochloride is toxic, mutagenic, and can cause a form of anemia. Avoid contact.

Reaction:

$$R-\underset{\underset{R'}{|}}{\overset{\overset{O}{\|}}{C}} + H_2N-OH \longrightarrow R-\underset{\underset{R'}{|}}{C}=N-OH + H_2O$$

R, R′ = alkyl, aryl, or H

Take Care! Avoid contact with hydroxylamine hydrochloride.

Prepare the oxime following the procedure given for semicarbazones (**D-4**), using hydroxylamine hydrochloride in place of semicarbazide hydrochloride. It is usually necessary to heat the reactants with a boiling-water bath or steam bath for 10 minutes or more. Adding a few milliliters of cold water to the reaction mixture may facilitate precipitation.

Derivatives of Amides

The acid and amine portions of an amide can be obtained by hydrolysis, as described in Procedure **D-6**, and one or both of them may be characterized by a melting point or derivative preparation. Melting points of the carboxylic acids obtained from amides are given in Table 4 of Appendix VI. Melting points of amine derivatives can be found in Table 5 and Table 6; melting points of carboxylic acid derivatives are in Table 7. You can also prepare a derivative of a primary amide by performing Procedure **D-7**.

D-6 *Hydrolysis Products*

If the amide is known to be primary, omit Procedure **A**. For microscale work, all quantities should be divided by 2.

Safety Notes

Reactions: $RCONR'_2 + NaOH \longrightarrow RCOONa + R'_2NH$

$RCOONa + H^+ \longrightarrow RCOOH + Na^+$

R, R' = H, alkyl, or aryl

If the alkaline hydrolysis classification test (C-2) suggests that the amide is difficult to hydrolyze, use 6 M NaOH, a longer reaction time, or both.

Measure 0.60 g of the unknown amide and 10 mL of 3 *M* sodium hydroxide into a small round-bottom flask. Add a boiling chip or two, attach a water-cooled condenser, and heat the mixture under reflux for 15 minutes or more. Using the reaction flask and a water-cooled condenser, assemble an apparatus for small-scale or microscale simple distillation [OP-30]. Place 4 mL of 3 *M* hydrochloric acid in the receiving flask, or in a collecting tube if you are using a Hickman still. If you can't carry out the reaction under a hood, attach a gas trap [OP-14] that contains dilute HCl to the vacuum adapter outlet (SS) or one that contains pelletized Norit to the condenser (μS). Distill the reaction mixture until about 6 mL of distillate has been collected in the receiving flask or collecting tube.

Take Care! Wear gloves, and avoid contact with and inhalation of the arenesulfonyl chloride.

A. Characterization of the Amine. *Under the hood*, add 10 mL of 3 *M* sodium hydroxide to the distillate; then add 0.40 mL of benzenesulfonyl chloride *or* 0.60 g of *p*-toluenesulfonyl chloride. Proceed according to the directions given in **D-9** (beginning at "Stopper the test tube . . .") for preparing arenesulfonamide derivatives of amines. Note that you may not obtain a derivative if the "amine" is ammonia or a gaseous amine that escapes during the reaction or distillation.

B. Characterization of the Carboxylic Acid. Carefully acidify the residue in the boiling flask with 6 *M* HCl. If a precipitate forms (the carboxylic acid), collect it by vacuum filtration [OP-16], wash it [OP-26a], and recrystallize [OP-28] it from water, ethanol/water, or another suitable solvent. If no precipitate forms, you can try to prepare a *p*-nitrobenzyl derivative with this solution by following the directions in **D-15**.

Safety Notes

D-7 N-*Xanthylamides*

This procedure is suitable only for primary amides. For microscale work, all quantities may be divided by 2.

Reaction:

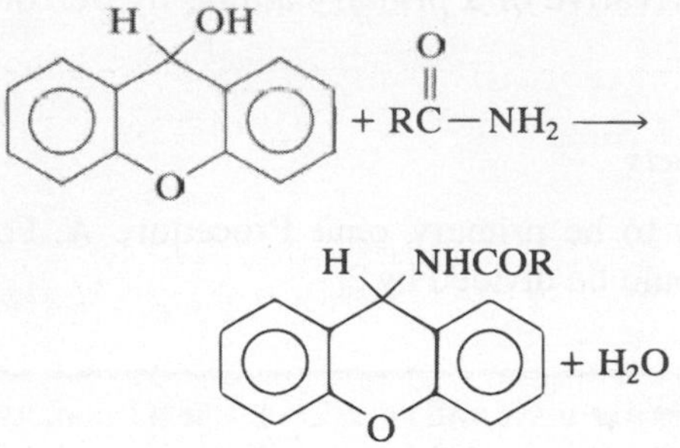

Take Care! Wear gloves, and avoid contact with and inhalation of acetic acid.

Under the hood, dissolve 0.40 g of xanthydrol in 5.0 mL of glacial acetic acid in a test tube, stopper it, and shake until most of the solid has dissolved. Separate the solution from undissolved residue, if there is any. Then add 0.20 g (or as close to 1.5 mmol as you can estimate) of the unknown amide to the solution, and heat the reaction mixture in an 85°C water bath for 20 minutes. (If the amide is insoluble in acetic acid, dissolve it in a minimal volume of ethanol before adding it to the solution; then add 1 mL of water to the warm reaction mixture after the reaction is complete.) Let the solution cool until precipitation is complete. Collect the solid by vacuum filtration [OP-16], and recrystallize [OP-28] it from an ethanol/water mixed solvent.

Derivatives of Primary and Secondary Amines

See **D-12** for directions for preparing picrate derivatives of amines.

D-8 *Benzamides*

For microscale work, all quantities may be divided by 2.

Safety Notes

> Benzoyl chloride is corrosive, a lachrymator, and a possible carcinogen. Use gloves and a hood, avoid contact, and do not breathe its vapors.

Reaction:

R, R′ = alkyl, aryl, or H

Take Care! Wear gloves, and avoid contact with and inhalation of benzoyl chloride.

Under the hood, combine 0.20 g of the unknown primary or secondary amine (or as close to 2.0 mmol as you can estimate) with 2.0 mL of 3 *M* sodium hydroxide in a small test tube. Then add 0.80 mL of benzoyl chloride, drop by drop, with swirling or shaking. Continue to shake the stoppered test tube for about 5 minutes; then carefully neutralize the solution to a pH of 8 with 3 *M* HCl (use pH paper). Break up the solid mass with a stirring rod, if necessary, and collect the derivative by vacuum filtration [OP-16]. After washing the product thoroughly with cold water [OP-26a], recrystallize [OP-28] it from an ethanol/water mixed solvent.

D-9 *Benzenesulfonamides, p-Toluenesulfonamides*

A precipitate that forms in the Hinsberg test (**C-15**) can be purified and used as a *p*-toluenesulfonamide derivative. For microscale work, all quantities may be divided by 2.

> **Arenesulfonyl chlorides are toxic and corrosive. Use a hood, avoid contact, and do not breathe their vapors.**

Safety Notes

Reactions:

$$RNH_2 + ArSO_2Cl \xrightarrow{NaOH} \xrightarrow{HCl} ArSO_2NHR + HCl$$

$$R_2NH + ArSO_2Cl \xrightarrow{NaOH} ArSO_2NR_2 + HCl$$

Under the hood, combine 0.20 g (or as close to 2.0 mmol as you can estimate) of the unknown primary or secondary amine with 10 mL of 3 *M* sodium hydroxide in a test tube. Add 0.40 mL of benzenesulfonyl chloride *or* 0.60 g of *p*-toluenesulfonyl chloride. Stopper the test tube, and shake it vigorously for 3 to 5 minutes. Check the pH of the solution to make sure it is basic; add more 3 *M* NaOH if it is not. Loosen the stopper, and heat the test tube in a boiling-water bath or over a steam bath for about 2 minutes. Let the solution cool to room temperature.

Take Care! Wear gloves, and avoid contact with and inhalation of the arenesulfonyl chloride.

(a) If a precipitate forms, collect it by vacuum filtration [OP-16], wash it with water [OP-26a], and recrystallize [OP-28] it from an ethanol/water mixed solvent.

(b) If no precipitate forms after cooling, acidify the solution to pH 6 with 6 *M* HCl and cool it in an ice/water bath. Collect the precipitate by vacuum filtration [OP-16], wash it with cold water [OP-26a], and recrystallize [OP-28] it from an ethanol/water mixed solvent.

D-10 *α-Naphthylthioureas, Phenylthioureas*

Note that the reagents are iso*thio*cyanates; don't use the corresponding isocyanate by mistake. Protect the reactants and the reaction mixture from water. For microscale work, all quantities may be divided by 2.

> **The isothiocyanates are corrosive and toxic, and α-naphthylisothiocyanate is a lachrymator. Use gloves and a hood, avoid contact, and do not breathe their vapors.**

Safety Notes

Reaction:

$$ArN{=}C{=}S + \underset{\underset{R'}{|}}{RNH} \longrightarrow Ar\underset{\underset{R'}{|}}{NH}\overset{\overset{S}{\|}}{C}NR$$

R, R' = alkyl, aryl, or H

Take Care! Wear gloves, and avoid contact with and inhalation of the isothiocyanate.

Under the hood, dissolve 0.20 g (or as close to 2.0 mmol as you can estimate) of the unknown primary or secondary amine in 2.0 mL of *absolute* ethanol in a *dry* 15-cm test tube or a conical vial. Add 0.20 mL of phenylisothiocyanate *or* 0.30 g of α-naphthylisothiocyanate. Attach an air condenser if you are using a conical vial. Add a boiling chip or two, and gently boil the mixture under the hood for 5 minutes with a hot-water bath or steam bath. If you are using a test tube, replace any ethanol that evaporates. Let the reaction mixture cool, and scratch the sides of the container to induce crystallization or cause any oil to crystallize. If no crystals form, boil the mixture gently (use a hood!) for another 20 minutes or so, replacing any ethanol that evaporates, and again try to induce crystallization. Adding water, drop by drop, until the solution becomes cloudy may help.

Using a small amount of aqueous 50% ethanol for the transfer, collect the derivative by vacuum filtration [OP-16], and wash it [OP-26a] once with 50% ethanol and once with 95% ethanol. If the solid appears quite impure, you can extract impurities by boiling and stirring it with 4 mL of petroleum ether. Recrystallize [OP-28] the derivative from ethanol or an ethanol/water mixed solvent.

Derivatives of Tertiary Amines

D-11 *Methiodides*

For microscale work, all quantities may be divided by 2.

Safety Notes

> Iodomethane is toxic and irritant, and it is a suspected human carcinogen and mutagen. Use gloves and a hood, avoid contact, and do not breathe its vapors.

Reaction: $R_3N + CH_3I \longrightarrow R_3NCH_3^+I^-$

R = alkyl, aryl, or a combination
of the two

Take Care! Wear gloves, and avoid contact with and inhalation of iodomethane.

Under the hood, combine 0.20 g of the unknown tertiary amine with 0.20 mL of iodomethane in a small test tube or a Craig tube, and heat the mixture in a 50–60°C water bath for 5 minutes. Cool the mixture in ice, collect the product by vacuum filtration [OP-16]—or by centrifugation [OP-17], if you used a Craig tube—and recrystallize [OP-28] it from ethanol, ethyl acetate, or a mixture of the two.

D-12 *Picrates*

Picrates of primary and secondary amines and aromatic hydrocarbons can also be prepared by this method. Picrates of many aromatic hydrocarbons dissociate when heated and therefore cannot be recrystallized. For microscale work, all quantities may be divided by 2.

Safety Notes

Reaction:

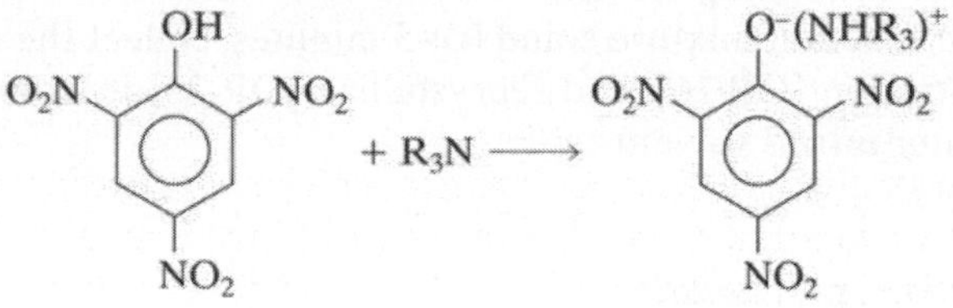

R = alkyl, aryl, or a combination of the two

Dissolve 0.20 g of the unknown amine (or aromatic hydrocarbon) in 5.0 mL of 95% ethanol in a test tube, and add 5.0 mL of a saturated solution of picric acid in ethanol. Heat the solution just to boiling over a steam bath or in a boiling-water bath, and then let it cool to room temperature. Collect the crystals by vacuum filtration [OP-16], and wash them [OP-26a] with cold ethanol or methanol. Recrystallize [OP-28] the derivative from ethanol, if necessary (some picrates are pure enough to use without recrystallization). Some picrates may explode when strongly heated, so use caution when obtaining the melting point.

Take Care! Avoid contact with the picric acid solution. Don't let the heated solution boil over.

Derivatives of Carboxylic Acids

D-13 *Amides*

This derivative is suitable for aromatic acids and for most aliphatic acids that have six or more carbon atoms. Because Procedures **D-13** and **D-14** both involve preparation of the acid chloride, it is convenient to make enough acid chloride to prepare one of the **D-14** derivatives as well. In that case, double the amounts given for the preparation of the acid chloride, add half of it to the aqueous ammonia as described here, and save the other half for the **D-14** derivative. For microscale work, all quantities may be divided by 2.

Safety Notes

Reactions: $RCOOH + SOCl_2 \longrightarrow RCOCl + HCl + SO_2$

$RCOCl + NH_3 \longrightarrow RCONH_2 + HCl$

After drying its components in an oven for 20 minutes or more, assemble an apparatus for heating under reflux. For microscale work, use a conical vial and a water-cooled condenser. Carry out the reaction under the hood or use a gas trap [OP-14]. Mix 0.40 g of the unknown carboxylic acid with 2.0 mL of thionyl chloride, add a boiling chip, and heat the mixture under gentle reflux for 20–30 minutes, using a steam bath or hot-water bath. Cool the resulting acid chloride in an ice/water bath. *Under the hood,* add the acid chloride slowly, with constant stirring [OP-10], to a small beaker containing 5.0 mL of ice-cold concentrated aqueous ammonia. Let the reaction mixture stand for 5 minutes, collect the derivative by vacuum filtration [OP-16], and recrystallize [OP-28] it from water or an ethanol/water mixed solvent.

Take Care! Wear gloves, and avoid contact with and inhalation of thionyl chloride and the acid chloride.

Take Care! A violent reaction is possible. Wear gloves, and avoid contact with and inhalation of NH_3.

D-14 *Anilides,* p-*Toluidides*

If you divided all quantities for preparation of the acid chloride (in **D-13**) by 2, do so for this procedure as well.

Safety Notes

> The aromatic amines are toxic if inhaled, ingested, or absorbed through the skin. Use gloves, avoid contact, and do not breathe their vapors.
> Acid chlorides are toxic and corrosive, and their vapors are harmful. Avoid contact, and do not breathe their vapors.

Reactions: $RCOOH + SOCl_2 \longrightarrow RCOCl + HCl + SO_2$
$RCOCl + ArNH_2 \longrightarrow RCONHAr + HCl$

The reaction apparatus used for preparing the acid chloride must be dry. If you already carried out Procedure **D-13** with double the amounts of reactants, use the acid chloride you saved from that preparation. Otherwise, prepare the acid chloride of the unknown carboxylic acid as directed in Procedure **D-13.**

Take Care! Wear gloves, and avoid contact with and inhalation of thionyl chloride and the acid chloride.

Take Care! Wear gloves, and avoid contact with and inhalation of the aromatic amine.

Under the hood, dilute the cooled acid chloride with 2.0 mL of anhydrous diethyl ether (if necessary, transfer it to a larger container after dilution). Then add in portions, shaking or stirring [OP-10] after each addition, a solution that contains 0.70 mL of aniline *or* 0.80 g of *p*-toluidine dissolved in 10 mL of anhydrous diethyl ether. Continue the addition until the odor of the acid chloride has disappeared. If the odor persists after all of the aromatic amine solution has been added, heat the mixture over a steam bath or in a boiling-water bath for a minute or two. Using a separatory funnel or centrifuge tube, wash [OP-24] the ether solution with 5 mL of 1.5 *M* HCl, followed by 5 mL of water. Evaporate [OP-19] the solvent from the organic layer. Recrystallize [OP-28] the derivative from water or an ethanol/water mixed solvent.

D-15 p-*Nitrobenzyl Esters*

Preparation of this derivative is recommended only when the previous derivatives are not suitable or when the carboxylic acid is obtained in aqueous solution. It is important that *p*-nitrobenzyl chloride not be present in excess, because it is difficult to remove from the product. For microscale work, all quantities should be divided by 2.

Safety Notes

Reaction:

$$RCOONa + O_2N-\bigcirc-CH_2Cl \longrightarrow RCOOCH_2-\bigcirc-NO_2 + NaCl$$

If the carboxylic acid was obtained by hydrolysis of an unknown ester (Procedure **D-16**) or amide (Procedure **D-6**), identify the alcohol or amine portion of the unknown first, and estimate the molecular weight of the acid portion from your list of possibilities. Then estimate the amount of acid in the hydrolysis solution, and measure out enough of the solution to provide ~2.0 mmol of the acid.

Mix an estimated 2.0 mmol of the unknown carboxylic acid with 3 mL of water (or use the measured hydrolysis solution) in a small round-bottom flask, and add a drop of phenolphthalein indicator solution. Add 3 *M* NaOH, drop by drop, until the solution turns pink. If necessary, heat to dissolve the acid salt; then add a drop or so of 1.5 *M* HCl to just discharge the pink color. *Under the hood,* add 0.30 g (1.75 mmol) of *p*-nitrobenzyl chloride dissolved in 10 mL of 95% ethanol. Drop in a boiling chip or two, and heat the mixture under gentle reflux for about 90 minutes (di- and triprotic acids should be heated for 2 and 3 hours, respectively). Transfer the solution to a small Erlenmeyer flask, and let it cool to room temperature. If crystallization hasn't occurred by then, add 1 mL of water and scratch the sides of the flask. When crystallization is complete (it may take 20 minutes or more), collect the derivative by vacuum filtration [OP-16]; wash it twice [OP-26a] with small portions of 5% sodium carbonate, and then once with water. Recrystallize [OP-28] the derivative from ethanol or an ethanol/water mixed solvent.

Take Care! Wear gloves, and avoid contact with and inhalation of *p*-nitrobenzyl chloride.

Take Care! Wear gloves, and avoid contact with the derivative.

Derivatives of Esters

The acid and alcohol portions of an ester can be obtained by hydrolysis, as described in **D-16**, and one or both of them may be characterized by a melting point or derivative preparation. Melting points of solid carboxylic acids and alcohols are given in Table 8 of Appendix VI. Melting points of alcohol and carboxylic acid derivatives are given in Table 1 and Table 7. You can also prepare a derivative from the ester itself by following either Procedure **D-17** or Procedure **D-18**. Procedure **D-17** forms a derivative of its carboxylic acid portion, and Procedure **D-18** forms a derivative of its alcohol portion.

D-16 *Hydrolysis Products*

For microscale work, all quantities may be divided by 4.

Safety Notes

Reactions: RCOOR′ + NaOH $\longrightarrow$ RCOONa + R′OH

RCOONa + H$^+$ $\longrightarrow$ RCOOH + Na$^+$

Take Care! Wear gloves, avoid contact with the NaOH solution.

The organic layer may be an alcohol, in which case it can be used to prepare a derivative, after purification if necessary.

Take Care! Wear gloves, and avoid contact with and inhalation of HCl.

If the unknown may be an ester of a phenol, test a small amount of the precipitate for solubility in 5% NaHCO$_3$ (see "Solubility Tests").

Mix 2.0 mL of the unknown (or 2.0 g, if it is a solid) with 20 mL of 6 *M* sodium hydroxide, and heat the mixture under reflux [OP-7c] for 30 minutes or more. If there are two layers, separate them and save the aqueous layer (the larger one). *Under the hood,* acidify the aqueous layer by adding concentrated HCl, drop by drop. If a solid carboxylic acid precipitates, collect it by vacuum filtration [OP-16], and recrystallize [OP-28] it from water or an ethanol/water mixed solvent. Use it as a derivative, convert it to one of the carboxylic acid derivatives, or both. If no precipitate forms, make the solution basic to litmus with dilute sodium hydroxide, and distill [OP-30] it until about 4 mL of distillate has been collected (save the distillate, which may contain an alcohol). Acidify the solution remaining in the reaction vessel, and either (a) use the solution to prepare a *p*-nitrobenzyl ester, as described in Procedure **D-15**; or (b) extract [OP-18] the solution with diethyl ether, and evaporate [OP-19] the ether to isolate the carboxylic acid for a derivative preparation.

The alcohol portion of the ester may separate if the distillate is saturated with solid potassium carbonate. It can then be isolated by removing the aqueous layer with a Pasteur pipet or by extracting [OP-18] the distillate with diethyl ether and evaporating [OP-19] the ether. After purification (if necessary), the alcohol can be used to prepare an alcohol derivative.

D-17 N-*Benzylamides*

This procedure works well only with methyl and ethyl esters. If your unknown may be an ester of a higher alcohol, heat 1.0 g of the ester under reflux with 5 mL of 5% sodium methoxide in methanol for 30 minutes, and then evaporate [OP-19] the methanol. Use all of the resulting methyl ester in the following procedure. For microscale work, all quantities may be divided by 2.

Safety Notes

Benzylamine is corrosive and lachrymatory. Use gloves and a hood, avoid contact, and do not breathe its vapors.

Reactions:

RCOOR′ + CH$_3$OH $\xrightarrow{\text{CH}_3\text{ONa}}$ RCOOCH$_3$ + R′OH (optional)

RCOOCH$_3$ + PhCH$_2$NH$_2$ $\xrightarrow{\text{NH}_4\text{Cl}}$ RCONHCH$_2$Ph + CH$_3$OH

or

RCOOCH$_2$CH$_3$ + PhCH$_2$NH$_2$ $\xrightarrow{\text{NH}_4\text{Cl}}$ RCONHCH$_2$Ph + CH$_3$CH$_2$OH

Take Care! Wear gloves, and avoid contact with and inhalation of benzylamine.

Under the hood, combine 1.0 g of an unknown methyl or ethyl ester with 2.0 mL of benzylamine and 0.10 g of powdered ammonium chloride in a conical vial or small round-bottom flask. Heat the mixture under reflux for 1 hour. Cool the reaction mixture, and wash it with 6 mL of water in a centrifuge tube (or a conical vial, if you reduced the quantities), removing the water with a Pasteur pipet. If no precipitate forms, add a drop or two of 3 *M*

HCl and scratch the sides of the tube. If a precipitate still does not form, transfer the mixture to a small beaker (use a little water in the transfer), and boil it for a few minutes to remove any excess ester. Then cool it and try to induce crystallization. Collect the derivative by vacuum filtration [OP-16], wash it with cold petroleum ether [OP-26a], and recrystallize [OP-28] it from an ethanol/water mixed solvent or from ethyl acetate.

D-18 *3,5-Dinitrobenzoates*

This procedure is not satisfactory for esters of tertiary and some unsaturated alcohols. If the 3,5-dinitrobenzoic acid takes more than 15 minutes to dissolve, increase the reaction time to 1 hour. For microscale work, all quantities may be divided by 2.

Safety Notes

> Sulfuric acid causes chemical burns that can seriously damage skin and eyes. Use gloves and avoid contact.
> 3,5-Dinitrobenzoic acid is an irritant. Avoid contact.

Reaction:

$$O_2N\text{-}C_6H_3(NO_2)\text{-}COOH + RCOOR' \xrightarrow{H_2SO_4} O_2N\text{-}C_6H_3(NO_2)\text{-}COOR' + RCOOH$$

Combine 1.0 g of the unknown ester with 0.80 g of 3,5-dinitrobenzoic acid in a conical vial or small round-bottom flask, and add a drop of concentrated sulfuric acid and a boiling chip or two. If the ester boils below 150°C, heat the mixture under reflux [OP-7c] until the 3,5-dinitrobenzoic acid dissolves, and then continue heating for an additional 30 minutes. Otherwise, heat it for the same time period with a 150°C aluminum block, sand bath, or oil bath, while stirring. Dissolve the cooled reaction mixture in 20 mL of anhydrous diethyl ether. Wash the ether solution twice with 10-mL portions of 0.5 *M* sodium carbonate, and then with water. Evaporate [OP-19] the ether, and dissolve the residue (often an oil) in 2–3 mL of boiling ethanol. Filter the hot solution by gravity [OP-15], add water until the mixture becomes cloudy, and cool the solution to crystallize the product. Recrystallize [OP-28] the derivative from an ethanol/water mixed solvent.

Take Care! Wear gloves, and avoid contact with 3,5-dinitrobenzoic acid and sulfuric acid.

Take Care! Foaming will occur during the sodium carbonate wash.

Derivatives of Alkyl Halides

In addition to the following derivative, density (Test **C-10**) and refractive index values are useful for characterizing alkyl and aryl halides.

D-19 S-*Alkylthiuronium Picrates*

Tertiary alkyl halides will not form this derivative. If the unknown is an alkyl chloride, use Procedure **B**. For microscale work, all quantities may be divided by 2.

Safety Notes

> As the dry solid, picric acid is unstable and can explode when subjected to heat or shock. Do not let the picric acid solution dry out. It is also toxic and corrosive. Avoid contact with solutions that contain picric acid.
> Thiourea is toxic if absorbed through the skin. Avoid contact.

Reaction:

$$RX + 2H_2N-\overset{\overset{S}{\|}}{C}-NH_2 + \underset{NO_2}{\underset{\displaystyle}{O_2N}\!\!\bigcirc\!\!{NO_2}}^{OH} \longrightarrow$$

$$\left[\begin{array}{c} R-S \\ | \\ H_2N-C=NH \end{array}\right]^+ \underset{NO_2}{O_2N\!\!\bigcirc\!\!NO_2}^{O^-} + H_2NCSNH_3{}^+X^-$$

X = Cl, Br, I   R = alkyl

Take Care! Avoid contact with thiourea and the picric acid solution. Do not allow the solution to evaporate to dryness; that could cause an explosion.

A. Mix together 0.50 g of the unknown alkyl bromide or iodide, 0.50 g of powdered thiourea, and 5.0 mL of 95% ethanol in a small round-bottom flask. Add a boiling chip or two, and heat the mixture under reflux for 20 minutes if the halide is primary, or 2–3 hours if it is secondary. Then add 5.0 mL of a saturated solution of picric acid in ethanol, and heat the mixture under reflux until a clear (but not necessarily colorless) solution is obtained. Allow the solution to cool, collect the derivative by vacuum filtration [OP-16], and recrystallize [OP-28] it from ethanol or an ethanol/water mixed solvent. If a derivative fails to form under these conditions, try Procedure **B**.

Take Care! Avoid contact with thiourea and the picric acid solution.

B. Mix together 0.20 g of the unknown alkyl halide, 0.20 g of powdered thiourea, and 6 mL of ethylene glycol in a test tube. Insert a clamped thermometer, and heat the solution at 120°C—using an oil bath, an aluminum block, or a sand bath—for 30 minutes. Then add 2.0 mL of a saturated solution of picric acid in ethanol, and continue heating the reaction mixture at 120°C for 15 minutes. Add 6 mL of water, and cool the mixture in an ice/water bath to induce crystallization. Collect the derivative by vacuum filtration [OP-16], and recrystallize [OP-28] it from ethanol or an ethanol/water mixed solvent.

Derivatives of Aryl Halides

In addition to preparing the following derivative, you can characterize aryl halides that have alkyl side chains by oxidizing the side chain (Procedure **D-21**). Density (Test **C-10**) and refractive index values are also useful.

D-20 *Nitro Compounds*

Procedure **A** yields mononitro derivatives of comparatively reactive aryl halides and aromatic hydrocarbons. Procedure **B** should yield dinitro or trinitro derivatives of reactive compounds and mononitro derivatives of un-reactive ones. Most di- and trialkylbenzenes yield trinitro derivatives by Procedure **B**, whereas monoalkylbenzenes yield dinitro derivatives. Because di- and trinitro derivatives are often easier to purify than mononitro derivatives, Procedure **B** is usually preferred. For microscale work, all quantities may be divided by 2.

> Sulfuric acid, nitric acid, and (especially) fuming nitric acid are toxic, highly reactive, and very corrosive. Use gloves and a hood, avoid contact, and do not inhale vapors or any brown fumes that may be generated during the reaction.

Safety Notes

Reaction: $ArH + HNO_3 \xrightarrow{H_2SO_4} ArNO_2 + H_2O$
(and di- or trinitro derivatives in some cases)

A. *Under the hood,* mix 0.50 g of the unknown aryl halide (or aromatic hydrocarbon) with 2.0 mL of concentrated sulfuric acid. Cautiously add 2.0 mL of concentrated nitric acid, drop by drop, with shaking or stirring. Then heat the mixture in a 60°C water bath for 10 minutes, with magnetic stirring [OP-10] or frequent shaking. Cautiously pour the mixture onto 15 mL of cracked ice in a small beaker, with manual stirring. After the ice has melted, collect the precipitate by vacuum filtration [OP-16], wash it with water [OP-26a], and recrystallize [OP-28] it from an ethanol/water mixed solvent. Repeated recrystallization may be necessary if the product melts at a lower temperature than expected, or over a wide range.

Take Care! Wear gloves, and avoid contact with and inhalation of the acids.

Take Care! A violent reaction is possible.

B. Follow Procedure **A**, but use 2.0 mL of fuming nitric acid in place of concentrated nitric acid, and heat the solution for 10 minutes over a steam bath or in a boiling-water bath. Add the acid slowly to minimize the generation of brown fumes of nitrogen dioxide. If the product separates as an oil, it is probably a mixture of compounds with different numbers of nitro groups.

Take Care! Wear gloves, and avoid contact with and inhalation of the acid.

Derivatives of Aromatic Hydrocarbons

In addition to preparing the following derivative, you can characterize aromatic hydrocarbons by the preparation of picrates (**D-12**) and nitro compounds (**D-20**). The picrates of many aromatic hydrocarbons dissociate when heated and cannot be recrystallized.

D-21 *Aromatic Carboxylic Acids*

The following procedure is for an aromatic hydrocarbon or aryl halide with one alkyl side chain. If the unknown may have more than one side chain, increase the quantities of potassium permanganate and 6 *M* NaOH in proportion to the anticipated number of side chains. For microscale work, all quantities may be divided by 5.

> Sodium hydroxide is toxic and corrosive, and it causes severe damage to skin, eyes, and mucous membranes. Use gloves, and avoid contact with the NaOH solution.
> Potassium permanganate can react violently with oxidizable materials. Keep it away from other chemicals and combustibles.

Safety Notes

Reaction: $\text{ArR} \xrightarrow{\text{KMnO}_4} \text{ArCOOH}$

In a round-bottom flask of appropriate size, dissolve 1.5 g of potassium permanganate in 25 mL of water. Add 0.50 g of the aromatic hydrocarbon (or alkyl-substituted aryl halide), followed by 0.50 mL of 6 M sodium hydroxide. Heat the mixture under reflux, with magnetic stirring [OP-10] or occasional shaking, for 1 hour or until the purple permanganate color has disappeared. Cool the reaction mixture to room temperature, acidify it with 6 M sulfuric acid, and boil it under reflux for about 5 minutes. If a brown precipitate of manganese dioxide is present, stir just enough solid sodium bisulfite into the hot solution to remove it, keeping the solution acidic with 6 M H_2SO_4 during this treatment. Cool the reaction mixture, collect the product by vacuum filtration [OP-16], and recrystallize [OP-28] the carboxylic acid from water or an ethanol/water mixed solvent.

Derivatives of Phenols

D-22 *Aryloxyacetic Acids*

For microscale work, all quantities may be divided by 5. The equivalent weight of an aryloxyacetic acid (and thus of the unknown phenol) can be determined by measuring its neutralization equivalent (Test **C-18**).

Safety Notes

Chloroacetic acid is corrosive and toxic. Use gloves, avoid contact, and do not breathe its vapors.
Sodium hydroxide is toxic and corrosive, and it may cause severe damage to skin, eyes, and mucous membranes. Use gloves, and avoid contact with the NaOH solution.
Some aryloxyacetic acids, such as 2,4-dichlorophenoxyacetic acid (2,4-D), are suspected human carcinogens. Avoid contact with the derivative.

Reaction: $\text{ArOH} + \text{ClCH}_2\text{COOH} \longrightarrow \text{ArOCH}_2\text{COOH} + \text{HCl}$

Under the hood, combine 0.50 g of the unknown phenol with 0.70 g of chloroacetic acid and 3.0 mL of 8 M sodium hydroxide. Heat the mixture over a steam bath or in a boiling-water bath for 1 hour. Then cool it to room temperature, and add 6 mL of water. Acidify the solution to pH 3 with 6 M hydrochloric acid, extract [OP-18] it with 20 mL of diethyl ether, and wash [OP-24] the ether extract with 5 mL of cold water. Extract the derivative from the ether using about 10 mL of 0.5 M sodium carbonate, and then acidify the sodium carbonate solution with 6 M hydrochloric acid. Collect the derivative by vacuum filtration [OP-16], and recrystallize [OP-28] it from boiling water.

D-23 *Bromo Derivatives*

For microscale work, all quantities may be divided by 3.

Bromine is toxic and corrosive, and its vapors are harmful. Use gloves and a hood, avoid contact, and do not breathe the vapors.

Reaction:

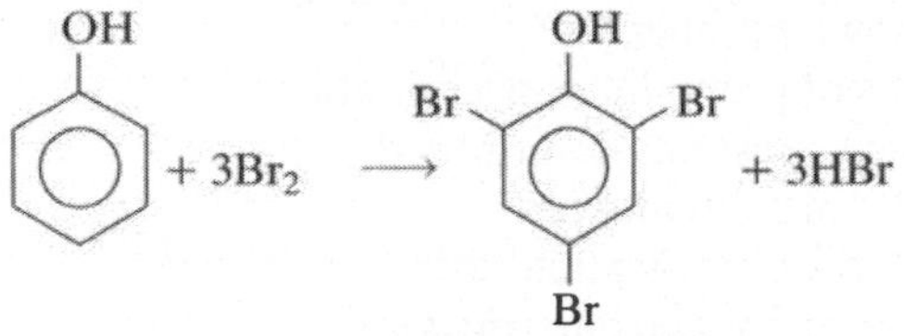

Reaction is for phenol; aromatic amines and substituted phenols undergo similar reactions.

The brominating solution may be prepared beforehand. If not, prepare the brominating solution *under the hood* by dissolving 4.5 g of potassium bromide in 30 mL of water and *carefully* adding 1.0 mL (about 3 g) of pure bromine. Dissolve 0.30 g of the unknown phenol in 6 mL of 50% ethanol (try 95% ethanol or acetone if it doesn't dissolve) in an Erlenmeyer flask. Still under the hood, add [OP-11] the brominating solution slowly, with stirring [OP-10], until the bromine color persists for 1 minute. Add 15 mL of water with stirring, and then collect the derivative by vacuum filtration [OP-16]. Wash it on the filter [OP-26a] with 1 M sodium bisulfite to remove any unreacted bromine. Recrystallize [OP-28] the derivative from 95% ethanol or an ethanol/water mixed solvent.

Take Care! Wear gloves, and avoid contact with and inhalation of bromine.

D-24 *α-Naphthylurethanes*

Pyridine is toxic, an irritant, and has an unpleasant odor. Use a hood, avoid contact, and do not breathe the vapors.
α-Naphthyl isocyanate is lachrymatory and a strong irritant. Use gloves and a hood, avoid contact, and do not breathe its vapors.

Reaction:

$$ArN=C=O + Ar'OH \longrightarrow ArNHC\overset{\displaystyle O}{\overset{\|}{-}}OAr'$$

Under the hood, carry out the procedure for preparing α-naphthylurethanes of alcohols (**D-2**), using 0.20 g of your unknown phenol in place of the alcohol and adding a drop of pyridine to catalyze the reaction. For particularly unreactive phenols, it may be helpful to add 1.0 mL of pyridine and a drop of 10% triethylamine in petroleum ether to the reaction mixture, and to heat the mixture at 70°C for about 30 minutes. If the urethane doesn't precipitate on cooling, add 1.0 mL of 0.5 M sulfuric acid.

Take Care! Avoid contact with and inhalation of pyridine and triethylamine.

Report

Your report should include a statement of the problem and an account of how you applied scientific methodology to solve it. It should also include the following information, or other information requested by your instructor:

- Unknown number
- Results of preliminary examination
- Physical constants determined
- Results of solubility tests
- Results of classification tests
- Spectra and spectrometric data
- Interpretation of tests and spectra
- Original list and short list of possibilities
- Melting points of derivatives
- Discussion and conclusion
- Answers to assigned exercises

Your report should reveal the thought processes that led you to your conclusion, as well as the physical and chemical information supporting it. For example, the "Interpretation" section should tell how your observations led you to make tentative assumptions about the nature of the functional group(s) or other structural features. You should also tell how you eliminated compounds from your original list of possibilities to arrive at your short list. When feasible, you should tabulate your data and observations to present them clearly and concisely.

Exercises

1. Write balanced equations for the chemical reactions undergone by your unknown, including those involved in classification tests, derivative preparations, and all solubility tests except the one with water.
2. Indicate the solubility class to which each of the following is most likely to belong: (a) propanoic acid; (b) toluene; (c) p-anisidine; (d) p-cresol; (e) 3-methylpentanal; (f) p-toluic acid; (g) 2-chlorobutane; (h) butylamine; (i) ethylene glycol; (j) acetophenone.
3. Deduce the functional class (chemical family) of each of the following unknowns, and give any additional structural information suggested by the results. If sufficient information is provided, give one or more possible structures for the unknown, assuming that it is one of the compounds listed in Appendix VI. Explain the reasoning behind your conclusions.
    (a) Unknown A is insoluble in water but soluble in 5% NaOH. It decolorizes a dilute, neutral solution of potassium permanganate, yielding a brown precipitate. Addition of bromine water to a solution of the unknown yields a white precipitate.
    (b) Unknown B is in solubility class **B** and yields an infrared spectrum with no absorption band above 3100 cm^{-1}. The unknown is insoluble in a pH 5.5 buffer, and treatment with p-toluenesulfonyl chloride in aqueous sodium hydroxide leaves a liquid residue that is soluble in dilute HCl.

(c) Unknown C burns with a sooty, yellow flame, and its infrared spectrum has strong bands at 1660, 3180, and 3370 cm^{-1}. When the unknown is heated with 6 M sodium hydroxide, a gas is generated that turns red litmus paper blue. Acidification of the alkaline hydrolysis solution yields a white precipitate.

(d) Unknown D is insoluble in cold, concentrated sulfuric acid, and a drop of the unknown in water sinks to the bottom. A solution of the unknown in chloroform gives an orange–red color on sublimed aluminum chloride. The unknown reacts immediately with both ethanolic silver nitrate and sodium iodide in acetone to form precipitates. Adding dichloromethane and chlorine water to its sodium fusion solution yields a red–orange color.

(e) Unknown E boils near 100°C, is water soluble, and reacts with acetyl chloride to yield a pleasant-smelling liquid. It dissolves in the Lucas reagent, giving a cloudy solution after 4 minutes. Treating the unknown with iodine in sodium hydroxide forms a yellow precipitate with a medicinal odor.

(f) Unknown F is water soluble, and its infrared spectrum has a strong band at 1691 cm^{-1}. It gives an orange–red precipitate with 2,4-dinitrophenylhydrazine reagent, and a blue–green suspension with chromic acid reagent.

(g) Unknown G is insoluble in water and 5% NaHCO$_3$, and it gives no precipitate with 2,4-dinitrophenylhydrazine. When the unknown is heated with 6 M NaOH and the reaction mixture acidified, a vinegar-like odor is detected. When the reaction mixture is then made basic and distilled, extraction of the distillate yields a liquid that forms a blue–green precipitate with chromic acid.

(h) Unknown H is a water-insoluble solid that dissolves in 5% NaHCO$_3$. It decolorizes a solution of bromine in dichloromethane. An aqueous solution containing 0.195 g of the unknown is titrated to a phenolphthalein end point by 32.0 mL of 0.106 M NaOH.

(i) Unknown I is in solubility class **X**, burns with a clean yellow flame, and floats on water. It reacts with both silver nitrate/ethanol and sodium iodide/acetone after heating, but not at room temperature.

(j) Unknown J is a water-insoluble liquid and has strong infrared bands at 690, 746, and 1688 cm^{-1}. The unknown gives a precipitate with 2, 4-dinitrophenylhydrazine reagent, but no precipitate with either chromic acid reagent or iodine in sodium hydroxide.

4. Give reasonable mechanisms for the reactions involved in each of the following classification tests or derivative preparations: (a) the alkaline hydrolysis of N-ethylbenzamide; (b) the reaction of p-cresol with bromine water; (c) the preparation of the semicarbazone of acetophenone; (d) the reaction of ethyl acetate with hydroxylamine in alkaline solution; (e) the reaction of cyclohexylamine with p-toluenesulfonyl chloride in aqueous sodium hydroxide; (f) the reaction of 2-propanol in the Lucas test; (g) the reaction of 2-chloro-2-methylbutane with ethanolic silver nitrate; (h) the reaction of 1-bromobutane with sodium iodide in acetone; (i) the mononitration of toluene by a mixture of nitric and sulfuric acids; (j) the preparation of the aryloxyacetic acid of p-cresol; (k) the formation of the 3,5-dinitrobenzoate of 2-butanol; (l) the iodoform reaction of acetophenone.

PART V

Laboratory Operations

This section describes all of the operations you should need to know to successfully complete an organic chemistry laboratory course or carry out a research project involving organic synthesis or analysis. Each operation is designated by a number, which is listed in large type on the top right-hand corner of every odd-numbered page and can be located quickly by thumbing through the pages. The operations are separated into the following categories:

A. Basic Operations
B. Operations for Conducting Chemical Reactions
C. Separation Operations
D. Washing and Drying Operations
E. Purification Operations
F. Measuring Physical Constants
G. Instrumental Analysis

There is some overlap between the categories. For example, gas chromatography is essentially a separation method because a gas chromatograph separates the components of a sample, but this operation is used primarily for quantitative analysis of samples, so it is placed in Section G rather than Section C.

Although the theoretical background and basic methodology for an operation are the same regardless of the scale on which the operation is performed, the equipment and procedures may be different for standard scale and microscale work. Therefore, always read the introductory material for each operation and any other parts that are not specifically designated for standard scale or microscale methods. Then read the appropriate parts designated by 🔆 if you will be using standard scale equipment or by 🔋 if you will be using microscale equipment. In cases for which the same methods or equipment can be used for both standard scale and microscale work, the parts will be designated by 🔆🔋.

A. Basic Operations

In this section, you will learn about some of the basic lab operations required for doing experiments in organic chemistry. Although you may already have used some of them in a general chemistry course, you should still read the descriptions carefully because an operation may require different equipment or be performed in a different way in the organic chemistry lab. For example, many volume measurements for microscale organic chemistry are carried out using Pasteur pipets or syringes rather than graduated cylinders.

The success of a reaction may depend on how clean and moisture-free your equipment is, so you must learn how to clean and dry glassware thoroughly, as described in Operation 1 [OP-1]. Most experiments in organic chemistry are conducted using specialized glassware components that are held together by ground joints or other connectors. Operation 2 tells you how to assemble and disassemble ground-joint components. For some experiments, you may have to cut, bend, seal, or fire-polish glass tubing or glass rods, as described in OP-3. Nearly all experiments require that you accurately weigh a specified quantity of a limiting reactant or another chemical. Weighings can be done easily using an electronic balance, as described in OP-4. Some of the many kinds of apparatus for measuring volume are illustrated, and their operation is described in OP-5. Operation 6 describes several methods for transferring solids and liquids from one container to another. The method used may depend on the amount of material being transferred.

OPERATION **1**

Cleaning and Drying Glassware

Cleaning Glassware

Clean glassware is essential for good results in the organic chemistry laboratory. Even small amounts of impurities can sometimes inhibit chemical reactions, catalyze undesirable side reactions, and invalidate the results of chemical tests or rate studies. Always clean your dirty glassware at the end of each laboratory period, or as soon as possible after the glassware is used. This way, your glassware will be clean and dry for the next experiment, and you will be ready to start work when you arrive. If you wait too long to clean glassware, residues may harden and become more resistant to cleaning agents; they may also attack the glass itself, weakening it and making future cleaning more difficult. It is particularly important to wash out strong bases such as sodium hydroxide promptly because they can etch the glass permanently and cause glass joints to "freeze" tight. When glassware has been thoroughly cleaned, water applied to its inner surface should wet the whole surface and not form droplets or leave dry patches. However, used glassware that has been scratched or etched may not wet evenly.

You can clean most glassware adequately by vigorous scrubbing with hot water and a laboratory detergent such as Alconox, using a brush of appropriate size and shape to reach otherwise inaccessible spots. A plastic trough or another suitable container can serve as a dishpan. A tapered centrifuge-tube brush can be used to clean conical vials as well as centrifuge tubes. A nylon mesh scrubber is useful for cleaning spatulas, stirring rods, beakers, and the outer surfaces of other glassware. Pipe cleaners or cotton swabs can be used to clean narrow funnel stems, eyedroppers, Hickman still side ports, and so on.

Organic residues that cannot be removed by detergent and water will often dissolve in organic solvents such as technical-grade acetone. (Never use reagent-grade solvents for washing.) For example, it is difficult—if not impossible—to scrub the inside of a porcelain Buchner or Hirsch funnel, but squirting a little acetone around the inside of the funnel stem and letting it drain through the porous plate should remove chemical residues that may have lodged there. Use acetone sparingly and recycle it after use (don't pour it down the drain), as it is much more costly than water and may harm the environment. Be certain that acetone is completely removed from glassware before you return it to a lab kit, because it will dissolve a foam lab-kit liner.

After washing, always rinse glassware thoroughly with water (a final distilled-water rinse is a good idea), and check it to see if the water wets its surface evenly rather than forming separate beads of water. If it doesn't pass this test, scrub it some more or use a cleaning solution such as Nochromix. Note that some well-used glassware may not pass the test because of surface damage, but it may still be clean enough to use after thorough scrubbing.

Drying Glassware

Always dry glassware thoroughly if it will be used with organic reactants and solvents under nonaqueous conditions. Don't waste time drying wet glassware if it will come into contact with water or an aqueous solution during an experiment. Just let it drain for a few minutes before you use it.

The easiest (and cheapest) way to dry glassware is to let it stand overnight in a position that allows easy drainage. You can dry the outer surfaces of glassware with a cloth or paper towel, but don't use a towel to dry any surfaces that will be in contact with chemicals because of the likelihood of contamination. If a piece of glassware is needed shortly after washing, drain it briefly to remove excess water, then rinse it with one or two small portions of wash acetone. Dry it in a stream of clean, dry air or put it in a drying oven for a few minutes. Compressed air from an air line may contain pump oil, moisture, and dirt, so don't use it directly from the line for drying. Air can be cleaned and dried as described in OP-27.

Glassware that is to be used for a moisture-sensitive reaction (such as the Grignard reaction in Experiment 30) must be dried very thoroughly before use. If possible, clean the glassware during the previous lab period, let it dry overnight or longer, and then dry it in an oven set at about 110°C for 20 to 30 minutes. Assemble the apparatus, and attach one or more drying tubes (see OP-12) as soon as possible after oven-drying; otherwise, moisture will condense inside it as it cools. If the glassware must be cleaned the same day as it is used, rinse it with acetone after washing and

Take Care! Use tongs or heat-resistant gloves when handling hot glass.

flush it with clean, dry air before you put it in the oven. You can also dry glassware by passing a "cool" Bunsen burner flame over the surface of the assembled apparatus, but this practice should never be used in laboratories where volatile solvents such as diethyl ether are in use. It should be done only with the instructor's permission and according to his or her directions.

OPERATION 2

Using Specialized Glassware

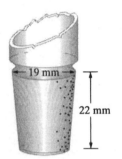

(a) standard scale (19/22)

(b) microscale (14/10)

Figure A1 Standard-taper joints

Most specialized glassware components used in organic chemistry have rigid ground-glass joints called *standard-taper* joints. The size of a tapered joint is designated by two numbers, such as 19/22 (for typical standard scale glassware) or 14/10 (for typical microscale glassware), in which the first number is the diameter at the top of the joint and the second is the length of the taper, measured in millimeters (see Figure A1).

Glassware from a commercial organic lab kit, or its equivalent purchased as separate parts, can be used to construct apparatus for many different laboratory operations. The glassware provided in typical standard scale lab kits and Mayo–Pike-style microscale lab kits is illustrated in Appendix I. Setups for the various operations are illustrated in the appropriate operation descriptions in this book. For example, to find an illustration of a setup for microscale fractional distillation, refer to the microscale section of operation OP-32.

An alternative type of microscale glassware developed by Kenneth L. Williamson uses elastomer connectors rather than ground-glass joints to hold glassware assemblies together. Williamson glassware can be used for many of the microscale experiments in this book, but no specific instructions are given for its use.

 ## Lubricating Joints

For some operations, such as vacuum distillation, glass joints should be lubricated with a suitable joint grease. For most other operations, particularly with microscale equipment, lubrication of glass joints is unnecessary and may be undesirable. Your instructor should inform you if lubrication will be necessary. To lubricate a ground-glass joint, apply a thin layer of joint grease completely around the top half of the inner (male) joint. Do not lubricate the outer (female) joint. Be careful to keep grease away from the open end of the joint, where it may come into contact with and contaminate your reaction mixture or product. When you assemble the components, press the outer and inner joints together firmly, with a slight twist, to form a seal around the entire joint, with no gaps. Grease should never extend beyond the joint inside the apparatus.

After disassembling the apparatus, remove the grease completely by using a suitable organic solvent. You can remove petroleum-based greases with petroleum ether or hexanes, and silicone greases by thorough cleaning with dichloromethane. An inner joint can be cleaned by wrapping a small amount of cotton loosely around the end of an applicator stick, dipping it in the solvent, and wiping the joint with the moist cotton.

 ## Assembling Standard Scale Glassware

Standard-taper joints are rigid, so a setup using standard scale glassware must be assembled carefully to avoid strain that can result in breakage. First, place the necessary clamps and rings at appropriate locations on the ring stand (use two ring stands for distillation setups). Then assemble the apparatus *from the bottom up, starting at the heat source.* Position the heat source on a ring or other support so that it can be removed easily when the heating period is over; otherwise, it may continue to heat a reaction mixture or an empty distilling flask even after it is switched off, causing a danger of breakage, tar formation, or even an explosion. Clamp the reaction flask or boiling flask securely at the proper distance from the heat source.

As you add other components, clamp them to the ring stand(s), but don't tighten the clamp jaws completely until all of the components are in place and aligned properly. Use as many clamps as are necessary to provide adequate support for all parts of the apparatus. A vertical setup, such as the one for addition under reflux [OP-11], requires at least two clamps for security because, if the setup is bumped, the clamp holding the reaction flask may rotate and deposit your glassware on the lab bench, with expensive consequences. Some vertical components, such as Claisen connecting tubes, need not be clamped if they are adequately supported by the component below. Non-vertical components, such as distillation condensers, should be clamped; otherwise, they may be jarred loose and fall. Clamping condensers and other components at an angle to a ring stand requires an adjustable clamp with a wing nut on the shaft. This wing nut is tightened after the apparatus is aligned. Distillation receivers should be supported by a ring and wire gauze or another suitable support. They should not be clamped because they may have to be replaced quickly during a distillation.

Some joints, such as the joint that connects a condenser to a vacuum adapter, tend to separate easily, so they should be held together with joint clips or strong rubber bands. For example, you can secure a vacuum adapter to a condenser by stretching a rubber band around the tubulation on both or by snapping a joint clip around the joint rim. Condensers and vacuum adapters should never be allowed to hang unsupported, even momentarily while you are assembling the apparatus.

Position the clamps so that all parts are aligned correctly and their glass joints slide together easily. Then seat the joints firmly, with a slight twist if necessary, and tighten all the clamps. Examine the joints for gaps, then check to make sure that the apparatus is held securely by the clamp jaws and that the clamp holders are secured tightly to the ring stand(s).

Figure A2 summarizes the steps followed in assembling one kind of ground-glass apparatus. (Most of the glassware setups you will be using are less complex than the one illustrated.)

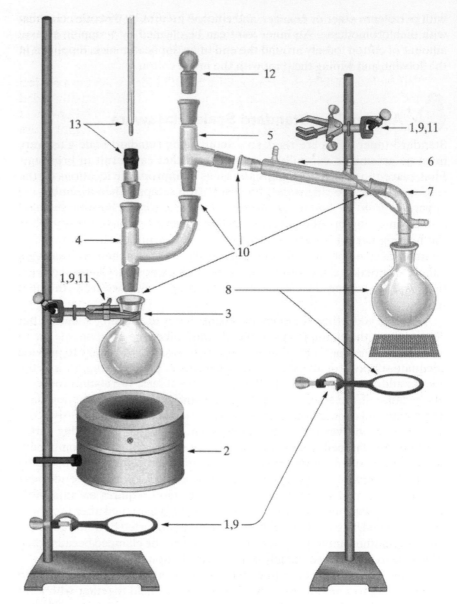

Steps

1. Position clamps, rings.
2. Position heat source.
3. Clamp boiling flask securely.
4, 5. Add Claisen adapter and connecting adapter.
6. Clamp West condenser in place.
7. Attach vacuum adapter with rubber band or spring clamp.
8. Attach receiving flask, support with ring and wire gauze.
9. Readjust all clamps to align parts.
10. Press joints together.
11. Tighten clamps.
12. Add stopper.
13. Add thermometer adapter and position thermometer.

Figure A2 Steps in the assembly of standard scale ground-glass apparatus

 Assembling Microscale Glassware

Microscale glassware comes in a variety of configurations. Most undergraduate microscale laboratory courses use glassware of the kind developed and tested by students at Bowdoin College and Merrimack College under the direction of professors Dana W. Mayo and Ronald M. Pike. The glassware provided in a typical Mayo–Pike-style microscale lab kit is illustrated in Appendix I. Variations exist in the construction of this type of glassware, but the components are usually held together by threaded plastic compression caps. These microscale components are connected with standard-taper joints, just as for standard scale equipment, but a compression cap and O-ring are used to give a tight, greaseless seal.

    You can assemble such a joint as illustrated in Figure A3 for a conical vial and a water-cooled condenser. First, put a compression cap, threaded side down, over the male (outer) joint of the condenser. Hold it in place as you roll an O-ring over the joint onto the clear part of the glass. Make sure that the entire O-ring is above the ground joint, and then release the cap, which should be held in place by the O-ring. Now insert the male joint of the condenser into the female (inner) joint of the conical vial, and screw the cap over the threads at the top of the vial, tightly enough so that the outer joint cannot be rotated around the inner joint. Be careful, because screwing it down too tightly may break the threads or cause strains in the glass that will lead to eventual breakage.

    Other microscale components, such as Claisen connecting tubes, drying tubes, and Hickman stills, can be connected to conical vials or microscale reaction flasks to perform a wide variety of laboratory operations, such as distillation (Figure E11, OP-30) and addition under reflux (Figure B15, OP-11). All the components are connected by compression caps, as shown by the appropriate illustrations in the operation descriptions.

    Unlike standard scale apparatus, microscale apparatus can be assembled on the benchtop and *then* clamped to a ring stand, often with a single

Rubber O-rings tend to deteriorate over time, so inspect O-rings before using them, and replace any that are cracked.

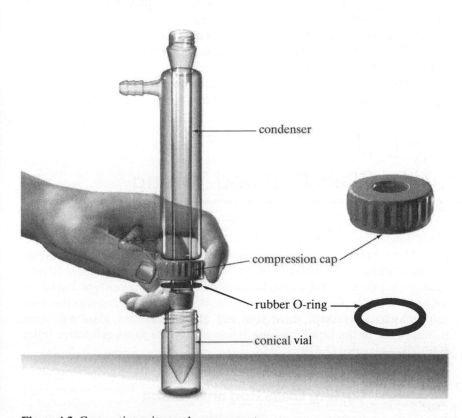

condenser

compression cap

rubber O-ring

conical vial

Figure A3 Connecting microscale components

microclamp, rather than being assembled from the bottom up on one or more ring stands. Because the reaction vessel (flask or conical vial) is not going to fall off the joint it is connected to, it need not be clamped. Instead, you can clamp the apparatus higher up—on a condenser, for example—to make it more stable. Be sure that the microclamp is held securely to the ring stand and that the clamp jaws are tightened securely around the apparatus, so that it doesn't wobble or fall to the bench and break. If you intend to heat a reaction mixture in the flask or the conical vial, clamp the apparatus so that, if necessary (as when a reaction mixture is boiling too vigorously), you will be able to loosen the clamp holder at the ring stand and raise the entire apparatus above the heat source quickly.

Disassembling Glassware

Disassemble (take apart) ground-joint glassware promptly after use because joints that are left coupled for an extended period of time may freeze together and become difficult or impossible to separate without breakage. Ground joints can usually be separated by pulling the components apart with a twisting motion. For microscale glassware, unscrew the compression cap completely before you separate the joints. If a joint is frozen, you can sometimes loosen it by tapping it gently with the handle of a wooden-handled spatula or by applying steam to the joint while rotating the apparatus slowly, and then pulling the components apart with a twisting motion. If this doesn't work, see your instructor. Clean [OP-1] the glassware thoroughly, and return each component to its proper location in the lab kit or to the stockroom. To reduce assembly time, caps and O-rings are sometimes left on microscale components when they are returned to their lab-kit case; this can make the components more difficult to clean thoroughly, so your instructor may prefer that you remove them.

Take Care! The glass may break, so protect your hands with heavy gloves.

OPERATION 3

Using Glass Rod and Tubing

Glass connecting tubes, stirring rods, and other simple glass items are required for certain operations in organic chemistry. Soft-glass rod and tubing can be worked easily with a Bunsen burner, but borosilicate glass (Pyrex, Kimax, etc.) requires the hotter flame provided by a Meker-type burner or an oxygen torch. To distinguish borosilicate from soft glass, dip the glass into anhydrous glycerol; most (but not all) borosilicate glass will seem to disappear in the liquid because it has nearly the same refractive index [OP-35] as glycerol (1.475).

Cutting Glass Rod and Tubing

Glass rods and tubes are cut by scoring them at the desired location and snapping them in two. Score the rod or tube by drawing a sharp triangular file (or other glass-scoring tool) across the surface at a right angle to the axis of the tubing. Often, only a single stroke is needed to make a deep scratch in the surface; don't use the file like a saw. To cut a thin, fragile glass tube, such as a melting-point tube or the capillary tip of a Pasteur pipet, it is best to use a special glass scorer, but a sharp triangular file may work if applied carefully so as not to crush the glass. Moisten the scratch with water or saliva. Using a towel or gloves to protect your hands, place your thumbs about 1 cm apart on the side opposite the scratch and, while holding the glass firmly in both hands, press forward against the glass with your thumbs as you rotate your wrists outward (Figure A4).

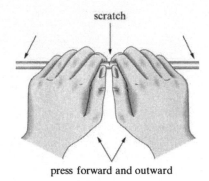

Figure A4 Breaking glass tubing

  ## Working Glass Rod and Tubing

The cut ends of a glass rod or tube should always be *fire-polished* to remove sharp edges and prevent accidental cuts. To fire-polish a glass rod or tube, hold it at a 45° angle to a burner flame (see OP-7a for directions on using a burner) and rotate its cut end slowly in the flame until the edge becomes rounded and smooth (Figure A5).

To round the cut end of a glass rod, rotate the rod in a burner flame, holding it at a 45° angle with its tip at the inner blue cone of the flame. The end should be hemispherical in shape, not rounded only at the edges and flat on the bottom.

To flatten one end of a glass rod, rotate it with its tip at the inner blue cone of the flame until it is incandescent and very soft, but not starting to bend. Then press the softened end straight down onto a hard surface, such as the base of a ring stand. The flattened end should be well centered and about twice the diameter of the rod.

To seal one end of a glass tube, hold the tube at a 45° angle to the burner, with its end just above the inner blue cone of the flame, and rotate it until the soft edges come together and eventually merge. Remove the tube from the flame as soon as it is closed, and immediately blow into the open end to obtain a sealed end of uniform thickness. Let the tube cool to room temperature. Then check it for leaks by connecting the open end to an aspirator or a vacuum line with a length of rubber tubing, placing the closed end in a test tube that contains a small amount of dichloromethane, and turning on the vacuum. (**Take Care!** Avoid contact with dichloromethane, and do not breathe its vapors.) If the tube is not properly sealed, the liquid will leak into it when you apply suction. To seal the end of a thin, fragile tube such as a melting-point capillary, rotate its open end in the *outer* edge of the flame.

To bend glass tubing, first place a flame spreader on the barrel of a Bunsen burner (or use a Meker-type burner). Hold the tubing over the burner flame, parallel to the long axis of the flame spreader, and rotate it constantly at a slow, even rate until it is nearly soft enough to bend under its own weight (see Figure A6). (The flame will turn yellow as the glass begins to soften.) Remove the hot tubing from the flame, and immediately bend it to the desired shape with a firm, even motion and a minimum of force (if much force is required, the glass isn't soft enough). Bend it in a vertical plane, with the ends up and the bend at the bottom; the bend should follow a smooth curve with no constrictions.

Take Care! Don't burn yourself on the hot end of a glass rod or tube, or lay the glass onto combustible materials.

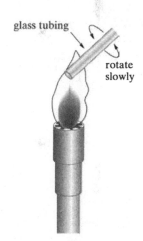

Figure A5 Fire-polishing

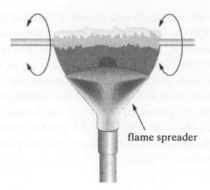

flame spreader

Figure A6 Bending tubing

Inserting Glass Items into Stoppers and Thermometer Adapters

Safety Notes

Improper insertion of glass tubes and thermometers through stoppers is one of the most frequent causes of laboratory accidents. The resulting cuts and puncture wounds can be severe, requiring medical treatment and sometimes causing the victim to go into shock. Thermometers are particularly easy to break, especially at the scored immersion line.

Cork borer

Take Care! Don't grasp the tube too far from the stopper. The glass may break and lacerate your hand.

Sometimes you may have to insert a glass tube through a hole bored in a cork or rubber stopper. To bore a hole in a solid stopper, obtain a *sharp* cork borer that is slightly smaller in diameter than the object to be inserted in the stopper. (If the borer is dull, use a special cork-borer sharpener to sharpen it.) Lubricate its cutting edge with a small amount of glycerine, and then *twist* it through the stopper using a minimum of force (don't try to "punch" out the hole). Rotate the borer and stopper in opposite directions, checking the alignment frequently to make sure that the borer is going in straight. When the borer is about halfway through, twist it out and start boring from the opposite end of the stopper until the holes meet. You can remove the plug left inside the cork borer with a rod that comes with a set of cork borers.

To insert a glass tube into a rubber stopper, first lubricate the hole lightly with glycerol or another suitable lubricant; water may work, if the hole isn't too tight. You can use a cotton swab or an applicator stick to apply the lubricant evenly. Protect your hands with gloves or a towel, then grasp the tube close to the stopper and twist it through the hole with firm, steady pressure. Apply force directly along the axis of the tube because any sideways force may cause it to break. Using excessive force or forcing the tube through a hole too small for it can also cause it to break. After the tube is correctly positioned, rinse off any glycerol with water. Follow the same directions to insert a thermometer through a rubber stopper or a standard scale thermometer adapter cap. A microscale thermometer adapter uses an O-ring rather than a rubber cap to hold the thermometer in place. Don't try to insert a thermometer into an assembled microscale thermometer adapter; instead, roll the O-ring onto the thermometer and then secure the thermometer in the adapter, as described in OP-9.

To remove a glass tube from a stopper, lubricate the part of the glass that will pass through the stopper with water or glycerol, protect your hands with gloves or a towel, and twist the tube out with a firm, continuous motion. Hold the tube close to the stopper or cap, and avoid applying any sideways force that could cause it to break. If you can't remove the tube by this method, obtain a cork borer of a size that will just fit around it, lubricate the borer's cutting edge, and twist it gently through the stopper until the tube can be pulled out easily. (Follow the same directions to remove a thermometer from a thermometer adapter cap.)

Weighing   OPERATION **4**

Most chemistry laboratories are equipped with electronic balances that display the mass directly, without any preliminary adjustments (Figure A7). If you will be using a different type of balance, your instructor will demonstrate its operation. For microscale experiments, chemicals should be weighed on balances that measure to at least the nearest milligram (0.001 g). For standard scale experiments, balances that measure to the nearest centigram (0.01 g) are acceptable for most purposes, but milligram balances are preferable. Most products obtained from a preparation are transferred to vials or other small containers, which should be *tared*—weighed empty— and then reweighed after the product has been added. As a rule, the container should be weighed with its cap and label on, and this *tare mass* should be recorded.

A balance is a precision instrument that can easily be damaged by contaminants, so avoid spilling chemicals on the balance pan or on the balance itself. If spillage does occur, *clean it up immediately.* If you spill a liquid or corrosive solid on any part of the balance, notify your instructor as well. Before you leave the balance area, replace the caps on all reagent bottles, return them to their proper locations (if you obtained them elsewhere), and ensure that the area around the balance is clean and orderly.

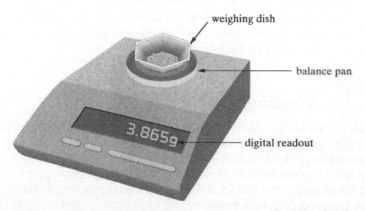

Figure A7 An electronic balance

Weighing Solids

Solids can be weighed in glass containers (such as vials or beakers), in aluminum or plastic weighing dishes, or on glazed weighing papers. In standard scale work, solid reactants are usually weighed on glazed paper or in weighing dishes and then transferred to the reaction flask. In microscale work, it is best to weigh solid reactants directly in the reaction vessel to avoid losses in transfer. A round-bottom flask or pear-shaped flask should be supported in a beaker or on a cork ring for weighing. Hygroscopic solids, those that absorb moisture from the atmosphere, should be weighed in screw-cap vials or other containers that can be capped immediately after the solid is added. Filter paper and other absorbent papers shouldn't be used for weighing because a few particles will always remain in the fibers of the paper.

To weigh a sample of a solid that is in a tared container, such as a preweighed screw-cap vial, set the digital readout to zero by pressing the appropriate button, and then place the container on the balance pan. Be sure that the draft shield (if there is one) is in place, then read the mass of the container and its contents from the digital display. Wait until the reading remains constant, and then record the mass in your laboratory notebook. Include all digits after the decimal point. For example, if the balance reads 3.610 g, don't record the mass as 3.61 g because zeroes following the decimal point are significant. Then subtract the tare mass to obtain the mass of the solid.

To weigh a sample of a solid that is to be transferred to another container, such as a weighing dish or storage vial, place the container on the balance pan, press the tare button to zero the digital display, and transfer the solid to the container. With the draft shield in place, wait until the reading has stabilized, and then read the mass of the sample directly from the digital display.

To measure out a specific quantity of a solid—such as a solid reactant—into a reaction flask or another container, first support the container on the balance pan and press the tare button to zero the digital display. Then use a spatula or Scoopula to add the solid in small portions, until the desired mass appears on the digital display. With the draft shield in place, wait until the reading has stabilized, and then read the mass of the sample directly from the digital display. Ordinarily, you need not measure out the exact mass specified in a procedure, but try not to deviate from the specified mass by more than 2% or so, especially for a limiting reactant. Because the theoretical yield of a preparation is based on the actual mass of a starting material, always use your measured mass—not the mass you calculated for the prelab assignment—for yield calculations.

For example, if a procedure requires 0.250 g of a limiting reactant, you should measure out between 0.245 g and 0.255 g of the reactant.

 Weighing Liquids

Organic liquids should be weighed in screw-cap vials or other closed containers to prevent damage to the balance from accidental spillage and losses by evaporation. If liquid must be added to or removed from a weighed container, the container should be removed from the balance pan first. Any excess liquid should be placed in a waste container or otherwise disposed of—*not* returned to a stock bottle.

To measure the mass of a liquid sample in a tared or untared container, follow the directions for solids, but be sure to keep the container capped while it is on the balance pan. When using a tared container, subtract the tare mass to obtain the mass of the liquid.

To measure out a specific mass of a liquid from a reagent bottle, you should first measure the approximate quantity of the liquid by volume and then weigh that quantity accurately in an appropriate closed container. For example, if you need 3.71 g of 1-butanol (d = 0.810 g/mL) for a standard scale experiment, you can use a small graduated cylinder or a measuring pipet to measure [OP-5] about 4.6 mL (3.71 g ÷ 0.810 g/mL) of the liquid into a tared container, then cap and weigh the container and liquid. (The balance can first be zeroed with the container and its cap on the balance pan—don't forget to include the cap!) If the measured mass is not close enough to 3.71 g, add or remove liquid with a clean Pasteur pipet or medicine dropper.

For microscale work, it is best to weigh liquid reactants in the reaction vessel to avoid losses in transfer. A round-bottom flask or pear-shaped flask should be supported in a beaker or on a cork ring for weighing. Use an automatic pipet, a measuring pipet, a graduated syringe, or a bottle-top dispenser to measure the estimated volume of the liquid into the reaction vessel, and cap it before you weigh it.

Always weigh liquid limiting reactants! Volume measurements are far less accurate than weight measurements.

Take Care! Be careful not to spill liquids on the balance pan. If you do, clean up the spill immediately and inform your instructor.

Measuring Volume   OPERATION **5**

Several different kinds of volume-measuring devices are used in the undergraduate organic chemistry laboratory. Although some kinds of measuring devices are used mainly for standard scale work, and others are used mainly for microscale work, most of the devices described here are applicable to both. Relatively large volumes of liquids are generally measured using graduated cylinders whose capacity may vary from 5 mL to 100 mL or more. Smaller volumes of liquids can be measured using various kinds of pipets and syringes. Reagent bottles containing liquids may be provided with bottle-top dispensers that measure out a preset volume of the liquid. For a few experiments, you may use a buret or a volumetric flask; their use is described in most general chemistry laboratory manuals.

  Graduated Cylinders

Graduated cylinders are not highly accurate, but in standard scale work they are often used to measure specified quantities of solvents and wash liquids, or even some liquid reactants that are used in excess. In microscale work, they are used mostly for measuring relatively large amounts of water or other solvents.

To use a graduated cylinder, transfer the liquid being measured to the cylinder by pouring it (for most standard scale work) or by using a Pasteur pipet (for microscale work), until the cylinder is filled to the graduation

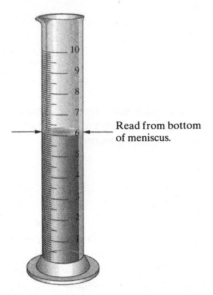

Read from bottom
of meniscus.

Figure A8 Reading the volume contained in a graduated cylinder—in this case, 6.0 mL

mark corresponding to the desired volume. Read the liquid volume from the bottom of the meniscus, as shown in Figure A8. If necessary, add or remove liquid with a Pasteur pipet.

Bottle-Top Dispensers

A typical adjustable bottle-top dispenser (see Figure A9) has a moveable plunger that pumps liquid into a glass cylinder, from which it is dispensed through a discharge tube. The cylinder is usually surrounded by a protective sleeve that is raised to fill the cylinder and lowered to dispense the liquid. The dispenser is screwed onto a bottle containing the liquid and can be adjusted to dispense a specified volume of liquid, which is read from a scale on the sleeve or cylinder. Before its initial use, the dispenser must be *primed* by pumping it several times to fill the cylinder and discharge tube and to expel any air bubbles.

To use a bottle-top dispenser, first check to see that there are no air bubbles in the discharge tube (if there are, prime the dispenser or inform your instructor). Then hold your container underneath the discharge tube outlet, and raise the sleeve as high as it will go. Release the sleeve so that it drops by gravity, and then push it down gently until it moves no further. Touch the tip of the discharge tube to an inside wall of your container to remove the last drop of liquid. If the liquid is the limiting reactant for a preparation, you should weigh it accurately, as described in OP-4.

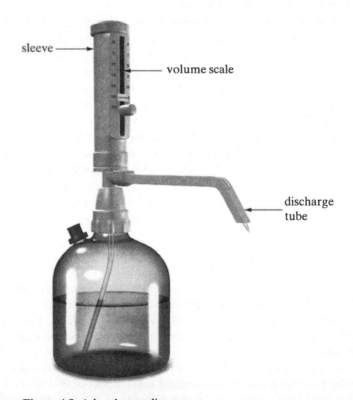

sleeve

volume scale

discharge tube

Figure A9 A bottle-top dispenser

Measuring Pipets and Volumetric Pipets

A *measuring pipet* has a graduated scale and is used to measure liquid volumes within a range of values; for example, a typical 1-mL measuring pipet can measure volumes up to 1.00 mL to the nearest 0.01 mL. A *volumetric pipet* measures only a single volume, but it is more accurate than a measuring pipet. Suction is required to draw the liquid into a measuring or volumetric pipet, but you should never use mouth suction because of the danger of ingesting toxic or corrosive liquids. A pipet pump is a simple and convenient suction device for filling such pipets. Other pipet fillers, such as large rubber bulbs, can also be used.

To use a measuring pipet with a pipet pump of the type shown in Figure A10, first see that the plunger is as far down as it will go. Then insert the wide (untapered) end of the pipet firmly into the opening at the bottom of the pump. Place the tip of the pipet in the liquid, and rotate the front of the thumbwheel downward (moving your thumb back toward you) until the liquid meniscus rises a few millimeters above the zero graduation mark; be careful not to draw any liquid into the pump itself. Slowly rotate the front of the thumbwheel upward (moving your thumb away from you) until the meniscus drops just to the zero mark. Measure the desired volume of liquid into a clean container by placing the pipet tip over the container and rotating the thumbwheel upward until the meniscus drops to the graduation mark corresponding to the desired volume (Figure A11). Touch the tip of the pipet to the inside of the container to remove any adherent drop of liquid. If the pipet is one dedicated for use with a particular reagent bottle, the excess liquid can be drained into the bottle by depressing the pump's quick-release lever (if it has one) or by rotating the thumbwheel upward as far as it will go. Otherwise, the liquid should be drained into another container or disposed of as directed by your instructor.

To use a volumetric pipet, obtain a bulb-type pipet filler or a pipet pump with a quick-release lever that allows the liquid to drain by gravity. Use the bulb or pump to fill the volumetric pipet to its calibration mark, hold the pipet tip over a receiving container, and use the quick-release lever or another device to let the liquid drain out until only a small amount of liquid is left in the tip. Touch the tip of the pipet to the inside of the container to remove any adherent drop of liquid, but do not expel the liquid in the pipet tip—its volume is accounted for when the pipet is calibrated.

 Automatic Pipets

Automatic pipets (also called *pipetters*) provide a quick, convenient way to deliver a specified volume of liquid with a high degree of reproducibility (Figure A12). Most automatic pipets measure comparatively small volumes of liquids and are therefore most useful for microscale experiments. A variable-volume automatic pipet can be set to a specified volume within a certain range of volumes, such as 20 to 200 μL (0.020–0.200 mL). The volume is displayed on a digital display or an analog scale, usually in microliters (μL). To prevent contamination, liquid is drawn into a disposable tip and never inside the pipet itself. Whenever the pipet is used for a different liquid, the

*A convenient "homemade" pipetting bulb is described in J. Chem. Educ. **1974**, 51, 467.*

Be careful not to raise the pipet tip out of the liquid while filling a pipet by this or any other method.

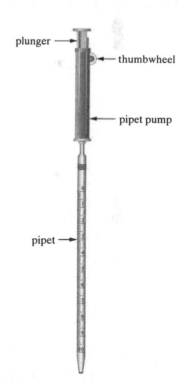

Figure A10 Pipet pump and measuring pipet

Figure A11 Reading the volume delivered from a measuring pipet—in this case, 3.0 mL

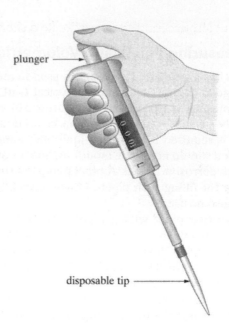

plunger

disposable tip

Figure A12 An automatic pipet

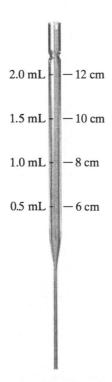

2.0 mL — 12 cm

1.5 mL — 10 cm

1.0 mL — 8 cm

0.5 mL — 6 cm

Figure A13 A calibrated Pasteur pipet

volume is reset (if necessary) and a new pipet tip is installed. The instructor or a lab assistant will ordinarily set the volume of an automatic pipet and designate it for a specific liquid. Do *not* try to reset the volume or use the pipet for a different liquid without explicit permission from your instructor.

To use an automatic pipet, depress the plunger to the first *detent* (stop) position, when you will feel resistance to further movement. (Using excessive force will move the plunger to its second detent position, causing an inaccurate measurement.) Insert the pipet tip into the liquid to a depth of about 1 cm or less; don't let it touch the bottom of the liquid's container, where impurities may be concentrated. Slowly release the plunger to draw liquid into the pipet tip. Place the tip inside the receiving container, and depress the plunger to the first detent position; pause for a second or two, then push the plunger down to the second detent position and touch the tip to the inner wall of the receiving container to expel the last droplet of liquid.

 ## Calibrated Pasteur Pipets

A calibrated Pasteur pipet (Figure A13) can be used to measure approximate volumes of liquids such as washing and extraction solvents. For measuring volatile liquids, a filter-tip pipet (see OP-6) that has been calibrated should work better than an ordinary calibrated pipet.

To calibrate a Pasteur pipet, first attach a latex rubber bulb to its wide end. Measure 0.50 mL of water into a conical vial or small test tube, using a measuring pipet or another accurate measuring device. Carefully draw all of the liquid into the Pasteur pipet so that there are no air bubbles in its tip (if necessary, squeeze the bulb *gently* to expel any air), and mark the position of the meniscus with an indelible glass-marking pen. Expel all the water and repeat this operation using 1.00 mL of water, and other volumes as desired.

A quicker but less accurate way to calibrate a short ($5\frac{3}{4}$ inch) Pasteur pipet is to use a ruler to mark lines at distances of 6 cm, 8 cm, 10 cm, and 12 cm from the narrow (capillary) tip of the pipet (see Figure A13). These lines mark volumes of approximately 0.5 mL, 1.0 mL, 1.5 mL, and 2.0 mL. Make sure that the capillary tip is intact; if part of it is broken off, this calibration method won't work.

To use a calibrated pipet, hold the pipet (with its attached bulb) vertically over the liquid to be measured, squeeze the bulb to expel some of the air (ideally, an amount of air nearly equal to the volume of liquid required), and insert the tip in the liquid. With practice, you should learn how far to squeeze the bulb in order to draw in the desired amount of liquid. Then release the bulb until the liquid meniscus is at the level of the appropriate calibration mark. Without delay, raise the pipet tip out of the liquid, move it into position over the receiving container, and squeeze the bulb to expel all of the liquid into the container. It takes practice to transfer the liquid without losing some in the process, so read OP-6 for additional tips about the use of Pasteur pipets.

  ## Syringes

A syringe (Figure A14) can be used to measure and deliver small volumes of liquid, often by inserting its needle through a *septum*—a rubber or plastic disk that can be penetrated by a needle but that remains more-or-less air-tight after the needle is withdrawn. A syringe of appropriate size can be used to inject liquid samples into a gas chromatograph and (in some microscale experiments) to add liquid reagents to a reaction mixture during a reaction.

To fill a syringe, hold it vertically with the needle pointing down, then place the needle tip in the liquid and slowly pull out the plunger until the barrel contains a little more than the required volume of liquid. If there are air bubbles in the liquid, remove them by holding the syringe vertically—with the needle pointing up—and tapping the barrel with your fingernail, or by expelling the liquid and filling the syringe again, more slowly. Hold the syringe with the needle pointing up, and slowly push in the plunger to eject the excess liquid (collect it for disposal, if requested) until the bottom of the liquid column is at the appropriate graduation mark. Wipe off the tip of the needle with a tissue, place the needle tip into the receiving vessel or through a septum, and expel the liquid by gently pushing the plunger in as far as it will go. Clean the syringe immediately after use by flushing it repeatedly with an appropriate solvent, such as acetone, or a soap solution. If you use soap for washing, rinse the syringe thoroughly with water afterward. Dry the syringe by pumping the plunger several times to expel excess solvent. Then remove the plunger to let the barrel dry. If the syringe is to be used again shortly, you can dry it by drawing air through the barrel with an aspirator or a vacuum line.

The plastic 1-mL syringes provided in some microscale lab kits are subject to contamination and aren't compatible with certain organic solvents. For some volume-measuring applications, the barrel of such a syringe can be connected to the wide end of a clean Pasteur pipet with a small length of plastic or rubber tubing, so that the measured volume of liquid is drawn into the Pasteur pipet rather than the body of the syringe (see *J. Chem. Educ.* **1993**, *70*, A311).

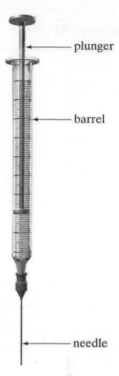

plunger

barrel

needle

Figure A14 A syringe

Take Care! Don't stick yourself with the needle!

Take Care! Don't bend the plunger.

OPERATION **6**

Making Transfers

In many organic syntheses, losses during transfers constitute a substantial part of the total product loss, so they can have a major impact on your yield. Such losses can occur whenever you transfer a liquid or a solid from one container to another, whether the original container is a stock bottle, reaction flask, beaker, or funnel. Making complete transfers is particularly important in microscale work, where losing just a few crystals of a solid product or a drop of a liquid product may reduce your percent yield significantly.

  Transferring Solids

Bulk solids (such as those from a lab stock bottle) can be transferred from one container to another using spatulas of various shapes and sizes (Figure A15). For standard scale work, a Scoopula is preferred because it is curved to help keep the solid from sliding off. A flat-bladed spatula will also work, but unless you are careful, some of the solid may spill over its sides. For microscale work, the U-shaped or V-shaped end of a Hayman-type microspatula (see Figure A15) can be used to transfer solids. Small amounts of solids can also be transferred with a plastic microscoop, made by cutting a 1-mL automatic pipet tip in half.

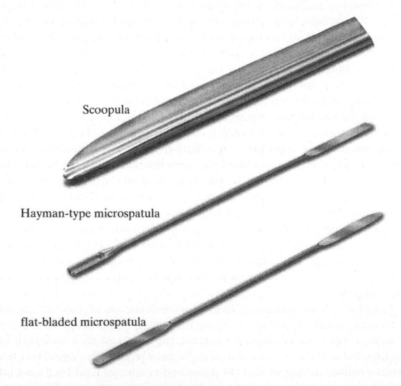

Scoopula

Hayman-type microspatula

flat-bladed microspatula

Figure A15 Spatulas for transferring solids

Solids can be conveniently transferred to small-mouthed containers such as test tubes and storage vials using a folded square of weighing paper or a square plastic weighing dish as a makeshift funnel. To transfer a solid from a plastic weighing dish, hold opposite corners of the dish between your thumb and middle finger, and bend the dish to form a "spout" from which you can pour it or scrape it out. During such transfers, place the receiving container on a square of weighing paper or in a weighing dish (or clamp it above the paper or dish), so that any solid that misses the container can be recovered. If the solid you are transferring sticks to the sides of its container (such as a reaction vial or a Buchner funnel), use a flexible flat-bladed spatula or microspatula to scrape as much as you can off the sides. If you need to transfer the last traces of a solid, you can dissolve the residual solid in a volatile solvent, make the transfer, and evaporate the solvent as described next for liquid transfers.

Transferring Liquids

In standard scale work, liquid transfers are usually accomplished by *decanting* (pouring) the liquid from its original container into another container. Various kinds of pipets and dispensers [OP-5] can also be used for standard scale liquid transfers.

In microscale work, most liquids (especially liquid reactants and products) should *not* be decanted because too much liquid will adhere to the inside of the original container and be lost. Instead, liquids are transferred using pipets or syringes.

A Pasteur pipet fitted with a latex rubber bulb (Figure A16) can be used for most microscale transfers. Volatile liquids such as dichloromethane tend to partially vaporize during a transfer (especially on a warm day or when the pipet is warmed by your hand), causing some of the liquid to spurt out of the tip of the pipet. You may be able to avoid this problem by drawing in and expelling the liquid several times to fill the pipet with solvent vapors before you use it for the transfer. Alternatively, you can use a *filter-tip pipet*.

To make a filter-tip pipet, obtain a *very* small wisp of clean cotton, roll it into a loose ball, and use a straight length of thin (~20 gauge) copper wire to push it past the narrow neck of a $5\frac{3}{4}$-inch Pasteur pipet into its capillary end. Hold the pipet with the capillary tip pointed up as you use the wire to push the cotton as close to the tip of the pipet as you can (see Figure A16). If the cotton ball is too large, it will get hopelessly stuck in the capillary, and you will have to start over with another pipet and cotton ball. You may have to poke the cotton plug repeatedly with the wire to get it in place; the capillary is very fragile, so be careful you don't break it. Mayo and Pike et al. [Bibliography, D4] recommend that the cotton plug in a filter-tip pipet be washed with 1 mL of methanol and 1 mL of hexanes, and then dried before use, but this measure should be necessary only when the liquid transferred must be very pure and dry (when in doubt, follow your instructor's recommendation).

A filter-tip pipet is useful for transferring all types of liquids, not just volatile ones, because the cotton plug helps remove solid impurities from the liquid (if any are present). It also gives you better control over the transfer process, reducing the likelihood that some of your product will drip onto

Pipets and syringes are a common cause of contamination, so never allow a liquid to be sucked into a rubber bulb or pipet pump, and clean [OP-1] all pipets and syringes thoroughly after use.

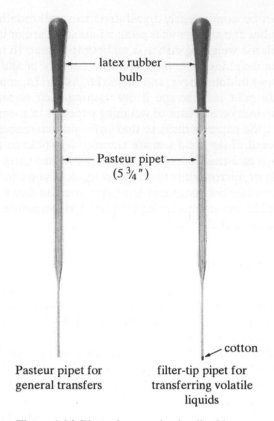

latex rubber
bulb

Pasteur pipet
(5 ¾")

cotton

Pasteur pipet for
general transfers

filter-tip pipet for
transferring volatile
liquids

Figure A16 Pipets for transferring liquids

the benchtop on the way to the collecting container. The main drawbacks of this kind of filter-tip pipet are that (1) it takes some time and practice to prepare one properly, (2) the cotton plug in an improperly prepared pipet may be so tight that it impedes liquid flow or so loose that it won't stay in place, and (3) it is difficult to get the cotton plug out without breaking the fragile tip. A shortened filter-tip pipet has few of these disadvantages. You can prepare one by cutting off [OP-3] all but about 5 mm of the capillary tip of a $5\frac{3}{4}$-inch Pasteur pipet and pushing a wisp of cotton to the end of its shortened tip. A shortened filter-tip pipet is particularly useful for transferring hot recrystallization [OP-28] solutions.

A 1-mL (or smaller) syringe of the kind that comes with most microscale lab kits can also be used for microscale liquid transfers. It is particularly useful for transferring liquids to or from containers that are sealed with plastic or rubber septum caps to keep out air or moisture. To inject liquid through a septum with a syringe, fill the syringe with the desired volume of liquid (see OP-5), carefully push its needle through the septum while holding the needle to keep it from bending, and then gently push the plunger in as far as it will go. To withdraw liquid through a septum, push the plunger in as far as it will go, insert the syringe needle through the septum until its tip is below the liquid surface, and pull the plunger to withdraw the desired amount of liquid. See OP-5 for additional information about the use and care of syringes.

When you are transferring a liquid from one container to another, you can avoid losses by keeping the containers as close together as possible. For example, if you are transferring a liquid from a conical vial to a screw-cap storage vial, hold the vials together in the same hand—with their mouths at the same level—and then use your free hand to make the transfer. This way, any dripping liquid should be caught by one or the other container rather than ending up on the benchtop. Even after a careful transfer, an appreciable amount of liquid may remain behind in the original container. You can recover that liquid by adding a small amount of a volatile solvent to the original container, tilting and rotating the container to wash all of the liquid off its sides, transferring the resulting solution to the receiving container, and evaporating [OP-19] the solvent with a stream of dry air or nitrogen. The volatile solvent must be one in which the liquid is appreciably soluble. Dichloromethane and diethyl ether are suitable solvents for most organic liquids.

B. Operations for Conducting Chemical Reactions

Conducting a chemical reaction is a little like baking a cake. You need to measure the ingredients accurately using basic operations discussed in the last section, combine them, heat the mixture (or cool it) while keeping its components well mixed, and occasionally mix in additional ingredients. In this section, you will learn about a number of different methods for heating [OP-7] and cooling [OP-8] a reaction mixture, and how to monitor the temperature of the mixture [OP-9]. You will also learn how to keep the reactants mixed [OP-10] and how to incorporate additional reactants during the course of a reaction [OP-11]. Certain reactions must be carried out in a dry atmosphere [OP-12] or an oxygen-free atmosphere [OP-13]. Other reactions generate toxic or otherwise harmful gases and must be conducted using a gas trap [OP-14].

Beginning in Part B, certain operation descriptions, such as the one for heating under reflux [OP-7c], will contain a troubleshooting section entitled "When Things Go Wrong." Whenever you encounter problems while performing an operation, see this section for help and advice.

OPERATION 7   Heating

a. Heat Sources

Chemical reactions are accelerated by heat because heat (thermal energy) speeds up the reactant molecules so that they collide more often, and increases the energy of those collisions so that they are more likely to generate product molecules. Therefore, most organic reactions are performed using some kind of heat source so that they can be carried out in a reasonable period of time. Heating devices are used for other purposes as well, such as distilling liquid mixtures and evaporating volatile solvents.

A variety of heat sources are used in the organic chemistry laboratory. The choice of a heat source for a particular application depends on such factors as the temperature required, the flammability of a liquid being heated, the need for simultaneous stirring, and the cost and convenience of the heating device. Of the heat sources described here, heating mantles, steam baths, and oil baths are used mostly for standard scale work, whereas hot plates, heating blocks, sand baths, and hot-water baths are used mostly for microscale work. Some heat sources, such as hot-water baths, are useful for both standard scale and microscale work.

When a reaction mixture is being heated, there is always a chance that an exothermic reaction will "take off" (become too vigorous), in which case the reaction mixture may spew out of the reaction apparatus and create a potentially dangerous situation. For that reason, it is always a good idea to have a container with cold water handy so that you can chill the reaction flask (after separating it from the heat source) to bring the reaction under control. If that can't be done safely, and the reaction is being carried out under a fume hood, close the hood sash to isolate the reaction mixture and turn off the heat source by pulling the plug or by any other appropriate means. If a reaction becomes too vigorous while a reagent is being added [OP-11], the addition should be stopped or the rate of addition reduced. Some reactions mixtures will boil up vigorously if boiling chips (see OP-7b) have not been added, or if the stirring rate [OP-10] is too slow. If you forgot to use boiling chips, be sure to cool the reaction mixture well below the boiling point before adding them.

Heating Mantles. A heating mantle (Figure B1) is generally used to heat a round-bottom flask during a reaction or distillation. It is always used in conjunction with a voltage-regulating or time-cycling ("on–off") heat control to vary its heat output. A mantle can be used with a magnetic stirrer (see OP-10), and its heat output can be varied over a wide range, but its operating temperature cannot be monitored with a thermometer. Certain heating mantles, such as Thermowell ceramic flask heaters, are designed to heat round-bottom flasks over a range of sizes. For example, a 100-mL ceramic mantle can be used to heat 25-mL, 50-mL, and 100-mL round-bottom flasks efficiently. Most other mantles are designed for a specific flask size, so a 100-mL fiberglass heating mantle should only be used to heat a 100-mL round-bottom flask; the mantle will not heat efficiently and could even burn out if used with a flask of another size. Don't turn on an empty heating mantle or use it to heat an empty flask because that might burn out its heating element. If you spill any chemicals into the well of a heating mantle, particularly if it is hot, unplug it and notify your instructor.

To operate a heating mantle, first support it on a ring support or a set of wood blocks so that it can be lowered and removed quickly if the heating rate becomes too rapid. If one is available, you can use a *lab jack* instead. A lab jack is an adjustable platform that can be raised or lowered by rotating a knob. Clamp the flask in place so that it is in direct contact with the well of the heating mantle. If you are heating a small flask in a larger mantle, filling the well with glass wool up to the flask's liquid level may help distribute the heat more evenly (this is said to be unnecessary with a Thermowell mantle). See that the heat-control dial is set to zero, then plug the mantle into it— *never* directly into an electrical outlet—and adjust the heat-control dial until the desired rate of heating is attained. Note that the dial controls only the rate of heating and cannot be set to a specific temperature. Because a heating mantle responds slowly to changes in the control setting, it is easy to exceed the desired heating rate by setting the dial too high at the start. If that happens, lower the mantle so that it is no longer in contact with the flask, reduce the dial setting, and allow sufficient time for the temperature to drop before raising the mantle again. Further adjustments may be needed to maintain heating at the desired rate. When you are done heating, lower the mantle, adjust the heat-control dial to its lowest or "off" setting, and let the mantle cool down before you attempt to remove it.

Steam Baths. A steam bath (Figure B2) is a metal container with metal rings that can be removed or added to accommodate glassware of different sizes. It uses externally generated steam for heating, so it has only one operating temperature, 100°C. This limits its usefulness somewhat (e.g., a steam bath cannot be used to boil water or an aqueous solution), but the

well

Figure B1 Heating mantle and heat control

steam inlet   rings

water outlet

Figure B2 Steam bath

relatively low temperature helps prevent decomposition of heat-sensitive substances. Steam baths are often used to heat recrystallization mixtures, evaporate volatile solvents, and heat low-boiling liquids under reflux. Condensation of steam in the vicinity of a steam bath may be a nuisance, but it can be reduced by maintaining a slow rate of steam flow and by using enough rings to bridge any gaps between a flask (or another container) and the steam bath. Beyond a certain point, there is no advantage to increasing the steam flow rate since the steam temperature is constant. If the flask and rings are positioned correctly, heating is quite uniform and efficient.

To use a steam bath, obtain two lengths of rubber tubing, attach one to the steam bath's *water outlet* tube and the other to the steam valve over the sink, and place the open ends of both rubber tubes in the sink. (If your steam bath has no water outlet tube, you will have to turn off the steam periodically to empty it of water.) Remove inner rings from the steam bath, leaving enough rings to safely support the container you wish to heat (unless it is supported by a clamp), but providing an opening large enough so that the steam will contact most of the container's bottom. If the container is a round-bottom flask that is clamped to a ring stand, remove enough rings so that the flask can be lowered through the rings to about its midpoint, leaving the smallest possible gap between the innermost ring and the flask.

Directing the steam into the sink drain, open the steam valve fully and let it run until little or no water drips from the end of the rubber tube. Close the steam valve, connect it to the steam bath's *steam inlet* tube, and then open it just enough to maintain the desired rate of heating with the container in place. You can adjust the heating rate somewhat by adding or removing rings, raising or lowering a clamped flask, or changing the steam flow rate. When you are done heating, turn off the steam valve completely and let the steam bath cool down. Then remove the rubber tubes, drain any water that remains in the steam bath, and put it and the rubber tubes back where you found them. (Don't leave rubber tubing in the sink!)

Take Care! Avoid contact with the steam, which can cause serious thermal burns.

🔆 *Oil Baths.*   An oil bath (Figure B3) provides very uniform heating and precise temperature control, thereby reducing the likelihood of decomposition and side reactions caused by local overheating, and its operating temperature can be measured with a thermometer. But oil baths are messy to work with, difficult to clean, and potentially hazardous. Hot oil can cause severe injury if accidentally spilled on the skin; the oil, which is difficult to remove and slow to cool, remains in contact with the skin long enough to produce deep, painful burns. An oil bath liquid can suddenly burst into flames if it is heated above its *flash point* when an ignition source, such as a spark or burner flame, is present. Hot oil can also catch fire if it splatters onto a hot surface, such as the top of a hot plate. Most oil fires can be extinguished by dry-chemical fire extinguishers or powdered sodium bicarbonate. Water must be kept away from most oil baths because spilling water into a hot oil bath causes dangerous splattering. Oil that contains water shouldn't be used until the water is removed, and a bath liquid that is dark and contains gummy residues should be replaced.

The flash point of a liquid is the minimum temperature at which its vapors can be ignited by a small flame.

Mineral oil is probably the most commonly used oil bath liquid, but it presents a potential fire hazard and is hard to clean up. High–molecular-weight polyethylene glycols (such as Carbowax 600) are water soluble,

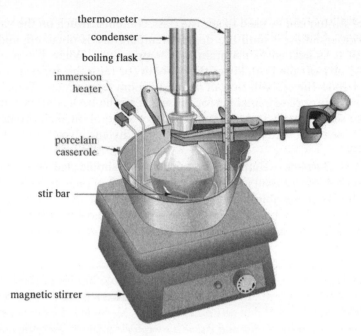

thermometer
condenser
boiling flask
immersion heater
porcelain casserole
stir bar
magnetic stirrer

Figure B3 Oil bath assembly

which makes cleanup much easier, and they can be used at comparatively high temperatures without appreciable decomposition. Some silicone oils can be used at even higher temperatures, but they are considerably more expensive than the other bath liquids. Flash points and other information about selected oil bath liquids are given in the margin. Note that flash points may vary with composition; check the label or ask your instructor if you aren't sure about the flash point of a specific oil bath liquid.

An oil bath is ordinarily heated by a removable heating element, such as a coil of resistance wire or an immersion heater. (A hot plate can also be used, but it may cause a fire if any bath liquid spills onto the hot surface.) The output of the heating element is controlled by a variable transformer, and the temperature of the bath is measured with a thermometer suspended in the liquid. A large porcelain casserole (see Figure B3) makes a convenient bath container because it is less easily broken than a glass container and has a handle for convenient placement and removal.

To use an oil bath, first place it on a lab jack, a set of wood blocks, or some other support that will allow it to be removed from contact with the reaction apparatus quickly in case a reaction becomes violent. If that isn't possible, make sure that the reaction apparatus can be raised out of the oil bath quickly. Don't set an oil bath on a ring support because of the danger of spilling hot oil when the ring is raised or lowered. See that the apparatus containing the reaction flask or boiling flask is clamped securely to a ring stand. Then loosen (at the ring stand) the clamp holding the flask, and lower the flask into the bath so that the liquid level inside it is 1 to 2 mm below the oil level. Clamp a thermometer so that its bulb is immersed in the oil but doesn't touch anything else in the oil bath. Drop a stir bar into the bath if desired, and stir the bath gently to ensure more even heat distribution. A

Oil bath liquids
Mineral oil
  Flash point ~190°C, but varies with composition
  Potential fire hazard

Glycerol
  Flash point 160°C
  Water soluble, viscous

Dibutyl phthalate
  Flash point 171°C
  Viscous at low temperatures

Triethylene glycol
  Flash point 165°C
  Water soluble

Polyethylene glycols (Carbowaxes)
  Flash point varies with molecular weight
  Water soluble, some are solids at room temperature

Silicone oil, high temperature
  Flash point 315°C, usable range −40°C to 230°C
  Expensive; decomposition products are very toxic.

smaller stir bar can be used to stir the flask contents. Switch on the variable transformer, adjust it until the desired temperature is obtained, and then readjust it as needed to maintain that temperature. When you are done heating, turn off the heat, lower the oil bath (or raise the apparatus out of it), and allow the oil bath to cool nearly to room temperature. Transfer the oil to an appropriate container for reuse. Clean the bath container using a suitable solvent, such as petroleum ether for mineral oil, dichloromethane for silicone oil, or water for glycerol and polyethylene glycol.

Burners.   Bunsen-type burners are simple and convenient to operate, but they present a serious risk of fire in an organic chemistry lab, in which highly flammable solvents are often used. For that reason, burners should be used mainly for operations that cannot be conducted with flameless heat sources, such as bending and fire-polishing glass tubing.

Safety Notes

> **Always check to see that there are no flammable liquids in the vicinity before you light a burner. Never use a burner near a heated oil bath or to heat a flammable liquid in an open container. Never leave a burner flame unattended; it may go out and cause an explosion due to escaping gas.**

To operate a typical burner with a needle valve at the base, connect it to a gas outlet with a rubber hose and make sure that the valve at the gas outlet is turned off. Close the needle valve on the burner by rotating the knurled wheel clockwise until you feel resistance (don't close it tightly), and then open it a turn or two. Open the gas valve and—without delay—ignite the burner with a burner lighter. If it doesn't light, rotate the barrel of the burner clockwise (or close the sleeve-type regulator, if it has one) and try again. When the burner is lit, adjust the needle valve and rotate the barrel or sleeve to obtain a flame of the desired size and intensity. Rotating the barrel counterclockwise or opening the sleeve regulator to introduce more air produces a hotter, bluer flame. If you are using a burner to heat a non-flammable liquid in a beaker or other container, place the container on a ring support using a ceramic-centered wire gauze to spread out the flame and prevent superheating. The ring support should be positioned so that the bottom of the wire gauze is at the top of the inner blue cone of the flame, where it is hottest.

Hot Plates.   A hot plate (Figure B4) can be used to heat most liquids and solutions in flat-bottomed containers, such as Erlenmeyer flasks and beakers. It should *not* be used to heat low-boiling, flammable liquids that could splatter on the hot surface and ignite or to heat round-bottom flasks directly. Hot plates can also be used to heat water baths, oil baths, sand baths, and heating blocks, which are in turn used to heat reaction mixtures and other liquids or solutions. Hot plates with built-in magnetic stirrers [OP-10], which can be used for operations that require simultaneous stirring and heating, are particularly useful in the microscale laboratory.

To use a hot plate, plug it into an electrical outlet and adjust the heat-control dial to obtain the desired temperature or heating rate. If you are using a hot plate with a sand bath or an aluminum block, it's a good idea to prepare

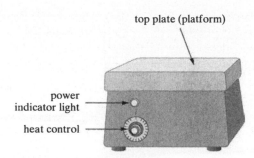

Figure B4 Hot plate

a calibration curve by measuring the equilibrium temperature at each dial setting (wait 10–15 minutes for the temperature to equilibrate at each setting) and plotting the temperature against the dial setting. Then you can adjust the heat control for the desired operating temperature when you use the same sand bath or aluminum block again. Note that the volume of sand in a sand bath must be kept constant in order for the calibration to be valid. Keep tongs, heat-resistant gloves, or other insulating materials handy so that you can quickly remove the container being heated when necessary. For example, you can fold a rectangle cut from a paper towel lengthwise several times and loop it around the neck of a hot Erlenmeyer flask to remove the flask from a hot plate.

Hot-Water Baths. Hot-water baths are useful for heating low-boiling reaction mixtures, evaporating [OP-19] volatile solvents, and in other applications that require gentle heating. Although special metal water baths that resemble steam baths are available, a beaker can be used for most purposes. A typical hot-water bath for microscale work is illustrated in Figure B5. Note that the water should fill the water-bath container about three-fourths full when the container being heated is immersed in it. The usual function of the air condenser shown is to return solvent vapors to a boiling reaction mixture (this process is described in OP-7c), but it also makes a convenient "handle" that can be used to lower or raise the container being heated and keeps it from tipping over in the water bath. So, when you heat a jointed microscale container in a hot-water bath, it is often a good idea to attach a condenser—whether or not the mixture will be boiling.

To prepare a hot-water bath, measure an appropriate amount of water into the bath container and set it on the platform of a hot plate or hot plate–stirrer. Secure the container being heated inside the water bath so that the liquid level in the container is below the water level. Clamp a thermometer with its bulb beneath the water surface and at the same level as the mixture to be heated; its bulb should not touch the bath container or the container being heated. If you are using a magnetic stirrer [OP-10], the stirring device inside the container should be close enough to the center of the platform to allow efficient stirring. If a specific bath temperature is required, adjust the heat setting and observe the thermometer reading until that temperature is reached. If the bath temperature rises above the specified value by 5°C or more, withdraw some of the bath water and replace it by an equal volume of cold water. A 10-mL (or larger) pipet equipped with a pipet pump can be used for this purpose. For most purposes, the bath temperature can be allowed to vary by ±5°C or so from the specified value. If a

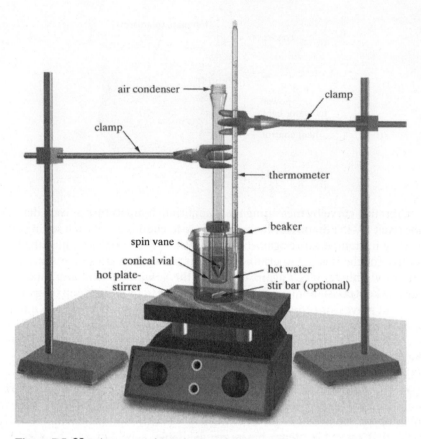

Figure B5 Heating a reaction mixture with a hot-water bath

boiling-water bath is required, add boiling chips or a stir bar to the water before you heat it to boiling. A stir bar is desirable even when the water isn't boiling because it ensures more uniform heat distribution.

If precise temperature control is not necessary, you can fill a beaker with preheated water from a hot-water tap or another source, and adjust the temperature by adding hot or cold water. As the bath cools, withdraw some of the bath water and replace it by fresh heated water.

Heating Blocks. Aluminum heating blocks (see Figure B6) with holes or wells designed to accommodate small test tubes, round-bottom flasks, reaction vials, and similar containers can be used to conduct microscale reactions and for such operations as recrystallization [OP-28] and distillation [OP-30]. Copper heats and cools faster than aluminum, so copper heat-transfer plates may also be used. These plates aren't commercially available, but they can easily be fabricated [Bibliography, D4].

To use a heating block, set it on a hot plate or hot plate–stirrer and insert a thermometer (such as a nonmercury glass thermometer or a dial thermometer with a metal probe) to monitor its temperature, if necessary. If you will be using a magnetic stirrer [OP-10], position the heating block so that the well holding the container being heated is close to the center of the hot plate–stirrer. A glass thermometer should be secured by a three-finger clamp on a ring stand and *carefully* lowered into a small hole (one drilled in

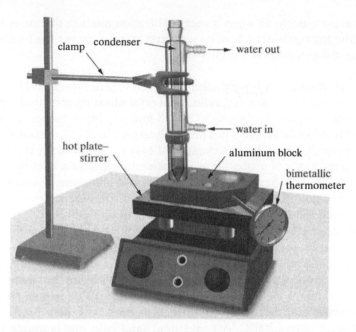

clamp condenser
→ water out

→ water in

hot plate–stirrer

aluminum block

bimetallic thermometer

Figure B6 Heating a reaction mixture with a heating block

the face of the block to accommodate it) until its bulb just rests on the bottom of the hole. Position a glass thermometer in the block *before* you begin heating, or the thermometer bulb may break. The metal probe of a bimetallic dial thermometer can be inserted into a small hole drilled in one corner of a typical heating block. Note that it is not always necessary to monitor the temperature of the block, which is invariably higher than the temperature inside the container it is heating; but by knowing the block temperature, you can control the heating rate more accurately and avoid overheating. Because a heating block takes some time to reach a desired temperature, it is a good idea to start heating it well before it will be needed, using a calibration curve (if you have prepared one) to select an appropriate heat-control setting.

Place the container to be heated in a well of the appropriate size. For the most uniform heating, the liquid level in the container should be just below the top of its well. If the liquid level is above the well top, you can insulate the container with glass wool held in place by aluminum foil. When especially high temperatures are required, a conical vial can be provided with a commercially available split aluminum collar. Most glassware setups should be clamped to a ring stand, but a small test tube, a Craig tube, or a similar container may be supported adequately by the walls of its well. Adjust the heat control on the hot plate so that the temperature of the heating block is at least 20°C higher than the temperature you wish to attain inside the container you are heating. Then readjust the heat control, as necessary, until the desired heating rate is attained. For example, if you want to boil a reaction mixture in which water is the solvent, first raise the block temperature to 120°C. If the reaction mixture does not boil when the block is at that temperature, advance the heat control gradually until it does boil. You can control the heating rate to some extent by raising and lowering a container in its well without changing the heat setting. If you need to lower the

Take Care! If the bulb of a mercury thermometer breaks, especially in a heated block, it will release toxic mercury vapors into the atmosphere. Notify your instructor at once if this happens.

Take Care! A hot metal block looks just like a cold one, so never touch a heating block unless you are sure it is cold.

Take Care! Wear gloves while handling glass wool.

temperature quickly, as when a recrystallization mixture threatens to boil over, raise the container out of its well first and *then* lower the heat setting or clamp the container at a higher level.

Sand Baths.   A typical sand bath (see Figure B7) consists of a flat-bottomed container, such as a cylindrical crystallization dish, that has been filled with fine sand to a depth of 10–15 mm. (Using a deeper sand layer may overload and damage a hot plate's heating element, especially at high temperatures.) A sand bath is cheap and easy to set up and it can be used for the same kinds of processes as a heating block. Like a heating block, a sand bath is usually heated on a hot plate or hot plate–stirrer, using a thermometer to monitor its temperature. For uniform heating, the container being heated should be pushed far enough into the sand so that the liquid level in the container is just below the top of the sand. When necessary, heating can be made more uniform and a higher temperature can be attained at a given heat setting by covering the bath container with aluminum foil. Holes must be cut in the foil to accommodate the thermometer and the container being heated. Although sand can be heated to a very high temperature, the glass container of a sand bath may break if it is heated much above 200°C. A convenient sand bath that is usable at high temperatures can be constructed by partly filling the ceramic well of a 100-mL Thermowell heating mantle with sand.

Sand baths heat and cool more slowly than aluminum blocks, but it is easier to observe changes in a reaction mixture and to swirl or shake a mixture in a sand bath. A sand bath also provides a temperature gradient, with lower temperatures near the top of the sand layer and higher temperatures near the bottom. Thus, it isn't necessary to control the measured temperature of a sand bath precisely because you can vary the amount of heat applied to a container

Take Care! Do not touch a sand bath or its container unless you are sure it is cold.

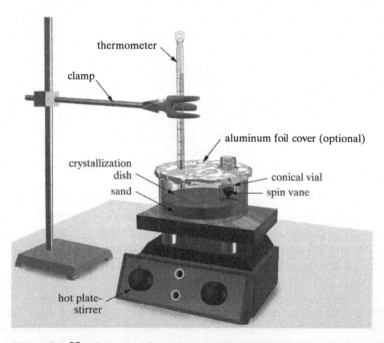

Figure B7 Heating a reaction mixture with a sand bath

by varying its depth in the sand bath. For example, you can bring a reaction mixture to the boiling point quickly by immersing its container deep in the sand, and then raise the container just enough to keep it boiling gently.

To use a sand bath, set it on a hot plate or hot plate–stirrer, clamp a thermometer to a ring stand, and lower it deep enough into the sand so that its bulb is completely covered but is not touching the bath container. Try to place the thermometer bulb at the same depth in the sand each time because the temperature reading will vary with its depth. Begin heating the sand bath well before it will be needed, using a calibration curve (if you have prepared one) to select an appropriate heat setting. Adjust the heat control on the hot plate so that the temperature reading is at least 20°C higher than the temperature you wish to attain inside the container you are heating. Position the container, using clamps for support as necessary, with its bottom immersed in the sand. If you are using a magnetic stirrer, position the apparatus close to the center of the hot plate–stirrer. Raise or lower it in the sand, or readjust the heat control, until the desired heating rate is attained.

Other Heat Sources. Heating devices such as infrared heat lamps (Figure B8) and electric forced-air heaters (heat guns) can be used in some heating applications. A heat lamp plugged into a variable transformer provides a safe and convenient way to heat comparatively low-boiling liquids. The boiling flask is usually fitted with an aluminum foil heat shield to concentrate the heat on the reaction mixture.

b. Smooth Boiling Devices

When a liquid is heated at its boiling point, it may erupt violently as large bubbles of superheated vapor are discharged from the liquid; this phenomenon is called *bumping*. A *boiling chip* prevents bumping by providing nucleating sites on which smaller bubbles can form. Boiling chips (also called boiling stones) are made from porous pieces of alumina, carbon, glass, marble (calcium carbonate), Teflon, and other materials. Alumina and calcium carbonate boiling chips may break down in strongly acidic or alkaline solutions, so boiling chips made of carbon, Teflon, or other chemically resistant materials should be used with such solutions. Wooden applicator sticks can be broken in two, and the broken ends used to promote smooth boiling in nonreactive solvents; they should not be used in reaction mixtures because of the possibility of contamination. Boiling chips aren't needed when a liquid being heated is stirred at a moderate rate with a magnetic stir bar or spin vane because stirring [OP-10] causes turbulence that breaks up the large bubbles responsible for bumping.

Unless you are instructed differently, always add one or more boiling chips to any liquid or liquid mixture that will be boiled without stirring, such as a liquid to be distilled or a reaction mixture to be heated under reflux (see section **c**). One or two small boiling chips are usually sufficient for microscale work; several boiling chips should be used for standard scale work. It is important to add boiling chips *before* heating begins because the liquid may froth violently and boil over if you add them when it is hot. If you let a boiling liquid cool below its boiling point, add a fresh boiling chip if you reheat it later because liquid fills the pores of a boiling chip and reduces its effectiveness when boiling stops.

Take Care! If the bulb of a mercury thermometer breaks in a heated sand bath, it will release toxic mercury vapors into the atmosphere. Notify your instructor at once if this happens.

Figure B8 Heat lamp bulb

Microporous carbon boiling chips work well for most purposes. Teflon chips are suitable with most organic solvents, but they float on water and other dense solvents.

c. Heating Under Reflux

Most organic reactions are carried out by heating the reaction mixture to increase the reaction rate. The temperature of a reaction mixture can be controlled in several ways, the simplest and most convenient being to use a reaction solvent that has a boiling point within the desired temperature range for the reaction. Sometimes, a liquid reactant itself may be used as the solvent. The reaction is conducted at the boiling point of the solvent, using a *condenser* to return solvent vapors to the reaction vessel so that no solvent is lost. This process of boiling a reaction mixture and condensing the solvent vapors back into the reaction vessel is known as *heating under reflux* (or more informally as "refluxing"), where the word reflux refers to the "flowing back" of the solvent. Usually, a reaction time is specified for a reaction conducted under reflux. That interval should be measured from the time the reaction mixture begins to boil, *not* from the time heating is begun.

Round-bottom flasks are ordinarily used as the reaction vessels for a standard scale reaction. A typical standard scale lab kit contains round-bottom flasks with capacities of 25, 50, 100, 250, and 500 mL. A microscale lab kit may contain 3-mL and 5-mL conical vials, a 5-mL pear-shaped flask, and a 10-mL round-bottom flask, any of which can be used to carry out a reaction. As a rule, the reaction vessel should be the smallest appropriate container that will be about half full or less when all of the reactants have been added. For example, if you will be dissolving 8 mL of reactant A in 20 mL of solvent before starting a reaction, and adding 6 mL of reactant B during the reaction, the maximum volume of liquid in the reaction vessel will be approximately 34 mL. Because that volume would fill a 50-mL flask more than half full, a 100-mL round-bottom flask should be used.

Several different kinds of reflux condensers are available. A *water-cooled condenser* consists of two concentric tubes, with cold tap water circulating through the outer tube, and solvent vapors from a boiling reaction mixture rising up the inner tube. The circulating water cools the walls of the inner tube, cooling the vapors and causing them to condense to liquid droplets that flow back into the reaction vessel. An *air condenser* is ordinarily a single tube whose walls transfer heat to the surrounding air, cooling and condensing the vapors of a boiling liquid. For standard scale work, a water-cooled West condenser is used for most reactions conducted under reflux (see Figure B9). Sometimes a distilling column is used as a standard scale air condenser, but no water is circulated through its jacket, if it has one.

A typical microscale lab kit contains both a water-cooled condenser and an air condenser. As a rule, air condensers should be used with nonaqueous solvents that boil at 150°C or above, or with small amounts of lower boiling solvents that are heated gently. Air condensers can also be used with aqueous solutions because any loss of water vapor into the laboratory air doesn't present a safety hazard. When in doubt, it is best to use a water-cooled condenser for its more efficient cooling action.

Figure B10(a) shows a microscale reflux apparatus with a round-bottom flask and a water-cooled condenser, and Figure B10(b) illustrates one with a conical vial and an air condenser. Either type of condenser can be used with either kind of reaction vessel.

A West condenser (also called a Liebig–West condenser) is provided in standard scale lab kits. Don't mistake a jacketed distilling column for a West condenser; the condenser has a smaller diameter.

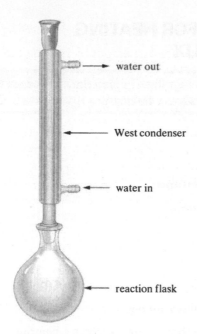

Figure B9 Standard scale apparatus for heating under reflux

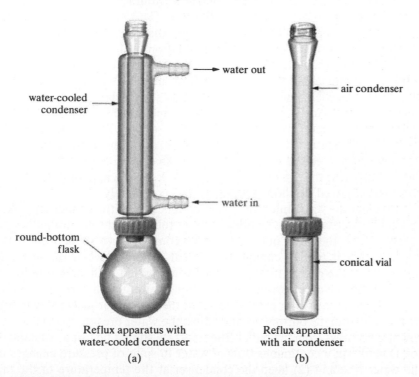

Reflux apparatus with water-cooled condenser
(a)

Reflux apparatus with air condenser
(b)

Figure B10 Microscale apparatus for heating under reflux

A reflux apparatus consisting of a cold-finger condenser (a water-cooled tube) inserted through a notched rubber stopper into a test tube is convenient for some small-scale reactions, such as those used in qualitative analysis. If you have such a condenser, your instructor can show you how to use it.

DIRECTIONS FOR HEATING UNDER REFLUX

> **Never heat the reaction flask before the condenser water is turned on; solvent vapors may escape and cause a fire or create a health hazard.**

 ### Standard Scale

Equipment and Supplies

- heat source
- round-bottom flask
- West condenser
- boiling chips or stir bar
- two lengths of rubber tubing

Select an appropriate heat source, such as a heating mantle or steam bath. Position the heat source at the proper location on or near a ring stand so that it can be removed quickly if the flask should break or the reaction become too vigorous. Select a round-bottom flask of a size such that the reactants fill it about half full or less. Clamp this *reaction flask* securely to the ring stand at the proper location in relation to the heat source. Transfer [OP-6] the reactants and any specified solvent to the reaction flask. Solids should be added through a powder funnel, or with a weighing dish or a square of weighing paper, and liquids should be added through a stemmed funnel. Add a few boiling chips or a magnetic stir bar (see OP-10), and mix the reactants by swirling or stirring. Insert a West condenser into the flask, making sure that the joint is tight. Do *not* stopper the condenser—that will create a closed system, which may shatter violently when heated.

Take Care! Never heat a closed system.

Put a clamp near the top of the condenser to keep the apparatus from toppling over if jarred, but don't tighten its jaws completely.

Connect the water inlet (the lower connector) on the condenser jacket to a cold-water tap with a length of rubber tubing, and run another length of tubing from the water outlet (the upper connector) to a sink drain, making sure that it is long enough to prevent splashing when the water is turned on. If the rubber tubing slips off when pulled with moderate force, replace it by tubing of smaller diameter or secure it with wire or a tubing clamp. Turn on the water carefully so that the condenser jacket slowly fills with water from the bottom up, and adjust the water pressure so that a narrow stream flows from the outlet. The flow rate should be just great enough to (1) maintain a continuous flow of water in spite of pressure changes in the water line and (2) keep the condenser at the temperature of the tap water during the reaction. Excessively high water pressure may force the tubing off the condenser and spray water on you and your neighbors.

If you are using a stir bar, begin stirring at a moderate rate, unless the experiment's directions specify a faster rate. Turn on the heat source, and adjust it to keep the solvent boiling gently; measure the reaction time from the time that boiling begins, when a continuous stream of bubbles will rise through the liquid. Reflux has begun when liquid begins to drip into the flask from the condenser. The vapors passing into the condenser will then form a *reflux ring* of condensing vapors that should be clearly visible. Below this point, liquid will be seen flowing back into the flask; above it, the condenser should be dry. If the reflux ring is more than halfway up the condenser, reduce the heating rate or increase the water flow rate (for a water-cooled condenser) to prevent the escape of solvent vapors.

At the end of the reaction period, turn off the heat source and remove it from contact with the flask. Let the apparatus cool; then turn off the condenser water. Unless the next operation will be carried out in the reaction vessel, decant the reaction mixture into a container suitable for that operation (leave any boiling chips behind). Clean [OP-1] the reaction flask as soon as possible so that residues don't dry on the glass.

Summary

1. Position heat source.
2. Clamp flask in or over heat source.
3. Add solvent and reactants.
4. Add boiling chips or a stir bar.
5. Insert condenser, clamp in place, and attach tubing.
6. Turn on condenser water and adjust flow rate.
7. Start stirrer (if used); adjust heat control so that reaction mixture boils gently.
8. Readjust water flow or heating rate as necessary; boil gently until end of reflux period.
9. Turn off and remove heat source, let flask cool, and transfer reaction mixture.
10. Disassemble and clean apparatus.

 Microscale

Equipment and Supplies

heat source
conical vial or round-bottom flask
air condenser or water-cooled condenser
boiling chip(s) or stirring device
two lengths of rubber tubing (for water-cooled condenser only)

For the *reaction vessel*, select a conical vial or round-bottom flask of a size such that the reactants fill it about half full or less. Transfer [OP-6] the reactants and any specified solvent to the reaction vessel. It is best to weigh limiting reactants directly into the reaction vessel. Add a boiling chip or a magnetic stirring device (see OP-10), and mix the reactants by swirling or stirring. Attach an appropriate condenser to the reaction vessel, making sure that the compression cap is screwed on securely (see OP-2). Do *not* stopper the condenser—that will create a closed system, which may shatter

Take Care! Never heat a closed system.

violently when heated. Clamp the apparatus to a ring stand, and lower it into a heat source such as a heating block or sand bath.

If you are using an air condenser, go on to the next paragraph. If you are using a water-cooled condenser, connect the water inlet (the lower connector) on the jacket to a cold-water tap with a length of rubber tubing, and run another length of tubing from the water outlet (the upper connector) to a sink, making sure that it is long enough to prevent splashing when the water is turned on. If the rubber tubing slips off when pulled with moderate force, replace it with tubing of smaller diameter or secure it with wire or a tubing clamp. Turn on the water carefully so that the condenser jacket slowly fills with water from the bottom up, and adjust the water pressure so that a narrow stream flows from the outlet. The flow rate should be just great enough to (1) maintain a continuous flow of water in spite of pressure changes in the water line and (2) keep the condenser at the temperature of the tap water during the reaction. Excessively high water pressure may force the tubing off the condenser and spray water on you and your neighbors.

If you are using a stirring device, begin stirring at a moderate rate. Adjust the heat setting or the depth of the reaction vessel in the heat source to keep the solvent boiling gently; measure the reaction time from the time that boiling begins, when a continuous stream of bubbles will rise through the liquid. If there is sufficient liquid in the reaction vessel, its vapors should form a *reflux ring* of condensing vapors in the condenser. Below this point, liquid will be seen flowing back into the reaction vessel; above it, the condenser should be dry. If the reflux ring is more than halfway up the condenser, reduce the heating rate or increase the water flow rate to prevent the escape of solvent vapors.

At the end of the reaction period, turn off the heat source and raise the apparatus on the ring stand, clamping it several inches above the heat source. When the reaction vessel has cooled nearly to room temperature, turn off the condenser water (if used). Unless the next operation will be carried out in the reaction vessel, transfer its contents to a container suitable for that operation (leave any boiling chips behind). Clean [OP-1] the reaction vessel as soon as possible so that residues don't dry on the glass.

Summary

1. Transfer reactants and solvent to reaction vessel.
2. Add boiling chip or a stirring device.
3. Attach appropriate condenser.
4. Clamp apparatus over heat source.
   IF an air condenser is being used, GO TO 7.
5. Attach tubing to water-cooled condenser.
6. Turn on condenser water and adjust flow rate.
7. Start stirrer (if used); adjust heat so that reaction mixture boils gently.
8. Readjust water flow or heating rate as necessary; boil gently until end of reaction period.
9. Turn off heat source, let reaction vessel cool, and transfer reaction mixture.
10. Disassemble and clean apparatus.

When Things Go Wrong

If, when you turn on the cooling water, the condenser fills from the top down rather than the bottom up, you connected the rubber tubes to the wrong hose connectors. Turn off the water, reattach the tube from the water tap to the condenser's bottom connector and the other tube to its top connector, and turn on the water again.

If, as you heat a reaction mixture, the liquid bumps or foams up, you probably forgot to add boiling chips or to use a magnetic stirrer. Drop in a stirring device and start stirring, or let the apparatus cool for several minutes and then drop one or more boiling chips down the top of the condenser. If you were already using boiling chips or a stirrer, you are probably heating the reaction mixture too strongly. Reduce the heating rate by raising the apparatus or lowering the heat source a few millimeters (for rapid cooling) or by turning down the heat control (for slower cooling), or both. You can always return the apparatus to its original location once the heating rate has decreased.

If, as you heat a reaction mixture, the liquid level in the reaction vessel goes down or the reflux ring of condensing vapors rises above the midpoint of the condenser, either the cooling water isn't flowing fast enough (or at all), you are overheating the reaction mixture, or you are using an air condenser when you should be using a water-cooled condenser. If you are using a water-cooled condenser, it should be cool to the touch. If it isn't, adjust (or turn on) the cooling water so that a steady stream flows through the condenser—not a strong stream that may force the hose off the condenser. If the reflux ring is still too high, reduce the heating rate as described previously until the reflux ring stays in the bottom half of the condenser. If you are using an air condenser, replace it with a water-cooled condenser (let the reaction mixture cool down before switching condensers). If the liquid level in the reaction vessel has gone down, add more solvent to replace any that boiled away.

If, when you are taking the apparatus apart, you can't separate the condenser from the reaction flask or vial, the glass joints have probably frozen. See "Disassembling Glassware" in OP-2.

Cooling

Some reactions proceed too violently to be conducted safely at room temperature, or involve reactants or products that decompose at room temperature. In such cases, the reaction mixture is cooled with some kind of cold bath, which can be anything from a beaker filled with cold water to an electrically refrigerated device. Cold baths are also used to increase the yield of crystals from a reaction mixture or recrystallization mixture.

A setup like the one shown in Figure B5 (OP-7) for a hot-water bath can also be used for a cold bath. A cold bath can be prepared using any suitable container, such as a beaker of suitable size, a crystallization dish, an evaporating dish, or a pair of nested Styrofoam cups. A beaker can be wrapped with glass wool or another insulating material and placed inside a larger beaker to keep it cold longer, if necessary.

Take Care! Wear gloves while handling glass wool.

Temperatures below −40°C cannot be measured using a mercury thermometer because mercury freezes at that temperature.

Take Care! Never handle dry ice with bare hands.

A number of cooling media are used for cold baths. A mixture of ice (or snow) and water can be used for cooling in the 0–5°C range. The ice should be finely divided, and enough water should be present to just cover the ice, because ice alone is not an efficient heat-transfer medium. An ice–salt bath consisting of three parts of finely crushed ice or snow to one part of sodium chloride can attain temperatures down to −20°C, and mixtures of $CaCl_2 \cdot H_2O$ containing up to 1.4 g of the calcium salt per gram of ice or snow can provide temperatures down to −55°C. In practice, these minimum values may be difficult to attain because the actual temperature of an ice–salt bath depends on such factors as the fineness of the ice and salt and the insulating ability of the container. Temperatures down to −75°C can be attained by mixing small chunks of dry ice (solid carbon dioxide) with acetone, ethanol, or another suitable solvent in a vacuum-jacketed container such as a Dewar flask.

DIRECTIONS FOR COOLING

   Standard Scale and Microscale

Equipment and Supplies

> cold bath container
> cooling medium
> thermometer
> air condenser (µS, optional)

Obtain a suitable cold bath container, and fill it with the cooling medium to a level depending on the size of the container to be cooled. When this container is immersed in the cold bath, the cooling medium should fill the cold bath container about three-fourths full. Clamp a thermometer [OP-9] so that its bulb is entirely immersed in the cooling medium but not touching either container. If you are using an ice–salt bath, mix in the appropriate salt in small portions; wait for the temperature to equilibrate after each addition, until the desired temperature is attained. Lower the container to be cooled into the cooling bath so that the liquid level in that container is below the cooling fluid level. For microscale work, attach an air condenser to any threaded container being cooled (unless experimental conditions preclude this), and clamp the condenser to a ring stand. Otherwise, either clamp the neck of the container to a ring stand or hold the container in your hand so that it doesn't tip over. Keep the contents of the cold bath mixed by occasional stirring or swirling. The contents of the container being cooled can also be swirled or stirred for more efficient cooling. Add small portions of ice, as needed, to keep the temperature in the desired range, removing an equal amount of water (with a pipet, etc.) to make room for it.

Summary

1. Fill container with cooling medium.
2. Insert thermometer in cooling medium.
3. Insert container to be cooled.
4. Keep contents of container and cooling bath mixed, and adjust temperature as needed.

Temperature Monitoring

In the organic chemistry lab, thermometers are used to monitor the temperatures of heating devices, cooling baths, reaction mixtures, distillations, and for many other purposes. Such thermometers should have a range of at least −10°C to 260°C, and a wider range is desirable for some purposes. Most broad-range glass thermometers contain mercury, which is toxic and presents a safety hazard if a thermometer is broken, but broad-range non-mercury thermometers are also available. Short glass thermometers (about 15 cm long) are available for microscale work, and bimetallic thermometers with metal probes can be used to measure the temperatures of some heating devices. For the most accurate temperature readings, a thermometer should be *calibrated* and an *emergent stem correction* applied as described in OP-33, but this is generally not necessary for routine temperature monitoring.

To read a thermometer accurately, rotate it so that its mercury column is adjacent to its graduation marks, and view it with your line of sight perpendicular to the thermometer and extending to the top of the mercury column. If the thermometer is vertical, for example, your eyes should be at about the same level as the top of the mercury column. You should then be able read the temperature to at least the nearest half degree.

You can monitor the temperature of a liquid or solid heating medium (such as water, oil, or sand) using a thermometer clamped with its bulb entirely immersed in the heating medium. It should be held in place by a three-fingered clamp or a special thermometer clamp, or inserted into a stopper that is held by a utility clamp. The thermometer should not touch the side or bottom of the container, or anything inside the container.

To monitor the temperature of a reaction mixture that will be stirred [OP-10] in an open container such as an Erlenmeyer flask, clamp a thermometer so that its bulb is completely immersed in the mixture but doesn't contact the stirring device (a large stir bar could break the thermometer bulb). If a magnetic stirrer is not available, you may have to hold a thermometer inside the reaction vessel as it is being swirled or shaken. Do this by holding the neck of the flask and nesting the thermometer stem in the "vee" between your thumb and index finger, so that the bulb of the thermometer is held securely inside the flask and continuously immersed in the liquid. With a little practice, you should be able to mix the contents of the flask quite vigorously without damage to the thermometer. If continuous mixing is not necessary, you can insert the thermometer each time you stop shaking or swirling the reaction flask, read it when the temperature has stabilized, then remove it and resume mixing. Never use the thermometer itself for stirring because the bulb is fragile and breaks easily.

Using a Thermometer Adapter

You will ordinarily need a *thermometer adapter* to monitor the temperature of an operation (such as distillation) conducted in a jointed glassware setup (see Figure B11). Be certain that the thermometer adapter, when inserted in the apparatus, doesn't create a closed system. For example, never put a

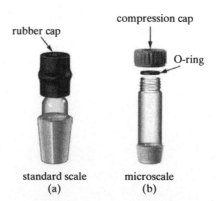

rubber cap

compression cap

O-ring

standard scale
(a)

microscale
(b)

Figure B11 Thermometer adapters

sealed thermometer adapter assembly on top of a reflux condenser that is attached directly to a reaction flask because heating such a system may cause it to shatter.

To use a standard scale thermometer adapter, carefully insert the bulb of the thermometer through the rubber cap of the adapter using an appropriate lubricant (see OP-3). Then secure the adapter in the appropriate joint on the apparatus, and carefully raise or lower the thermometer so that its bulb is positioned correctly. To prevent accidental breakage, remove the thermometer assembly from the apparatus before repositioning the thermometer.

To use a microscale thermometer adapter, first slide a small rubber O-ring down the thermometer stem to near its center (the O-ring should come with the adapter). Secure the adapter, without its upper compression cap, in the appropriate joint on the apparatus. Insert the thermometer (bulb end down) through the adapter, and move the O-ring up or down until its bulb is positioned correctly when the O-ring is resting on the adapter. Then slide the adapter's threaded cap down the thermometer stem, and use it to secure the thermometer assembly to the apparatus.

OPERATION **10**   Mixing

Reaction mixtures are often stirred, shaken, or agitated in some other way to promote efficient heat transfer, prevent bumping, increase contact between the components of a heterogeneous mixture, or mix in a reactant as it is being added.

Manual Mixing

If you are carrying out a reaction in an Erlenmeyer flask or a test tube, the reactants can be mixed using a stirring rod or spatula, or by manual shaking or swirling. A motion that combines shaking with swirling is more effective than swirling alone. If you are carrying out a standard scale reaction under reflux, you can sometimes mix the reactants adequately by clamping the apparatus *securely* to a ring stand and carefully sliding the base of the ring stand back and forth. But when more efficient and convenient mixing is required, particularly over a long period of time, it is best to use a magnetic stirrer, as described in a following section.

Manual mixing may be used at other times than during reactions. For example, liquids can be dried [OP-25] by swirling the liquid with a drying agent in an Erlenmeyer flask. This increases the amount of contact between the liquid and the particles of drying agent, increasing drying efficiency.

Small quantities of liquids are often dried by stirring the liquid with the drying agent in a conical vial. You can do this by twirling the pointed end of a microspatula in the bottom of the vial. Similarly, you can twirl the rounded end of a flat-bladed microspatula inside a Craig tube or a small test tube to stir recrystallization solutions and other mixtures.

Mechanical Stirring

A mechanical stirrer consists of a stirring motor connected to a paddle or agitator by means of a shaft that extends through the neck of the reaction vessel. A glass sleeve or bearing is used to align the shaft, which is ordinarily made of glass to reduce the likelihood of contamination. Mechanical stirrers exert more torque than magnetic stirrers and are preferred when viscous liquids or slurries must be stirred. A variety of stirring paddles made of Teflon, glass, and chemically resistant wire are available.

A slurry is a thick suspension of solid in a liquid.

Magnetic Stirring

A *magnetic stirrer* (Figure B12) is an enclosed unit containing a motor that rotates a bar magnet underneath a metal or ceramic platform. As the bar magnet rotates, it in turn spins a Teflon-coated stirring device inside a container placed on or above the platform. The most common stirring device, called a *stir bar*, is an oblong (usually cylindrical) Teflon-coated magnet. Because no moving parts extend outside of the container in which stirring occurs, a reaction assembly that is to be stirred magnetically can be completely enclosed if necessary. The rate of stirring is controlled by a dial on the magnetic stirrer. For efficient stirring, the vessel (flask, beaker, conical vial, etc.) containing the stirring device should be positioned near the center of the stirring unit and as close to its platform as practicable.

Magnetic stirrers can be used in conjunction with heating mantles, oil baths, steam baths, and other heat sources that are constructed of nonferrous materials. A *hot plate–stirrer* has a heating device in the same unit that

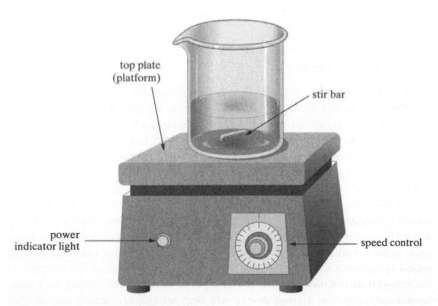

Figure B12 Magnetic stirrer

houses the magnetic stirrer, so it has two dials: one to control the heating unit, and the other to control the stirrer. Hot plate–stirrers can be used to heat and stir flat-bottomed containers such as Erlenmeyer flasks directly, but they are also used in conjunction with heating devices that require an external heat source, such as aluminum blocks, hot-water baths, and sand baths [OP-7]. Figure B5 (OP-7) shows a hot plate–stirrer being used to heat a hot-water bath and stir both the bath liquid and a reaction mixture at the same time.

A hot plate–stirrer is nearly indispensable in the microscale laboratory. The stirring device can be either a *spin vane*, which is used in conical vials, or a small stir bar, which is used in round-bottom flasks, small Erlenmeyer flasks, beakers, and other vessels that have flat or gently rounded bottoms. To visualize a spin vane, imagine a wedge-shaped piece of Teflon with a small bar magnet set crosswise on its short side (see Appendix I for an illustration). When the spin vane is inserted into a conical vial with its point down, the magnetic bar is quite distant from the platform, so the spin vane may not rotate properly unless it is centered correctly and the stirring rate is relatively low. If necessary, you can use a small stir bar to stir the contents of a conical vial. At low speeds, the stir bar wobbles around in the conical end of the vial and doesn't stir very efficiently, but at higher speeds, it should spin horizontally in the wider part of the vial and create a vortex that promotes efficient mixing.

DIRECTIONS FOR STIRRING A REACTION MIXTURE MAGNETICALLY

     Standard Scale and Microscale

Equipment and Supplies

> stirrer or hot plate–stirrer
> heating device
> reaction vessel (flask, conical vial, etc.)
> stir bar or spin vane

Set the heating device (heating mantle, aluminum block, sand bath, etc.), if any, directly on the platform of the magnetic stirrer or hot plate–stirrer. Position the reaction vessel in the heating device so that it is close to the center of the stirring unit's platform, secure it with a clamp (if necessary), and drop in a stir bar or spin vane. (Don't add boiling chips; the stirring action prevents bumping.) If you are using a spin vane, position it with its sharply pointed end facing down. If you need to stir a heating bath as well, use a stir bar that is larger than the one in the reaction mixture. If necessary, attach a condenser or other device to the reaction vessel. Start circulating water through a water-cooled condenser, if you are using one. Start the magnetic stirrer, and adjust the stirring rate dial carefully so that the stirring action is vigorous (you should see a vortex in the middle of the container) but smooth. If the stirring rate is too high or the reaction vessel isn't positioned correctly, the stirring device will flop around erratically rather than rotate smoothly. If that happens, reset the dial to a low value and increase it gradually until a suitable rate is attained, or reposition the reaction vessel to bring it closer to the top and center of the stirring unit's platform. High stirring rates may be needed for heterogeneous reaction mixtures, such as those involving two immiscible liquids, but in most cases a moderate stirring rate is suitable. If you are to heat the stirred reaction mixture, adjust the heating rate as described in OP-7 for the heating device you are using.

Summary

1. Place heating device (if used) on stirring unit.
2. Secure reaction vessel on or inside heating device.
3. Drop in stir bar or spin vane.
4. Adjust stirrer for appropriate stirring rate.

When Things Go Wrong

If, as you increase the spinning rate of a stirring device (stir bar or spin vane), the stirring device wobbles or otherwise moves erratically in its container, try the following remedies in order. Make sure you're not using a ferrous container, such as a stainless-steel beaker. Reduce the stirring rate, and move the container horizontally until it is centered over the platform; then advance the speed control *slowly* until you attain a suitable stirring rate. If the stirring device still turns erratically, try lowering the container so that it is closer to the top of the platform. If you are using a large beaker for a water bath, for example, replace it by a smaller, lower beaker or a porcelain dish. If that doesn't help, try a different magnetic stirrer or stirring device.

If the stir bar you are using for a reaction that requires thorough mixing (such as a heterogeneous reaction) is not stirring the reaction mixture vigorously enough (it should produce a vortex in the liquid at high speed), switch to a larger stir bar.

Addition of Reactants   OPERATION **11**

In many organic preparations, the reactants are not all combined at the start of the reaction. Instead, one or more of them is added during the course of the reaction. This is necessary when the reaction is strongly exothermic or when one of the reactants must be kept in excess to prevent side reactions. Solid reactants can be added slowly or at regular intervals from a plastic weighing dish that is bent to form a pouring spout. Solids can also be divided into small portions that are added at regular intervals. For standard scale work, liquids are added in portions or drop by drop using a separatory funnel or a special addition funnel. For microscale work, liquids are generally added using a syringe or a Pasteur pipet.

 ### Standard Scale Addition

An *addition funnel* has a cylindrical body, a drain tube controlled by a stopcock, and a pressure-equalizing tube to equalize the pressure in the reaction vessel and addition funnel, allowing its contents to flow freely into the reaction vessel. A *separatory funnel* usually has a pear-shaped body attached to a similar

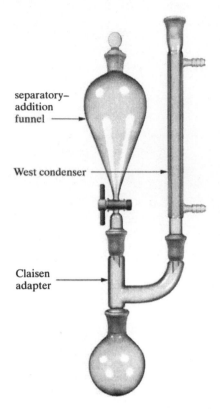

separatory–addition funnel

West condenser

Claisen adapter

Figure B13 Apparatus for standard scale addition under reflux

drain tube, but it lacks a pressure equalizing tube (see Figure B13). Because addition funnels are seldom available in undergraduate labs, a separatory funnel (which we will call a separatory–addition funnel here) is generally used for that purpose. An opening must be left at the top of the funnel for air to enter; otherwise, the liquid outflow will create a vacuum, and the flow will eventually stop. If a reaction is run in an open container, such as an Erlenmeyer flask, the separatory–addition funnel can simply be clamped to a ring stand above the flask, which is swirled or stirred during the addition. For a reaction conducted under reflux, see the directions for standard scale addition that follow.

 ## Microscale Addition

Small amounts of reactants can be added directly to a reaction vessel using a short Pasteur pipet or through a reflux condenser into the reaction vessel using a long (9-inch) Pasteur pipet. When an addition must be made over an extended period, it is more convenient to use a syringe. The syringe is filled with a measured amount of the liquid to be added, and then inserted through a septum so that its needle is directly over the reaction mixture. A rubber septum should remain airtight even after it has been punctured by a syringe needle. A Teflon-lined septum (the kind that fits inside a compression cap) may not remain airtight after being punctured, so if you are using such a septum, try to find an intact septum or one that has already been punctured but still fits tightly around the syringe needle. (Your instructor may want you to use a punctured one to keep the others intact.) Remember that a syringe needle is very sharp (unless it has been blunted to prevent injury) and may be contaminated with dangerous biological or chemical substances, so be careful not to stick yourself or anyone else with it.

DIRECTIONS FOR ADDITION UNDER REFLUX

 ## Standard Scale

Equipment and Supplies

> round-bottom reaction flask
> Claisen adapter
> separatory–addition funnel
> West condenser
> stopper (can be omitted for most aqueous solutions or other nonvolatile liquids)

Measure the appropriate reactants into the flask, and assemble the apparatus shown in Figure B13, placing the separatory–addition funnel on the straight arm of the Claisen adapter so that it is directly over the reaction flask. Clamp the flask and the Claisen adapter securely to a ring stand. Make sure the stopcock is closed; then place the liquid to be added in the separatory–addition funnel. Unless this liquid must be protected from atmospheric moisture, place a strip of filter paper between the stopper and the funnel's ground-glass joint. (If the liquid is moisture sensitive, insert a drying tube [OP-12a] filled with drying agent in the top of the funnel.) Add the liquid either in portions or continuously, as directed in the experiment. For portionwise addition, add small portions of the liquid at regular intervals by opening the stopcock momentarily while stirring magnetically or shaking to mix the reactants. For continuous addition, open the stopcock just far enough so that the liquid drips or drizzles slowly into the reaction flask, and adjust the stopcock position to provide the desired rate of addition. Continuous addition is usually carried out dropwise (drop by drop), with magnetic stirring or periodic shaking [OP-10] to keep the reactants mixed.

Some reactions conducted under reflux also require that the temperature of the reaction mixture be monitored [OP-9] or that the mixture be stirred with a mechanical stirrer (see OP-10), in which case the flask and Claisen adapter shown in Figure B13 are replaced by a three-necked flask (Figure B14). For temperature monitoring, the addition funnel should be inserted in the middle neck, and the reflux condenser and thermometer in the outer necks. For mechanical stirring, the stirrer shaft is inserted in the middle neck, and the addition funnel and reflux condenser in the outer necks.

Figure B14 Three-necked flask

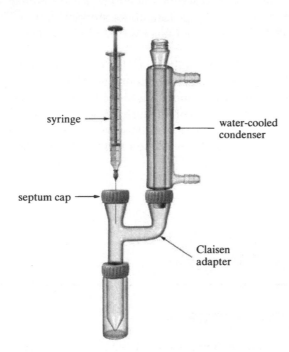

Figure B15 Apparatus for microscale addition under reflux

 Microscale

Equipment and Supplies

> reaction vessel (conical vial or boiling flask)
> Claisen adapter
> septum cap
> air condenser or water-cooled condenser
> syringe

Measure the appropriate reactants into the reaction vessel. Assemble the apparatus illustrated in Figure B15 by inserting a Claisen adapter in the reaction vessel (conical vial or round-bottom flask) and attaching an appropriate condenser to its long arm and a septum cap (a compression cap with a septum inside) to its short, straight arm. Clamp the apparatus securely to a ring stand. Fill the syringe with the desired volume of the liquid to be added (see OP-5). Hold the syringe vertically with its needle pointing down, and carefully insert the needle through the septum. Add the liquid in small portions during the reaction, as directed in the experiment, by depressing the plunger. If necessary, remove the syringe to refill it, and then immediately replace it on the apparatus. When the addition is complete, remove the syringe and clean it (see OP-5) without delay.

When Things Go Wrong

If, during a standard scale reaction, the liquid you are adding stops draining from a separatory–addition funnel, its stopper may be inserted too tightly. Remove the stopper, and place a folded piece of paper between it and the joint.

If the liquid still doesn't drain, close the stopcock and pour the liquid out the top of the funnel into another container. Filter [OP-15] the liquid if it contains solid impurities. Remove the stopcock, use a piece of wire (or a toothpick, etc.) to clean any debris out of the hole, and rinse the hole with distilled water or an appropriate organic solvent, and let it dry. Then insert the stopcock in the separatory-addition funnel, return the liquid to the funnel, and continue.

OPERATION 12

Excluding Water from Reaction Mixtures

a. Using Drying Tubes

Some chemicals react with water vapor from the air, and some reactions are inhibited or prevented by traces of water. Water-sensitive reactions can be carried out and water-sensitive chemicals protected by attaching *drying tubes* (see Figure B16 and B17) wherever an apparatus is open to the atmosphere. The drying tube is filled with a suitable desiccant (drying agent) such as calcium chloride, calcium sulfate (Drierite), granular alumina, or silica gel. Calcium chloride is the least efficient of these, but it is adequate in many cases. When a very dry atmosphere is required, the apparatus should be swept out by passing dry nitrogen or another dry gas through it, as described in Operation 13. Unless your instructor directs otherwise, put used desiccant in a designated container (*not* the container you got it from) when you are done. If you leave calcium chloride in a drying tube exposed to the atmosphere, its granules will eventually clump together in a solid mass that can only be removed by immersing the drying tube in water overnight or longer, until the solid dissolves.

To prepare a standard scale drying tube, use a glass rod or applicator stick to push a small plug of dry cotton into the drying tube until it covers the narrow opening, and tamp it down gently to hold it in place. Add calcium chloride or another drying agent through the top of the drying tube until it is filled to within a few centimeters of the top; then insert another plug of cotton in the top to prevent spills. Push the connector at the bottom of the drying tube into a thermometer adapter, and insert the adapter into the top of a reflux condenser (or into any other part of an apparatus that is open to the atmosphere), as shown in Figure B16. If the apparatus includes a vacuum adapter, the drying tube can be attached to its sidearm using a short length of rubber tubing.

To prepare a microscale drying tube (Figure B17), use an applicator stick or glass rod to push a plug of cotton through its long end nearly to the bend in the tube. Holding the drying tube with its long arm upright (open end up), use a plastic weighing dish to add enough calcium chloride (~1.5 g) or another drying agent to form a layer 3–4 cm deep; then insert another plug of cotton to keep the desiccant in place. Insert the drying tube into the top of a reflux condenser or any other part of an apparatus that is open to the atmosphere.

b. Water Separation

During some reactions that yield water as a by-product, it may be necessary to remove the water to prevent the decomposition of a water-sensitive product or to increase the yield. This is sometimes done by codistilling (see OP-20b) the water with an organic solvent that forms a low-boiling azeotrope (see OP-32) with water. This process is known as *azeotropic drying*. The solvent used must be less dense than water and immiscible in it. For example, a mixture of water and toluene (bp = 111°C; d = 0.866 g/mL) yields an azeotrope containing 13.5% water by mass that distills at 84°C, so toluene is often used to remove water from reaction mixtures.

The codistillation can be accomplished with an ordinary simple distillation apparatus [OP-30a], but for standard scale work it is more convenient to use a *water separator,* such as the Dean–Stark trap shown in Figure B18. The Dean–Stark trap is inserted in the reaction flask, filled to the level of its sidearm with the reaction solvent, and fitted with a reflux condenser. As water forms during the reaction, its vapors and those of the reaction solvent condense inside the reflux condenser and drip down into the water separator. The organic solvent, which separates on top of the water layer, overflows through the sidearm and returns to the reaction flask, while the water stays in the bottom of the separator. The theoretical yield of water from the reaction can be calculated, so the volume of water in the separator is monitored to determine when the reaction is nearing completion.

If a Dean–Stark trap is not available, the parts from a standard scale organic lab kit can be assembled as shown in Figure B19 so that the 25-mL flask, still head, and vacuum adapter together function like a Dean–Stark trap. When you assemble this apparatus, clamp both flasks securely and close the vacuum adapter outlet with a rubber bulb from a medicine dropper.

Take Care! Never stopper a drying tube because this will result in a closed system that might explode or fly apart when heated.

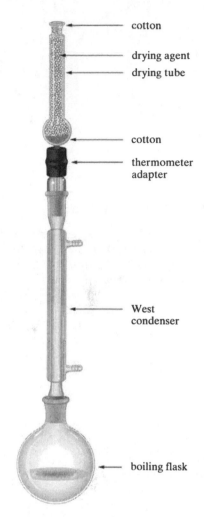

cotton

drying agent

drying tube

cotton

thermometer adapter

West condenser

boiling flask

Figure B16 Standard scale apparatus for heating under reflux in a dry atmosphere

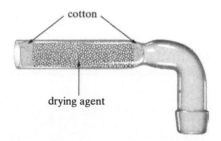

cotton

drying agent

Figure B17 Microscale drying tube

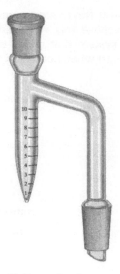

Figure B18 Dean-Stark trap

*A "homemade" Dean–Stark trap can be constructed as described in J. Chem. Educ, **1963**, 40, 349.*

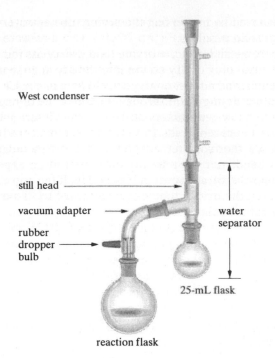

Figure B19 Apparatus for standard scale water separation

Use a funnel to fill the water separator with the organic solvent to a level just below the bottom of the sidearm. Heat the reaction mixture under gentle reflux, being careful that the adapter's drip tip does not become flooded with liquid (an adapter with a missing drip tip works better). When disassembling the apparatus after the reaction, leave the water separator clamped while the other components are removed, and then tilt it carefully to pour liquid from its sidearm into a beaker.

🗑 For microscale work, a Hickman still can function as a water separator in an apparatus such as the one pictured in Figure E11 of OP-30. The well of the Hickman still, which corresponds to the solvent reservoir of a Dean–Stark trap, can be previously filled with toluene or another suitable organic solvent. Alternatively, an amount of excess organic solvent equal to the well's capacity (1–2 mL) can be added to the reaction vessel, from which it distills into the well during the reaction. Any water that forms during the reaction condenses inside the Hickman still and collects in the bottom of its well, and the organic solvent overflows from the well into the pot.

OPERATION 13

Excluding Air from Reaction Mixtures

Some chemicals react readily with oxygen from the air, so reactions using such chemicals must be conducted in an inert (oxygen-free) atmosphere. The simplest and least expensive way to provide an inert atmosphere is to flush all parts of a reaction apparatus with nitrogen. This process also removes water vapor and thus provides a dry atmosphere as well.

To flush a standard scale reflux assembly with nitrogen, first assemble the apparatus pictured in Figure B20(a). Use glassware components that have been oven-dried and then cooled. Coat all of the joints with a thin layer of joint grease (see OP-2), and use joint clips to keep them from separating. Fold a rubber septum over the straight arm of the Claisen adapter and another rubber septum over the top of the condenser. Insert syringe needles (but not the syringes) through both septa. To make a gas bubbler that will monitor the nitrogen flow, attach a short Pasteur pipet to one end of a length of rubber or plastic tubing and clamp it over a test tube partly filled with mineral oil, inserting its narrow end in the oil; then attach the other end of the tubing to the base of the syringe needle at the top of the condenser. Use another piece of tubing to attach the needle on the Claisen adapter to a nitrogen source. Open the nitrogen flow valve just far enough to produce a gentle stream of bubbles in the mineral oil. After a few minutes, reduce the flow to maintain a small positive nitrogen pressure in the apparatus, and then carry out the reaction. If the reaction mixture is

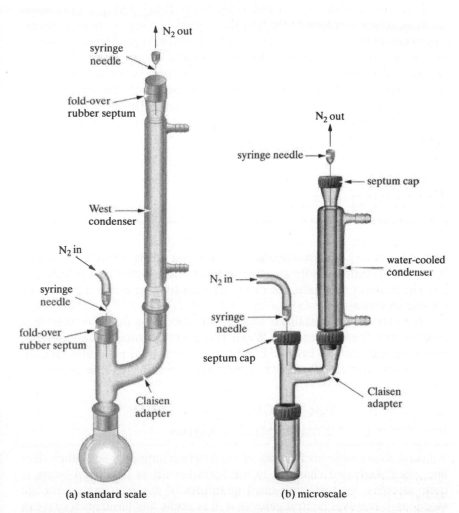

(a) standard scale   (b) microscale

Figure B20 Apparatus for conducting a reaction in a dry, oxygen-free atmosphere (a) Standard scale (b) Microscale

being heated, increase the flow rate at the end of the heating period to maintain a positive pressure.

To flush a microscale reflux assembly with nitrogen, assemble an apparatus like that shown in Figure B20(b). The glassware components should have been oven-dried and then cooled. Be sure that all compression caps have undamaged O-rings and are screwed down tightly. Attach a septum cap to the top of the condenser, and insert a syringe needle through it. To make a gas bubbler that will monitor the nitrogen flow, attach a short Pasteur pipet to one end of a length of rubber or plastic tubing and clamp it over a test tube partly filled with mineral oil, inserting its narrow end in the oil; then attach the other end of the tubing to the base of the syringe needle at the top of the condenser. Use another piece of tubing to attach the needle on the Claisen adapter to a nitrogen source. Open the nitrogen flow just far enough to produce a gentle stream of bubbles in the mineral oil. After a few minutes, reduce the flow to maintain a small positive nitrogen pressure in the apparatus, and then carry out the reaction. If the reaction mixture is being heated, increase the flow rate at the end of the heating period to maintain a positive pressure while the reaction flask cools down.

If it will be necessary to add reactants [OP-11] during a microscale reaction, attach a balloon to the barrel of a plastic syringe (it may be necessary to cut off the top of the barrel) and fill it with nitrogen through a plastic tube attached to the syringe's tip (remove the needle first). When the balloon is full, pinch its neck to keep nitrogen from escaping, remove the tube, attach a needle, and immediately insert the needle through the condenser's septum. When the addition syringe is inserted through the adapter's septum cap, enough air should escape to allow the apparatus to fill with nitrogen.

OPERATION **14**   # Trapping Gases

The best way to keep toxic and smelly gases out of the laboratory air is to conduct all reactions under an efficient fume hood. If that isn't possible, or if the hood is not adequate, gases can be removed using either a gas trap or a water aspirator.

A gas trap that contains a suitable gas-absorbing liquid or solid will remove most gases effectively. Water alone will dissolve some gases, but dilute aqueous sodium hydroxide (about 5% or 1 M) is generally used for acidic gases, such as HBr or SO_2. It converts them to salts that dissolve in the water.

$$HBr + NaOH \longrightarrow NaBr + H_2O$$

$$SO_2 + NaOH \longrightarrow NaHSO_3$$

Similarly, dilute aqueous HCl can be used to trap ammonia and other alkaline gases. Activated charcoal, in the form known as pelletized Norit, is quite effective for removing small quantities of gases during microscale reactions. It removes neutral gases as well as acidic and basic ones, so it can also be used to keep strong or offensive odors out of the lab. A drying tube (see OP-12a) filled with cotton that is carefully moistened with water can trap some gases and remove some odors, but it is only effective for water-soluble gases and organic vapors, and precautions must be taken to keep water from dripping into the apparatus.

🔥 You can construct a simple gas trap for standard scale work by clamping an inverted narrow-stemmed funnel over a beaker containing a suitable gas-absorbing liquid, and then lowering the funnel so that its rim just touches the surface of the liquid, as shown in Figure B21. Connect the gas trap to the reaction apparatus at any point that is open to the atmosphere (usually the top of a reflux condenser) using rubber tubing and a short length of fire-polished glass tubing (see OP-3) that is inserted into a thermometer adapter or rubber stopper.

You can remove water-soluble gases such as hydrogen halides by using a water aspirator. Attach a vacuum adapter to the top of your reflux condenser, or any other part of your apparatus that is open to the atmosphere, and use a length of heavy-walled rubber tubing to connect the sidearm of the adapter to the aspirator. Turn on the aspirator partway while the gas is

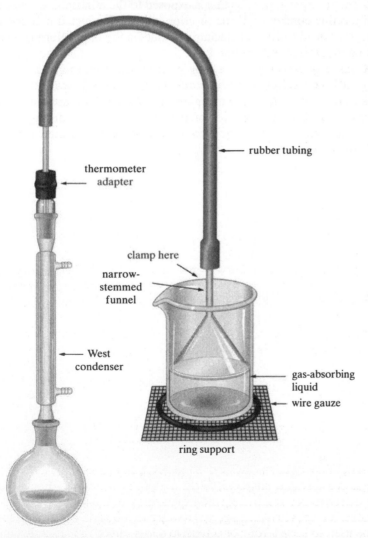

Figure B21 Apparatus for trapping gases during reflux

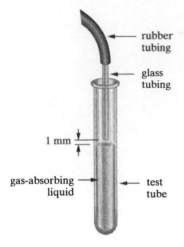

Figure B22 Small-scale gas trap

being generated. The gas should be drawn into the aspirator, dissolve in the water, and pass down the drain. Before using an aspirator for this purpose, make sure that it is legally permissible in your city or state to flush such gases into the wastewater system.

🧪 🧪 For small amounts of gases, a straight glass tube inserted into a test tube containing the gas-absorbing liquid may be adequate. Clamp the outlet of the glass tube about a millimeter *above* the surface of the liquid to keep it from backing up into the reaction apparatus when gas evolution ceases or heating is discontinued (see Figure B22). Connect it to the reaction apparatus as shown in Figure B21, using a thermometer adapter or rubber stopper.

🧪 For microscale work, you can use a Norit gas trap, which consists of a layer of pelletized Norit in a microscale drying tube (see Figure B17). To construct the gas trap, push a plug of cotton nearly to the bend in the drying tube, then hold it with the long arm upright (open end up) and use a plastic weighing dish to add enough pelletized Norit (~0.5 g) to form a layer 3–4 cm deep. Insert another plug of cotton to keep the Norit in place. Insert the drying tube in any part of the reaction apparatus that is exposed to the atmosphere—usually the top of a reflux condenser. If the reaction is to be conducted in a dry atmosphere, you can add a layer of calcium chloride on top of the Norit layer before inserting the second cotton plug.

A gas trap consisting of a plug of moistened cotton in a microscale drying tube can effectively trap some water-soluble gases, but care must be taken to keep water from dripping into the reaction apparatus. Such a trap is prepared by filling most of the long arm of the drying tube with cotton and using a Pasteur pipet to drop water onto it until it is moist but not dripping wet.

C. Separation Operations

After a chemical reaction has been carried out using operations from Section B, the product must be *separated* from the other components of the reaction mixture. Solid impurities can be removed from liquids by gravity filtration [OP-15], which is also used for the recrystallization operation [OP-28] described in Section E. A solid product can be separated from the liquid part of a reaction mixture by vacuum filtration [OP-16] or, for some microscale experiments, by centrifugation [OP-17]. If the product is dissolved in an aqueous reaction mixture, it is often separated by extraction [OP-18] with a volatile organic solvent, which is then removed by evaporation [OP-19]. Some water-insoluble liquid products are separated from an aqueous reaction mixture by steam distillation [OP-20]. Column chromatography [OP-21] is a versatile separation method by which a liquid or solid product is separated from other components of a mixture as the mixture passes down a column of adsorbent material. Both thin-layer chromatography [OP-22] and paper chromatography [OP-23] can separate the components of very small samples; they are generally used to detect or identify components in a mixture rather than to separate reaction mixtures.

Most separation operations can be used for purposes other than separating the components of a reaction mixture. For example, paper chromatography [OP-23] and thin-layer chromatography are often used to separate and identify the components of natural or commercial products (see Minilabs 9 and 11). Gravity filtration can be used to filter a hot recrystallization solution [OP-28], and vacuum filtration or centrifugation to collect the crystals that form after the solution has cooled. Extraction and steam distillation are used to obtain useful substances from natural or commercial products (see Minilab 7 and Experiment 10), and to recover reusable chemicals from waste material. Column chromatography can be used to separate the organic components of natural products, such as tomatoes (see Experiment 9).

Gravity Filtration

OPERATION **15**

Filtration is used for two main purposes in organic chemistry:

- To remove solid impurities from a liquid or solution
- To separate an organic solid from a reaction mixture or a crystallization solvent

Gravity filtration is generally used for the first purpose, and *vacuum filtration* [OP-16] for the second. *Centrifugation* [OP-17] can be used for either. In a gravity filtration, the liquid component of a liquid–solid mixture drains through a filtering medium (such as cotton or filter paper) by gravity alone, leaving the solid on the filtering medium. The filtered liquid, called the *filtrate,* is collected in a flask or another container. Gravity filtration is often used to remove drying agents from dried organic liquids or solutions, and solid impurities from hot recrystallization solutions.

If the solid being removed is coarse and quite dense, it can sometimes be removed from a liquid by letting it settle to the bottom of the container (preferably an Erlenmeyer flask) and then slowly and carefully pouring the liquid into another container, leaving the solid behind. Some of the liquid may remain behind in the flask, but it can be transferred [OP-6] using a Pasteur pipet or a filter-tip pipet, if necessary. This process, called *decanting,* should not be used with finely divided solids because some of the solid will inevitably be poured out with the liquid and contaminate it.

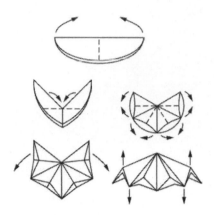

Figure C1 Making a fluted filter paper

Take Care! Wear gloves when handling glass wool.

 Standard Scale Gravity Filtration

Standard scale gravity filtration of organic liquids (see Figure C2) can be carried out using a funnel with a short, wide stem (such as a powder funnel) and a relatively fast, fluted filter paper. Circles of ordinary filter paper, such as 12.5 cm Whatman #1 (for fine particles) or Whatman #4 (for coarser particles), can be fluted (folded) as shown in Figure C1, but commercial fluted filter papers are available from chemical supply houses. Glass wool is sometimes used for very fast filtration of coarse solids. A thin layer of glass wool is placed inside the cone of a short-stemmed funnel, covering the outlet hole, and the mixture to be filtered is poured directly onto the glass wool. Because fine particles will pass through the glass wool fibers, this method is most often used for prefiltration of mixtures that will be filtered again.

 Microscale Gravity Filtration

Small amounts of solid–liquid mixtures (~10 mL or less) can be filtered using a *filtering pipet*—a Pasteur pipet that contains a small plug of cotton (see Figure C3). A filtering pipet is usually made with a standard $5\frac{3}{4}$-inch Pasteur pipet. For filtering hot recrystallization [OP-28] solutions, it is best to use a shortened filtering pipet made by cutting off [OP-3] most of the capillary tip to leave a 5-mm stub; otherwise, crystals may form in the narrow capillary and block the liquid flow. A glass-wool plug can be used when large particles are being removed or when the mixture being filtered contains an acid or another substance that may react with cotton. Because glass wool is unpleasant to handle and doesn't filter out fine particles, cotton is preferred for most applications. Very fine particles may pass through cotton also; a filtering pipet that contains a 2-mm layer of chromatography-grade alumina or silica gel on top of a cotton plug can be used to remove such particles from a mixture.

A microscale gravity filter with a larger capacity can be constructed by cutting the rounded top off the bulb of a plastic Beral-type pipet and packing some cotton in its neck (see *J. Chem. Educ.* **1993,** *70,* A204). The plastic may not be compatible with some organic solvents, however.

A filter-tip pipet, prepared as described in OP-6, can also be used to filter small amounts of liquids. This method is not really gravity filtration,

fluted filter paper

powder funnel

bent wire

collecting flask

Figure C2 Apparatus for standard scale gravity filtration

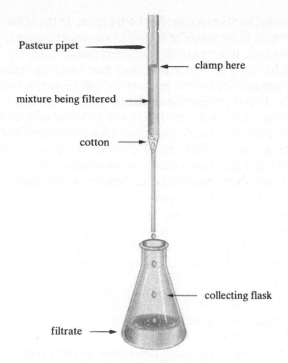

Pasteur pipet

clamp here

mixture being filtered

cotton

collecting flask

filtrate

Figure C3 Filtration with a filtering pipet

but it accomplishes the same purpose: removing a solid from the liquid being filtered. It has the disadvantage that some solid may adhere to the cotton and be transferred to the collecting container. When the solid particles are fairly coarse, like the sodium sulfate granules used for drying liquids [OP-25], you may be able to use a Pasteur pipet without a filter tip to remove them. Use the pipet tip to push aside any solid that is in the way, and then hold it flat against the bottom of the container as you draw liquid into it.

DIRECTIONS FOR GRAVITY FILTRATION

 Standard Scale

Equipment and Supplies

    powder funnel
    fluted filter paper
    bent wire or paper clip
    Erlenmeyer flask or other collecting container

If you are filtering the solid–liquid mixture into a narrow-necked container such as an Erlenmeyer flask, support the funnel on the neck of the flask, placing a bent wire or a paper clip between them to leave a gap for pressure equalization (Figure C2). Alternatively, you can set the funnel in a ring support or funnel support positioned directly over the collecting container. Open the fluted filter paper to form a cone and insert it snugly into the funnel, trying not to flatten out any of its folds. If the solid is not finely divided, or if there is not much of it, decant (pour) the mixture directly into the filter paper cone. If the mixture contains a considerable amount of finely divided solid, let the solid settle first, and then carefully decant the liquid into the filter paper cone so that most of the solid remains behind until the end of the filtration (this helps keep the fine solid from clogging the pores of the filter paper and slowing the filtration). In either case, add the mixture fast enough to keep the filter paper cone about two-thirds full, without allowing any liquid to rise above the top of the filter paper, until it has all been added. Swirl a small amount of an appropriate pure solvent (usually the solvent present in the mixture being filtered) in the decanting container to wash any residual solid, then pour it into the filter paper cone and let it drain into the receiving container. Wash the solid on the filter paper with this solvent by stirring gently as the solvent drains, but be careful not to tear the filter paper with your stirring rod. This washing step should reduce losses due to adsorption of dissolved organic materials on the solid.

Unless you need to save the solid as well as the filtrate, there is no need to transfer all of the solid to the filter paper.

Summary

1. Support funnel over collecting container.
2. Insert fluted filter paper.
3. Pour mixture being filtered into filter cone and let drain.
4. Wash solid in decanting vessel and on filter paper.
5. Clean up.

 Microscale

Equipment and Supplies

two $5\frac{3}{4}$-inch Pasteur pipets
rubber bulb (2-mL capacity)
cotton
applicator stick or stirring rod
collecting containers

Roll a small amount of cotton between your fingers to form a loose ball, and insert it in the top of a $5\frac{3}{4}$-inch Pasteur pipet. (Alternatively, you can use a Beral-type pipet with the top cut off.) Then use a small stirring rod or a wooden applicator stick to push it down the body of the pipet, forming a cotton plug that ends about where the capillary section of the pipet begins, as shown in Figure C3. Don't pack it too tightly because that will slow down the filtration. Clamp the resulting filtering pipet vertically over a small beaker. Rinse the plug with a suitable wash solvent (usually the solvent present in the mixture being filtered) by using a second Pasteur pipet to transfer about 0.5 mL of the solvent to the top of the filtering pipet, letting it drain, and using a rubber bulb to force any remaining solvent through. Replace the beaker by another collecting container, such as a conical vial or a small flask, and use the second Pasteur pipet to transfer the mixture being filtered—in several portions, if necessary—to the top of the filtering pipet. Let the liquid drain by gravity into the collecting container. If the filtration rate is very slow, you can use a rubber bulb or a pipet pump (see OP-5) to apply a gentle, constant pressure to the top of the filtering pipet. Don't use excessive pressure, because that may force particles into the filtrate. Depress the pipet pump's quick-release lever (if it has one) before you remove it. Wash the solid and the plug with a small amount of wash solvent as described previously, collecting the solvent in the container that holds the filtrate. Use a rubber bulb or a pipet pump to force out the last few drops of liquid. If you wish to reuse the Pasteur pipet, remove the plug (when it is dry) either by pulling it out with a wooden applicator stick (twirl it to snag the fibers) or by snagging it with a copper wire bent to form a "J" at one end.

Summary

1. Prepare filtering pipet by inserting cotton plug in Pasteur pipet.
2. Clamp filtering pipet over beaker, and rinse with solvent.
3. Replace beaker with collecting container.
4. Transfer mixture being filtered to filtering pipet and let drain.
5. Wash filtering pipet with solvent.
6. Clean up.

When Things Go Wrong

If a liquid is filtering very slowly, the filter paper or other filtering medium may be too retentive or the particles may be so fine that they plug the pores in the filter paper. Try using a coarser filtering medium, such as a coarse pre-folded filter paper rather than one folded from Whatman #1 paper (the most widely used grade of filter paper). For a microscale filtration, try using glass wool (wear gloves) rather than cotton in a filtering pipet; if necessary, you can *gently* force solvent through a filtering pipet with a rubber bulb or a pipet pump. If fine particles pass into the filtrate, refilter using a more retentive filtering medium.

DIRECTIONS FOR FILTRATION WITH A FILTER-TIP PIPET

Equipment and Supplies

$5\frac{3}{4}$-inch Pasteur pipet
rubber bulb (2-mL capacity)
cotton
collecting containers

Construct a filter-tip pipet as described in OP-6, and rinse it with a suitable wash solvent (usually the solvent present in the mixture being filtered) by drawing in about 0.5 mL of the solvent and slowly ejecting it into a waste container. Use the pipet and attached bulb to draw up liquid from the mixture being filtered, and transfer it to a suitable collecting container—leaving the solid behind in the original container—until all of the liquid has been transferred. To avoid transferring adherent solid along with the liquid, try to keep the pipet's tip away from the solid when you draw liquid into it. To transfer the last few drops of liquid, push the solid aside with the tip of the pipet and hold it flat against the bottom of the original container as you withdraw the liquid. Stir a little wash solvent into the solid, draw it into the filter-tip pipet, and combine it with the rest of the filtrate.

Summary

1. Construct filter-tip pipet; rinse with wash solvent.
2. Draw liquid being filtered into pipet.
3. Transfer liquid to collecting container.
4. Wash solid; transfer wash solvent to collecting container.
5. Clean up.

OPERATION 16   # Vacuum Filtration

Vacuum filtration (also called suction filtration) provides a fast, convenient method for isolating a solid from a liquid–solid mixture and for removing solid impurities from a relatively large quantity of liquid. In a typical standard scale vacuum filtration, a circle of filter paper is laid flat on a perforated plate inside a porcelain *Buchner funnel,* which is attached by an airtight connector to a thick-walled *filter flask* that has a sidearm on its neck (see Figure C4). The filter flask's sidearm is connected to the inlet of a *water aspirator* or to a vacuum line, often by way of a trap (described in the "Experimental Considerations" section), with a short length of thick-walled rubber tubing. In the water aspirator, a rapid stream of water passes by a small hole at the inlet, creating a vacuum there and in the attached filter flask, and exits into a sink. An aspirator should always be run "full blast" because its efficiency decreases and the likelihood of water backup increases at lower flow rates. When the mixture being filtered is poured into the Buchner funnel, the liquid is forced through the paper by the unbalanced external pressure and collects in the filter flask, while the solid remains on the filter paper as a compact *filter cake.*

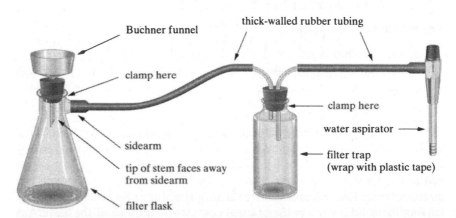

Figure C4 Apparatus for standard scale vacuum filtration

Small quantities of solids can be filtered by essentially the same method using a *Hirsch funnel* attached to a small filter flask or a sidearm test tube (see Figure C5). This kind of apparatus is suitable for many microscale experiments and can be used for some standard scale experiments as well.

A porcelain Hirsch funnel contains an integral perforated plate about 1–2 cm in diameter; plastic Hirsch-type funnels with separate fritted disks (which don't require filter paper) are also available. Hirsch funnels use very small filter paper circles. These are available commercially, but they can also be cut from ordinary filter paper using a sharp cork borer on a flat cutting surface, such as the bottom of a large cork. For a porcelain Hirsch funnel, the filter paper should be about equal in size to the perforated plate, or slightly smaller, but large enough to completely cover all of its holes.

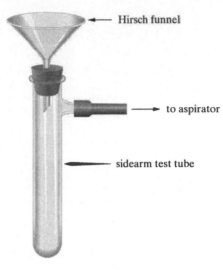

Figure C5 Apparatus for small-scale vacuum filtration with sidearm test tube

  ## Experimental Considerations

Filter Traps and Cold Traps.   You should ordinarily interpose a *filter trap* between the filter flask (or sidearm test tube) and a water aspirator to keep water from backing up into the flask when the water pressure changes, as it often does. Using a filter trap is most important when the filtrate is to be saved because any backed-up water will contaminate the filtrate, but it is a good idea to use the trap for all vacuum filtrations involving an aspirator. A suitable filter trap can be constructed by wrapping a thick-walled Pyrex jar with transparent plastic tape (to reduce the chance of injury in case of implosion) and inserting a rubber stopper fitted with two L-shaped connecting tubes, as described in Minilab 1. Note that one of the connecting tubes should be longer than the other (see Figure C4). Another kind of filter trap with a pressure-release valve is illustrated in Figure E15 of OP-31.

If you are using a vacuum line connected to a central mechanical vacuum pump, you may need to use a *cold trap* to protect the pump from solvent vapors that might damage it (your instructor will inform you if this is necessary). A filter trap can function as a cold trap if it is immersed in an appropriate cold bath [OP-8].

Filtering Media.   Because of the external pressure on the mixture being filtered, solid particles are more likely to pass through the filter paper than with gravity filtration, so a slower (finer-grained) grade of filter paper should be used. An all-purpose filter paper, such as Whatman #1, is adequate for filtration of most solids. When filtering a finely divided solid impurity from a liquid, you may need to use a *filtering aid* (such as Celite) to keep the solid from plugging the pores in the filter paper. In a stoppered flask, shake the filtering aid vigorously with a suitable solvent to form a slurry (a thick suspension). Without delay, pour the slurry onto the filter paper while applying a vacuum, until a bed about 2–3 mm thick has been deposited. Remove the solvent from the filter flask before continuing with the filtration. This method cannot be used when the solid is to be saved because it would be contaminated with the filtering aid.

Washing.   Unless otherwise instructed, you should always *wash* the solid on the filter paper with an appropriate solvent—usually the same solvent as the one from which it was filtered. To reduce losses, the wash solvent should be cooled in ice water. For example, if you filter a solid from an aqueous solution, use cold distilled water as the wash solvent. If you filter a solid from a mixture of solvents, as in a mixed-solvent recrystallization [OP-28b], you should ordinarily use the solvent in which the solid is least soluble. For more information about washing solids see OP-26a.

Take Care! Never use a thin-walled container, such as an Erlenmeyer flask, as a trap; it may shatter under vacuum.

Drying. A solid that has been collected by vacuum filtration is usually *air-dried* after the last washing by leaving it on the filter for a few minutes with the vacuum turned on. The vacuum draws air through the solid, which increases the drying rate. If the solid is still quite wet, you can place a *rubber dam* (a thin, flexible rubber sheet) or a sheet of plastic wrap over the mouth of the funnel. The vacuum should cause the sheet to flatten out on top of the filter cake, forcing water out of it. Unless a solid is filtered from a very low-boiling solvent, it should be dried further by one of the methods described in OP-26b.

  # DIRECTIONS FOR VACUUM FILTRATION

Equipment and Supplies

Buchner funnel or Hirsch funnel
filter flask (or sidearm test tube)
1-hole rubber stopper or neoprene adapter
filter trap
filter paper
thick-walled rubber tubing
flat-bottomed stirring rod (optional)
flat-bladed spatula
wash solvent

Replace the term filter flask *by* sidearm test tube *if you are using the latter.*

Clamp the filter flask and trap (if you are using one) securely to a ring stand, and connect them to an aspirator or a vacuum line, as shown in Figure C4. Use thick-walled rubber tubing that will not collapse under vacuum for all connections. If you are using a water aspirator, connect the longer glass tube on the filter trap (the tube that extends farther into the trap) to the aspirator, and the shorter glass tube to the filter flask. If you are using a vacuum line that must be protected by a cold trap, connect the trap to the vacuum line and filter flask, and secure it inside a cooling bath as directed by your instructor. Insert a Buchner or Hirsch funnel into the filter flask, using a neoprene filter flask adapter or a snug-fitting rubber stopper to provide a tight seal. Obtain a circle of filter paper of the correct diameter, and place it inside the funnel so that it covers all of the holes in the perforated plate but doesn't extend up the sides of the funnel.

Moisten the filter paper with a few drops of wash solvent—a solvent that is present in the mixture being filtered, or one that is miscible with it. Open the aspirator tap or vacuum-line valve as far as it will go. Direct the water stream from an aspirator into a large beaker or another container to prevent splashing. If the solid is finely divided, let it settle before you decant the liquid into the funnel, and transfer the bulk of the solid near the end of the filtration. Otherwise, stir or swirl the mixture just before decanting to transfer more of the solid and leave less behind in the decanting vessel. If the volume of the filtration mixture is greater than the capacity of the funnel, add the mixture rapidly enough to keep the funnel about two-thirds full throughout the filtration, until it has all been added. Transfer any remaining solid to the filter paper with a flat-bladed spatula, using a small

Do not attach a rubber tube to the aspirator outlet to reduce splashing, because it will also reduce the aspirator's effectiveness.

amount of the filtrate or some cold wash solvent to facilitate the transfer. Leave the vacuum on until only an occasional drop of liquid emerges from the stem of the funnel. If there is a possibility that water collecting in a trap will back up into the filter flask, or if you are using an aspirator with no filter trap, break the vacuum using a pressure-release valve or disconnect the rubber tubing at the vacuum source before you turn off the vacuum.

With the vacuum off, add enough previously chilled wash solvent to cover the solid. Being careful not to disturb the filter paper, stir the mixture *gently* with a spatula or a flat-bottomed stirring rod until the solid is suspended in the liquid. (For microscale work, stirring may be omitted because of the likelihood of product loss.) Without delay, turn on the vacuum to drain the wash liquid. For standard scale work, the washing step can be repeated with another portion of chilled wash solvent; one portion is usually adequate for microscale work. Work quickly to avoid dissolving an appreciable amount of solid in the wash solvent. After the last washing, leave the vacuum on for 3–5 minutes (longer if the solvent is water) to air-dry the solid on the filter and make it easier to handle. Run the tip of a small flat-bladed spatula around the circumference of the filter paper to dislodge the filter cake; then invert the funnel carefully over a square of glazed paper, a watch glass, a weighing dish, or another suitable container to remove the filter cake and filter paper. Use your spatula to scrape any remaining particles onto the paper or into the container. Dispose of the filtrate as directed by the experimental procedure or your instructor, and dry the solid by one of the methods described in OP-26b. To reduce losses, dry the filter paper along with the filter cake and scrape off any additional solid after it is dry, being careful not to scrape any filter paper fibers into your product.

Rule of Thumb: Use about 1–2 mL of wash solvent per gram of solid unless directed otherwise.

Summary

1. Assemble apparatus for vacuum filtration.
2. Position and moisten filter paper, and turn on vacuum.
3. Add mixture being filtered to funnel.
4. Transfer any remaining solid to funnel.
5. Wash solid on filter with chilled wash solvent.
6. Air-dry solid on filter paper.
7. Transfer solid to container, and remove filtrate from filter flask.
8. Disassemble and clean apparatus.

When Things Go Wrong

If a liquid is filtering very slowly, the filter paper may be too retentive, or its pores may be plugged with fine particles. Replace the used filter paper with a new one (keep any solid you collected on the used one), let the solid settle to the bottom of the mixture you are filtering, then carefully decant the liquid into the filtering funnel and wait until the end of the filtration process to transfer the solid, along with any remaining liquid. If the filtration rate is still slow, consider using a larger filtering device, such as a Buchner funnel rather than a Hirsch funnel. You can also try using a coarser filtering medium, such as a circle of Whatman #4 paper rather than Whatman #1, but you may have to re-filter the filtrate if fine particles pass through the paper. If you don't need to save the solid, you can use a filtering aid such as Celite. (See the section entitled "Filtering Media.") Slow filtration rates with a water aspirator may also be caused by low water pressure when too many aspirators are running at the same time. Be patient, or wait until later to compete your filtration.

If water backs up into the filter flask when you turn off an aspirator, you probably didn't use a filter trap. Remove the water, and then connect a trap between the filter flask and the aspirator, as shown in Figure C4. Alternatively, pull off the tubing at the aspirator before you turn it off. (See "Filter Traps and Cold Traps.")

If an appreciable amount of solid product disappears when you wash it, the wash solvent may not have been adequately chilled, you may have used too much of it, or it may be inappropriate for washing your product. If the filtrate contains a relatively low-boiling solvent, you should be able to recover the solid by evaporating [OP-19] the solvent, but it should then be purified and washed more carefully. Alternatively, some solid may have passed under the filter paper and into the filtrate. Try re-filtering the filtrate, being careful not to displace the filter paper when you wash the recovered solid. (See "Washing.")

OPERATION 17   # Centrifugation

Centrifugation is used to separate different phases from one another by centrifugal force. When a mixture in a centrifuge tube is placed inside a *centrifuge* (Figure C6) and whirled around a circular path at high speed, the denser phase (often a solid) is forced to the bottom of the tube, leaving the

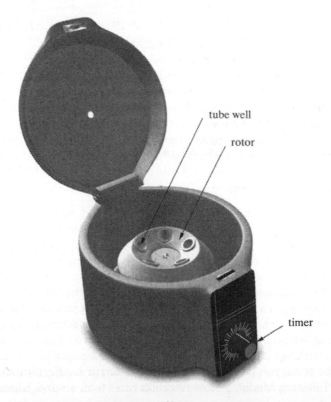

tube well

rotor

timer

Figure C6 A benchtop centrifuge

other phase on top. In the microscale laboratory, centrifugation is often used to collect solids that have crystallized from solution in a *Craig tube*. Centrifugation may also be used to separate a finely divided solid from a liquid, to separate two immiscible liquids sharply after an extraction [OP-18], and to collect small amounts of liquids that have been separated by preparative gas chromatography [OP-37].

  ## DIRECTIONS FOR CENTRIFUGATION

Equipment and Supplies

> benchtop centrifuge
> two centrifuge tubes
> Pasteur pipet (optional)
> flat-bladed spatula (optional)

Transfer the mixture to be centrifuged to a conical centrifuge tube with a capacity of ~15 mL or another centrifuge tube specified by your instructor or the experimental procedure. (If you are using a Craig tube, see OP-28.) Obtain an empty matched centrifuge tube, and add enough water to it so that the two tubes, with their contents, have approximately equal masses. Usually, you can estimate the amount of water by volume, but you may have to weigh the tubes to ensure proper balance. Place the two centrifuge tubes directly opposite one another in the centrifuge's rotor; they fit into tube wells, which may be cushioned to help prevent breakage. Close and lock the centrifuge lid, set the centrifuge's timer (if it has one) to 3–5 minutes, and start the centrifuge. When the time is up (or when you switch off the centrifuge), the rotor will slowly come to a stop. Wait until its whirring sound has stopped; then open the lid and remove the centrifuge tubes. If you are centrifuging a liquid–solid mixture and the solid isn't firmly packed in the bottom of the tube, continue centrifuging until the solid is compacted and there are no floating particles. Then carefully decant the liquid or remove it with a Pasteur pipet or a filter-tip pipet, leaving the solid behind. Use the pointed end of a flat-bladed microspatula to remove the solid. If you are centrifuging a mixture of two immiscible liquids, separate the liquids after centrifugation by removing the lower layer with a Pasteur pipet, as described in OP-18. Use a tapered centrifuge brush, if one is available, to clean the centrifuge tube.

Alternatively, find another student who is doing the same operation, and use his or her centrifuge tube to balance your own. Label the tubes so that you don't mix them up.

Summary

1. Transfer mixture to centrifuge tube.
2. Place centrifuge tube and a second tube of comparable mass in opposite tube wells.
3. Run centrifuge for 3–5 minutes.
4 Let centrifuge stop, and remove tubes.
5. Separate liquid layer from solid or second liquid layer.

When Things Go Wrong

If the centrifuge vibrates badly, rattles loudly, or stops before the time is up, the centrifuge tubes aren't properly balanced. Remove and balance them, and then resume centrifugation.

If a centrifuge tube breaks while the centrifuge is operating, the broken tube may have been faulty, it may have been the wrong kind for the centrifuge you are using, it may not have been balanced properly, or the tube wells may not be adequately cushioned. Clean up the mess, and try to identify the problem so that it doesn't happen again. If there is little or no cushioning in the wells, you may be able to push in some Styrofoam that has been cut to fit. See your instructor first because the padding may raise the tubes so high that they contact the lid of the centrifuge when it spins.

OPERATION **18**

Extraction

If you shake a bromine/water solution with some dichloromethane, the red–brown color of the bromine fades from the water layer and appears in the dichloromethane layer as you shake. The color changes show that the bromine has been transferred from one solvent (water) to another (dichloromethane). The process of transferring a substance from a liquid or solid mixture to a solvent is called *extraction,* and the solvent is called the *extraction solvent.* An extraction solvent is usually a low-boiling organic solvent that can be evaporated [OP-19] after extraction to isolate the desired substance.

Extraction is used for the following purposes in organic chemistry:

- To separate a desired organic substance from a reaction mixture or some other mixture
- To remove impurities from a desired organic substance, which is usually dissolved in an organic solvent

The second process is described in OP-24, "Washing Liquids."

a. Liquid–Liquid Extraction

Principles and Applications

Liquid–liquid extraction is based on the principle that if a substance is soluble to some extent in two immiscible liquids, most of it can be transferred from one liquid to the other by a process that involves thorough mixing of the liquids. For example, acetanilide is partly soluble in both water and dichloromethane. If a solution of acetanilide in water is shaken with a portion of dichloromethane, some of the acetanilide will be transferred to the organic (dichloromethane) layer (see Figure C7). The organic layer, being denser than water, separates below the water layer and can be removed and replaced with another portion of dichloromethane. When that portion of dichloromethane is shaken with the aqueous solution, more acetanilide passes into the new organic layer. This new layer can then be removed and combined with the first. By repeating this process enough times, virtually all of the acetanilide can be transferred from the water to the dichloromethane.

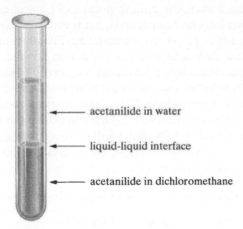

Figure C7 Distribution of a solute between two liquids

The ability of an extraction solvent (S_2) to remove a solute (A) from another solvent (S_1) depends on the partition coefficient (K) of solute A in the two solvents, as defined in Equation (1):

$$K = \frac{\text{concentration of A in } S_2}{\text{concentration of A in } S_1} \qquad \textbf{(1)}$$

In the example of acetanilide in water and dichloromethane, the partition coefficient is given by

$$K = \frac{[\text{acetanilide}]_{\text{dichl.}}}{[\text{acetanilide}]_{\text{water}}}$$

The larger the value of K, the more solute will be transferred to the organic layer with each extraction, and the fewer portions of dichloromethane will be required for essentially complete removal of the solute. A rough estimate of K can be obtained by using the ratio of the solubilities of the solute in the two solvents—that is,

$$K \sim \frac{\text{solubility of A in } S_2}{\text{solubility of A in } S_1}$$

This approximate relationship can be helpful in choosing a suitable extraction solvent.

Extraction Solvents

Most extraction solvents are organic liquids that are used to extract nonpolar and moderately polar solutes from aqueous solutions. A good organic extraction solvent should be immiscible with water, dissolve a wide range of organic substances, and have a low boiling point so that it can be removed by evaporation after the extraction. The substance being extracted should be more soluble in the extraction solvent than in water; otherwise, too many steps will be required to extract it.

Diethyl ether and dichloromethane (methylene chloride) are the most commonly used organic extraction solvents. Diethyl ether (also called ether or ethyl ether) has a very low boiling point (35°C) and can dissolve both polar and nonpolar organic compounds, but it is extremely flammable and tends to form explosive peroxides on standing. Dichloromethane is denser than water, which usually simplifies the extraction process, and it isn't flammable. Dichloromethane has a tendency to form emulsions, which can make it difficult to separate cleanly, and it must be handled with caution because it is a suspected carcinogen. These and other extraction solvents and their properties are listed in Table C1. Organic extraction solvents that are less dense than water ($d = 1.00$ g/mL) will separate as the top layer during the extraction of an aqueous solution; extraction solvents that are more dense than water will ordinarily separate as the bottom layer.

Table C1 Properties of commonly used extraction solvents

Solvent	bp, °C	d, g/mL	Comments
water	100	1.00	for extracting polar compounds, generally using a reactive solute such as NaOH or HCl
diethyl ether	35	0.71	good general solvent; absorbs some water; very flammable
dichloromethane	40	1.33	good general solvent; suspected carcinogen
toluene	111	0.87	for extracting aromatic and nonpolar compounds; difficult to remove
petroleum ether	~35–60	~0.64	for extracting nonpolar compounds; very flammable
*hexane	69	0.66	for extracting nonpolar compounds; flammable

*The mixture of C_6H_{14} isomers called hexanes is cheaper than pure hexane and is often used in place of it.

Just as organic solvents are used to extract substances from aqueous solutions, water and aqueous solutions can be used to extract certain polar substances from organic solutions. An aqueous solution may function as a *chemically active* extraction solvent if it contains a solute that reacts with the substance to be extracted, thus changing its distribution between the aqueous and organic layers. For example, dilute aqueous sodium hydroxide can be used to extract carboxylic acids from organic solvents by first converting them to carboxylate salts, which are much more soluble in water and less soluble in organic solvents than are the original carboxylic acids.

$$RCOOH + NaOH \longrightarrow RCOO^- Na^+ + H_2O$$

If the carboxylic acid is sufficiently insoluble in water, it can be recovered by acidifying the aqueous extract to precipitate the acid, which is then collected by vacuum filtration [OP-16]. Similarly, dilute hydrochloric acid is used to extract basic solutes such as amines from organic solvents by converting the amines to ammonium salts, which are much more soluble in water and less soluble in organic solvents than are amines.

$$RNH_2 + HCl \longrightarrow RNH_3^+Cl^-$$

Potential hazards should be considered when selecting and using an extraction solvent. For example, solvents such as benzene, trichloromethane (chloroform), and tetrachloromethane (carbon tetrachloride) should not be used as extraction solvents in an undergraduate laboratory because of their toxicity and carcinogenic potential. Precautions must be taken with all organic solvents to minimize skin and eye contact and inhalation of vapors. Flames must not be allowed in the laboratory when highly flammable solvents, such as diethyl ether and petroleum ether, are in use.

Experimental Considerations

Extraction Methods.   A standard scale liquid–liquid extraction is ordinarily carried out by shaking the liquids in a *separatory funnel* (see Figure C9), allowing time for the liquid layers to separate sharply, and opening the separatory funnel's stopcock to drain the lower layer into a separate container. The extraction is usually repeated several times to transfer most of the desired substance to the extraction solvent.

Separatory funnels are expensive and break easily. Never prop a separatory funnel on its base; set it in a ring support or some other stable support. If your separatory funnel has a glass stopcock, lubricate it by applying thin bands of stopcock grease on both sides, leaving the center (where the drain hole is located) free of grease to prevent contamination (see Figure C8). A glass stopcock is secured to the separatory funnel by a compression clip or a rubber ring, which should be tight enough to keep it from leaking. A Teflon stopcock (which should *not* be lubricated) is secured by a Teflon washer, rubber ring, and Teflon nut, in that order. The nut is screwed in tightly enough to prevent leakage, but not so tightly as to prevent smooth rotation of the stopcock.

In the microscale laboratory, a liquid–liquid extraction is usually performed by shaking the liquids in a conical vial or conical centrifuge tube and separating them with a Pasteur pipet. A 5-mL conical vial can be used with liquid volumes up to ~4 mL, and a 15-mL centrifuge tube can be used with liquid volumes up to ~12 mL. A screw-cap centrifuge tube is preferable to one with a snap-on cap because it is less likely to leak. A conical vial is usually capped with a compression cap that has a Teflon-faced silicone liner; the liner should be inserted in the cap so that its Teflon-coated (white) side faces down when the vial is capped. A conical vial may leak if its rim is chipped or if the liner is damaged, so shake some water in the capped vial to check for leaks before using the vial for an extraction. Do this for a centrifuge tube also, and replace the cap or the centrifuge tube if it leaks.

Liquid layers are ordinarily separated by removing the *lower* layer with a Pasteur pipet and transferring it to another container. This way, the interface between the layers is at the narrowest part of the container when the last of the lower layer is removed, making a sharp separation possible. It takes some practice and a steady hand to remove all of the bottom layer without including any of the top layer, but it is important that you learn how to do so. Otherwise, you will lose part of your product, or the product will be contaminated with material from the layer being extracted. Most extraction solvents have a high vapor pressure, which may cause them to spurt out of the tip of a Pasteur pipet during transfer. Product loss due to

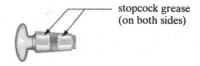

stopcock grease
(on both sides)

Figure C8 Lubricating a glass stopcock

spurting can be reduced or prevented by one or more of the following measures:

- Make sure that the extraction solvent, the liquid being extracted, and the Pasteur pipet are at room temperature or below.
- Rinse the Pasteur pipet with the extraction solvent two or three times to fill it with solvent vapors just before use.
- Use a filter-tip pipet.

For either extraction method, accurate separation of the layers is most important for the last extraction step because any extraction solvent that is not recovered during earlier steps can be recovered in the last one.

Volume of Extraction Solvent. The volume of extraction solvent and the number of extraction steps are sometimes specified in an experimental procedure. If they are not, use a volume of extraction solvent about equal to the volume of liquid being extracted, divided into at least two portions. For example, you can extract 12 mL of an aqueous solution with two successive 6-mL (or three 4-mL) portions of extraction solvent. Note that it is more efficient to use several small portions of extraction solvent rather than one large portion of the same total volume.

Getting Good Separation. Under some conditions, the liquid layers do not separate sharply, either because an *emulsion* forms at the interface between the two liquids or because droplets of one liquid remain in the other liquid layer. Emulsions can often be broken up by using a wooden applicator stick to stir the liquids gently at the interface. If that doesn't work, mix in some saturated aqueous sodium chloride solution (or enough solid NaCl to saturate the aqueous layer), and allow the extraction container to stand open and undisturbed for a time.

To consolidate the liquid layers, use an applicator stick to rub or stir any liquid droplets that form on the sides or bottom of the extraction container. You can also use an applicator stick to remove small amounts of insoluble "gunk" that sometimes form near the interface. Larger amounts of insoluble material can be removed by filtering [OP-15] the mixture through a loose pad of glass wool in a powder funnel or filtering pipet.

Saving the Right Layer. *Always keep both layers until you are certain which layer contains the desired product!* All too often, a student will unthinkingly discard the extraction layer that contains the product and will have to repeat an experiment from the beginning. The safest practice is to keep both layers until you have actually isolated the product from one of them, but you can usually determine which is the right layer before then. In most extractions, the product is extracted from an aqueous solution into an organic solvent such as dichloromethane or diethyl ether. If you make careful observations when you add the extraction solvent, you can usually tell whether it floats on top of the aqueous layer or sinks below it. Because diethyl ether is less dense than water, it will form the upper layer when it is used to extract an aqueous solution. Dichloromethane is denser than water, so it will ordinarily form the lower layer with an aqueous solution (but see "When Things Go Wrong").

Rule of Thumb: *Total volume of extraction solvent ≈ volume of liquid being extracted.*

An emulsion usually contains microscopic droplets of one liquid suspended in another.

DIRECTIONS FOR EXTRACTION

 Standard Scale

Equipment and Supplies

> separatory funnel with stopper
> ring stand
> support for separatory funnel
> narrow-stemmed funnel
> extraction solvent
> graduated cylinder
> wooden applicator stick
> 2 flasks

Support a separatory funnel on a ring support of suitable diameter or another appropriate support. Close the stopcock by turning its handle to a horizontal position, and pour the liquid to be extracted into the separatory funnel, preferably using a narrow-stemmed funnel to avoid getting liquid on the glass joint. The liquid should be at room temperature (or below) to prevent vaporization of the extraction solvent. Measure the required volume of extraction solvent using a graduated cylinder (the exact volume isn't crucial), and pour it through the stemmed funnel into the separatory funnel. The total volume of both liquids should not exceed three-quarters of the separatory funnel's capacity. If it does, obtain a larger separatory funnel or carry out the extraction in two or more steps, using a portion of the liquid to be extracted in each step.

If you use a metal ring support, cushion it with three short lengths of split rubber tubing to prevent damage to the separatory funnel.

Moisten the stopper with water, and insert it firmly with a twisting motion. Then pick up the funnel in both hands and partly invert it, with your right hand holding the stopcock (or your left hand, if you're a southpaw) and the first two fingers of your left hand holding the stopper in place (see Figure C9). Holding the separatory funnel with its outlet above the liquid level and its stem pointed away from you and your neighbors, *vent* it by slowly opening the stopcock to release any pressure buildup. Close the stopcock, shake the separatory funnel gently for a few seconds (still keeping its stem end higher than its stoppered end), and vent it as before. Then shake the funnel more vigorously, with occasional venting, for 2 to 3 minutes. As you shake the funnel, rotate the wrist holding its stem end so that its contents are swirled as well as shaken; this motion is more efficient than shaking alone. Avoid overly vigorous mixing if the solvent tends to form emulsions.

Take Care! Wear gloves during an extraction to protect your hands in case of leakage.

Venting should not be necessary after there is no longer an audible hiss of escaping vapors when the stopcock is opened.

Replace the funnel on its support, remove the stopper, and allow the funnel to stand until there is a sharp dividing line between the two layers. If the layers don't separate cleanly, take the appropriate measures described in the section entitled "Getting Good Separation." Begin to drain the bottom layer into a labeled Erlenmeyer flask (flask **A**) by opening the stopcock fully. As the interface approaches the bottom of the funnel, partly close the stopcock to slow the drainage rate. Close it completely, separating the layers cleanly, just as the interface reaches the stopcock. Next, follow method **1** if the extraction solvent is *more* dense than the liquid being extracted (forming the lower layer), and method **2** if it is *less* dense than the liquid being extracted (forming the upper layer).

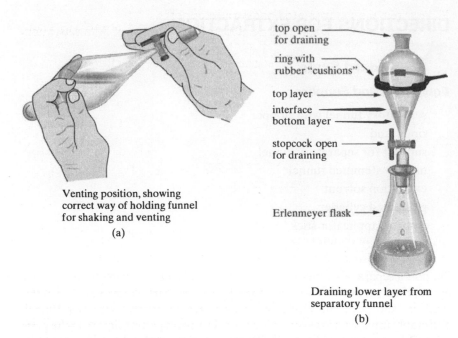

Venting position, showing
correct way of holding funnel
for shaking and venting

(a)

top open
for draining

ring with
rubber "cushions"

top layer

interface
bottom layer

stopcock open
for draining

Erlenmeyer flask

Draining lower layer from
separatory funnel

(b)

Figure C9 Standard scale extraction techniques

1. Extract the liquid that remains in the separatory funnel (the original top layer) with a fresh portion of the same extraction solvent; then drain the bottom layer into container **A** as before, combining the extracts. Repeat the process, as necessary, with fresh extraction solvent. After the bottom layer has been removed following the last extraction, pour the remaining liquid out of the *top* of the separatory funnel into a separate labeled container (**B**), and retain it for later disposal.

2. Pour the liquid that remains in the separatory funnel (the original top layer) out of the *top* of the separatory funnel into a separate labeled container (flask **B**). Then return the liquid in **A** to the separatory funnel, and extract it with a fresh portion of extraction solvent. Again drain the bottom layer into **A**, and pour the top layer into **B**. Repeat the process, as necessary, with fresh extraction solvent, combining all extracts in **B**. Retain the liquid in flask **A** for later disposal.

Summary

1. Add liquid to be extracted to separatory funnel.
2. Add extraction solvent, stopper funnel, invert, and vent.
3. Shake and swirl funnel, with venting, to extract solute into extraction solvent.
4. Remove stopper and let layers separate.
5. Drain lower layer into flask **A**.
   IF extraction solvent was the lower layer, GO TO 6.
   IF extraction solvent was the upper layer, GO TO 7.
6. Stopper flask **A**.
   IF another extraction step is needed, GO TO 2.
   IF extraction is complete, empty and clean separatory funnel; STOP.

7. Pour remaining layer into flask **B** and stopper it.
IF another extraction step is needed, return contents of **A** to separatory funnel; GO TO 2.
IF extraction is complete, clean separatory funnel; STOP.

 Microscale

Equipment and Supplies

conical vial or centrifuge tube with cap
support for extraction container
2 Pasteur pipets with bulbs, 1 calibrated
extraction solvent
wooden applicator stick
1–2 containers (conical vials, screw-cap vials, test tubes, etc.)

Depending on the amount of liquid to be extracted, obtain a 3- or 5-mL conical vial with a compression cap and unperforated liner or a 15-mL conical centrifuge tube with a screw cap. Check the extraction container for leaks. To keep a conical vial from tipping over, place it in a small beaker; set a centrifuge tube in a test-tube rack or another suitable support. Add the liquid to be extracted, which should be at room temperature or below. If its volume is less than 1 mL, it is advisable to add enough of a suitable solvent (usually water) to give it a total volume of at least 1 mL. Use a calibrated Pasteur pipet (or other measuring device) to add a measured portion of extraction solvent, and cap the container tightly. Shake the extraction container gently, and unscrew the cap slightly after 5–10 shakes to release any pressure inside the container. Tighten the cap and shake the mixture vigorously for at least 1 minute with occasional venting. Shake less vigorously but for a longer time if the extraction solvent is dichloromethane, which tends to form emulsions. (Alternatively, you can use a spin vane to stir [OP-10] the contents of a conical vial vigorously for at least 1 minute, or use a vortex mixer as directed by your instructor.) Loosen the cap, and let the mixture stand until there is a sharp interface between the layers. Use a wooden applicator stick to help consolidate the layers, if necessary. If you are using a centrifuge tube, it can be spun in a centrifuge [OP-17] to facilitate layer separation. If the layers don't separate cleanly, take the appropriate measures described in the section "Getting Good Separation." Follow method **1** (illustrated in Figure C10) if the extraction solvent is *more* dense than the liquid being extracted (forming the lower layer), and method **2a** (illustrated in Figure C11) or **2b** if it is *less* dense than the liquid being extracted (forming the upper layer). Method **2b** can be used only if both liquid layers will fit into the Pasteur pipet. Although this method requires fewer transfers than method **2a**, it is more difficult to perform proficiently.

Take Care! Wear gloves during an extraction to protect your hands in case of leakage.

1. Squeeze the bulb of a Pasteur pipet to expel air, and insert the pipet vertically so that its tip barely touches the bottom of the "vee" in the conical extraction container. Slowly withdraw the *bottom* (organic) layer, taking care not to mix the layers, and transfer it to a labeled test

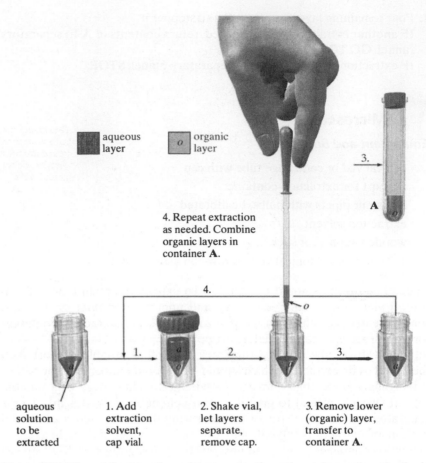

aqueous layer

organic layer

3. →

A

4. Repeat extraction as needed. Combine organic layers in container **A**.

4.

_o_

aqueous solution to be extracted

1. Add extraction solvent, cap vial.

2. Shake vial, let layers separate, remove cap.

3. Remove lower (organic) layer, transfer to container **A**.

Figure C10 Microscale extraction using an extraction solvent denser than the liquid being extracted

The kind of container you use for A depends on the next operation (washing, drying, etc.) that you will use.

tube or another small container (container **A**). Add another measured portion of pure extraction solvent to the liquid that remains in the extraction container (the original top layer), and shake to extract as before, transferring the extract (the bottom layer) to **A**. If another extraction is necessary, repeat the process, combining all of the extracts in **A**. Retain the liquid in the extraction container for later disposal.

2a. Squeeze the bulb of a Pasteur pipet to expel air, and insert the pipet vertically so that its tip just touches the bottom of the "vee" in the conical extraction container. Slowly withdraw the _bottom_ (aqueous) layer, taking care not to mix the layers, and transfer it to a labeled test tube or another small container (**A**). Transfer the contents of the extraction container to a different labeled container (**B**), and return the contents of **A** to the extraction container (see Figure C11). Add another measured portion of pure extraction solvent, and shake to extract as before; then transfer the lower layer to **A**, and combine the upper layer with the extract in **B**. If another extraction is necessary, return the contents of **A** to the extraction container and repeat the process. Retain the liquid in **A** for later disposal.

The kind of container you use for B depends on the next operation (washing, drying, etc.) that you will use.

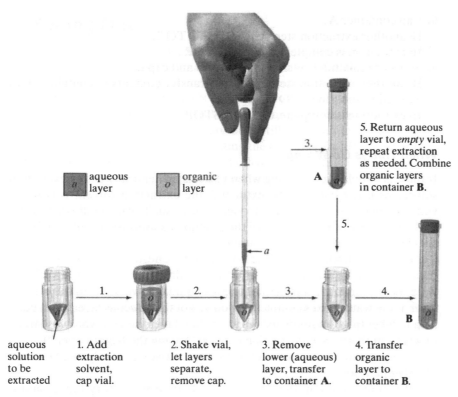

aqueous *a* layer   organic *o* layer

3. →   **A** *a*

5. Return aqueous layer to *empty* vial, repeat extraction as needed. Combine organic layers in container **B**.

5. ↓

← *a*

aqueous solution to be extracted

1. →   2. →   3. →   4. →   **B** *o*

| aqueous solution to be extracted | 1. Add extraction solvent, cap vial. | 2. Shake vial, let layers separate, remove cap. | 3. Remove lower (aqueous) layer, transfer to container **A**. | 4. Transfer organic layer to container **B**. |

Figure C11 Microscale extraction using an extraction solvent less dense than the liquid being extracted

2b. (For small amounts of liquid.) Slowly draw *both* liquid layers into the Pasteur pipet (avoid drawing in much air), and wait until a sharp interface forms between the layers. Then carefully return the bottom layer to the empty extraction container, and transfer the top layer to a labeled container (**A**). Add another measured portion of pure extraction solvent to the liquid in the extraction container, and shake to extract as before. Again draw both layers into the Pasteur pipet, let them separate, and then return the bottom layer to the empty extraction container; transfer the top layer to **A**. Repeat this process for any subsequent extractions, combining all of the extracts in **A**. Retain the liquid in the extraction container for later disposal.

Summary (Methods 1 and 2a)

1. Add liquid to be extracted to extraction container.
2. Add extraction solvent to extraction container and cap tightly.
3. Shake gently, vent, and continue shaking to extract solute into extraction solvent.
4. Loosen cap and let layers separate.
5. Uncap extraction container; transfer lower layer to container **A**.
    IF extraction solvent was the lower layer, GO TO 6.
    IF extraction solvent was the upper layer, GO TO 7.

sequence several times. Centrifuge [OP-17] the mixture and transfer the extract to a suitable container, leaving the residue in the centrifuge tube. Alternatively, use a filter-tip pipet to separate the extract from the solid residue. Repeat the extraction as many times as necessary, and combine the liquid extracts in a single collecting container.

Liquid–solid extractions can also be carried out by treating the solid with hot or boiling solvent, often under reflux [OP-7c], and filtering the mixture by gravity [OP-15], as described in Minilabs 7 and 44.

OPERATION 19   # Evaporation

Evaporation is the conversion of a liquid to vapor at or below the boiling point of the liquid. Evaporation can be used to remove a volatile solvent, such as diethyl ether or dichloromethane, from a comparatively involatile liquid or solid. Complete solvent removal is used to isolate an organic solute after such operations as extraction [OP-18] or column chromatography [OP-21]. Partial solvent removal, or *concentration,* can be used to bring a recrystallization solution to its saturation point (see OP-28).

Experimental Considerations

Because of possible health and fire hazards, you should never evaporate an organic solvent by heating an open container outside a fume hood. Even when using the methods described here, you should know and allow for the hazards associated with each solvent. In standard scale work, solvents are generally removed by distillation or under vacuum, whereas in microscale work, they are more often evaporated using a stream of nitrogen or dry air—but there are exceptions to these practices. For example, the apparatus shown in Figure C12d can be used for microscale evaporation under vacuum, and a Hickman still can be used for solvent removal by distillation. With any evaporation method, it's important to make sure that all of the solvent has evaporated. This can be done by weighing the evaporation container after evaporation, as described in the directions for evaporation under vacuum.

Evaporation Under a Fume Hood. The easiest (but slowest) way to evaporate small quantities of a volatile solvent from a solution is to put the solution in a tared wide-mouth container, such as a large vial (set inside a beaker for stability) or a small beaker, and to leave the container under a fume hood for several hours. Make sure that the hood is turned on. Large quantities of solution may need to be left under the hood overnight or for several days. The process can be accelerated by clamping an inverted stemmed funnel over the container and drawing air through it with an aspirator or vacuum pump. Solvents evaporated by this method end up in the atmosphere, so it should not be used for large quantities of solvents.

Whenever possible, it is best to use an evaporation method that allows recovery of the evaporated solvent.

Distillation. High-boiling solvents and relatively large quantities of low-boiling solvents can be removed by simple distillation [OP-30] or vacuum distillation [OP-31]. This procedure is often used when a reaction mixture contains a liquid product in a volatile solvent. After the solvent has distilled, the product of the reaction can be transferred to a smaller boiling flask (to avoid losses) and purified by distillation in the same apparatus. Distillation can also be used to concentrate a solution that is then evaporated further by one of the methods described later. In microscale work, for example, a solution can be concentrated to a volume of 0.5–1.0 mL by distillation into a Hickman still, and the remaining solvent can be evaporated under a stream of nitrogen or dry air, as described in the section "Evaporation Under Nitrogen or Dry Air."

Waste Disposal: Place the solvent in an appropriate solvent recovery container.

Evaporation Under Vacuum. Solvents can be evaporated under vacuum using one of the setups pictured in Figure C12. The test tube or flask containing the liquid to be evaporated is heated [OP-7a] gently with a

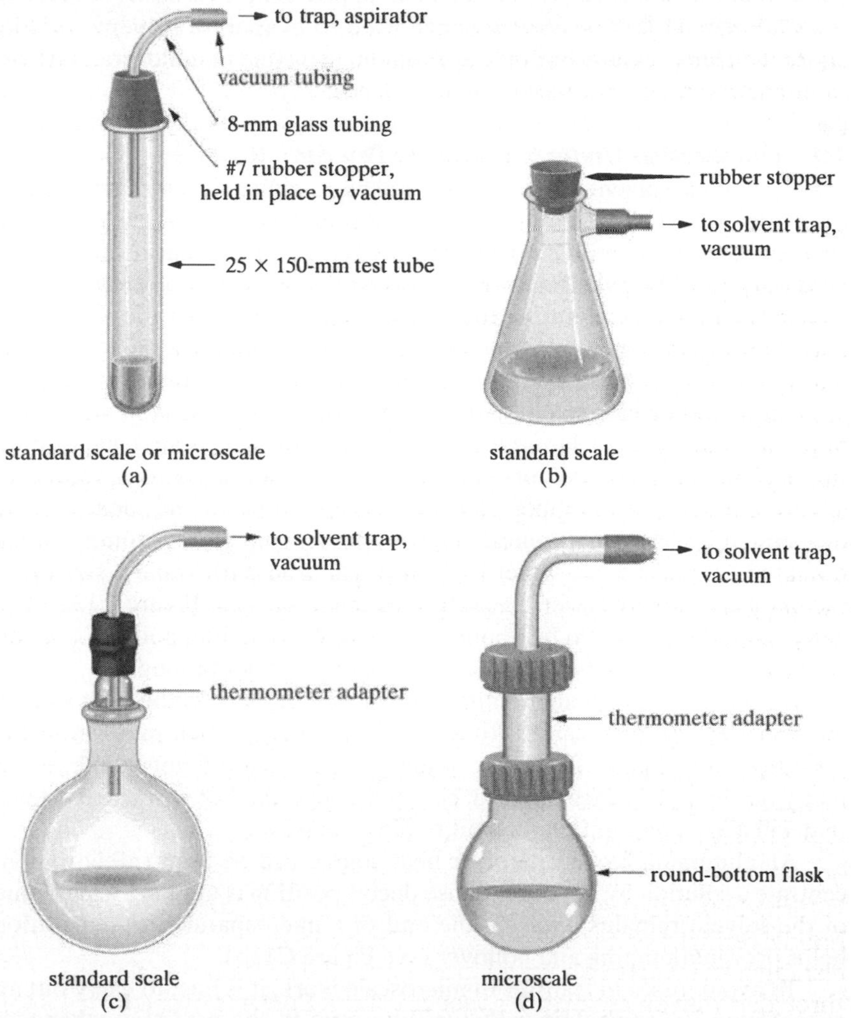

→ to trap, aspirator

vacuum tubing

8-mm glass tubing

#7 rubber stopper, held in place by vacuum

25 × 150-mm test tube

standard scale or microscale
(a)

rubber stopper

→ to solvent trap, vacuum

standard scale
(b)

→ to solvent trap, vacuum

thermometer adapter

standard scale
(c)

→ to solvent trap, vacuum

thermometer adapter

round-bottom flask

microscale
(d)

Figure C12 Apparatus for evaporation under vacuum

hot-water bath or steam bath, and an aspirator or vacuum line is used to reduce the pressure inside the apparatus, thereby increasing the evaporation rate. Swirling or stirring the solution continuously during evaporation speeds up the process and reduces foaming and bumping. Magnetic stir bars, because they tend to retain some of the residue, are not recommended for microscale evaporation unless the residue will later be dissolved in another solvent or will undergo an operation that requires magnetic stirring.

Evaporation under vacuum requires constant attention because excessive heat or a sudden pressure decrease may cause liquid to foam up and out of the container. One way to control the vacuum and reduce the likelihood of boilover is to replace the stopper shown in Figure C12b with a Hirsch funnel assembly. If you hold your thumb over the holes in the porcelain plate of the Hirsch funnel, you can decrease the internal pressure by pressing down with your thumb or increase the pressure by raising it.

A trap similar to the one pictured in Figure C4 of OP-16 should be interposed between the evaporation container and the aspirator to collect the evaporated solvent. To recover a low-boiling solvent such as diethyl ether, the solvent trap should be immersed in an appropriate cold bath (see OP-8).

Commercial *flash evaporators* are used to evaporate solvents rapidly under reduced pressure, but they are seldom available in undergraduate organic chemistry labs because of their high cost.

Evaporation Under Nitrogen or Dry Air.

Relatively small quantities of a volatile solvent can be evaporated by passing a slow stream of nitrogen or dry air over the solution. Nitrogen is preferred because the oxygen in air may react with easily oxidized solutes, but clean, dry air is suitable for most purposes. The gas stream sweeps solvent molecules away from the surface of the liquid, accelerating the evaporation rate. Evaporation cools the remaining liquid, however, so heating is needed to maintain a rapid evaporation rate and to prevent condensation of water vapor in the product. This operation must be carried out under a fume hood to keep solvent vapors out of the laboratory. Your laboratory may have a hood with an "evaporation station," where a number of Pasteur pipets are attached to a source of nitrogen or dry air and supported above a large hot plate. The solution to be evaporated is placed in a conical vial (or another suitable container), which is heated gently in a hot-water bath or warm sand bath while a stream of the dry gas is directed over the surface of the liquid (see Figure C13a). The bath temperature should be about 10°C below the boiling point of the solvent so that the solvent evaporates rapidly, but without boiling.

It is possible to use an aluminum block or hot plate as the heat source, but you must be very careful to avoid overheating, which may cause the residue to decompose. The evaporation container should not be placed directly on the hot surface; instead, clamp it above the hot surface at a level that will allow evaporation without boiling the solvent.

An aluminum block or similar heat source can be used safely to concentrate a solution by boiling because decomposition is unlikely while some of the solvent remains. Twirling the end of a microspatula in the solution helps prevent bumping and boilover (see Figure C13b).

To avoid losses in transfer in microscale work, it is best to carry out an evaporation in the container that will be used in the next step whenever possible. For example, if the residue left after evaporation will be the final

Waste Disposal: Place the solvent in an appropriate solvent recovery container.

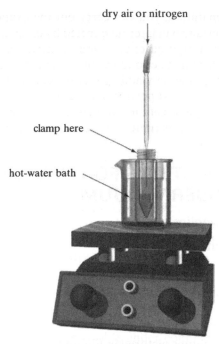

dry air or nitrogen

clamp here

hot-water bath

Evaporation under a stream
of dry air or nitrogen
(a)

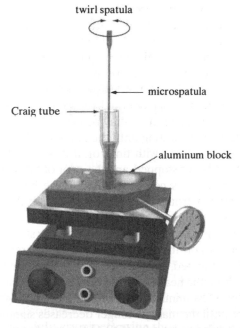

twirl spatula

microspatula

Craig tube

aluminum block

Concentration of a recrystallization solution
(b)

Figure C13 Apparatus for microscale evaporation

Table C2 Boiling points and compositions of heterogeneous mixtures of various organic compounds, with water as Component B

Component A	bp of A (°C)	bp of A/B mixture (°C)	mass % of A in distillate
toluene	111°	85°	80%
chlorobenzene	132°	90°	71%
bromobenzene	156°	95°	62%
iodobenzene	188°	98°	43%
quinoline	237°	99.6°	10%

of the organic liquid, the lower will be its proportion in the distillate, and the closer the mixture boiling point will be to 100°C.

Because the distillation boiling point is never higher than 100°C at 1 atm—well below the normal boiling points of most water-immiscible organic liquids—thermal decomposition of the organic component is minimized.

 a. External Steam Distillation

Externally generated steam is preferred for most standard scale steam distillations, especially those involving solids or high-boiling liquids because external steam produces a rapid distillation rate and helps prevent bumping caused by solids and tars. The steam is usually obtained from a steam line; if another kind of steam generator is to be used, your instructor will show you how to use it. A *steam trap* is needed to remove condensed water and foreign matter, such as grease or rust, from externally generated steam. A steam trap that includes a valve for draining off excess water, such as the one illustrated in Figure C14, works best. With other kinds of traps, distillation may have to be interrupted periodically to drain the trap.

The capacity of the boiling flask should be at least three times the volume of the liquid being distilled, so that it won't become much more than half full throughout the distillation. Some steam will condense during the distillation, raising the water level in the boiling flask; during an extended distillation, excessive water can be removed by external heating, if necessary. A Claisen adapter is used to help prevent mechanical transfer of liquids or particles from the boiling flask to the receiver. If the organic distillate is quite volatile, a thermometer can be used to indicate when the end of the distillation is near. For example, with a toluene–water mixture, the temperature will rise rather rapidly from 85°C to about 100°C when the toluene is nearly gone. With liquids that have boiling points of 200°C or higher, a thermometer is of little use because the vapor temperature will be close to 100°C throughout the distillation. The distillation should be carried out rapidly to reduce condensation in the boiling flask and to compensate for the large volume of water-laden distillate that may have to be collected to yield much of the organic component. Owing to the rapid distillation rate and the high heat content of steam, efficient condensing is essential. The vacuum adapter should be cool to the touch throughout the distillation, and no steam should escape from its outlet.

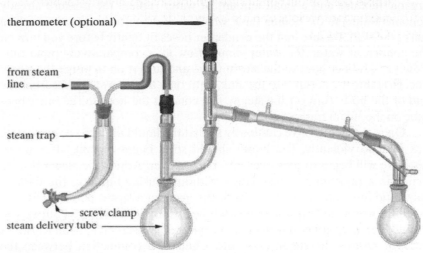

thermometer (optional)

from steam line

steam trap

screw clamp

steam delivery tube

If the thermometer is not used, replace it and the thermometer adapter with a stopper.

Figure C14 Apparatus for standard scale external steam distillation

DIRECTIONS FOR EXTERNAL STEAM DISTILLATION

 Standard Scale

Equipment and Supplies

  heat source
  ring stand, ring supports, clamps
  rubber tubing
  steam delivery tube
  large round-bottom flask
  Claisen adapter
  still head (connecting adapter)
  thermometer and thermometer adapter (optional) or stopper
  West condenser
  vacuum adapter
  receiving flask
  steam trap (bent adapter, two-hole rubber stopper, bent glass tubes,
      rubber tubing, screw clamp)

Assemble the apparatus pictured in Figure C14 using a large round-bottom boiling flask and, as the steam delivery tube, a 6-mm o.d. (outer diameter) glass tube extending to within about 0.5 cm of the bottom of the flask (it must not touch the bottom). Use a stopper in place of the thermometer adapter and thermometer if the component being separated boils above ~200°C. Position the boiling flask high enough so that external heat can be applied, if necessary. Use a length of rubber tubing to connect the steam delivery tube to a bent glass tube on the steam trap, which should be clamped to a ring stand over a beaker. See that the screw clamp on the steam trap is closed. Add the organic mixture and a small amount of water (unless the mixture already contains water) to the boiling flask, which should be no more than one-third full at the start. Be sure that the condenser hoses fit tightly before you turn on the condenser water; the water should flow at a comparatively rapid rate. Connect a rubber hose to the steam valve and turn it on to purge the steam line, directing the steam into the sink, until only a little water drips from the end of the hose. Turn off the steam, and connect the hose to the other bent tube on the steam trap.

Take Care! Do not burn yourself with the steam.

Open the steam valve cautiously so that the liquid in the flask is agitated, but not too violently. The liquid should soon begin to boil, after which distillate will begin to pass over into the receiver. Adjust the steam flow to maintain a rapid rate of distillation without causing liquid in the flask to splash up into the condenser. Check the vacuum adapter periodically; if it becomes warm, and especially if vapor begins to escape from its outlet, you should increase the cooling water flow rate, cool the receiver in an ice/water bath, or reduce the steam flow rate. Check the connection between the condenser and still head frequently to make sure that no vapor is escaping; this joint sometimes separates because of the violent action of the steam (you can use a rubber band or a joint clip to prevent this). Drain the trap periodically to remove condensed water. If you must interrupt the distillation for any reason, open the steam-trap valve (if there is one) or raise the steam delivery tube out of the liquid *before* you turn off the steam; otherwise, liquid in the boiling flask may back up into the steam trap.

When the distillate appears clear *and* the temperature is near 100°C (if you used a thermometer), collect and examine a few drops of fresh distillate on a watch glass. Continue distilling if the fresh distillate is cloudy, contains oily droplets, or has a pronounced odor, and collect and examine more distillate at 5- or 10-min intervals. When the distillate is water clear and distillation appears complete, open the steam-trap valve fully (or raise the steam delivery tube out of the liquid), and then turn off the steam.

The organic liquid can be separated from the distillate using a separatory funnel, or by extraction [OP-18] with diethyl ether or another suitable solvent. Extraction is advisable if the volume of the organic liquid is small compared to that of the water. If the aqueous layer is cloudy, you can saturate it with sodium chloride or another salt to salt out [OP-18b] the organic liquid.

Summary

1. Assemble apparatus for external steam distillation.
2. Add organic mixture and water (if necessary) to boiling flask.
3. Turn on condenser water.
4. Purge steam line, connect to steam trap, and turn on steam.
5. Distill rapidly until distillate is clear; drain trap periodically.
6. Open steam-trap valve and turn off steam.
7. Separate organic liquid from distillate.
8. Disassemble and clean apparatus.

When Things Go Wrong

Most of the things that go wrong during a simple distillation can also go wrong during an external steam distillation, so you can refer to "When Things Go Wrong" in OP-30 for help. The following cases apply only to external steam distillation.

If, during a steam distillation, the water level in the boiling flask rises well above its midpoint, check to make sure that water from the steam trap is not passing over into the boiling flask. If it is, drain the steam trap and monitor its water level more carefully. If not, heat the boiling flask externally with a steam bath or heating mantle to reduce condensation.

If, during a steam distillation, vapor escapes from the vacuum adapter outlet, first check to see that the condenser is cool to the touch; if not, increase the cooling water's flow rate. If that doesn't help, cool the receiver in an ice/water bath. It may also be necessary to reduce the steam flow rate.

b. Internal Steam Distillation

An organic liquid can sometimes be separated from a reaction mixture or another mixture by internal steam distillation (codistillation with water). The procedure is essentially the same as that for simple distillation [OP-30], except that more water may need to be added during the distillation. If water will be added during a standard scale internal steam distillation, the apparatus illustrated in Figure C15 should be used; otherwise, a simple distillation apparatus is suitable. If the organic distillate is quite volatile, a thermometer can be used to indicate when the end of the distillation is near.

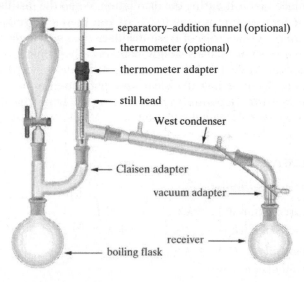

separatory–addition funnel (optional)

thermometer (optional)

thermometer adapter

still head

West condenser

Claisen adapter

vacuum adapter

receiver

boiling flask

If the thermometer is not used, replace it and the thermometer adapter with a stopper.

Figure C15 Apparatus for standard scale internal steam distillation

DIRECTIONS FOR INTERNAL STEAM DISTILLATION

See OP-30 for more detailed directions for conducting a distillation.

Standard Scale

Equipment and Supplies

heat source
ring stand, ring supports, clamps
condenser tubing

round-bottom flask

boiling chips or stir bar

still head (connecting adapter)

thermometer and thermometer adapter or stopper

West condenser

vacuum adapter

receiver

Claisen adapter (optional)

separatory–addition funnel (optional)

If it will be necessary to add more water during the distillation, assemble the apparatus shown in Figure C15; otherwise, assemble the apparatus pictured in Figure E7 of OP-30. Replace the thermometer adapter and thermometer by a stopper if the component being separated boils above ~200°C. Add the mixture to be steam distilled, boiling chips or a stir bar, and enough water to fill the boiling flask about one-third to one-half full (unless enough water is already present). Turn on the condenser water and the stirrer (if you are using one), and heat the flask with an appropriate heat source [OP-7a] to maintain a rapid rate of distillation. If necessary, add water to replace that lost during the distillation. When the distillate appears clear *and* the temperature is near 100°C (if you used a thermometer), collect and examine a few drops of fresh distillate on a watch glass. Continue distilling if the fresh distillate is cloudy, contains oily droplets, or has a pronounced odor, and collect and examine more distillate at 5- or 10-min intervals. When the distillate is water clear and distillation appears complete, discontinue heating. Separate the organic liquid from the distillate as described for external steam distillation.

See the Summary following the Microscale directions.

 Microscale

Equipment and Supplies

heat source (aluminum block or sand bath)

round-bottom flask

Hickman still

water-cooled condenser

stir bar (optional)

condenser tubing

ring stand, clamp

thermometer (optional)

$5\frac{3}{4}$-inch Pasteur pipet

9-inch Pasteur pipet (optional)

collecting container

If it will be necessary to add more water during the distillation, measure out the approximate amount of water that will be needed. Assemble an apparatus similar to the one pictured in Figure E11 of OP-30, but attach the Hickman still to a round-bottom flask and use a water-cooled condenser. If there is any likelihood that the mixture being distilled will foam up (as when certain plant products, such as ground cloves, are subjected to steam distillation), use the largest available round-bottom flask for boiling. Add the mixture to be steam distilled, a stir bar, and enough water to fill the boiling flask about one-half full (unless enough water is already present). In some cases, a stir bar may cause excessive foaming and should be omitted. Turn on the stirrer, if you are using one, and heat the flask with an appropriate heat source to maintain a rapid rate of distillation without allowing any boilover into the Hickman still. As the well of the Hickman still fills with liquid, use a short Pasteur pipet to transfer the distillate to an appropriate collecting container. As necessary, use a long Pasteur pipet to add water through the condenser to replace that lost during distillation. Discontinue heating when the fresh distillate appears to contain no more of the organic component *or* after a designated volume of liquid has been collected. When distillation is complete, the distillate should no longer be cloudy or contain droplets of organic liquid. If droplets of the organic component have collected on the inner walls of the Hickman still, use a Pasteur pipet to rinse the walls into the well with some of the distillate or an appropriate solvent, and transfer the contents of the well to the collecting container. Separate the organic liquid from the distillate by microscale extraction [OP-18] with a suitable solvent.

Summary

1. Assemble apparatus for internal steam distillation.
2. Add organic mixture and water to boiling flask.
3. Turn on stirrer (if used) and condenser water.
4. Distill until distillate is clear, adding water as necessary.
5. Separate organic liquid from distillate.
6. Disassemble and clean apparatus.

When Things Go Wrong

Most of the things that go wrong during a simple distillation can also go wrong during an internal steam distillation, so you can refer to "When Things Go Wrong" in OP-30 for help.

Column Chromatography

OPERATION **21**

If you touch the tip of a felt-tip pen to a piece of absorbent paper, such as a coffee filter, and then slowly drip isopropyl rubbing alcohol onto the spot with a medicine dropper, the spot will spread and separate into rings of different color—the dyes of which the ink is composed. This is a simple example of *chromatography,* the separation of a mixture by distributing its components between two phases. The *stationary phase* (the coffee filter, in this example) remains fixed in place, while the *mobile phase* (the rubbing alcohol) flows through it, carrying components of the mixture along with it. The stationary phase acts as a "brake" on most components of a mixture, holding them back so that they move along more slowly than the mobile phase itself. Because of differences in such factors as the solubility of the components in the mobile phase and the strength of their interactions with the stationary phase, some components move faster than others, and the components therefore become separated from one another.

If the spots for some components are too close together to identify from their R_f values, try another developing solvent or solvent mixture. Be sure that the solvents are not contaminated by water or other impurities. (See "Choosing a Developing Solvent.")

If you used iodine vapor for visualization and the entire TLC plate has become quite dark, you probably didn't let it dry long enough. If you can't locate all of the expected spots, you will have to prepare, develop, thoroughly dry, and visualize another plate. (See "Visualization.")

It's also possible that the plate has an organic binder, in which case a different type of TLC plate or a different visualization method should be used.

If you don't see the expected spots on your developed TLC plate, think about what you might have done wrong. Were your spots so small or diffuse that they could no longer be seen after development? (See "Spotting.") Did you use too much developing solvent or draw your starting line too low on the TLC plate, so that the solvent covered the starting line and washed out the components of the spots? (See "Development.") If you used a UV lamp to visualize the spots, did you irradiate the wrong side of the TLC plate or use the wrong UV wavelength? (See "Visualization.") If you put your TLC plate in an iodine-vapor chamber, did you set the plate aside for so long that the iodine spots faded before you examined it? (See "Visualization.") If you used a visualizing reagent such as phosphomolybdic acid, did you fail to dry the plate completely before applying the reagent, or did you not heat the plate long enough for the spots to appear? (See "Visualization.") If you think you may have done (or not done) any of these things, read the indicated section carefully, then prepare, develop, and visualize another plate, taking steps to correct any possible mistakes.

OPERATION 23

Paper Chromatography

Principles and Applications

Paper chromatography is similar to thin-layer chromatography [OP-22] in practice but quite different in principle. As for TLC, a square or rectangular piece of chromatography paper is spotted with solutions of the sample and standards, and the chromatogram is developed with a suitable mobile phase. Although paper consists mainly of cellulose, the stationary phase is not cellulose itself but the water that is adsorbed by it. Chromatography paper can adsorb up to 22% water, and the developing solvents usually contain enough water to keep it saturated. During development, a comparatively nonpolar mobile phase seeps up through the cellulose fibers, partitioning the solutes between the bound water and the mobile phase. Paper chromatography thus operates by a liquid–liquid partitioning process rather than by adsorption on the surface of a solid.

Because only polar compounds are appreciably soluble in water, paper chromatography is most frequently used to separate polar substances such as amino acids and carbohydrates. Manufactured chromatography paper is quite uniform, and the activity of cellulose doesn't vary as much as the activity of most TLC adsorbents, so R_f values obtained by paper chromatography may be more reproducible than those from thin-layer chromatography. However, the resolution of spots is often poorer, and the development times

microscale work. After the last washing, leave the vacuum turned on for several minutes to partially dry the solid. If you experience difficulties while washing a solid by vacuum filtration, refer to "When Things Go Wrong" in OP-16.

  To wash a solid by trituration, place it in a glass container (such as a test tube, beaker, or Erlenmeyer flask), and add enough of the wash solvent to completely cover the solid, or the amount of solvent specified by the procedure you are following. Using the tip of a glass stirring rod, rub and grind the solid against the sides of the container for several minutes. It is important to grind the solid finely to increase the amount of its surface area exposed to the solvent. Then remove the solvent by vacuum filtration [OP-16].

b. Drying Solids

Experimental Considerations

Solids that have been collected by vacuum filtration [OP-16] are usually air-dried on the filter by leaving the vacuum on for a few minutes after filtration is complete. Unless the solvent is very volatile, further drying is required. Comparatively volatile solvents can be removed by simply spreading the solid on a watch glass or evaporating dish (covered to keep out airborne particles) and placing the container in a location with good air circulation, such as a hood, for a sufficient period of time (Figure D2). Clamping an inverted funnel above the watch glass or evaporating dish and passing a gentle stream of dry air or nitrogen over it will accelerate the drying rate.

A very wet solid can be partially dried by transferring it to a filter paper on a clean surface and blotting it with another filter paper to remove excess solvent. The solid is then rubbed against the filter paper with the blade of a flat-bladed spatula until it is finely divided and friable, using fresh filter paper if necessary. It should then be dried completely by one of the methods described next. Some of the solid will adhere to the filter paper, so this method is not recommended for microscale work.

Many wet solids can be spread out in a shallow ovenproof container and dried in a laboratory oven set at 110°C or another suitable temperature. The expected melting point of the solid should be at least 20°C above the oven temperature, and the solid should not be heat sensitive or sublime readily at the oven temperature. It isn't unusual for a student to open an oven door and discover that the product he or she worked many hours to prepare has just turned into a charred or molten mass, or disappeared entirely. Aluminum weighing dishes and other commercially available containers made of heavy aluminum foil are usually suitable for oven drying because the aluminum conducts heat well, cools quickly, and isn't likely to burn your fingers. Aluminum reacts with acids and bases, so acidic and basic solids (or solids that may be wet with acidic or basic liquids) should be oven-dried in Pyrex or porcelain containers, such as watch glasses or evaporating dishes.

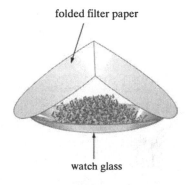

folded filter paper

watch glass

Figure D2 Covered watch glass for drying solids

Take Care! Don't blow the crystals away.

If you are not sure whether your product can be oven-dried safely, consult your instructor.

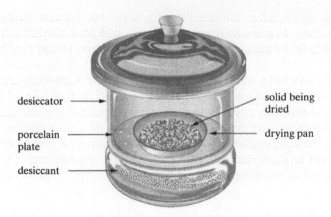

Figure D3 Commercial desiccator

A *vacuum oven* combines the use of heat with low pressure for very fast, efficient drying. A simple vacuum oven can be constructed by clamping a sidearm test tube horizontally and connecting it to a vacuum source (see *J. Chem. Educ.* **1988**, *65,* 460). The sample, in an open vial, is inserted in the sidearm test tube, which is stoppered and heated with a heat lamp while the vacuum is turned on.

When time permits, the safest way to dry a solid is to leave it in a *desiccator* overnight or longer. A desiccator consists of a tightly sealed container partly filled with a *desiccant* (drying agent) that absorbs water vapor, creating a moisture-free environment in which the solid should dry thoroughly. Desiccators such as the one shown in Figure D3 are available commercially. A simple "homemade" desiccator for drying small amounts of solid can be constructed using an 8-oz (~250-mL) wide-mouth jar with a screw cap (see Figure D4). Its size is well suited to microscale work because several samples in small vials can be dried at the same time, but it is also useful for standard scale work. Enough of a solid desiccant (about 50 mL, measured in a graduated beaker) is added to form a 1-cm layer of desiccant on the bottom. The wet solid, in an appropriate container, is set inside the desiccator, which is capped and allowed to stand undisturbed until drying is complete. If there is any danger of the container tipping over, a wire screen can be cut to fit on top of the desiccant layer and provide a more stable surface. Except when a product is being added or removed, the desiccator must be kept tightly closed at all times to keep the dessicant active.

A similar desiccator with a polyethylene storage rack is available commercially.

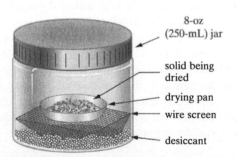

Figure D4 "Homemade" desiccator

Anhydrous calcium chloride is a good (if rather slow-working) desiccant because it is inexpensive and has a high water capacity. Drierite (anhydrous calcium sulfate) is faster and more efficient than calcium chloride, but it has a much lower capacity. A combination of calcium chloride with a small amount of indicating (blue) Drierite works better than either desiccant separately. The blue Drierite removes traces of moisture that calcium chloride cannot, and it turns pink when the desiccant is spent and needs to be replaced. Unless your instructor indicates otherwise, spent desiccant should be placed in a designated container for reactivation. Drierite can be reactivated by heating it in a 225°C oven overnight; calcium chloride should be heated overnight at 250–350°C.

DIRECTIONS FOR DRYING SOLIDS IN AN OVEN

 Standard Scale and Microscale

Obtain a wide, shallow, ovenproof container, such as a small evaporating dish or an aluminum weighing dish. Weigh it and label it to prevent mix-ups. Spread the solid on the bottom of the container in a thin, uniform layer, and place it in the oven, preferably where it is well separated from other containers. After 30 minutes or so, remove the container (wear gloves when handling a glass container), let it cool to room temperature, and weigh it. Then put it back in the oven for 5–10 minutes, let it cool, and weigh it again. If the mass has decreased by 1% or more, repeat this process until the mass does not change significantly between weighings.

Be sure the oven temperature is at least 20°C below the expected melting point of your solid.

DIRECTIONS FOR DRYING SOLIDS IN A DESICCATOR

 Standard Scale and Microscale

If the sample will remain in the desiccator until the next lab period, you can dry it in a tared, labeled storage vial with the cap removed. (At the beginning of the next lab period, you should cap the vial and weigh it.) If the sample will only be in the desiccator overnight or for a day or two, spread it out in a shallow, tared container, such as a polystyrene or aluminum weighing dish or a square drying tray made by folding a square of heavy aluminum foil. Label the container with the name of the compound, your name or initials, and the tare mass. Set the container inside a desiccator provided with fresh desiccant, taking care to place it securely so that it won't tip over. With a homemade desiccator, vials can be pushed down into the desiccant layer, and low containers can be set on a rack made of wire screen or another material (see Figure D4). A commercial desiccator has a porcelain plate or another kind of rack to hold the samples. Cap or cover the desiccator securely, and let it stand overnight or longer (preferably longer). Remove and weigh the container with the sample in it, then return it to the desiccator and reweigh it after an hour or so. If the mass has decreased by 1% or more, return the container to the desiccator and leave it there until the mass does not change significantly between weighings.

When Things Go Wrong

If a solid being dried in an oven begins to discolor, it is probably beginning to decompose. Dry it at a lower temperature or by a different method.

If a solid being dried in an oven is decreasing in volume, it is probably undergoing sublimation (conversion from a solid to a vapor). Dry it by a different method.

If a solid being dried in a desiccator is not dry after standing overnight or longer, check the appearance of the desiccant. Calcium chloride granules and some other desiccants clump together when exhausted, and indicating Drierite turns pink. If the desiccant appears to be exhausted, remove the old desiccant, clean and dry the inside of the desiccator, and add fresh desiccant. Then resume drying.

OPERATION **27**

Cleaning and Drying Gases

Air and nitrogen are often used to evaporate a solvent [OP-19] from a desired product, nitrogen and other inert gases are used to provide an inert atmosphere [OP-13] for reactions of oxygen-sensitive compounds, and reactive gases such as carbon dioxide are used in certain chemical syntheses. Gases must ordinarily be clean and dry for such applications. Gases can be dried using desiccants like the ones described in OP-26 for drying solids.

Many gases, such as nitrogen, are available in cylinders and can be purchased in a form that is pure enough for most applications. Other gases, especially compressed air obtained from a laboratory air line, may have to be cleaned and dried before use. For most purposes, air from an air line and other impure gases can be cleaned and dried by passing the gas slowly through a standard scale drying tube or a U-tube filled with a suitable desiccant (drying agent) and plugged with a layer of cotton at both ends (read about the use of drying tubes in OP-12). Indicating silica gel and granular alumina are very efficient desiccants; indicating Drierite and calcium chloride are satisfactory for many purposes. Silica gel has the advantage of being chemically inert, but calcium chloride is cheaper and easier to use. The cotton plugs remove most particles, grease, and other impurities from the air line. One end of the drying tube should have a connector that is inserted in a rubber or plastic tube going to the air line; the other end should have a connecter that is inserted in a similar flexible tube going to a Pasteur pipet or a gas delivery tube. If necessary, you can make a connector by inserting a short length of fire-polished glass tubing (see OP-3) into a one-hole rubber stopper of a size that will fit in the drying tube.

When it is important that a gas be very clean and dry, it can be bubbled through a gas-washing bottle such as the one in Figure D5. The bottle is partly filled with concentrated sulfuric acid or another suitable liquid. The

Take Care! Avoid contact with sulfuric acid, and use it under a fume hood.

gas in ⟶   ⟶ gas out

concentrated
sulfuric acid

Figure D5 Gas-washing bottle

gas is bubbled into the liquid through the long glass tube and exits through the short tube, from which it is conveyed through a flexible tube to wherever it is needed. To make sure that the acid is not carried with the airstream into a reaction flask or another vessel, it is a good idea to attach an empty trap (see Figure C4, OP-16) at the outlet of the gas-washing bottle. The acid should be replaced after extended use. Note that many reactive gases, such as ammonia, can't be dried in sulfuric acid.

E. Purification Operations

Once a product has been separated from a reaction mixture, it must ordinarily be *purified* to remove any residual impurities. Solids are usually purified by recrystallization [OP-28], but solids with high vapor pressures can be purified by sublimation [OP-29], and a few low-melting solids can be purified by distillation [OP-30b]. Most liquid products of reactions are purified by simple distillation [OP-30a]. High-boiling liquids that may decompose during an ordinary distillation can be purified by vacuum distillation [OP-31]. When a liquid product contains a substantial amount of liquid impurities having boiling points close to that of the product itself, it should be purified by fractional distillation [OP-32]. Both liquid and solid products can sometimes be purified by column chromatography [OP-21], which was described in Section C.

OPERATION **28**   ## Recrystallization

The simplest and most widely used operation for purifying organic solids is *recrystallization*. Recrystallization is so named because it involves dissolving a solid that (in most cases) had originally crystallized from a reaction mixture or another solution, and then causing it to *again* crystallize from solution. In a typical recrystallization procedure, the crude solid is dissolved by heating it in a suitable *recrystallization solvent*. The hot solution is then filtered by gravity, and the filtrate is allowed to cool to room temperature or below, whereupon crystals appear in the saturated solution and are collected by vacuum filtration. The crystals are ordinarily much purer than the crude solid because most of the impurities either fail to dissolve in the hot solution, from which they are separated by gravity filtration or transfer, or remain dissolved in the cold solution, from which they are separated by vacuum filtration or centrifugation.

Recrystallization is based on the fact that the solubility of a solid in a given solvent increases with the temperature of the solvent. Consider the recrystallization from boiling water of a 5.00-g sample of salicylic acid contaminated by 0.25 g of acetanilide. The solubility of salicylic acid in water at 100°C is 7.5 g per 100 mL, so the amount of water required to just dissolve 5.00 g of salicylic acid at the boiling point of water is 67 mL.

$$5.00 \text{ g} \times \frac{100 \text{ mL}}{7.5 \text{ g}} = 67 \text{ mL of water}$$

All of the acetanilide impurity will also dissolve in the boiling water. If the solution is cooled to 20°C, at which temperature the solubility of salicylic acid is only 0.20 g per 100 mL, about 0.13 g of salicylic acid will remain dissolved.

$$67 \text{ mL} \times \frac{0.20 \text{ g}}{100 \text{ mL}} = 0.13 \text{ g of salicylic acid}$$

The dissolved salicylic acid will end up in the filtrate during the vacuum filtration; the remaining 4.87 g will crystallize from solution (if sufficient time is allowed) and will be collected on the filter. The solubility of acetanilide in water is 0.50 g per 100 mL at 20°C, so up to 0.35 g of acetanilide can dissolve in 67 mL of water at 20°C.

$$67 \text{ mL} \times \frac{0.50 \text{ g}}{100 \text{ mL}} = 0.35 \text{ g of acetanilide}$$

This means that all 0.25 g of acetanilide in the crude product should remain in solution and end up in the filtrate. Therefore, under ideal conditions, the recrystallization should yield a 97% recovery of salicylic acid uncontaminated by acetanilide.

$$\frac{4.87 \text{ g}}{5.00 \text{ g}} \times 100 = 97\% \text{ recovery}$$

The recovery could be increased by cooling the mixture in an ice/water bath to further lower the solubility of salicylic acid, but even then, some of the salicylic acid would remain in solution. You can never recover all of your product after a recrystallization, but by allowing plenty of time for the product to crystallize and making careful transfers, you should be able to minimize your losses.

This is a simplified description of a rather complex process. A number of factors may bring about results different from those calculated.

- Crystals of the desired solid may adsorb impurities on their surfaces or trap them within the crystal lattice.
- The solubility of a solute in a saturated solution of a different solute may not be the same as its solubility in the pure solvent.
- Using only enough recrystallization solvent to dissolve a solid can result in premature crystallization, so additional solvent may be added to prevent this.

a. Recrystallization from a Single Solvent

Experimental Considerations

Most experimental procedures that involve recrystallization specify a suitable recrystallization solvent in the directions. If the solvent is not specified, see section **c**, "Choosing a Recrystallization Solvent."

In its simplest form, the recrystallization of a solid is carried out by dissolving the impure solid in the hot (usually boiling) recrystallization solvent and letting the resulting solution cool to room temperature or below to allow crystallization to occur. Additional steps, such as filtering or decolorizing the hot solution, may also be necessary. Sometimes it is desirable to collect a second or third crop of crystals by concentrating (see OP-19) the *mother liquor* (the liquid from which the crystals are filtered) from the previous crop. These crystals will contain more impurities than the first crop and may require recrystallization from fresh solvent. A melting-point determination [OP-33] or thin-layer chromatography (TLC) analysis [OP-22] can be used to assess the purity of a recrystallized solid.

point. Next, add enough of the original solvent to cause the cloudiness or crystals to disappear from the boiling solvent, and let it cool.

As a last resort, remove all of the solvent by evaporation and try a different recrystallization solvent—but see your instructor for advice first.

Using a lower-boiling solvent usually results in a lower percent recovery.

Dealing with Oils and Colloidal Suspensions.   When the solid being recrystallized is quite impure or has a low melting point, it may separate as an *oil* (a second liquid phase) upon cooling. Oils are undesirable because, even if they solidify on cooling, the solid retains most of the original impurities.

If the solid to be purified has a melting point below the boiling point of the recrystallization solvent, it may be possible to prevent oiling by substituting a lower-boiling solvent with similar properties. For example, methanol (bp 65°C) might be substituted for ethanol (bp 78°C), or acetone (bp 57°C) for 2-butanone (bp 80°C). Oiling may also be prevented by using more recrystallization solvent, adding seed crystals, or both. Seed crystals can sometimes be obtained by dissolving a small amount of the oil in an equal volume of a volatile solvent in a small, open test tube and letting the solvent evaporate slowly.

If oiling occurs, try the following remedies, in order:

1. Heat the solution until the oil dissolves completely—adding more solvent, if necessary—and then cool it slowly while rubbing the inside of the container (see "Inducing Crystallization").
2. Add an amount of pure recrystallization solvent equal to about 25% of the total solvent volume, and repeat the process described in step **1**.
3. Follow the procedure in step **1**, but add a seed crystal or two at the approximate temperature where oiling occurred previously.
4. Try to crystallize the oil by either (a) cooling the solution in an ice–salt bath, rubbing the oil with a stirring rod and adding seed crystals, if necessary, or (b) removing all of the oil with a Pasteur pipet, dissolving it in an equal volume of a volatile solvent, and letting the solvent evaporate slowly in an open test tube. Then collect the solid by vacuum filtration, and recrystallize it from the same solvent or a more suitable one. If necessary, use one or more of the previous methods to prevent further oiling.

A *colloid* is a suspension of very small particles dispersed in a liquid or another phase. Colloids generally have a cloudy appearance and cannot be filtered through ordinary filtering media because the particles pass right through. If a solid separates from a cooled solution as a colloidal suspension, the colloid can often be coagulated to form normal crystals by extended heating in a hot-water bath, or (if the solvent is polar) by adding an electrolyte such as sodium sulfate. Colloid formation can sometimes be prevented by treating a recrystallization solution with Norit, as described previously, or by cooling the solution very slowly.

DIRECTIONS FOR SINGLE-SOLVENT RECRYSTALLIZATION

Safety Notes

Unless you are informed otherwise, consider all recrystallization solvents (except water) to be flammable and harmful by ingestion, inhalation, and contact. Avoid contact with and inhalation of such solvents, and keep them away from flames and hot surfaces.

Standard Scale

Use this method (illustrated in Figure E1) when you have approximately 1 g
or more of crude solid.

Equipment and Supplies

> 2 Erlenmeyer flasks
> recrystallization solvent
> graduated cylinder
> heat source
> boiling (applicator) stick or boiling chips
> flat-bottomed stirring rod
> small watch glass
> Buchner funnel with filter paper

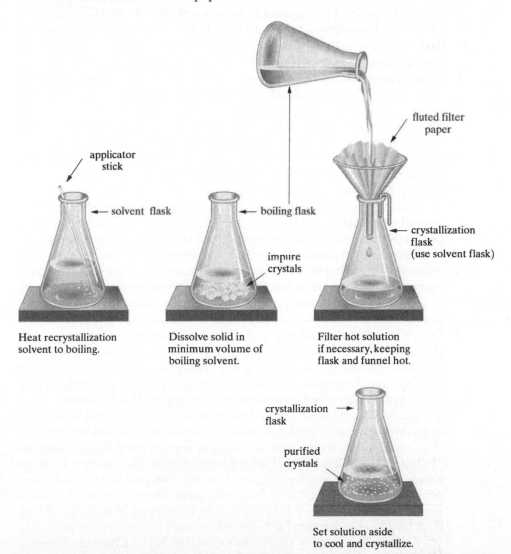

applicator
stick

←— solvent flask

←— boiling flask

impure
crystals

fluted filter
paper

←— crystallization
flask
(use solvent flask)

Heat recrystallization
solvent to boiling.

Dissolve solid in
minimum volume of
boiling solvent.

Filter hot solution
if necessary, keeping
flask and funnel hot.

crystallization —→
flask

purified
crystals

Set solution aside
to cool and crystallize.

Figure E1 Steps in the recrystallization of a solid

> filter flask
> cold washing solvent
> watch glass or beaker (to cover crystallization flask)
> powder funnel (optional)
> fluted filter paper (optional)
> Norit (optional)

If you know the solubility of the solid in the boiling recrystallization solvent, calculate the approximate volume of solvent that you will need to recrystallize it, and measure out that amount plus 10–20% extra. Otherwise, start with about 10 mL per gram of solid, and use more if needed. Measure the solvent into an Erlenmeyer flask—the *solvent flask*. Add a boiling stick or a few boiling chips, insert a powder funnel in the flask mouth, and heat the solvent to boiling with an appropriate heat source [OP-7a]. A steam bath is often preferred for organic solvents that boil below 100°C; a hot plate can be used for water and higher-boiling organic solvents. Place the solid to be purified in a second Erlenmeyer flask—the *boiling flask*—and add about one-quarter of the hot liquid in the solvent flask to the boiling flask. (If you've calculated the approximate volume of solvent needed, you can add about three-quarters of the calculated amount.) Heat the mixture *at the boiling point,* with continuous swirling or stirring—breaking up any large particles with a spatula or flat-bottomed stirring rod during this process—until it appears that no more solid will go into solution. If undissolved solid remains, add more portions of hot solvent—about 10% of the total each time—and heat the solution *at the boiling point,* with swirling or stirring after each addition. Continue this process until (1) the solid is completely dissolved *or* (2) no more solid dissolves when a fresh portion of solvent is added and it appears that only solid impurities remain.

See the section "Filtering the Hot Solution" for additional information about removing solid impurities.

If the solution has an intense color but the pure product should not be colored, decolorize it as directed in the section "Removing Colored Impurities." If the boiling solution contains no solid impurities, use the boiling flask as a crystallization flask and go to the next paragraph. If it does contain solid impurities (including Norit for decolorizing), add about one-tenth as much recrystallization solvent as you have used so far, and heat the mixture back to boiling. Put a preheated powder funnel on the neck of the emptied solvent flask (with a bent wire or paper clip between them), and set this flask (which is now the *crystallization flask*) on the heat source. Insert a coarse fluted filter paper in the funnel, and rapidly filter the hot solution while it is still near the boiling point, keeping any unfiltered solution hot throughout the filtration. If any solid crystallizes on the filter paper or inside the funnel, redissolve it as described in the section "Filtering the Hot Solution."

Set the crystallization flask on the benchtop, cover it with a watch glass or an inverted beaker, and let the solution cool slowly to room temperature. If no crystals form by the time the solution reaches room temperature, see "Inducing Crystallization." If an oil separates or the solution becomes cloudy but no solid precipitates, see "Dealing with Oils and Colloidal Suspensions." Once crystals have begun to form, allow at least 15 minutes (sometimes much longer) for complete crystallization. If desired, cool the flask further in an ice bath for 5 minutes or more to improve the yield.

Collect the crystals by vacuum filtration [OP-16] on a Buchner funnel or Hirsch funnel of appropriate size. Transfer any crystals remaining in the crystallization flask to the funnel with a small amount of ice-cold recrystallization solvent (or another appropriate solvent), and use more of the cold solvent to wash the solid on the filter [OP-26a]. Air-dry the crystals by leaving the vacuum on for a few minutes after the last washing, and then dry [OP-26b] them further as necessary.

Waste Disposal: Dispose of the filtrate as directed by your instructor.

Summary

1. Measure recrystallization solvent into solvent flask; heat to boiling.
2. Add some hot solvent to solid in boiling flask; boil with stirring.
3. Add more hot solvent in portions (as necessary) until solid dissolves.
   IF solution contains colored impurities, GO TO 4.
   IF solution contains undissolved impurities, add more hot solvent; GO TO 5.
   IF not, GO TO 6.
4. Cool below boiling point, stir in Norit, and heat to boiling.
5. Filter hot solution by gravity.
6. Cover flask; set aside to cool until crystallization is complete.
7. Collect crystals by vacuum filtration; wash and air-dry on filter.
8. Clean up; dispose of solvent.

 Microscale (Test-Tube Method)

Use this method (illustrated in Figure E2) when you have approximately 0.1 g to 1 g of crude solid.

Equipment and Supplies

> 2 test tubes, 13 × 100 mm or 15 × 125 mm
> recrystallization solvent
> calibrated Pasteur pipet (preferably filter-tipped)
> heat source
> boiling stick or boiling chip
> flat-bladed microspatula
> Hirsch funnel with filter paper
> small filter flask
> cold washing solvent
> small Erlenmeyer flask (to hold test tube)
> beaker (to cover flask and test tube)
> shortened filter-tip pipet or filtering pipet (optional)
> pelletized Norit (optional)

If you know the solubility of the solid in the boiling recrystallization solvent, calculate the approximate volume of solvent you will need to recrystallize it, and measure out that amount plus 20–50% extra (use the higher value if you think you will need to filter the hot solution). Otherwise, start with about 1 mL per 0.1 g of solid, and use more if needed. Obtain a test tube large enough that the solvent will fill it no more than half full. Measure the recrystallization solvent into the test tube (the *solvent tube*) with a calibrated Pasteur pipet, and add a boiling chip or boiling stick; heat it to

stirring, until saturation occurs. Then cool the mixture and try to induce crystallization.

Once a suitable solvent or solvent pair has been identified, estimate the volume of solvent needed to dissolve all of the solid to be purified, based on the volumes of solid and solvent you used in the test.

OPERATION 29   # Sublimation

Sublimation is a phase change in which a solid passes directly into the vapor phase without going through an intermediate liquid phase. Many solids that have appreciable vapor pressures below their melting points can be purified by (1) heating the solid to sublime it (convert it to a vapor), (2) condensing the vapor on a cold surface, and (3) scraping off the condensed solid. This method works best if impurities in the crude solid do not sublime appreciably. Sublimation is not as selective as recrystallization or chromatography, but it has some advantages in that no solvent is required, and losses in transfer can be kept low.

 Experimental Considerations

Sublimation is usually carried out by heating the *sublimand* (the solid before it has sublimed) with a suitable heat source, and collecting the *sublimate* (the solid after it has sublimed and condensed) on a cool surface. For best results, the sublimand should be dry and finely divided, and the distance between the sublimand and the condensing surface should be minimized. A simple but effective sublimator consists of two nested beakers of appropriate sizes. For example, a 100-mL beaker can be nested inside a 150-mL beaker, with the inner beaker rotated so as to leave a gap of about 1 cm at the bottom. In some cases, it may be necessary to place separators made of folded-over strips of filter paper or paper toweling between the beakers to get the right spacing. Good beaker combinations are 100 mL/ 150 mL (for microscale work), 250 mL/400 mL, and 400 mL/600 mL. The sublimand is spread out on the bottom of the outer beaker, and the

On humid days, adding ice may cause condensation of water on the sublimate.

condensing (inner) beaker is partially filled with cold water, with or without added ice. As the outer beaker is heated, crystals of sublimate collect on the bottom of the condensing beaker. Figure E4 illustrates a sublimator operating on the same principle, except that an Erlenmeyer flask is used as a condenser, and the temperature is controlled by flowing water.

Solids that do not sublime rapidly at atmospheric pressure may do so under vacuum. Figure E5a illustrates a vacuum sublimator that can be assembled by fitting a 15 × 125-mm test tube snugly inside an 18 × 150-mm sidearm test tube, using a rubber O-ring from a microscale lab kit to act as a vacuum seal. A short section of 15-mm i.d. Tygon tubing (or several layers of masking tape) is placed around the lip of the inner tube to keep it from slipping inside the sidearm test tube (see *J. Chem. Educ.* **1991**, *68*, A63). A commercial vacuum sublimator, such as the one in Figure E5b, is more efficient because the condenser has a flat, wide bottom that is close to the sublimate.

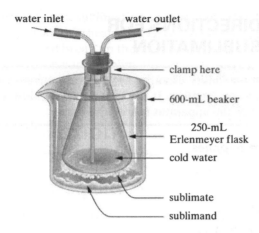

water inlet

water outlet

clamp here

600-mL beaker

250-mL
Erlenmeyer flask

cold water

sublimate

sublimand

Figure E4 Sublimation apparatus

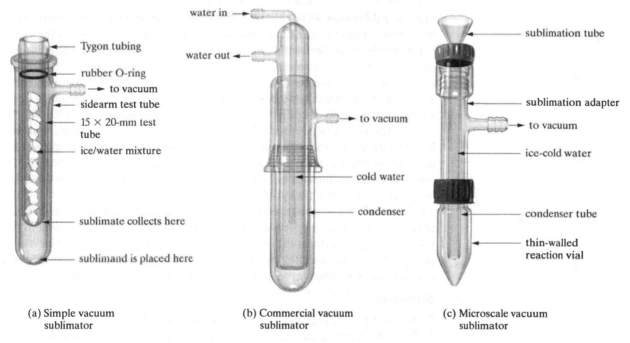

Tygon tubing

rubber O-ring

to vacuum

sidearm test tube

15 × 20-mm test
tube

ice/water mixture

sublimate collects here

sublimand is placed here

water in

water out

to vacuum

cold water

condenser

sublimation tube

sublimation adapter

to vacuum

ice-cold water

condenser tube

thin-walled
reaction vial

(a) Simple vacuum
    sublimator

(b) Commercial vacuum
    sublimator

(c) Microscale vacuum
    sublimator

Figure E5 Apparatus for vacuum sublimation

The microscale vacuum sublimation apparatus pictured in Figure E5c can be constructed using a special sublimation tube and adapter.

Depending on the temperature required and the nature of the sublimation apparatus, heat sources such as hot-water baths, oil baths, steam baths, hot plates (for nested beakers), heating blocks, and sand baths can be used for sublimation. An oil bath provides the most uniform heating, but oil baths are messy and somewhat hazardous to work with. With some of these heat sources, crystals tend to collect on the sides of the sublimation container as well as on the condenser. Wrapping the base of the sublimation container with aluminum foil or other insulation will help prevent this.

Presumably, entane and orctane exist only in J. R. R. Tolkien's Middle-Earth, where they are used for fuel by Ents and Orcs, respectively.

P is the total pressure over the mixture, assumed here to be 1 atm (760 torr).

In these expressions, P_A is the partial pressure of component A over the mixture, P_A^o is the equilibrium vapor pressure of pure A at the same temperature, X_A is the mole fraction of A in the liquid, and Y_A is the mole fraction of A in the vapor. Unfortunately, no real liquids obey these laws perfectly, so we shall consider the behavior of two imaginary hydrocarbons, *entane* (bp = 50°C) and *orctane* (bp = 100°C), which obey them both. If a mixture of entane and orctane is heated at normal atmospheric pressure, it will begin to boil at a temperature that is determined by the composition of the liquid mixture, producing vapor of a different composition. For example, an equimolar mixture of entane and orctane will start to boil at a temperature just above 66°C, and the vapor will contain more than four moles of entane for every mole of orctane. The liquid and vapor composition of an entane–orctane mixture at any temperature can be calculated using Equations **3** and **4**, which are derived from Dalton's law and Raoult's law.

$$X_A = \frac{P - P_B^o}{P_A^o - P_B^o} \qquad (3)$$

$$Y_A = \frac{P_A^o}{P} X_A \qquad (4)$$

For example, at 70°C the vapor pressure of orctane is 315 torr, and that of entane is 1370 torr (see Table E2), so the mole fraction of entane in a distilland that boils at 70°C will be (from Equation **3**)

$$X_{entane} = \frac{760 - 315}{1370 - 315} = 0.422$$

Its mole fraction in the vapor will be (from Equation **4**)

$$Y_{entane} = \frac{1370}{760} \times 0.422 = 0.761$$

showing that the vapor (and thus the distillate) is considerably richer in entane than is the liquid. The vapor pressures and approximate liquid–vapor compositions for entane and orctane at this and other temperatures are given in Table E2.

The key to an understanding of distillation is this: *The vapor over any mixture of volatile liquids contains more of the lower boiling component than does the liquid mixture itself.* So, at any time during a distillation, the liquid condensing into the receiver contains more of the lower-boiling component

Table E2   Equilibrium vapor pressures and mole fractions of entane and orctane at different temperatures

	Entane			Orctane		
T, °C	P^o, torr	X	Y	P^o, torr	X	Y
50°	760	1.00	1.00	160	0.00	0.00
60°	1030	0.67	0.90	227	0.33	0.10
70°	1370	0.42	0.76	315	0.58	0.24
80°	1790	0.24	0.57	430	0.76	0.43
90°	2300	0.11	0.32	576	0.89	0.68
100°	2930	0.00	0.00	760	1.00	1.00

Note: P^o = equilibrium vapor pressure of the pure liquid; X = mole fraction in liquid mixture; Y = mole fraction in vapor.

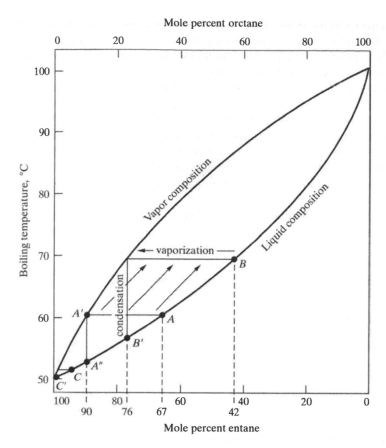

Figure E6 Temperature–composition diagram for entane–orctane mixtures

than does the liquid in the pot. As more of the lower-boiling component distills away, the pot liquid becomes richer in the higher-boiling liquid, so, by the end of the distillation, most of the lower-boiling liquid is in the receiver and most of the higher-boiling liquid is in the pot.

The purification process is shown by Figure E6, in which the liquid and vapor compositions are plotted against the boiling temperatures of entane–orctane mixtures. Suppose we distill a mixture that contains 2 moles of entane for every mole of orctane (67 mole percent entane). From the graph and Table E2, you can see that such a mixture will boil at 60°C (point A), and that its vapor will contain 90 mole percent (mol%) entane (point A′). Thus, the distillate that is condensed from this vapor (point A″) will be much richer in entane than was the original mixture in the pot. As the distillation continues, however, the more volatile component will boil away faster, and the pot will contain progressively less entane. Therefore, the vapor will also contain less entane, and the boiling temperature will rise. When the percentage of entane in the pot has fallen to 42 mol% (point B), the boiling temperature will have risen to 70°C, and the distillate will contain only 76 mol% entane (point B′). Only if the distillation were to be continued after nearly all of the entane had distilled would the distillate contain more of the less volatile component; at 90°C, for example, more than two-thirds of the molecules in the distillate would be orctane molecules.

thermometer records will always be higher than the still-head temperature, so it is no substitute for an internal thermometer, which records the actual vapor temperature of the liquid being distilled.

 Boiling Range.   An approximate boiling range for a distillation may be specified in an experimental procedure. For example, when isopentyl acetate is prepared by the reaction of isopentyl alcohol and acetic acid in Experiment 5, the product is collected over a boiling range of 137°C to 143°C.

$$
\underset{\substack{\text{acetic acid}}}{CH_3\overset{\overset{\displaystyle O}{\|}}{C}OH} + \underset{\substack{\text{isopentyl alcohol}\\ \text{b.p. }130°C}}{HOCH_2CH_2\overset{\overset{\displaystyle CH_3}{|}}{C}HCH_3} \longrightarrow \underset{\substack{\text{isopentyl acetate}\\ \text{b.p. }142°C}}{CH_3\overset{\overset{\displaystyle O}{\|}}{C}OCH_2CH_2\overset{\overset{\displaystyle CH_3}{|}}{C}HCH_3} + H_2O
$$

Because the major impurity in this case is the more volatile isopentyl alcohol, most of the isopentyl acetate should distill below its normal boiling point of 142°C; using 143°C as the end of the range allows for experimental error. If the boiling range for a distillation is not specified, you should collect the *main fraction* (the distilled liquid that contains the desired component) over a relatively narrow boiling range—usually 4–6°C—that brackets the boiling point of the desired component. A liquid fraction that distills below the expected boiling range for the main fraction is called a *forerun.* It should be collected in a different container than the main fraction, saved until distillation is complete, and then disposed of as directed. Sometimes, because of improper thermometer placement or an excessive heating rate, the internal thermometer will record a temperature lower than the actual vapor temperature. In that case, some or all of the liquid collected as forerun will actually be part of the expected main fraction and should *not* be discarded. So if you collect more "forerun" than expected, save it and redistill it later, after readjusting the heating rate or thermometer position. It may be advisable to redistill *all* of the liquid that distilled previously because the rest of the distillate may also have been collected over the wrong temperature range.

DIRECTIONS FOR SIMPLE DISTILLATION

Standard Scale

Equipment and Supplies

    heat source
    supports for heat source and receiver
    clamps, ring stands
    round-bottom flask
    boiling chips *or* stir bar and magnetic stirrer
    connecting adapter (still head)
    thermometer adapter
    thermometer

> condenser
> condenser tubing
> vacuum adapter
> receiver(s)
> joint clip(s) or rubber band

For distilling ~10 mL of liquid or more, assemble [OP-2] the conventional distillation apparatus pictured in Figure E7. As the pot, use the smallest round bottom flask for which the liquid's volume is roughly half or less of the container's capacity. For distilling less than 10 mL of liquid, assemble the compact apparatus pictured in Figure E9; use a 25-mL round bottom flask as the pot. Be sure to position the thermometer correctly in the still head (see Figure E8). If the liquid being distilled is quite volatile or hazardous, use a round-bottom flask as the receiver; otherwise, you can use an open container (usually tared), such as an Erlenmeyer flask, graduated cylinder, or large vial. Remove the thermometer assembly, add the distilland to the boiling flask through a stemmed funnel, and then drop in a few boiling chips or a stir bar. Replace the thermometer assembly and, if you are using the conventional apparatus, turn on the condenser water to provide a slow but steady stream of coolant. Note that the condenser water should flow *in* the lower end of the condenser and *out* the upper end. If you are using the compact apparatus, immerse the receiver in a suitable cooling bath.

Start the stirrer (if you are using one) and turn on the heat source, adjusting the heating rate so that the liquid boils gently and a reflux ring of condensing vapors rises slowly into the still head. Shortly after the reflux ring reaches the thermometer bulb, the temperature reading should rise rapidly, and vapors should begin passing through the sidearm into the condenser or vacuum adapter, coalescing into droplets that run into the receiving flask. As the first few droplets come over, the thermometer reading should rise to an equilibrium value and stabilize at that value. At this time, the entire thermometer bulb should be covered by a thin film of condensing liquid, which will drip off the end of the bulb and into the pot. Record the temperature at which the thermometer reading stabilizes; if it is lower than expected, check the thermometer placement and adjust it if necessary. Distill the liquid at a rate of about 1–3 drops per second for the conventional apparatus, or about 1 drop per second or less using the compact apparatus, monitoring the temperature frequently throughout the distillation.

If the initial thermometer reading is below the expected boiling range, carry out the distillation until the lower end of the range is reached, collecting the forerun in the receiver; then replace the receiver by another one. Save any forerun for later disposal or possible redistillation. Try to make the switch quickly enough so that no distillate is lost. (Stop the distillation before changing receivers if you are using the compact apparatus.) If the initial thermometer reading is within the expected boiling range, there is no need to change receivers. Continue distilling until the upper end of the expected boiling range is reached or until only a small volume of liquid remains—enough to just moisten the bottom of the boiling flask. Turn off and remove the heat source before the boiling flask is completely dry; heating a dry flask might cause tar formation or even an explosion. Disassemble and clean the apparatus as soon as possible after the distillation is completed.

Waste Disposal: Dispose of the residue from the pot and any forerun as directed by your instructor.

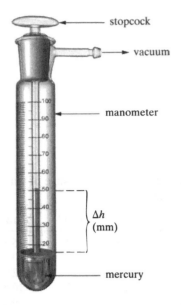

stopcock

vacuum

manometer

Δh
(mm)

mercury

Figure E13 A closed-end manometer

(Δh, in millimeters) between the mercury levels in the inner tube and the cylinder. Another kind of closed-end manometer is shown in Figure E15, which follows; its pressure reading (in torr) is the difference in height (in millimeters) between the mercury levels in the two arms of the bent tube. The mercury in a manometer can present a hazard if the vacuum is broken suddenly—air rushing in can push the mercury column forcefully to the closed end of the tube, breaking it and releasing toxic mercury into the laboratory. For this and other reasons, the vacuum must always be released *slowly.* It is advisable to open the valve connecting a manometer to an evacuated system only while a pressure reading is being made.

When the boiling points of any impurities are quite different from that of the main fraction, you may get by without a manometer if you can make a rough estimate of the pressure. For example, if you are using a water aspirator, you can measure the temperature of the water, estimate its vapor pressure from Table E4, and estimate the minimum boiling temperature of the liquid as described in the next paragraph. The product should distill somewhat *above* that temperature; its actual boiling range will depend on the efficiency of the aspirator and the air-tightness of your apparatus. You can also use a vacuum gauge to measure the pressure at the outlet of an aspirator or vacuum line, keeping in mind that the pressure in your distillation apparatus will be somewhat higher than the measured pressure.

Boiling Points Under Reduced Pressure.   If the boiling point of a substance at a given pressure is not known, it can be estimated using the vapor pressure–temperature nomograph shown in Figure E14. More precise estimates can be made using tables such as those in R. R. Dreisbach, *Pressure–Volume–Temperature Relationships of Organic Compounds* (New York: McGraw-Hill, 1952), or by using various empirical relationships. The main fraction should be collected over a range that brackets the expected boiling point, keeping in mind that the distillation temperature of a liquid may vary by 10°C or more under vacuum because of pressure fluctuations and other factors.

Heat Sources.   The heat source should be capable of providing constant, uniform heating to prevent bumping and superheating, and to maintain a constant distillation rate. For a typical standard scale vacuum distillation, a good heating mantle or an oil bath should be suitable. A microscale vacuum distillation can be carried out using a heating block or sand bath. See OP-7a for information about the use of these heat sources.

Smooth-Boiling Devices.   You can reduce bumping and foaming during a vacuum distillation by using microporous boiling chips, a magnetic stirring device, or (for standard scale vacuum distillation) a bubbler. Your lab kit may contain a narrow-tipped tube with a very fine hole at the outlet, which can be used as a bubbler. Otherwise, you can construct a flexible capillary bubbler, about as fine as a cat's whisker, by drawing it from a length of *thick-walled* capillary tubing (capillary bubblers drawn from thin-walled tubing break easily). See your instructor for help in constructing one. A short rubber tube with a screw clamp should be placed at the top of either kind of bubbler to control the rate of bubbling. The bubbler is inserted through a

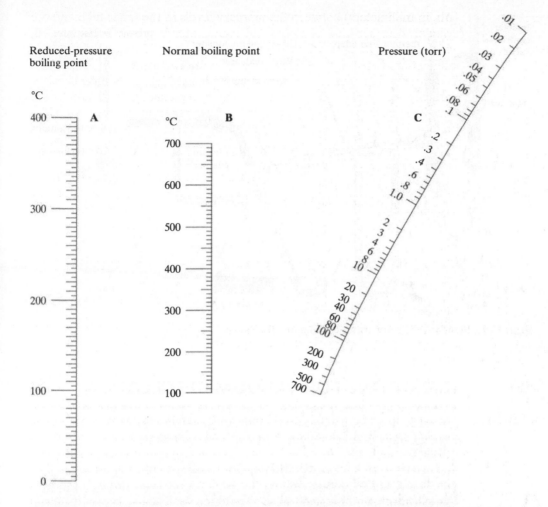

To estimate the boiling point at pressure P given the boiling point at another pressure P' : (a) connect pressure P' in **C** with the boiling point at that pressure in **A** using a ruler, and place a sharp pencil point where the ruler intersects line **B**; (b) pivot the ruler around the pencil point until it reaches the desired pressure (P) in **C**, and then read the boiling point at that pressure from **A**.

Example: To estimate the boiling point of dibutyl phthalate at 10 torr from its reported boiling point of 236° at 40 torr, place a ruler at 40 torr in **C** and 236° in **A**, causing it to intersect line **B** at about 345°. Then hold a pencil point at 345° on **B**, pivot the ruler about that point to 10 torr in **C**, and read the boiling point from **A**. This yields an estimated boiling point of 197° at 10 torr.

Figure E14 Reduced-pressure boiling-point nomograph

thermometer adapter (or a rubber stopper, if necessary) so that its tip extends to within a millimeter or two of the bottom of the boiling flask. Under vacuum, this device should deliver a very fine stream of air bubbles, preventing development of the large bubbles that cause bumping. However, a bubbler has several drawbacks. Air entering the system raises the pressure slightly and may oxidize the product at high temperatures, and a capillary bubbler may plug up when the vacuum is broken. Nevertheless, a well-constructed capillary bubbler works better than any other smooth-boiling device.

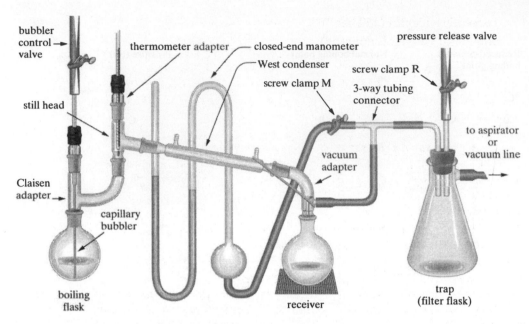

Figure E15 Standard scale apparatus for vacuum distillation

DIRECTIONS FOR VACUUM DISTILLATION

Safety Notes

> Because of the possibility of an implosion, safety glasses *must* be worn during a vacuum distillation. Work behind a hood sash or safety shield while the apparatus is under vacuum. A rapid pressure increase, accompanied by a thick fog in the distilling flask, indicates decomposition of the distilland. If this occurs, unplug the heat source *immediately*, and get away (warning others to do so also) until the flask cools. Report the incident to your instructor.

 Standard Scale

Before beginning a vacuum distillation, you should make a rough estimate of the boiling temperature of your sample under vacuum, or be ready to estimate it using the nomograph in Figure E14 once you obtain a manometer reading. Italicized instructions apply only if you are using a manometer; otherwise, disregard them.

Equipment and Supplies

>   heat source
>   rings, clamps, supports
>   round-bottom flask
>   bubbler or other smooth-boiling device
>   Claisen adapter

connecting adapter (still head)

stopper (if bubbler is not used)

thermometer

thermometer adapter

condenser

vacuum adapter

receiving flask(s)

joint clips (or wire, etc.)

condenser tubing

thick-walled rubber tubing

screw clamps

trap with pressure-release valve

manometer (optional)

glass tee (optional)

Inspect all glassware and rubber tubing, and replace any damaged items; if you have any doubt about their condition, see your instructor. For distilling ~10 mL of liquid or more, assemble [OP-2] the conventional vacuum-distillation apparatus as pictured in Figure E15. Be sure that the thermometer is placed correctly, as shown in Figure E8 of OP-30. (For distilling less than 10 mL of liquid, assemble the compact apparatus pictured in Figure E9, but connect it to the rest of the system as shown in Figure E15; interpose a Claisen head between the boiling flask and still head if you will be using a capillary bubbler or if carryover may be a problem.) Apply vacuum grease at all joints, as described in OP-2. If you aren't using a manometer, omit the three-way tubing connector shown. Connect the vacuum adapter to a trap with a pressure-release valve, and connect the trap to the vacuum source. If you are using a capillary bubbler, provide it with a screw clamp on a short length of rubber tubing to control the bubbling rate. If you are using micro-porous boiling chips or a stir bar to prevent bumping, drop them into the re-action flask and insert a ground-glass stopper into the short arm of the Claisen adapter (if your apparatus has one). If you are using a vacuum line rather than an aspirator, cool the trap if directed to do so by your instructor.

Make sure that all joints and connections are tight; then add the liquid to be distilled through a funnel. (If the liquid contains a volatile solvent, re-move it first by distilling at atmospheric pressure, and then let the apparatus cool before proceeding.) If you are using a bubbler, open its screw clamp a turn or two. Raise the heat source into position, but do not begin heating yet. Turn on the condenser cooling water (or immerse the receiving flask of the compact apparatus in a suitable cooling bath), open screw clamp R, and turn on the vacuum fully. Slowly close clamp R, and adjust the screw clamp on the bubbler (if you are using one) so that it emits a fine stream of bub-bles. (If bumping and foaming occur, there may be some residual solvent in the distilland; open clamp R slowly, and then close it down to a point at which the solvent will evaporate without excessive bumping. If a rubber tube collapses under vacuum, open clamp R slowly to break the vacuum, and replace it with sturdier tubing.) *Slowly open clamp M, wait a minute or two until the pressure equilibrates, then read the manometer and close clamp M.*

If the observed pressure is more than ~10 torr above the estimated pressure, check the system for leaks caused by loose joints, cracked tubing, and so on. If you find any leaks, release the vacuum by slowly opening clamp R, and fix them. If the pressure is satisfactory, use the nomograph shown in Figure E14 to estimate the boiling range at that pressure.

If you are using a magnetic stirrer, turn it on. Begin heating to bring the mixture to the boiling point. If you are using a bubbler, adjust the bubbler clamp as necessary to maintain a very fine stream of bubbles as the temperature rises. If excessive foaming occurs on boiling, reduce the heating rate. If bubbles form around any joint during the distillation, that joint is leaking air into the system; remove the heat source, release the vacuum, and regrease the joint or replace the glassware part by another one. When liquid begins to condense into the receiver, record the temperature reading. *Slowly open clamp M, let the pressure equilibrate, and record the pressure reading; then close clamp M and leave it closed, except when you need to make another pressure reading.* Adjust the heat source so that a distillation rate of about one drop per second or less is attained. If the temperature at the still head jumps up or down while the liquid is distilling, the pressure may be fluctuating because of changes in the aspirator flow rate; adjust the heating rate as necessary to maintain a suitable distillation rate. (To minimize such fluctuations, only a few students should use aspirators at the same time.)

If the initial distillation temperature is markedly lower than the estimated boiling range for the product, you are probably distilling a volatile forerun. Continue distilling until the temperature reaches the low end of the expected boiling range. Then change receivers without turning off the vacuum using the following procedure:

1. Lower the heat source and let the system cool down.
2. Open the bubbler clamp (if you are using one); then open clamp R slowly to bring the system to atmospheric pressure.
3. Replace the receiver with another one. If you are using microporous boiling chips, add another chip or two.
4. Slowly close clamp R; adjust the bubbler (if used).
5. Heat until distillation resumes.
6. Record the boiling temperature.

A capillary bubbler will sometimes plug up when the vacuum is broken; if that happens, you will have to replace it with a new one. Continue distilling until the upper end of the estimated boiling range is reached, or until a significant drop in temperature indicates that the product is completely distilled. Stop the distillation before the boiling flask is completely dry.

When the distillation is complete, follow steps **1** and **2** for bringing the system back to atmospheric pressure, and then turn off the vacuum. Disassemble the apparatus, and clean the glassware promptly.

Waste Disposal: Dispose of any residue and forerun as directed by your instructor.

Summary

1. Inspect glassware and tubing, assemble apparatus, and check connections and joints.
2. Add distilland and smooth-boiling device.

3. Position heat source, start cooling water, open clamp R, and turn on vacuum.
4. Close R; let pressure equilibrate.
5. *Open M, read pressure, close M, and estimate boiling range.*
6. Heat until distillation begins; adjust bubbler (if used).
7. Record temperature *and pressure.*
   IF temperature is below estimated range, GO TO 8.
   IF temperature is within estimated range, GO TO 12.
8. Adjust heat; distill until temperature reaches lower end of expected boiling range.
9. Lower heat source, let cool, and open bubbler clamp and clamp R.
10. Change receiver and close R.
11. Adjust bubbler (if used), heat until distillation resumes, and record temperature.
12. Distill until upper end of temperature range is attained or only a little distilland remains.
13. Lower heat source, let cool, and open R.
14. Turn off vacuum; remove distillate.
15. Disassemble and clean apparatus; dispose of residue and forerun.

 ## Microscale

Before beginning a vacuum distillation, you should have made a rough estimate of the boiling temperature of your sample under vacuum, or be ready to estimate it using the nomograph in Figure E14 once you obtain a manometer reading. Italicized instructions apply only if you are using a manometer; otherwise, disregard them.

Equipment and Supplies

> heat source
> clamps, supports
> boiling flask
> smooth-boiling device
> Hickman still
> *Claisen adapter
> thermometer
> *2 thermometer adapters (or 1 adapter and a 1-hole rubber stopper)
> *bent glass tube (8 mm o.d.)
> thick-walled rubber tubing
> screw clamps
> trap with pressure-release valve
> manometer (optional)
> 3-way tubing connector (optional)

> *These parts can be replaced by a multipurpose adapter, which is provided in some microscale lab kits.

Inspect all glassware, O-rings, and rubber tubing, and replace any damaged items; if you have any doubt about their condition, see your instructor.

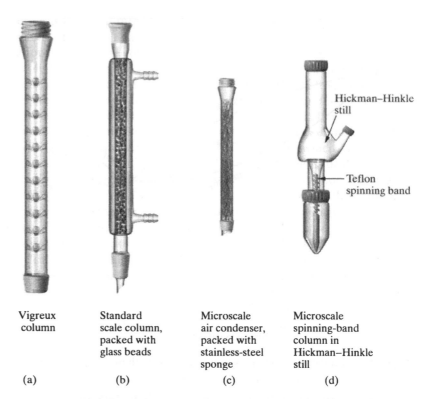

Vigreux
column

(a)

Standard
scale column,
packed with
glass beads

(b)

Microscale
air condenser,
packed with
stainless-steel
sponge

(c)

Microscale
spinning-band
column in
Hickman–Hinkle
still

(d)

Figure E22 Some columns for fractional distillation

Take Care! Stainless steel sponge has sharp edges; wear gloves while handling it.

are lower. The packing is introduced into a wide-bore jacketed column (not the narrower West condenser) from a standard scale lab kit, or into an air condenser from a microscale lab kit. Packing materials include metal turnings and glass or porcelain beads, rings, helices, and saddles. Highly efficient packing materials such as glass helices may provide HETP ratings down to about 1 cm, but they are quite expensive. Glass beads and stainless-steel sponge are more practical for use in most undergraduate laboratories. The jacketed standard scale column shown in Figure E22b is packed with glass beads, and the microscale column in Figure E22c is constructed of an air condenser packed with stainless-steel sponge. Stainless-steel sponge pads can be stretched and cut into 6–8 inch lengths for use in a typical standard scale distilling column. Approximately 1.5 g of stainless-steel sponge can be stretched to pack a microscale column. With stainless-steel packing, the column is sometimes deliberately flooded by strong heating to wet the packing (see the section entitled "Flooding"). Then the heat is reduced to drain the column before distillation is begun. Stainless-steel packing should not be used to distill halogen compounds, which corrode it.

The apparatus for standard scale fractional distillation is like that for simple distillation, except that a distilling column is interposed between the pot and the still head, as shown in Figure E23. For high-boiling liquids, the column should be insulated to prevent heat losses that may reduce efficiency or prevent distillation entirely. It can be covered by one or more layers of crumpled aluminum foil (shiny side in), or glass wool (wear gloves) can be

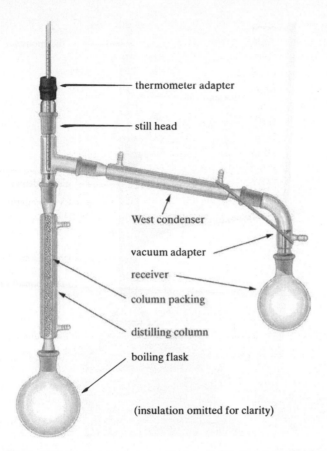

Figure E23 Apparatus for standard scale fractional distillation

wrapped around it and held in place by aluminum foil. The insulation should provide "windows" that can be opened for observation of the vapors in the still head and the packing near the bottom of the column. The still head can be insulated with the same materials as the column.

Typical microscale parts can be used to construct fractional-distillation setups like the one illustrated in Figure E24. Unless you are using a spinning-band column or another high-throughput column, it is seldom practical to distill less than 3–5 mL of liquid through a fractionating column, so the pot should ordinarily be a 10-mL round-bottomed flask. A microscale column made from an air condenser should be insulated. The insulating material can be glass wool (wear gloves) or aluminum foil, as described for a standard scale column, or two concentric layers of clear PVC tubing as shown in Figure E24. To insulate an air condenser with PVC tubing, obtain two split 20-cm lengths of tubing of different diameters; then wrap the smaller (in diameter) tube around the column and the larger tube around the smaller one. For an air condenser having an outer diameter (o.d.) at its narrowest of $\frac{1}{2}$ inch, use $\frac{1}{2}$-inch i.d. (inner diameter) by $\frac{5}{8}$-inch o.d. and $\frac{5}{8}$-inch i.d. by $\frac{7}{8}$-inch o.d. tubing.

A Hickman still is set atop the column to collect the condensing vapors. The narrow neck of the still should be insulated by wrapping it with glass wool (wear gloves), which can be held in place with aluminum foil, if

The throughput of a column is the volume of distillate collected per unit of time.

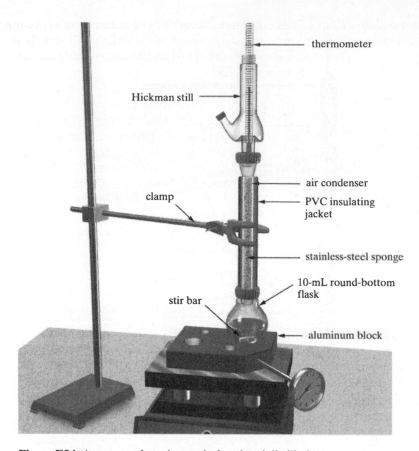

Figure E24 Apparatus for microscale fractional distillation

desired. If the distilland contains components that boil much below 100°C, it is a good idea to attach a condenser to the Hickman still. For most fractional distillations, however, no condenser is needed if the heating rate is kept low enough to prevent the escape of distillate vapors from the top of the still. If desired, an *uncapped* (important!) thermometer adapter or a multipurpose adapter with a sidearm can be inserted on top of the Hickman still to align the thermometer and reduce the likelihood of vapor escape.

Take Care! Capping the thermometer adapter will create a closed system, which could shatter and cause serious injury.

Heat Sources.   For good results, the heat source should provide constant, uniform heating. An oil bath works best, but a heating mantle will suffice if its heat output is adjusted carefully to bring about the desired distillation rate. A heating block or sand bath is suitable for microscale work. See OP-7a for information about the use of these heat sources.

Flooding.   One problem often encountered during a fractional distillation is *flooding,* in which the column becomes partly or entirely filled with liquid. Flooding is usually caused by an excessive heating rate, but it may also be caused by poor insulation, an unsuitable packing support, or improper packing. For example, sponge packing that is too tightly compressed or a glass-wool plug used as a packing support may hold up enough liquid to cause flooding. If flooding occurs, the apparatus must be separated from the heat source until all of the excess liquid has returned to the pot. Heating can then be resumed at a slower rate. Flooding will greatly decrease the efficiency of a separation because it reduces the surface area of packing available for the separation.

Chasers.   A column with a high holdup will retain a relatively large amount of distillate. To improve the distillate recovery, the held-up liquid can be driven off the column into the receiving container or the well of a Hickman still by a suitable high-boiling substance, called a *chaser*. For example, *p*-xylene (bp 138°C) is a good chaser for liquids that boil around 100°C or below. After the last fraction has distilled, the chaser is added to the pot and heated to boiling, and the temperature is monitored as it climbs up the column. When the temperature begins to rise sharply, indicating that the chaser has reached the still head, distillation is stopped immediately and the recovered distillate is collected.

DIRECTIONS FOR FRACTIONAL DISTILLATION

Standard Scale

Equipment and Supplies

    heat source
    clamps, rings, supports
    boiling flask (pot)
    boiling chips *or* stir bar and stirrer
    distilling column
    column packing
    insulating material (optional)
    connecting adapter (still head)
    thermometer
    thermometer adapter
    condenser
    condenser tubing
    vacuum adapter
    fraction collectors
    joint clips or rubber bands

If you are using column packing, pack the column to within a centimeter or so of the upper ground joint. To pack a column with stainless-steel sponge, *pull* it into the column using a copper wire bent into a hook at one end, making sure that it is as uniform as possible. Wear gloves, or you might cut yourself on the sharp edges of the packing. To pack a column with glass beads, hold the column nearly horizontal with your hand over the bottom opening, and place a few large beads in the top of the column. Then quickly pivot the column to an upright position so that (with a little luck) the beads will jam together at the constriction and support the remainder of the packing. (A small plug of stainless-steel sponge can also serve as a support.) Slowly pour in the rest of the packing from a beaker, with continuous shaking, so that it is as uniform as possible. Other packing can be added similarly, except that glass helices should be dropped in one at a time, with shaking.

Assemble the apparatus illustrated in Figure E23, using a boiling flask large enough that it will be no more than half full of distilland. The fraction collectors can be screw-cap vials or other containers of an appropriate size; they should be numbered and tared. For very volatile distillates, small ground-joint flasks can be used as fraction collectors. The vacuum adapter drip tube should extend into the collector to reduce losses by evaporation. Make sure that all joints are tight, the column is perpendicular to the benchtop, the boiling flask and fraction collector are supported properly, and none of the joints are under excessive strain. If the boiling temperature will exceed 100°C or so during the distillation, it is advisable to insulate the apparatus from the bottom of the column to the top of the still head. Position the thermometer correctly, as illustrated in Figure E8 of OP-30. Add the distilland to the distilling flask, and drop in a few boiling chips or a stir bar. Start cooling water flowing through the condenser, but *not* through the column jacket.

Position the heat source, start the stirrer (if you are using one), and begin heating to bring the mixture to the boiling point. When it boils, adjust the heating rate so that the reflux ring of condensing vapor passes up the column at a slow, even rate—it should take 5–10 min or more to reach the top of the column. Watch the packing at the bottom of the column closely for evidence of flooding. If flooding occurs, remove the heat source immediately, and let the liquid drain into the boiling flask; then resume heating at a lower rate. If flooding is still a problem, you may need to re-insulate or repack the column. When the vapors rise above the column packing, adjust the heat to keep the reflux ring between the packing and the sidearm for a minute or so, giving the column time to equilibrate. After vapors begin to condense into the collector, read the thermometer when the temperature reading stabilizes. Distill at a rate of about 1 drop every 1–3 seconds, or at a rate that gives the desired reflux ratio. (Estimate the reflux ratio by counting the drops that drip into the pot and those that drip into the receiver during a short time period.) If the initial distillate is cloudy (due to dissolved water), change receivers when it becomes clear.

If the column is not very efficient or the components' boiling points are close together, the temperature may rise only gradually throughout the distillation. In that case, it is best to collect fractions continuously at regular temperature intervals and redistill them as needed. Otherwise, continue distilling until the still-head temperature begins to rise sharply, or until a predetermined target temperature is reached; then change fraction collectors, and record the temperature. Change collectors again when the temperature begins to stabilize at a higher value, or when the next target temperature is reached, and record the temperature. Increase the heating rate as necessary to maintain a suitable distillation rate. Continue to collect fractions over the appropriate temperature ranges until the pot is nearly dry, the temperature drops sharply, or the final target temperature is reached. (Note that the temperature may drop if the heating rate is too low, so that the hot vapors no longer reach the thermometer bulb.) Then lower and turn off the heat source, and let the column drain. Any fractions collected while the temperature was rising rapidly are impure; unless you wish to redistill them, they should be placed in a solvent recovery container. Disassemble and clean the apparatus; remove and clean stainless-steel packing without delay.

Summary

1. Pack column; assemble apparatus.
2. Add distilland and boiling chips or stir bar.
3. Turn on cooling water, stirrer (if used), and heat source.
4. Adjust heat so that reflux ring passes slowly up the column.
5. Record temperature after distillation begins, when thermometer reading stabilizes.
6. Distill until temperature rises sharply or target temperature is reached; record temperature.
   IF more fractions are to be collected, change collector; REPEAT 6.
   IF you are distilling the last (or only) fraction, CONTINUE.
7. Distill until temperature drops sharply or final target temperature is reached.
8. Remove heat source; drain column.
9. Disassemble and clean apparatus; dispose of residue and any impure fractions.

 ## Microscale

Note: The italicized instructions apply only if you are using a Hickman–Hinkle still or another apparatus that has a spinning band.

Equipment and Supplies

heat source
clamps, support
boiling flask or vial (pot)
boiling chips *or* stir bar and stirrer
air condenser (for distilling column)
column packing *or spinning band*
insulating material
Hickman still
thermometer
condenser (optional)
condenser tubing (optional)
fraction collectors

If you are using column packing, pack the column to within a centimeter or less of the upper ground joint. To pack a column with stainless-steel sponge, *pull* it into the column using a copper wire bent into a hook at one end, making sure that it is as uniform as possible. Wear gloves, or you might cut yourself on the sharp edges of the packing. *If you are using a Hickman–Hinkle still or a similar apparatus that has a magnetically rotated spinning band, insert the spinning band in the bottom of the still (pointed end down), and lower it into the conical vial when you assemble the apparatus.*

A Hickman–Hinkle still uses a thin-walled conidal vial as the pot.

Add the distilland to the boiling flask or vial, and add one or two boiling chips or a stir bar. Assemble the apparatus illustrated in Figure E24, using small screw-cap vials—numbered and tared—as fraction collectors. *If you are using a Hickman–Hinkle still, do not insert a separate column between the still and the pot; its column is an integral part of the still.* Make sure that all joints are tight, the column is perpendicular to the benchtop, and the apparatus and thermometer are supported securely. Position the thermometer correctly, as illustrated in Figure E12 of OP-30. Insulate the column and the narrow neck of the Hickman still.

Position the boiling flask or vial in the heat source, start the stirrer (if you are using one), and begin heating to bring the mixture to the boiling point. *A spinning band should be rotated at a low spin rate when heat is applied, changed to an intermediate spin rate when reflux begins, and then adjusted to the highest practicable spin rate when liquid begins to enter the column. It should rotate freely, without significant vibration.* When the liquid boils, adjust the heating rate so that the reflux ring of condensing vapor passes up the column at a slow, even rate—it should take 5 minutes or more to reach the top of the column. Watch the packing at the bottom of the column closely for evidence of flooding. If flooding occurs, raise the apparatus away from the heat source immediately, and let the liquid drain into the pot; then resume heating at a lower rate. If flooding is still a problem, you may need to re-insulate or repack the column. After distillate begins to collect in the well of the Hickman still, read the thermometer when the temperature reading stabilizes. Distill the liquid so that the liquid level in the well rises very slowly; it should take 10 minutes or more to fill the well.

If the column is not very efficient or the components' boiling points are close together, the temperature may rise only gradually throughout the distillation. In that case, it is best to collect fractions continuously at regular temperature intervals and redistill them as needed. Otherwise, continue distilling until the still-head temperature begins to rise sharply, or until a predetermined target temperature is reached, and then transfer the liquid from the well to the first fraction collector. Close the port (of a ported still) immediately after the liquid has been withdrawn. If you are collecting more than one fraction, transfer each fraction to a different collector, and record the temperature range over which it was collected. If necessary, increase the heating rate to maintain a suitable distillation rate. Continue to collect fractions over the appropriate temperature ranges until the pot is nearly dry, the temperature drops sharply, or the final target temperature is reached. (Note that the temperature may drop if the heating rate is too low, so that the hot vapors no longer reach the thermometer bulb.) Then remove the apparatus from the heat source, and let the column drain. Any fractions collected while the temperature is rising rapidly are impure; unless you wish to redistill them, they should be placed in a solvent recovery container. Disassemble and clean the apparatus; remove and clean stainless-steel packing without delay.

A fraction may require several transfers if the well fills while it is distilling.

Waste Disposal: Dispose of any residue and impure fractions as directed by your instructor.

Summary

1. Pack column; add distilland and boiling chips or stir bar.
2. Assemble apparatus.
3. Turn on stirrer (if used) and heat source.
4. Adjust heat so that reflux ring passes slowly up the column.

5. Record temperature after distillation begins, when thermometer reading stabilizes.
6. Distill until temperature rises sharply or target temperature is reached, transfer distillate to collector, and record temperature.
   IF more fractions are to be collected, change collector; REPEAT 6.
   IF you are distilling the last (or only) fraction, CONTINUE.
7. Distill until temperature drops sharply or final target temperature is reached.
8. Remove apparatus from heat source; drain column.
9. Disassemble and clean apparatus; dispose of residue and any impure fractions.

When Things Go Wrong

Most of the things that go wrong during a simple distillation can also go wrong during a fractional distillation, so you can refer to "When Things Go Wrong" in OP-30 for help. The following cases apply only to fractional distillation.

If, while you're collecting a fraction, the temperature drops below that fraction's boiling range when there is still liquid in the pot, it's likely that all of the liquid making up that fraction has distilled but the vapors of the next fraction have not yet reached the still head. Keep heating, increasing the heating rate as necessary so that the next fraction will start distilling. It is also possible that the heat setting was not high enough to maintain distillation of the first fraction, in which case it should resume distilling after you turn up the heat.

Suppose that, when you assembled your standard scale apparatus, you were careful to connect the cooling-water tap to all of the available hose connections. Now the liquid in the pot is boiling, but none of its vapors are reaching the still head, where the temperature is still below 30°C. By connecting your distilling column to the cooling water, you have turned it into a reflux condenser; any vapors that enter it will condense and drip back into the pot. Yes, a distilling column does look a lot like a condenser, but it's not to be used as one during a fractional distillation.

F. Measuring Physical Constants

After a reaction product has been purified, it is usually *analyzed* to find out whether it is, in fact, the desired product, and how pure it is. Another function of analysis is to determine the identity of an unknown compound. Analysis may involve measurement of a substance's physical properties, as described in this section, or recording a spectrum or chromatograph of the substance, as described in Section G. A solid substance is usually analyzed by measuring its melting point [OP-33], and a liquid by measuring its boiling point [OP-34]. Measuring a liquid's refractive index [OP-35] provides a good indication of its purity and can be used to help identify it. An optically active compound, either liquid or solid, can be characterized by measuring its optical rotation [OP-36].

OPERATION **33**   # Melting Point

Principles and Applications

The *melting point (mp)* of a pure substance is defined as the temperature at which the solid and liquid phases of the substance are in equilibrium at a pressure of 1 atmosphere. At a temperature slightly below the melting point, a mixture of the two phases solidifies; at a temperature slightly above the melting point, the mixture liquefies. Melting points can be used to characterize organic compounds and to assess their purity. The melting point of a pure compound is a unique property of that compound, which is essentially independent of its source and method of purification. This is not to say that no two compounds will have the same melting point; many compounds have melting points that differ by no more than a fraction of a degree. If two pure samples have *different* melting points, however, they are almost certainly different compounds.

The melting point of an organic solid is usually measured by grinding the solid to a powder and packing the powder inside a *melting-point tube,* a capillary tube that is closed at one end. The melting-point tube is then placed in an appropriate heating device, and the *melting-point range* of the sample—the range of temperatures over which the solid is converted to a liquid—is observed and recorded. A pure substance usually melts within a range of no more than 1–2°C; that is, the transition from a crystalline solid to a clear, mobile liquid occurs within a degree or two if the rate of heating is sufficiently slow and the sample is properly prepared.

The presence of impurities in a substance *lowers* its melting point and *broadens* its melting-point range. To better understand the effects of impurities on melting points, consider the phase diagram for phenol (P) and diphenylamine (D) in Figure F1. Pure phenol melts at 41°C, and pure diphenylamine at 53°C. If a sample of phenol contains diphenylamine as an impurity, its melting point will be lower than 41°C by an amount that

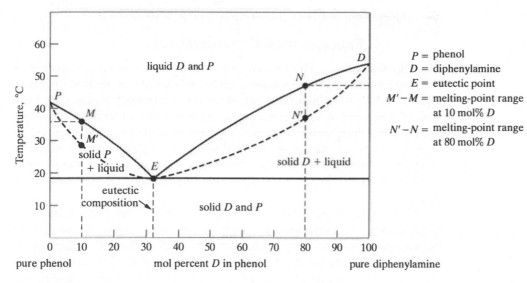

Figure F1 Phase diagram for the phenol–diphenylamine system

depends on the mole percent of diphenylamine present. Similarly, the melting point of diphenylamine will be lower than 53°C if i t contains phenol as an impurity. For example, the melting point of phenol containing 10 mol% diphenylamine is given by point *M* on the phase diagram, and that of diphenylamine containing 20 mol% phenol is given by point *N*.

Pure phenol and pure diphenylamine both have sharp melting points, meaning that the transition from solid to liquid occurs over a narrow temperature range. Mixtures of the two (except the *eutectic mixture* at the minimum in the diagram) exhibit broader melting-point ranges that depend on their composition. The approximate melting-point range for a mixture is given by the distance between the broken lines connecting points *P* and *E* or points *E* and *D* and the solid lines connecting the same points on the phase diagram. For example, the melting-point range of phenol containing 10 mol% diphenylamine is given by the distance between *M'* and *M*, and the melting-point range of diphenylamine containing 20 mol% phenol is given by the distance between *N'* and *N*.

Because the melting point decreases in a nearly linear fashion as the amount of impurity increases (until the eutectic point, E, is reached), the difference between the observed and expected values can make it possible to estimate a compound's purity, as is done for camphor in Experiment 7. The melting-point lowering effect can also be used to confirm the identity of a substance, such as the product of a reaction, when it is thought to be a certain known compound. The compound in question is mixed with a sample of the known compound, and the melting point of the mixture is measured. If the two compounds are identical, the mixture melting point will be essentially the same as that of the known compound. If they are not identical, the known compound will act as an impurity in the unknown, so the melting point of the mixture will be lower and its range broader than for the known compound.

Experimental Considerations

Melting Behavior.   The melting-point range of a sample is reported as the range between (1) the temperature at which the sample first begins to liquefy and (2) the temperature at which it is completely liquid, called the *liquefaction point*. When a single melting point is to be reported, the liquefaction point is generally used. A compound may also be characterized by its *meniscus point,* the temperature at which the liquid meniscus is barely clear of the solid below it. Some automatic melting-point devices report melting points that are closer to the meniscus point than to the liquefaction point.

If traces of solvent remain in a sample because of insufficient drying or other causes, you may observe "sweating" of solvent from the sample or bubbles in the molten sample, which may resolidify when all of the solvent is driven off. If a sample does show this behavior, it should be dried and the melting point remeasured. Even a dry sample will tend to soften and shrink before it begins to liquefy; this process begins at the *eutectic temperature* (point *E* in Figure F1). In any case, softening, shrinking, and sweating should not be mistaken for melting behavior. The melting-point range does not begin until the first free liquid is clearly visible, at which time you should see movement of both solid and liquid in the melting-point tube.

Some compounds sublime—change directly from the solid to the vapor state—when they are heated in an open container. Sublimation can be detected during a melting-point determination by a pronounced shrinking of the sample, accompanied by the appearance of crystals higher up inside the melting-point tube (Figure F2). The melting point of a sample that sublimes at or below its melting temperature can be measured using a sealed melting-point tube. An ordinary melting-point tube should be cut (see OP-3) short enough so that it doesn't project above the block of a melting-point apparatus, such as the one in Figure F4, or so that it can be entirely immersed in a heating-bath liquid. The sample is introduced, and the open end is sealed in a burner flame (see OP-3). Then the melting point is measured by one of the methods described in the "Directions" section.

If a sample becomes discolored and liquefies over an unusually broad range during a melting-point determination, it is probably undergoing thermal decomposition. Compounds that decompose on heating usually melt at temperatures that vary with the rate of heating. The approximate melting point (also called the *decomposition point*) of such a compound should be measured by heating the melting-point apparatus to within a few degrees of the expected melting temperature before inserting the sample, and then raising the temperature at a rate of about 3–6°C per minute.

Apparatus for Measuring Melting Points.   Melting points can be determined with good accuracy using a Thiele tube or Thiele–Dennis tube filled with a heating-bath liquid such as mineral oil, as illustrated in Figure F5 for a Thiele–Dennis tube. The design of such tubes promotes good circulation of the heating liquid without stirring. A melting-point tube containing the solid is secured to a thermometer, which is then immersed in the bath liquid. The solid is observed carefully for evidence of melting as the apparatus is heated. Melting points can also be measured in an ordinary beaker if the

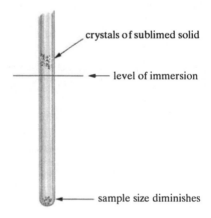

crystals of sublimed solid

level of immersion

sample size diminishes

Figure F2 Sublimation of a sample in a melting-point tube

bath liquid is stirred constantly (Figure F3), either manually or with a magnetic stirrer [OP-10].

Melting-point instruments that use capillary melting-point tubes, such as the Mel-Temp illustrated in Figure F4, are available commercially. As a rule, they are more accurate and easier to use than melting-point baths. The Mel-Temp and similar devices can be used to make several measurements at once which is convenient when a mixture melting point is being determined because it allows the melting points of the unknown compound, the known, and the mixture to be measured and compared at the same time. The heating rate is adjusted by a dial that controls the voltage input to a heating coil. The dial reading required to attain the desired heating rate at the sample's melting point can be estimated from a heating-rate chart furnished with the instrument. The dial is initially set higher than this to bring the temperature to within 20°C or so of the expected melting point, and then reset to the value estimated from the chart.

Either kind of apparatus can be used for both standard scale and microscale experiments, but commercial melting-point instruments are easier to use and provide more uniform heating than melting-point baths.

Thermometer Corrections. The observed melting point of a compound may be inaccurate because of defects in the thermometer used or because of the *emergent stem error* that results when a thermometer is not immersed to its intended depth in a heating bath. Many thermometers are designed to

Melting point tubes are available commercially, but one can be constructed by sealing one end of an open-ended capillary tube that is approximately 10 cm long and 1 mm in diameter.

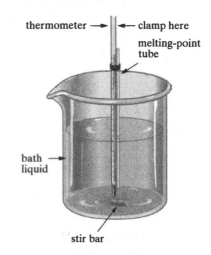

Figure F3 Stirred heating bath

Newer Mel-Temp models are provided with mercury-free precision digital thermometers.

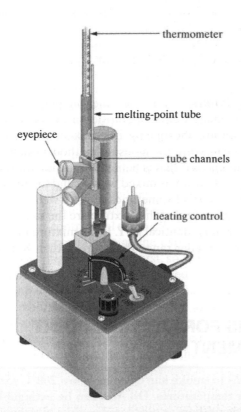

Figure F4 Apparatus for measuring melting points (Mel-Temp method)

You can use a similar method with other melting-point baths, such as the one shown in Figure F3, but a hot plate–stirrer or another flameless heat source will be required in that case.

You can use a thermometer clamp instead of a cutaway cork to hold the thermometer in place.

B. Thiele-Tube Method.   Clamp the Thiele tube or Thiele–Dennis tube securely to a ring stand, and add enough mineral oil (or another appropriate bath liquid) to just cover the top of the sidearm outlet, as shown in Figure F5a. (Refer to OP-7a for precautions to be followed when using oil baths.) Secure the melting-point tube to a broad-range thermometer as follows:

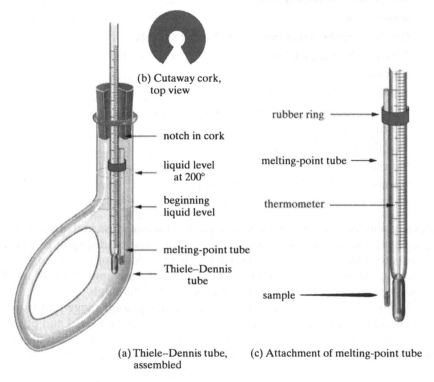

(b) Cutaway cork, top view

notch in cork

liquid level at 200°

beginning liquid level

melting-point tube

Thiele–Dennis tube

rubber ring

melting-point tube

thermometer

sample

(a) Thiele–Dennis tube, assembled

(c) Attachment of melting-point tube

Figure F5 Apparatus for measuring melting points (Thiele-tube method)

1. Cut a 3-mm-thick rubber ring from $\frac{1}{4}$-inch i.d. thin-walled rubber tubing (rubber rings may be provided).
2. Place the rubber ring around the thermometer, about 9 cm from its bulb end.
3. Pinch the rubber ring between your fingers to create a gap, and insert the open end of the melting-point tube through the gap.
4. Move the melting-point tube until the sample is adjacent to the middle of the thermometer bulb (see Figure F5c).

The cork is bored out to accommodate the thermometer, and then cut with a single-edged razor blade or a sharp knife so that the thermometer can be snapped into place from the side rather than inserted from the top.

Snap the thermometer into the center of a cutaway cork (Figure F5b) at a point above the rubber ring, with the melting-point tube and the degree markings on the same side as the opening in the cork. Insert this assembly into the bath liquid, and move the thermometer, if necessary, so that its bulb is centered in the tube about 3 cm below the sidearm junction and the temperature can be read through the opening in the cork (Figure F5a). The rubber ring should be 2–3 cm above the liquid level so that the bath liquid, as it expands on heating, will not come in contact with it. If the hot oil meets the rubber, it may soften and allow the melting-point tube to drop out.

Heat the bottom of the Thiele tube with a burner flame (or use a microburner, for more precise heat control) until the temperature is about 15°C below the expected melting point. Reduce the heating rate by turning down the flame and applying it at the sidearm, so that the temperature rises at a rate of 1–2°C per minute at the melting point. Continue heating at that rate as you observe the sample closely, and record (as the limits of the melting-point range) the temperatures (1) when the first free liquid appears in the melting-point tube and (2) when the sample is completely liquid. For best results, do at least two measurements on each compound. Let the heating bath cool to 15–20°C below the melting point before you do another measurement. Cooling can be accelerated by passing an airstream over the tube.

Clean up the apparatus, and either place the oil in a designated container or store it in the Thiele tube. Mineral oil can be removed from glassware by rinsing the glassware with petroleum ether followed by acetone, and then washing it with a detergent and water.

Summary

1. Assemble apparatus for melting-point determination.
2. Grind solid to a powder; fill melting-point tube(s) to depth of 1–2 mm. IF you are using method **B**, GO TO 4.
3. Insert sample in Mel-Temp heating block; GO TO 5.
4. Secure melting-point tube to thermometer; insert assembly in heating bath.
5. Heat rapidly to ~15–20°C below mp; then reduce heating rate to 1–2°C/min.
6. Observe and record melting-point range.
7. Disassemble apparatus as needed, and clean up.

When Things Go Wrong

If, during a melting-point determination, the solid sample begins to shrink before any liquid appears, don't assume that it is melting. The melting-point range doesn't begin until there is some liquid with the solid. But if the sample shrinks until there is little if any solid left at the bottom of the melting-point tube, your sample is subliming and may completely disappear before it starts to melt. In that case, you should prepare a new sample tube and seal it, as described in the section entitled "Melting Behavior."

If your sample discolors significantly during a melting-point determination, it is probably decomposing. Prepare a new sample tube, and proceed as described in "Melting Behavior."

If the melting point you measure for a substance is substantially higher than its expected value, you may have heated the sample too rapidly. If so, carry out another measurement using a new sample, with the temperature rising at a rate of no more than 2°C per minute at the melting point.

If the melting point you measure for a substance is substantially lower than its expected value, you may have recorded the temperature before it was completely melted. Try again with a new sample, making sure that it is entirely liquid before you record its melting point. If the melting point is still low, your product is probably wet or impure.

If the substance appears to melt over an excessively broad range, you may have used too much sample, or the sample may not have been packed tightly enough; the sample in the melting-point tube should be no more than 2 mm high. If you used the right amount of sample, you may have heated the sample too rapidly; the temperature should rise at a rate of no more than 2°C per minute at the melting point. Otherwise, you may have recorded the initial temperature before the sample began to liquefy, or your product may have decomposed near its melting point (see "Melting Behavior"). If repeating the melting-point measurement more carefully with a fresh sample (don't re-melt the original sample) still gives a broad range, your product may be wet or impure.

OPERATION **34**

Boiling Point

The *boiling point (bp)* of a liquid is defined as the temperature at which the vapor pressure of the liquid is equal to the external pressure at the surface of the liquid, and also as the temperature at which the liquid is in equilibrium with its vapor phase at that pressure. These definitions are the basis for various standard scale and small-scale methods for measuring boiling points. For example, the boiling point of a liquid can be determined by distilling a small quantity of the liquid and observing the temperature at the still head, where the liquid and its vapors are assumed to be in equilibrium. It can also be determined by measuring the temperature at which the liquid's vapor, trapped inside a capillary tube immersed in the liquid, exerts a pressure equal to the external pressure. Like the melting point of a solid, the boiling point of a liquid can be used to help identify it and assess its purity.

Boiling-Point Corrections

The *normal boiling point* of a liquid is its boiling point at an external pressure of 1 atmosphere (760 torr, 101.3 kPa). Because the atmospheric pressure at the time of a boiling-point determination is seldom exactly 760 torr, observed boiling points may differ somewhat from values reported in the literature and should be corrected. If a laboratory boiling-point determination is carried out at a location reasonably close to sea level, atmospheric pressure will rarely vary by more than 30 torr from 760 torr. For deviations of this magnitude, a *boiling-point correction, t*, can be estimated using Equation 1.

$$\Delta t \approx y(760 - P)(273.1 + t) \tag{1}$$

Δt = temperature correction, to be added to the observed boiling point
P = barometric pressure, in torr
t = observed boiling point, in °C

The value 1.0×10^{-4} is used for the constant y if the liquid is water, an alcohol, a carboxylic acid, or another associated liquid; otherwise, y is assigned the value 1.2×10^{-4}. For example, the boiling point of water at 730 torr is 98.9°C. Use of Equation **1** leads to a correction factor of

$[(1.0 \times 10^{-4})(760 - 730)(273.1 + 98.9)]°C = 1.1°C$, which yields the correct normal boiling point of 100.0°C.

At high altitudes, the atmospheric pressure may be considerably lower than 1 atmosphere, resulting in observed boiling points that are substantially lower than the normal values. For example, water boils at 93°C on the campus of the University of Wyoming at Laramie, which has an elevation of 2290 m (7520 ft). For major deviations from atmospheric pressure, Equation **2** can be used in conjunction with approximate entropy of vaporization values obtained from the section "Correction of Boiling Points to Standard Pressure" in older editions of the *CRC Handbook of Chemistry and Physics* [Bibliography, A15].

*Equation **2** is a simplified form of the Hass–Newton equation found in the* CRC Handbook, *64th Edition, p. D-189.*

$$\Delta t \approx \frac{(273 + t)}{\varphi} \log \frac{760}{P} \qquad (2)$$

$$\varphi = (\text{entropy of vaporization at normal boiling point})/2.303R$$

For example, hexane boils at 49.6°C at 400 torr. The value of φ for alkanes is found (from the *CRC Handbook*) to be about 4.65 at that temperature. Substituting these values into Equation **2** yields a correction factor of

$$\Delta t \approx \frac{(273°C + 49.6°C)}{4.65} \log \frac{760\ \text{torr}}{400\ \text{torr}} = 19.3°C,$$

which gives a normal boiling point of 68.9°C. A second approximation using the value of φ at the corrected boiling point gives 68.8°C, which compares very favorably to the reported normal boiling point of 68.7°C. As for melting-point determinations, it may be necessary to correct a boiling point for thermometer error, especially when working with high-boiling liquids. See "Thermometer Corrections" in OP-33 for instructions.

a. Distillation Boiling Point

During a carefully performed distillation of a pure liquid, the vapors surrounding the thermometer bulb are in equilibrium (or nearly so) with the liquid condensing on the bulb. Thus, the vapor temperature recorded during the distillation of a pure liquid should equal its boiling point. If the liquid is contaminated by impurities, the distillation boiling point may be either too high or too low, depending on the nature of the impurity. Volatile impurities in a liquid lower its boiling point, whereas nonvolatile impurities raise it; in either case, its boiling point will vary throughout its distillation. Therefore, if there is any doubt about the purity of a liquid, it should be distilled or otherwise purified prior to a boiling-point determination.

DIRECTIONS FOR DISTILLATION BOILING-POINT MEASUREMENT

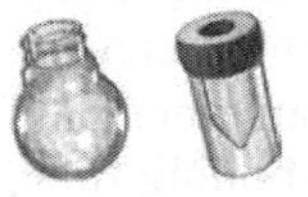

Standard Scale and Microscale

For standard scale work, assemble the compact distillation apparatus pictured in Figure E9 of OP-30, using a 25-mL round-bottom flask and placing the thermometer as shown in Figure E8. For microscale work, assemble the

So
to
cu
ni
tu

]
i

In this equation, $[\alpha]$ is the specific rotation of the mixture, $[\alpha]_A$ is the specific rotation of component A, X_A is the mole fraction of component A, and $[\alpha]_B$ is the specific rotation of component B. For example, an equilibrium mixture of α-D-glucose ($[\alpha] = 112°$) and β-D-glucose ($[\alpha] = 18.7°$) has a specific rotation of 52.7°. The mole fraction of α-D-glucose in the mixture can be calculated by substituting these values into Equation 2 and solving for X_A:

$$52.7° = (112°)\, X_A + (18.7°)(1 - X_A)$$

$$X_A = 0.364$$

Because both forms of glucose have the same molecular weight, the equilibrium mixture contains 36.4% α-D-glucose and 63.6% β-D-glucose by mass.

  ## Experimental Considerations

The specific rotation of an optically active sample can be determined using a polarimeter such as the one illustrated in Figure F13. A polarimeter includes a light source, a polarizing prism called the *polarizer,* a sample cell to hold the sample, and a second polarizing prism called the *analyzer* (see Figure F14). The traditional light source is a sodium lamp, which produces monochromatic light with a wavelength of 589 nm, but modern polarimeters may use a halogen lamp with an orange filter to provide light of that wavelength. The polarizer is fixed in place, and light that passes through it is polarized in the plane of its vertical axis—in other words, all light waves

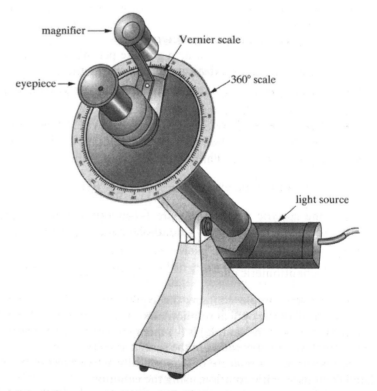

Figure F13 Cole–Parmer EW-81205 polarimeter

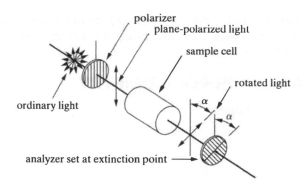

Figure F14 Schematic diagram of a polarimeter

except those parallel to the polarizer's axis are blocked out. The analyzer can be rotated so that its axis is at an angle to the polarizer's axis. When the axis of the analyzer is perpendicular to that of the plane-polarized light, the light is essentially blocked out so that its intensity is at a minimum; this condition is called the *extinction point*. It is easier for the human eye to match two intensities than to recognize a point of minimum intensity; therefore, in a precision polarimeter, the analyzer contains two or more prisms set at a small angle to each other, and it is rotated until the prisms bracket the extinction point, transmitting dim light of equal intensity. The angle by which the analyzer must be rotated to reach this point equals the angle by which the sample rotated the beam of plane-polarized light—its observed rotation, α. Using Equation **1**, we can convert the observed rotation of the sample to its specific rotation, given the sample's concentration and the length of the sample cell. The most commonly used sample cells have lengths of 1 dm (10 cm) and 2 dm (20 cm).

The optical rotation of a substance is usually measured in solution. Water and ethanol are common solvents for polar compounds, and dichloromethane can be used for less polar ones. Often, a suitable solvent will be listed in the literature, along with the light source and temperature used for the measurement. The volume of solution required depends on the size of the polarimeter cell, but 10–25 mL is usually sufficient. A solution for polarimetry ordinarily contains about 1–10 g of solute per 100 mL of solution, and it should be prepared using an accurate balance and a volumetric flask. If the solution contains particles of dust or other solid impurities, it should be filtered [OP-15]. When possible, the concentration should be comparable to that reported in the literature. For example, the *CRC Handbook of Chemistry and Physics* reports the specific rotation of (+)-menthol as "+49.2 (al, $c = 5$)," where the concentration (c) is given in grams per 100 mL of an alcoholic (al) solution (c is defined differently here than in Equation **1**). Thus, a (+)-menthol solution suitable for polarimetry can be prepared by accurately weighing about 1.25 g of (+)-menthol, dissolving it in ethyl alcohol in a 25-mL volumetric flask, adding more alcohol up to the calibration mark, and mixing the solution thoroughly.

Because the solvent you use may alter the observed rotation, you should always run a *solvent blank* by measuring the optical rotation of the pure solvent and subtract its rotation from that of your sample. Be sure

If, when you look through the eyepiece, the visual field is so dark that you can't compare the light intensities accurately, try the following remedies in order. Check to see that the sodium lamp (if you are using one) has warmed up enough to produce a bright light, and that it is positioned properly for maximum illumination of the visual field. Check to see whether there is a movable ring (possibly marked $+/-$) at the far end of the polarimeter that, when rotated, adjusts the light intensity; if so, adjust it for optimum intensity. Examine the sample in the polarimeter tube for turbidity (suspended solids); if it is not water clear, filter it by gravity filtration [OP-15].

If the specific rotation you calculate from your observed value is significantly different than the expected value, make sure that you subtracted the observed rotation of a solvent blank from that of your sample, and that your calculation is correct. Also check to see whether the solvent you used and the temperature of your measurement are similar enough to those used to obtain the expected value to make a comparison valid. If you were analyzing a chiral compound provided by a chemical supply company, it may not be enantiomerically pure, which would lead to a low specific rotation; check the label on the bottle the chemical came in (it should list the value of $[\alpha]$), or ask your instructor to do so. If you still think your result may be inaccurate, re-read the Directions and repeat the measurement more carefully. If necessary, prepare a fresh solution, making sure to weigh the sample and measure the solvent volume accurately,

nonpolar ones, giv␣
lar components. A␣
nents more strong␣

A column chr␣
room temperature␣
separation. In con␣
temperature, and t␣
according to a pr␣
increases the fract␣
retention time. The␣
because at excessiv␣
of their time in the␣

 In␣

In addition to the␣
some means of v␣
separation, detect␣
and recording dat␣
mined. A typical␣
diagrammed in Fi␣

Injection Port.␣
sage through the ␣
the column by ins␣
depressing the pl␣
about 1–2 μL, bu␣
With an open tu␣
about 1 nL (10^{-3}␣
carded. The inject␣
the sample, usuall␣
component.

G. Instrumental Analysis

Measurements of physical properties can help you identify substances whose identities you already suspect, and they often give at least a rough indication of the purity of a substance. But they don't reveal much about the molecular makeup of a compound, and they are of little use when you are trying to identify an unknown compound or analyze a mixture of compounds. For these purposes, you can use instruments that provide different kinds of information about compounds and mixtures. A gas chromatograph [OP-37] can separate the components of mixtures of liquids and volatile solids and often help you identify some or all of the components; a high-performance liquid chromatograph [OP-38] can do the same with mixtures of nonvolatile substances. An infrared spectrometer [OP-39] can detect the functional groups in an organic compound and provide additional information about its molecular structure, facilitating the identification of unknown compounds and confirming the identities of reaction products. A nuclear magnetic resonance spectrometer [OP-40] may provide enough detailed structural information about an unknown compound to reveal its entire molecular structure. An ultraviolet–visible spectrometer [OP-41] provides information about unsaturated systems in molecules and can be used to measure the concentrations of many compounds in solution. Mass spectrometers [OP-42] make it possible to identify many thousands of organic compounds by means of large databases of spectral information. They can also be used to determine molecular formulas and certain molecular structures or structural features.

Gas Chromatography

carrier-ga␣
tank

syringe —

injection␣
port

heaters —

chromat␣
recorder

Figure G␣

Gas chromatography (GC) affords a powerful method for the separation and analysis of volatile components of mixtures. Like all chromatographic methods, its operation is based on the distribution of the sample components between a mobile phase and a stationary phase. *Gas–liquid chromatography* is the most useful form of gas chromatography. The mobile phase for gas–liquid chromatography is an unreactive *carrier gas* such as helium, and the stationary phase consists of a high-boiling liquid on a solid support, contained within a heated column. The components of the sample must have reasonably high vapor pressures so that their molecules will spend enough time in the vapor phase to travel through the column with the carrier gas. Thus, gas chromatography can be used to separate gases, liquids that vaporize without decomposing when heated, and some volatile solids. (Solids must first be dissolved in a suitable solvent.) Less volatile liquids and solids can be separated by high-performance liquid chromatography [OP-38].

Analytical gas chromatography can be used for both the qualitative and quantitative analysis of mixtures; that is, to identify the components of a

product have chromatograms with similar peaks; if so, they may have come from traces of impurities in chemicals that were used to prepare the product. If a small extraneous peak precedes all of your sample peaks, it may be an air peak, due to air that was in the syringe needle, or the peak of a volatile syringe-washing solvent (such as dichloromethane) that hadn't completely evaporated before you filled the syringe with your sample. If you think the peak is from a syringe-washing solvent, you should run another sample using a clean, completely dry syringe. If one or more extraneous peaks are quite large, you may have injected your sample before another student's sample completely passed out of the column. Wait a minute or so after the last peak of your chromatogram has appeared, and then inject a fresh sample. If that doesn't make a difference and none of the previous possibilities seem likely, your product may need further purification.

OPERATION **38**

High-Performance Liquid Chromatography

Principles and Applications

High-performance liquid chromatography (HPLC) can be regarded as a hybrid of column chromatography and gas chromatography, sharing some features of both methods. As in column chromatography, the mobile phase is a solvent or solvent mixture (the eluant) that carries the sample through a column packed with fine particles that interact with the components of the sample to different extents, causing them to separate. As in gas chromatography, the sample is usually injected onto the column and detected as it leaves the column, and its passage through the column is recorded as a series of peaks on a chromatogram. The stationary phase may be a solid adsorbent, as in column chromatography, but it is more often an organic phase that is bonded to tiny beads of silica gel. The silica beads are, in effect, coated with a very thin layer of a liquid organic phase. Each component of the sample is partitioned between a liquid mobile phase and the liquid stationary phase according to a ratio—the *partition coefficient*—that depends on its solubility in each liquid. The components of a mixture generally have different partition coefficients in a given liquid phase, so they pass down the column at different rates.

Unlike gas chromatography, HPLC can be used to separate nonvolatile solids and liquids as well as substances that decompose at elevated temperatures. Substances that are often analyzed by HPLC include proteins, amino acids, carbohydrates, nucleic acids, steroids, drugs, pesticides, natural products, and inorganic compounds.

 Instrumentation

HPLC was developed as a means of improving the efficiency of a column chromatographic separation by reducing the particle size. Most column chromatography packings contain particles with diameters in the $75-175\ \mu m$ range, whereas most modern HPLC packings have particle sizes in the $3-10\ \mu m$ range, increasing separation efficiency dramatically. Solvents will not easily flow through such small particles by gravity alone, so a powerful pump is needed to force them through the column at pressures up to 6000 psi (~400 atm).

The basic components of an HPLC system are diagrammed in Figure G5. The instrument ordinarily has several large solvent reservoirs, each of

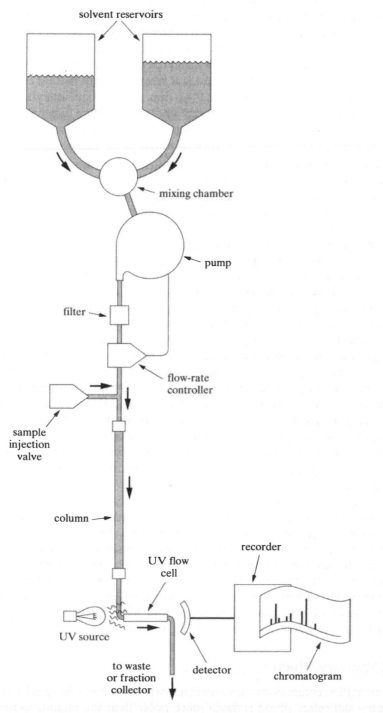

Figure G5 Schematic diagram of HPLC system

each point of contact, the wave penetrates a few micrometers into the sample. At frequencies where the sample absorbs energy, the IR beam is attenuated or altered. It is then directed to the instrument's detector, where the spectrum is generated.

A typical ATR accessory suitable for liquid samples has a recessed crystal surface in a horizontal plate. After a background scan is performed, the crystal is covered with a thin layer of the liquid, and the spectrum is recorded. Solids are best analyzed on an ATR accessory that has a diamond surface; the solid is forced onto the surface with a pressure tip that holds it in close contact with the crystal. In either case, the crystal surface must be cleaned thoroughly with a solvent-soaked tissue or cotton swab after a spectrum is run.

DIRECTIONS FOR RECORDING AN INFRARED SPECTRUM

 ## Standard Scale and Microscale

Equipment and Supplies

Starred items are needed only for the sample types indicated in parentheses.

> IR spectrometer
> sample
> Pasteur pipet
> IR sample cell(s) and windows, or other sampling device
> *Luer–Lok syringe, spacer (volatile neat liquids)
> *spectral-grade solvent, Luer–Lok syringe, spacer (solutions)
> *mortar & pestle, mulling oil, glass rod with rubber policeman (mulls)
> *dry potassium bromide, mortar & pestle, Mini-Press, vise, wrench (KBr disks)
> *hot plate and forceps, or oven (melts)
> *disposable IR card (IR cards)
> solvent for cleaning windows, etc.
> tissues
> desiccator for storing windows

Do not attempt to operate the instrument without prior instruction and proper supervision. The construction and operation of commercial IR spectrometers vary widely, so the following is meant only as a general guide to assist you in recording an IR spectrum. Specific operating techniques must be learned from the instructor, the operating manual, or both. It will be assumed that the necessary operational parameters have been set beforehand; if not, your instructor will show you what to do. If you are using an ATR accessory, your instructor should show you how to apply your sample. If you are using an FTIR spectrometer, follow Procedure **A**; for a dispersive IR spectrometer, follow Procedure **B**.

A. FTIR Spectrometer.   Your instructor will tell you which menu choices (if the spectrometer's operation is controlled by a computer) or keys to use for such processes as scanning a spectrum, using a cursor, subtracting a background scan, and printing or plotting a spectrum. If your compound is in solution, run a background spectrum with a cell containing the pure solvent in the sample compartment, and use the same cell for the solution. If you are using a disposable IR card, scan its spectrum before you apply the sample. Otherwise, run the background spectrum (if one is necessary) with the sample compartment empty just before you record your spectrum. Prepare a sample cell, IR card, or KBr disk by one of the methods described previously, and place the cell, card, or KBr disk holder in the sample cell holder. Select the desired number of scans (four are usually sufficient for a routine spectrum), and start scanning the spectrum. Wait until a spectrum appears on the monitor. If the instrument doesn't automatically subtract any background spectrum, do so as directed by your instructor. If the spectrum doesn't look right—for example, if the low or high wave-number end is missing, or you are seeing only a small part of the total spectrum—display the "normal" spectrum using the appropriate key(s) (some instruments use *Rerange* and *Rescale* keys for this purpose) or menu choices. The strongest bands should extend nearly to the bottom of your spectrum; if they do not, use a vertical-scale expansion option to improve the appearance of the spectrum. See that the printer or plotter is turned on and properly adjusted, and then use the appropriate key or menu choice to print or plot the spectrum. If the instrument you are using doesn't record wave numbers directly on the spectrum, use the cursor arrow keys to move the cursor to the significant bands, and write the displayed wave numbers below the corresponding IR bands on your spectrum. Reset the instrument to display a normal spectrum, if necessary. Then remove the sample cell and close the sample compartment. Clean, dry, and store the cell windows (if you are using them) as described previously.

B. Dispersive IR Spectrometer. Prepare a sample cell or KBr disk containing the sample by one of the methods described previously, and place the cell or KBr disk assembly in the sample cell holder. If you are running a solution spectrum, place an identical cell containing the solvent in the reference compartment; otherwise, leave it empty. If necessary, place chart paper on the paper carriage (or wrap it around a drum); then align the paper properly, and move the carriage or drum to the starting position. Set the 100% transmittance control so that the pen is at 85–90% T, lower the pen onto the chart paper, and scan the spectrum. Examine the spectrum to see that the absorption bands show satisfactory intensity and resolution. Ideally, the strongest absorption band should have a maximum transmittance of 5–10%. If your first spectrum is not acceptable, try varying the following parameters, depending on the sample preparation method:

Take Care! Make sure the instrument has been reset correctly before attempting to move the drum or carriage.

- *Neat liquid*—Vary cell path length or film thickness.
- *Solution*—Vary concentration or cell path length.
- *KBr disk*—Vary amount of sample or thickness of disk.
- *Mull*—Vary amount of sample or film thickness.

Remove the sample and spectrum, and reset the instrument, if necessary. Clean, dry, and store the sample cell or cell windows as described previously.

Summary

1. Put sample in sample cell, or prepare IR card or KBr disk.
2. Put sample cell, card, or KBr disk holder in instrument's sample holder.
   IF you are using an FTIR spectrometer, GO TO 6.

3. Align chart paper, and move drum or carriage to starting position.
   IF you are not analyzing a solution, GO TO 5.
4. Put solvent cell in reference beam.
5. Adjust 100% transmittance control; lower pen to paper.
6. Scan spectrum; subtract background spectrum, if necessary.
   IF you are using a dispersive IR spectrometer, GO TO 8.
7. Print or plot spectrum; record wave numbers, if necessary.
8 Disassemble cell; clean, dry, and store cell windows.
   Note: Additional steps are required for running solution spectra.

When Things Go Wrong

If you scan an IR spectrum and see significant absorption near 2350 cm^{-1} (due to CO_2 from the atmosphere), a background scan has probably not been run recently. Perform a background scan as described in the Directions.

If you scan a spectrum and see nothing but a flat line near the 100% transmittance level, you (or someone else) probably did a background scan with the sample in the cell compartment. Perform a background scan with nothing (or the solvent, if you are analyzing a solution) in the cell compartment, as described in the Directions.

If you scan an FTIR spectrum and see only a partial spectrum or a display that doesn't look like a normal spectrum, use the scale- and range-setting keys or menu choices to display a normal spectrum.

If the baseline of your mull, KBr disk, or melt spectrum begins (on the high-frequency end) well below the 100% transmittance level and slopes upward before flattening out near the 2500 cm^{-1} region, and especially if your peaks "tail off" (are distorted along their trailing edges), your sample (for a mull or KBr disk) was not ground finely enough or the melt formed unsuitably large crystals. Prepare a new mull or KBr disk, or try method **B** for a melt. If you still can't get a good spectrum, you may have to use a different sampling method.

If your IR spectrum shows significant absorption bands near 3500 cm^{-1} and 1650 cm^{-1}, especially if your compound doesn't contain OH or NH bonds, your sample is probably wet. If you are running a liquid film, solution spectrum, or mull, clean the IR windows immediately and thoroughly so that they won't be etched by the water, Then dry your product and run another spectrum. If you are using a KBr disk, the presence of a little water may be unavoidable, but preparing a new disk using oven-dried KBr and avoiding extended exposure to the atmosphere should help.

If some bands on your IR spectrum "bottom out" near 0% transmittance (they will usually be somewhat flattened out at the bottom), your sample film is too thick or (for a solution) the solution is too concentrated. On an FTIR spectrometer, you may be able to get a decent spectrum by using the "Autex" key or an equivalent scale expansion control. Otherwise, you will have to prepare the sample cell again, using less sample or a less concentrated solution.

Suppose the peaks on your IR spectrum are broad and indistinct, lacking fine structure. If your sample is a neat liquid, it has probably been evaporating or leaking out of the infrared beam area. Look at the infrared windows to see if there are areas between them where there is no liquid. If so, prepare another sample cell, using an additional drop of liquid, and try to record the spectrum more rapidly. If you prepared a mull or KBr disk with a solid sample, you probably didn't grind the solid finely enough. The spectrum of a mull may also have a sloping baseline in this case. See "Mulls" or "Potassium Bromide Disks," and prepare another mull or disk.

If you run a spectrum with a dispersive IR spectrometer and all of the wave numbers seem to vary by the same amount from the expected values, the chart paper wasn't aligned properly or the spectrometer wasn't calibrated properly. Check to see that the appropriate wave number on the chart paper is directly opposite the alignment mark on the instrument—if not, align it and run another spectrum. If the chart paper was aligned properly, ask your instructor to have the spectrometer recalibrated (or to help you do it), and then run another spectrum.

  # Interpretation of Infrared Spectra

Because most IR bands are associated with specific chemical bonds, it is usually possible to deduce the functional class of an organic compound from its IR spectrum. The *stretching* vibrations of chemical bonds resemble the vibrations of springs in that stronger bonds have higher vibrational energies and frequencies than weaker ones. Thus, triple bonds generally absorb at higher wave numbers than double bonds, and double bonds absorb at higher wave numbers than single bonds. However, because of the comparatively low mass of a hydrogen atom, single bonds to hydrogen (C—H, O—H, N—H, etc.) have even higher vibrational frequencies than double and triple bonds. Stretching bands involving single bonds to hydrogen occur at the high-frequency (left) end of an IR spectrum, in the region between 3700 and 2700 cm^{-1} (2.7–3.7 μm). Triple bonds usually absorb between 2700 and 1850 cm^{-1} (3.7–5.4 μm), and double bonds and aromatic bonds absorb between 1950 and 1450 cm^{-1} (5.1—6.9 μm). Most IR bands between 1500 and 600 cm^{-1} (6.7–16.7 μm) are produced by *bending* vibrations or single-bond stretching vibrations. It takes less energy to bend a bond than to stretch it, so bending vibrations tend to have comparatively low frequencies. An absorption band in the 1500–600 cm^{-1} region may be associated with more than one bond; for example, the so-called acyl–oxygen stretching band of an ester arises from the vibration of C—C—O units rather than isolated C—O bonds.

What to Look for in an IR Spectrum

Consider the IR spectrum of 2-methyl-1-propanol (isobutyl alcohol) in Figure G15. At first glance, it may seem indecipherable—just a series of dips and rises in a graph. But each "dip" (IR band) arises from a stretching or bending vibration of one or more bonds in the 2-methyl-1-propanol molecule, and some of the bands can tell you a great deal about the molecules that gave rise to them. First look at the WAVENUMBERS scale at the bottom of the spectrum; from this scale, you can read off the wave number, in cm^{-1}, of each band. For example, the first large band in the spectrum is between 3600 and 3000 cm^{-1}, and its minimum is at approximately 3330 cm^{-1}. Bands designated by tick marks (short lines) at the bottom of a spectrum have their exact wave numbers listed, so you can find a more accurate wave number for this band, 3328.1 cm^{-1}, in the list of numbers above the right-hand end of the spectrum.

The IR spectra in this book are reproduced from the Aldrich Library of FT–IR Spectra, Edition II, *with permission.*

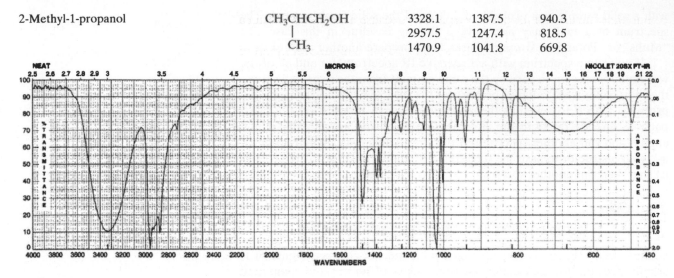

2-Methyl-1-propanol

CH₃CHCH₂OH
|
CH₃

3328.1	1387.5	940.3
2957.5	1247.4	818.5
1470.9	1041.8	669.8

Figure G15 Infrared spectrum of 2-methyl-1-propanol

Another numerical scale at the top of the spectrum indicates the wavelength in micrometers (microns). The numbers on the left side of the spectrum are transmittance values. For example, the minimum in the 3328 cm⁻¹ band has a transmittance of ~10%, meaning that only 10% of the 3328 cm⁻¹ IR radiation passed through the sample. The other 90% was absorbed during a change in the bond vibrational frequency of some bond in the compound—but which bond? Since the band is at the left end of the spectrum, the bond must have a high vibrational energy, and we have already noted that bands in the 3700–2700 cm⁻¹ region of the spectrum arise from vibrations of bonds to hydrogen atoms. There are only two bonds of this type in the molecule: C—H bonds and O—H bonds. Now note that there are two bands in the 3700–2700 cm⁻¹ region—the strong, broad, symmetrical one on the left, and a rather ragged band with several minima (centered around 2900 cm⁻¹) on the right. The ragged band is actually composed of several overlapping bands, arising from vibrations of several different bonds of the same general type. Since there is only one O—H bond in the molecule, and there are nine C—H bonds, it is reasonable to assume that the overlapping bands on the right arise from C—H stretching vibrations and that the band on the left is the O—H band. Note that the size of a band is not directly related to the number of bonds that give rise to it; the single O—H bond has a much broader band than the nine C—H bonds.

So the bond responsible for a given IR band can often be identified from its *location* on the spectrum (as indicated by its wave number), its *intensity* (relative strength), and its *shape*. Most O—H bands, like the one in the previous spectrum, are very broad and strong (a *strong* band is one whose minimum is near the bottom of the spectrum). Most C—H bands are relatively strong and give rise to a ragged array of overlapping bands.

Another very strong band appears at 1042 cm⁻¹ in the Figure G15 spectrum. This band, which is in the wave-number region for single-bond stretching vibrations (except those involving hydrogen), arises from stretching vibrations of the C—O single bond. The presence of both a C—O and an O—H band in the IR spectrum of a compound is good evidence that the compound is an alcohol (or possibly a phenol) because all alcohols contain a C—O—H grouping in their molecules.

Although we have now located bands corresponding to every kind of bond in the 2-methyl-1-propanol molecule (except C—C single bonds, which don't give prominent bands), there are still a number of bands left. This is because the same kind of bond can undergo different kinds of vibrations. For example, most of the bands just to the left of the C—O band arise from *scissoring, wagging,* and *twisting* vibrations of CH_2 and CH_3 groups (see Figure G16), and the very broad, weak band centered at 670 cm^{-1} arises from an O—H bending vibration.

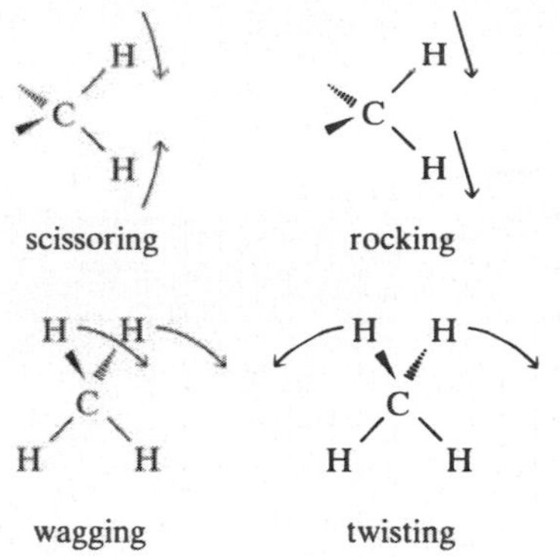

Figure G16 Some carbon–hydrogen vibrations

Spectral Regions

You can see that some IR bands, particularly the stretching bands we have discussed, are more easily recognized than others and are more useful in revealing the presence of functional groups. Many of the other bands can be ignored for the time being, although they may provide useful information to a chemist skilled in spectral interpretation. The key to efficient IR spectral interpretation is *knowing where to look* for the more useful bands. Examining the following regions of the IR spectrum will help you locate the most useful IR bands quickly:

Region 1: 3600–3200 cm^{-1} (2.8–3.1 μm). Bands in this region can arise from O—H and N—H stretching vibrations of alcohols, phenols, amines, and amides. O—H bands are generally very strong and broad; N—H bands are somewhat weaker, and, in the case of primary amines and amides, they have two peaks.

Region 2: 3100–2500 cm^{-1} (3.2–4.0 μm). This region contains most of the C—H stretching vibrations. A strong band in the 3000–2850-cm^{-1} region, arising from C—H bonds to sp^3 carbon atoms, is present for most organic compounds. The sp^2 C—H bonds associated with aromatic hydrocarbons and alkenes absorb at higher frequencies (3100–3000 cm^{-1}), and the C—H bonds of aldehyde (CHO) groups absorb at lower frequencies. The O—H bond of a carboxylic acid gives rise to a very broad absorption band in this region.

Region 3: 1750–1630 cm^{-1} (5.7–6.1 μm). This region contains most of the carbonyl (C=O) stretching bands of aldehydes, ketones, carboxylic acids, amides, and esters. The carbonyl band is usually strong and quite unmistakable. Unsaturated compounds may have a C=C stretching band in the 1670–1640-cm^{-1} region, but this band is nearly always weaker and narrower than a carbonyl band.

Region 4: 1350–1000 cm^{-1} (7.4–10.0 μm). This region is usually cluttered with many C—H bending bands and other bands, but it is often possible to identify the C—O stretching bands of alcohols, phenols, carboxylic acids, and esters, and some C—N stretching bands of amines and amides.

These four spectral regions are shaded in the IR spectrum illustrated in Figure G17. In this spectrum, the absence of any band in Region 1 (or a broad band in Region 2) eliminates from consideration all compounds containing O—H and N—H bonds, including alcohols, phenols, and primary or secondary amines and amides. In Region 2, the appearance of a weak "shoulder" on the C—H band at 3050 cm^{-1} indicates an sp^2 C—H bond associated with either an aromatic ring or a carbon–carbon double bond.

2981.9	1367.2	1108.5
1718.5	1275.8	1028.5
1451.4	1175.2	710.3

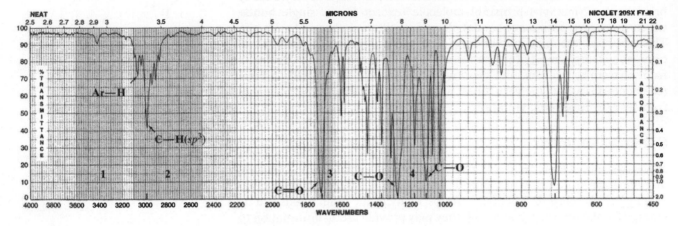

Figure G17 Classification of a compound from its IR spectrum

1719

1276   1109

ethyl benzoate

Region 3 has a strong C=O band at 1719 cm^{-1}, and Region 4 shows a strong C—O band at 1276 cm^{-1} as well as a weaker one at 1109 cm^{-1}. The absence of an O—H or N—H band and the presence of the C=O and two C—O bands suggest that the compound responsible for this spectrum is an ester. The compound is, in fact, the aromatic ester ethyl benzoate, whose structure and bond wave numbers are shown in the margin.

Table G2 summarizes the locations and characteristics of important absorption bands from the four spectral regions and tells you where to look

Table G2 Important bands in Regions 1–4 of infrared spectra

Region	Frequency range (cm^{-1})	Bond type	Family	Comments
1	3500–3200	N—H	amine, amide	weak–medium. 1°: 2 bands; 2°: 1 band; 3°: no bands; see also Region 3.
	3600–3200	O—H	alcohol, phenol	broad, strong; see Region 4.
2	3300–2500	O—H	carboxylic acid	very broad, strong, centered around 3000; see Regions 3 and 4.
	3100–3000	C—H	aromatic hydrocarbon, alkene	may be shoulder on stronger sp^3 C—H band.
	2850–2700	C—H	aldehyde	weak to medium, usually two sharp bands; see Region 3.
3	1740–1685	C=O	aldehyde	strong; see Region 2.
	1750–1660	C=O	ketone	strong.
	1725–1665	C=O	carboxylic acid	strong; see Regions 2 and 4.
	1775–1715	C=O	ester	strong; see Region 4.
	1695–1615	C=O	amide	strong; see Region 1.
4	1350–1210	C—O	carboxylic acid	medium–strong; see Regions 1 and 3.
	1300–1180	C—O	phenol	strong; see Region 1.
	1200–1000	C—O	alcohol	strong; see Region 1. Wave numbers in order 3° > 2° > 1°.
	1310–1160	C—O	ester	strong; see Region 3. Accompanied by weaker C—O band, as for alcohol.

Note: Tentative classifications must be confirmed by referring to the following descriptions of specific families.

for other bands that may help you confirm the presence of a particular functional group.

The best way to become proficient at identifying IR bands is to study spectra that contain those bands, such as the spectra in your lecture textbook, in the "Characteristic Infrared Bands" section that follows, and in collections of spectra described in Category F of the Bibliography. When you have learned to recognize the most important IR bands, you can take some shortcuts that will help you identify functional groups quickly—or at least eliminate the functional groups that aren't there. The following flowchart should help you do that. Just start at the top and work your way down, following the yes–no arrow that answers each question.

Possible family   C=O present?   *Possible family*
              yes /   \ no

carboxylic ←$\xleftarrow{yes}$ O—H present?   O—H present? $\xrightarrow{yes}$ alcohol
acid   or phenol
                    | no   no |

amide (1°, 2°) $\xleftarrow{yes}$ N—H present?   N—H present? $\xrightarrow{yes}$ amine (1°, 2°)
                    | no   no |

ester $\xleftarrow{yes}$ C—O present?   C=C present? $\xrightarrow{yes}$ alkene
                    | no   no |

aldehyde $\xleftarrow{yes}$ C—H at ~ 2700 cm^{-1}?   Ar—H present? $\xrightarrow{yes}$ aromatic
                                                                     hydrocarbon
                    | no   no |

ketone $\xleftarrow{yes}$ None of the above?   None of the above? $\xrightarrow{yes}$ alkane
or 3° amide   or 3° amine

Flowchart for detecting functional classes from IR bands

This flowchart is intended as a rapid screening device and is not infallible; some bands (such as the C=C stretching band) are hard to identify with certainty, and the locations of other bands may vary widely. Moreover, some compounds may contain more than one functional group; thus, hydroxyacetone (CH_3COCH_2OH) has both an O—H and a C=O band in its spectrum, but it isn't a carboxylic acid, as you could tell from the location of its O—H band. When you arrive at a tentative conclusion about the nature of the compound responsible for an IR spectrum, you should refer to Table G2 to see whether other bands in the spectrum are consistent with your initial choice. Then study the spectral characteristics of the appropriate class of compounds to confirm (or disprove) your tentative classification. The IR correlation chart on the back endpaper of this book may also help you identify some infrared spectral bands.

For example, suppose that the flowchart suggests that your compound may be an alcohol or phenol. You can first check Table G2 to see if any other bands characteristic of alcohols and phenols appear in its spectrum, such as a C—O band. If so, you should read the "Characteristic Infrared Bands" sections about alcohols and phenols to find out whether your compound is an alcohol or a phenol. If you find that your compound is an alcohol, you should then study its spectrum for clues to its structure. The frequency of its C—O band may tell you whether it is primary, secondary, or tertiary. By consulting the sections on aromatic hydrocarbons and alkenes (which also apply to other compounds that contain aromatic rings and C$=$C bonds), you can find out whether your alcohol is aromatic or contains a carbon–carbon double bond. Of course, if you find that your compound is *not* an alcohol or a phenol, you should continue down the chart or start back from the beginning.

Characteristic Infrared Bands

This section contains information about the most useful IR bands of the most commonly encountered kinds of organic compounds—alkanes, alkenes, aromatic hydrocarbons, alcohols, phenols, aldehydes, ketones, carboxylic acids, esters, amines, amides, and organic halides. Note that compounds other than hydrocarbons may contain bands characteristic of alkanes, alkenes, or aromatic hydrocarbons, so you can check the sections for these hydrocarbons when you are interpreting the spectra of other kinds of compounds. For each family of organic compounds, a summary of the main spectral features that characterize the family is followed by a description of individual bond vibrations and a representative IR spectrum. The wave-number ranges given are for solids (in Nujol mulls or KBr discs) or neat liquids; values for solutions may differ somewhat. Although the wave-number ranges apply to most of the organic compounds in each class, compounds with certain structural features (such as highly strained rings) may have bands outside of the ranges indicated. On the spectra, absorption bands are designated either as stretching (ν) or bending (δ) bands. Only those bands that are most useful for identifying functional groups or structural features are labeled. Note that the exact wave numbers of significant bands (designated by tick marks along the lower edge of the spectra) are listed with each spectrum.

Alkanes.   Alkanes are identified primarily by the absence of any IR bands characteristic of functional groups. Their spectra are quite simple, containing only the C—H stretching and bending vibrations characteristic of sp^3 hybridized carbon atoms. Because nearly all other organic compounds contain such C—H bonds, their spectra will also contain some or all of the bands described for alkanes. (See Figure G18.)

> C—H *stretch:* 3000–2800 cm^{-1} (multiple overlapping bands, strong to weak). CH$_3$ bands are near 2960 cm^{-1} and 2870 cm^{-1}. CH$_2$ bands are near 2925 cm^{-1} and 2850 cm^{-1} (nearly always to the *right* of 3000 cm^{-1}).
>
> C—H *bend:* 1465–720 cm^{-1} (moderate to weak). CH$_3$ bands are near 1450 cm^{-1} and 1375 cm^{-1}. CH$_2$ bands occur near 1465 cm^{-1}, between 1350 cm^{-1} and 1150 cm^{-1} (several weak bands), and sometimes around 720 cm^{-1}. The 720 cm^{-1} band is characteristic of unbranched alkanes that have seven or more carbon atoms.

Alkenes.   Most alkenes contain the same kinds of bands as alkanes, plus additional bands associated with carbon–carbon double bonds and vinylic ($=$C—H) carbon–hydrogen bonds. The presence of one or two strong bands in the 1000–650 cm^{-1} region and a sharp band near 1650 cm^{-1} suggests an alkene functional group, especially if the compound is not aromatic. (See Figure G19).

2,2,4-Trimethylpentane

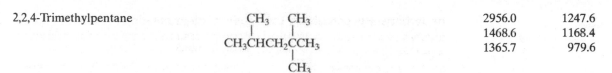

2956.0	1247.6
1468.6	1168.4
1365.7	979.6

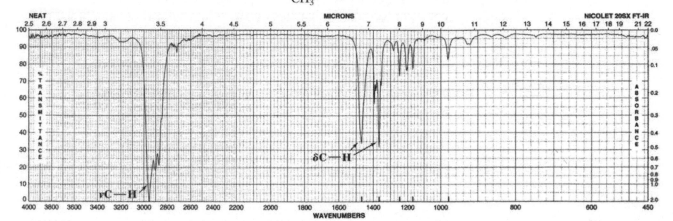

Figure G18 IR spectrum of an alkane, 2,2,4-trimethylpentane

1-Hexene

$CH_3CH_2CH_2CH_2CH=CH_2$

2962.1	1466.1	909.2
1821.3	1379.1	739.8
1641.8	992.7	630.8

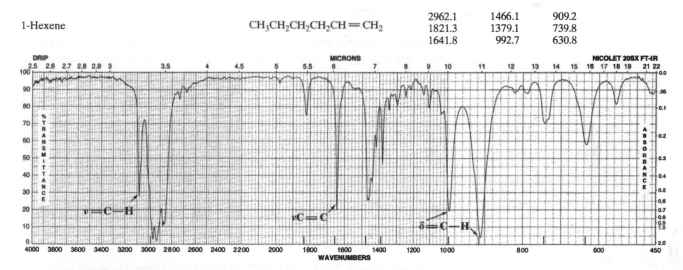

Figure G19 IR spectrum of an alkene, 1-hexene

$=C-H$ *stretch:* 3125–3030 cm^{-1} (moderate to weak). May appear as a shoulder on a stronger sp^3 C—H band, but nearly always to the *left* of 3000 cm^{-1}.

$C=C$ *stretch:* 1675–1600 cm^{-1} (moderate to weak; narrow). May be absent for symmetrical alkenes. Conjugation moves band to lower wavelengths.

$=C-H$ *out-of-plane bend:* 1000–650 cm^{-1} (usually strong). Position depends on type of substitution: $RCH=CH_2$ has bands at 995–985 and 915–905 cm^{-1}; *cis*-$RCH=CHR$ a band at 730–665 cm^{-1}; *trans*-$RCH=CHR$ a band at 980–960 cm^{-1}; and $R_2C=CH_2$ a band at 895–885 cm^{-1} (R = alkyl or aryl substituent).

Isopropylbenzene

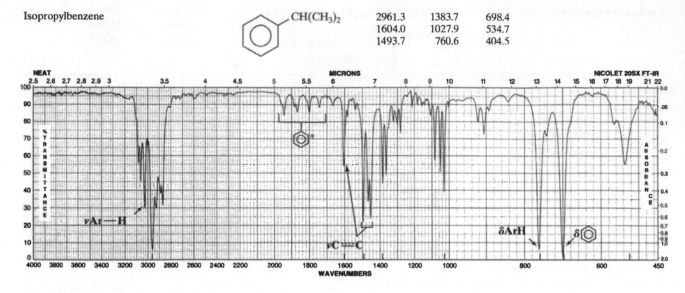

2961.3	1383.7	698.4
1604.0	1027.9	534.7
1493.7	760.6	404.5

Figure G20 IR spectrum of an aromatic hydrocarbon, isopropylbenzene. The bands marked ⬡* are aromatic overtone-combination bands.

Aromatic Hydrocarbons.
Most compounds containing benzene rings are characterized by (1) aromatic C—H (Ar—H) stretching bands near 3070 cm^{-1}, (2) a distinctive pattern of weak bands in the 2000–1650-cm^{-1} region, (3) two sets of bands near 1600 cm^{-1} and 1515–1400 cm^{-1}, and (4) one or more strong absorption bands in the 900–675-cm^{-1} region. The presence of such bands and the absence of absorption bands characteristic of functional groups suggest an aromatic hydrocarbon. (See Figure G20.)

Ar—H *stretch:* 3100–3000 cm^{-1} (moderate to weak). May appear as a shoulder on a stronger sp^3 C—H band, but nearly always to the *left* of 3000 cm^{-1}.

Overtone-combination vibrations: 2000–1650 cm^{-1} (multiple bands, weak). The band pattern is related to the kind of ring substitution, as shown in Figure G21.

C⋯C *stretch:* 1615–1585 cm^{-1} and 1515–1400 cm^{-1} (variable).

Ar—H *out-of-plane bend:* 910–730 cm^{-1} (strong). The band frequency varies with the number of adjacent ring hydrogens:

two adjacent hydrogens: 855–800 cm^{-1}

three adjacent hydrogens: 800–765 cm^{-1}

four or five adjacent hydrogens: 770–730 cm^{-1}

Monosubstituted, *meta*-disubstituted, and some trisubstituted benzenes show an additional ring-bending band around 715–680 cm^{-1}. For example, a *meta*-disubstituted benzene has three adjacent ring hydrogens, so it should have bands in the 800–765-cm^{-1} and 715–680-cm^{-1} regions.

Alcohols.
The presence of a strong, broad band centered around 3300 cm^{-1} and a strong C—O band in the 1200–1000-cm^{-1} region is good

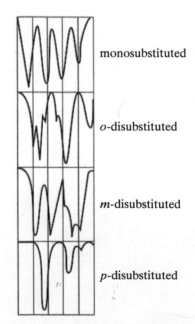

monosubstituted

o-disubstituted

m-disubstituted

p-disubstituted

Figure G21 Typical absorption patterns of substituted aromatic compounds in the 2000–1650-cm^{-1} region

2-Methyl-1-propanol

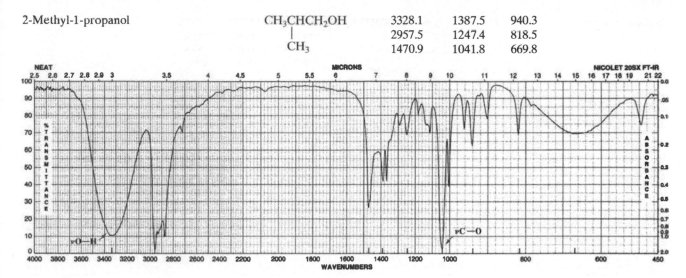

Figure G22 IR spectrum of a primary alcohol, 2-methyl-1-propanol

evidence for an alcohol. (See Figure G22.) A C—O band above 1200 cm^{-1} may suggest a phenol, particularly when it is accompanied by bands indicating an aromatic ring structure. (See Figure G23.)

> O—H *stretch:* 3600–3200 cm^{-1} (strong, broad). Usually centered near 3300 cm^{-1}.

> C—O *stretch:* 1200–1000 cm^{-1} (strong to moderate). Most saturated aliphatic alcohols absorb near 1050 cm^{-1} if they are primary, near 1110 cm^{-1} if they are secondary, and near 1175 cm^{-1} if they are tertiary. Alicyclic alcohols and alcohols with aromatic rings or vinyl groups on the carbon that is bonded to OH absorb at wave numbers about 25–50 cm^{-1} lower than these.

Phenols. Phenols are characterized by a strong, broad band centered around 3300 cm^{-1} and a strong band near 1230 cm^{-1}, accompanied by bands indicating an aromatic structure. (See "Aromatic Hydrocarbons" and Figure G23.)

> O—H *stretch:* 3600–3200 cm^{-1} (strong, broad).

> O—H *bend:* 1390–1315 cm^{-1} (moderate).

> C—O *stretch:* 1300–1180 cm^{-1} (strong); usually close to 1230 cm^{-1}. This band may be split, with several distinct peaks.

Aldehydes. The presence of a sharp, medium-intensity band near 2720 cm^{-1} and a strong carbonyl band near 1700 cm^{-1} is good evidence for an aldehyde. (See Figure G24.)

> $\overset{\text{(O)}}{\overset{\|}{C}}$—H *stretch:* 2850–2700 cm^{-1} (moderate to weak). From the carbonyl C—H bond; most aldehydes have two bands near 2850 and 2720 cm^{-1}, with the low-frequency band well separated from other aliphatic C—H bands.

Phenol

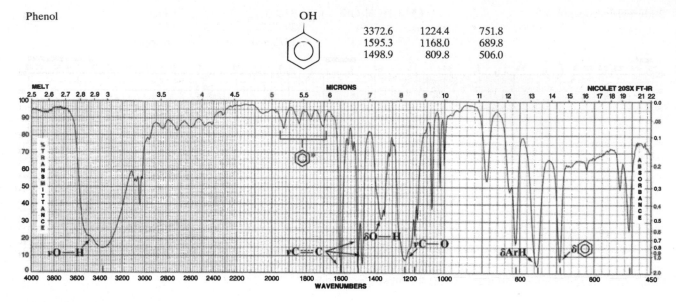

3372.6	1224.4	751.8
1595.3	1168.0	689.8
1498.9	809.8	506.0

Figure G23 IR spectrum of phenol.

The bands marked ⬡* are aromatic overtone-combination bands.

3-Methylbutanal

$$CH_3 \quad O$$
$$| \qquad ||$$
$$CH_3CHCH_2CH$$

2960.1	1468.3	1016.6
2718.7	1368.8	898.9
1727.6	1170.8	524.1

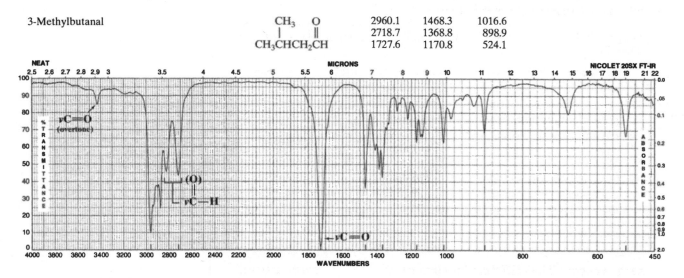

Figure G24 IR spectrum of an aldehyde, 3-methylbutanal

C＝O *stretch:* 1740–1685 cm^{-1} (strong). Most unconjugated aldehydes absorb near 1725 cm^{-1}; conjugation of the carbonyl group with an aromatic ring or another unsaturated system shifts the band to the 1700–1685-cm^{-1} region. A weak overtone of this band may appear near 3400 cm^{-1}.

Ketones.   The presence of a strong carbonyl band around 1700 cm^{-1} is good evidence for a ketone if other bands described in Table G2 (O—H, N—H, C—O, and aldehyde C—H) are absent. One or more bands in the 1300–1100-cm^{-1} region arise from C—C—C vibrations involving the

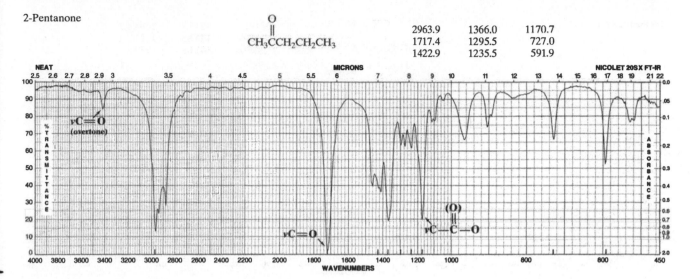

2-Pentanone

$$CH_3CCH_2CH_2CH_3$$

2963.9	1366.0	1170.7
1717.4	1295.5	727.0
1422.9	1235.5	591.9

Figure G25 IR spectrum of a ketone, 2-pentanone

carbonyl carbon. Such bands are generally weaker and narrower than C—O bands, for which they might otherwise be mistaken. (See Figure G25.)

C=O *stretch:* 1750–1660 cm⁻¹ (strong). Most unconjugated aliphatic ketones absorb around 1715 cm⁻¹, and conjugated ketones absorb near 1670 cm⁻¹. A weak C=O overtone band is usually evident near 3400 cm⁻¹.

(O)
‖
C—C—C *stretch–bend:* 1300–1100 cm⁻¹ (moderate). Often multiple bands; unconjugated ketones absorb around 1230–1100 cm⁻¹, and conjugated ketones absorb around 1300–1230 cm⁻¹.

Carboxylic Acids. The presence of a very broad band centered near 3000 cm⁻¹ and a carbonyl band around 1700 cm⁻¹ is good evidence for a carboxylic acid. (See Figure G26.)

O—H *stretch:* 3300–2500 cm⁻¹ (strong, very broad). C—H stretching bands are usually superimposed on this band.

C=O *stretch:* 1725–1665 cm⁻¹ (strong). Unconjugated acids absorb around 1725–1700 cm⁻¹; conjugated acids absorb around 1700–1665 cm⁻¹.

C—O *stretch:* 1350–1210 cm⁻¹ (strong). Long-chain acids may have a number of sharp peaks in this region.

O—H *bend:* 950–870 cm⁻¹ (moderate, broad).

Esters. The presence of a strong carbonyl band around 1740 cm⁻¹ and an unusually strong C—O band in the 1310–1160-cm⁻¹ region is good evidence for an ester, especially if there is no O—H band. (See Figure G27.)

C=O *stretch:* 1775–1715 cm⁻¹ (strong). Near 1770 cm⁻¹ for phenyl esters (RCOOAr) and vinyl esters, 1740 cm⁻¹ for most unconjugated esters, and 1730–1695 cm⁻¹ for formates and conjugated esters.

Hexanoic acid

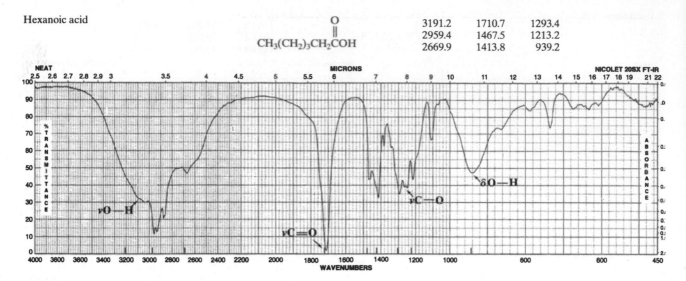

Figure G26 IR spectrum of a carboxylic acid, hexanoic acid

sec-Butyl acetate

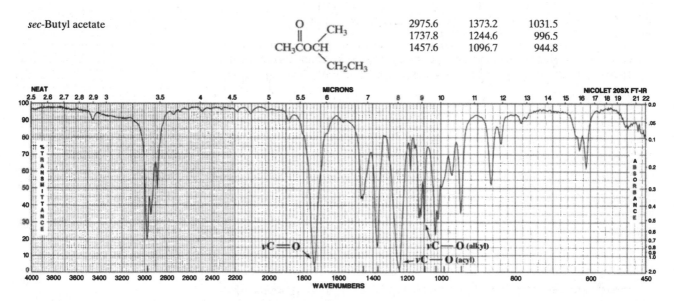

Figure G27 IR spectrum of an ester, *sec*-butyl acetate

C—O *stretch (acyl–oxygen):* 1310–1160 cm^{-1} (strong, broad). Occurs near 1310–1250 cm^{-1} for conjugated esters, 1240 cm^{-1} for unconjugated acetates, and 1210–1165 cm^{-1} for most other unconjugated esters. Both the acyl–oxygen and alkyl–oxygen bands arise from coupled vibrations involving C—C—O groupings.

C—O *stretch (alkyl–oxygen):* 1200–1000 cm^{-1} (moderate). Occurs in the same region as alcohol C—O bands, and varies in the same way with changes in the alkyl group's structure. Esters of phenols absorb at higher wave numbers.

Amines. Primary amines are characterized by a medium-intensity, two-pronged band near 3350 cm^{-1} and two medium–strong bands near 1615 and 800 cm^{-1}, the latter one being very broad. Secondary amines have a single weak band near 3300 cm^{-1} and a broad band near 715 cm^{-1}. Tertiary amines can sometimes be distinguished by the presence of a C—N band. (See Figure G28.)

N—H *stretch:* 3500–3200 cm^{-1} (moderate to weak, broad). Primary aliphatic amines give rise to a two-pronged band centered near 3350 cm^{-1}, secondary aliphatic amines have one weak band near 3300 cm^{-1}, and tertiary amines have none. Primary and secondary aromatic amines absorb near 3400 and 3450 cm^{-1}, respectively.

N—H *bend (scissoring):* 1650–1500 cm^{-1} (strong to moderate). Usually near 1615 cm^{-1} for primary amines. Seldom observed for secondary aliphatic amines; secondary aromatic amines absorb near 1515 cm^{-1}.

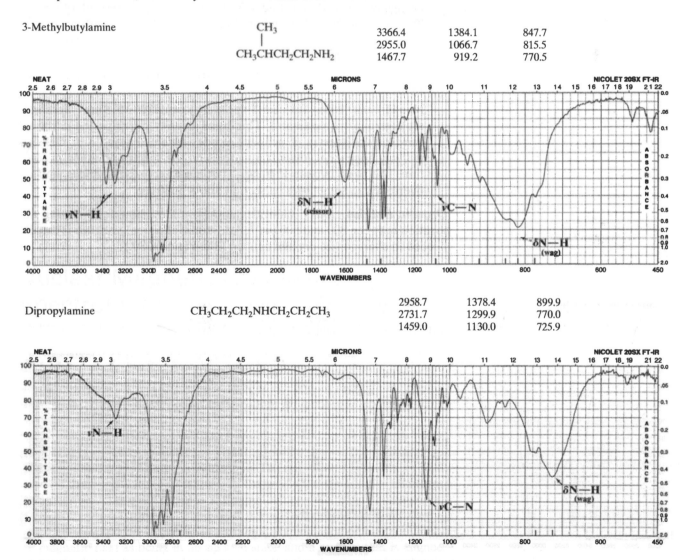

Figure G28 IR spectra of a primary amine, 3-methylbutylamine, and a secondary amine, dipropylamine

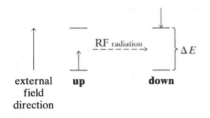

Figure G31 Spin transition of a magnetic nucleus

radiation of just the right frequency, some of its **up** nuclei will flip over, into the **down** spin state. This transition is illustrated in Figure G31. Because a nucleus in the **down** state is less stable (contains more energy) than a nucleus in the **up** state, the spin transition results in an absorption of energy by the nucleus. Such a transition is possible only if the energy of an RF photon, $h\nu$ is exactly equal to the energy of the transition, ΔE, so that $\nu = \Delta E/h$. When this is the case, the *resonance condition*—the condition under which nuclei of a given kind can undergo spin transitions—is fulfilled. The transition energy, ΔE, is directly proportional to the strength of the external magnetic field, H_o, so ν is also proportional to H_o. This means that the resonance condition for a nucleus can be attained either by adjusting the frequency of the RF radiation or by adjusting the strength of the external field.

a. ^{1}H NMR Spectrometry

Instrumentation

There are two fundamentally different ways of obtaining an NMR spectrum. With a *continuous-wave (CW) NMR spectrometer,* the sample is irradiated continuously with RF waves as the magnetic field or RF frequency is varied, and the electromagnetic signals generated by nuclei as they change spin states are converted to peaks on a moving chart. With a *Fourier-transform NMR (FT–NMR) spectrometer,* the sample is irradiated with intense pulses of full-spectrum RF radiation that displace the nuclei from their equilibrium distribution. Their response to the displacement is monitored, generating data that is converted by a microprocessor to an NMR spectrum.

Continuous-Wave NMR. In a continuous-wave NMR spectrometer, a glass tube containing the sample is placed between the poles of a magnet and irradiated with RF radiation from a transmitter coil while the magnetic field is "swept" (varied continuously) over a preset range. In an instrument of the type diagrammed in Figure G32, the magnetic field is swept from low to high field (*downfield* to *upfield*) by varying the strength of an electric current passing through the sweep coils. When the resonance condition for

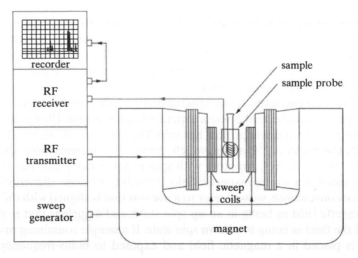

Figure G32 Schematic diagram of a continuous-wave NMR spectrometer

a particular kind of nucleus in the sample is met, nuclei of that kind flip from the **up** state to the **down** state. As they do so, they generate a small fluctuating magnetic field that can be detected by a receiver coil encircling the sample tube. The receiver coil sends an electronic signal to an RF receiver, which amplifies and modifies the signal so that it can be displayed on a recorder as part of an NMR spectrum.

An NMR spectrum is a record of all the signals generated by all of the different kinds of nuclei in the sample that absorb RF radiation over the range swept by the instrument. If the sweep range is one in which the resonance conditions for ^1H nuclei (protons) are met, the spectrum should display different signals for protons that are in different molecular environments. For example, protons on the benzene ring in *para*-xylene are in a different molecular environment than protons on the methyl groups, so the NMR spectrum of *p*-xylene will display two signals—one for each kind of proton, at different positions on the spectrum, as shown in Figure G33. The position of a signal relative to the position of a reference signal, usually that of tetramethylsilane (TMS), is called its *chemical shift*. A chemical shift, represented by the Greek letter δ, is ordinarily measured in parts per million (ppm). Because the TMS signal ($\delta = 0$) is on the right (upfield) side of a spectrum, chemical shifts increase from right to left.

A typical CW–NMR spectrometer suitable for use by undergraduate students may operate at a frequency of 60 MHz and a magnetic field strength of approximately 1.4 tesla (14,000 gauss). When an ^1H NMR spectrum is recorded using a 60-MHz spectrometer, the magnetic field is swept over a range of about 1.4×10^{-5} tesla (0.14 gauss), which is only 10 millionths of the external field strength, or 10 parts per million (ppm). This sweep range can be extended to 15 ppm or so to detect protons whose resonance conditions occur outside this range.

Fourier-Transform NMR. A Fourier-transform NMR (FT–NMR) spectrometer is capable of producing spectra with better resolution and a much higher signal-to-noise ratio than any CW instrument. In an FT–NMR instrument, the sample (in an appropriate sample tube) is placed between the poles of a powerful electromagnet and irradiated with a short (~10 μs) pulse of RF radiation that covers the entire frequency range of interest. The pulse

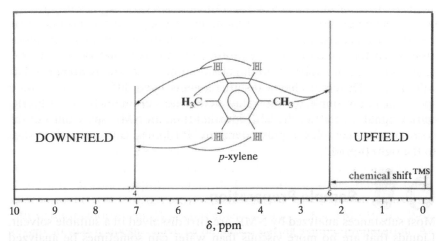

Figure G33 ^1H NMR spectrum of *p*-xylene

Integrating a Spectrum

An NMR spectrum is ordinarily *integrated* to measure the areas of its signals. With a typical CW-NMR instrument, the recorder pen traces a horizontal line until it reaches a signal; then it rises a distance that is proportional to the signal's area as it crosses the signal. Because the area of a signal on a proton NMR spectrum is proportional to the number of protons responsible for the signal, integrating the spectrum makes it possible to determine how many protons give rise to each signal.

Following is a summary of the steps in the integration of a typical ^{1}H NMR spectrum recorded with a CW-NMR spectrometer. If you will be expected to integrate your NMR spectrum, your instructor will provide more detailed directions.

1. The RF power is optimized to provide an acceptable signal-to-noise ratio.
2. The instrument is switched to the integral mode.
3. While the spectrum is scanned rapidly, the integral amplitude control is adjusted until the integrator trace spans the vertical axis of the chart.
4. With the sweep offset and sweep width controls set to scan a region free from NMR signals, the balance control is adjusted during a slow scan of that region to give a horizontal line.
5. While scanning a signal, the phasing control is adjusted to make the integrator traces before and after the signal as nearly horizontal as possible.
6. The integral over the entire spectrum is recorded (preferably once in each direction) using a sweep time that is about one-fifth to one-tenth that for the normal spectrum. The pen should be returned to the baseline after each scan.
7. The relative peak areas are determined by measuring the vertical distances between the integrator traces before and after each signal, and the results for successive scans are averaged (see Figure G38).

With an FT-NMR spectrometer, the signals are integrated electronically.

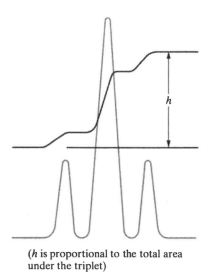

(*h* is proportional to the total area under the triplet)

Figure G38 Measuring signal areas

DIRECTIONS FOR OPERATING A CW–NMR SPECTROMETER

Standard Scale and Microscale

Equipment and Supplies

NMR spectrometer
sample
deuterated NMR solvent
TMS
NMR tube
Pasteur pipet
tissues
washing solvent

Do not attempt to operate the instrument without prior instruction and proper supervision. Do not make any adjustments other than the ones specified, except at the instructor's request and under his or her supervision. Some of the adjustments described here may be made in advance by the instructor or a lab technician. The following procedure applies to a typical 60-MHz

CW-NMR spectrometer; operating procedures for other instruments may vary considerably.

Prepare a solution of the sample in a suitable NMR solvent as described in "Sample Preparation," and add 1–3% TMS, if necessary. Fill the NMR tube to a depth of about 3 cm with this solution, and cap the tube. Wipe the outside of the NMR tube carefully with a tissue paper or lint-free cloth, insert it in the sample spinner using a depth gauge to adjust its position, wipe it again, and carefully place the assembly into the sample probe between the magnet pole faces. Adjust the air flow to spin the sample at 40–50 Hz; it may need to be readjusted later to minimize spinning sidebands. Align the chart paper on the recorder, and cover it with a sheet of scrap paper. Set the sweep controls to scan the desired range at a suitable rate. Typical settings for a 60-MHz instrument are: sweep offset, 0; sweep width, 600 Hz; and sweep time, 600 s. Set the RF power to about midrange and the filter response time to 1 s or less. Set the spectrum amplitude control to about midrange, and scan the spectrum to find the tallest peak. Readjust the spectrum amplitude to keep that peak on scale near the top of the chart during a scan. If necessary, optimize peak shape and ringing and adjust the phasing as directed by your instructor. Set the TMS peak to 0.0 δ with the sweep zero control; you may have to sweep through the TMS signal several times, adjusting the control each time, until it is lined up with the zero on the chart paper. Set the recorder baseline, if necessary, to a convenient location near the bottom of the spectrum. Remove the scrap paper, and record the spectrum. If you are to integrate your spectrum, cover it with scrap paper while you make the adjustments described in "Integrating a Spectrum," then remove the paper, and record the integral on the original spectrum.

When you have finished scanning and integrating your spectrum, remove the spectrum and record the control settings and other relevant information on it. Then remove the sample tube as demonstrated by your instructor; follow directions carefully or the tube may break. Clean the sample tube immediately and thoroughly using a Pasteur pipet and an appropriate solvent. The protic form of the solvent in which the sample was dissolved is generally used for cleaning. For example, if the solvent was $CDCl_3$, rinse the tube with $CHCl_3$—*not* the much more expensive deuterated solvent. Invert the tube in a suitable rack, and let it drain dry. Before being reused, an NMR tube should be dried in an oven to remove all traces of the wash solvent.

Take Care! Handle NMR tubes with great care; they are fragile and may break.

Specal NMR-tube cleaners are available commercially.

Waste Disposal: Dispose of the sample and solvent as directed by your instructor.

Summary

1. Prepare solution; add TMS, if necessary.
2. Transfer solution to NMR tube, and cap tube.
3. Wipe tube, and insert in sample spinner.
4. Insert spinner in probe; adjust spinning rate.
5. Align chart paper, and cover with scrap paper.
6. Set sweep, RF power, and filter response time controls.
7. Scan spectrum and adjust spectrum amplitude control.
8. Zero TMS signal.
9. Set baseline; remove scrap paper.
10. Scan spectrum.
11. Integrate spectrum.
12. Remove and clean sample tube; dispose of solution.

When Things Go Wrong

If the NMR spectrum of a sample run in $CDCl_3$ has a small extraneous peak at $\delta 7.3$, don't worry about it; the peak arises from the small amount of $CHCl_3$ in the solvent. If you are using some other deuterated solvent, check Table G3 to see where the signal of the protic form of that solvent occurs, and disregard any small peaks at that location. (See "NMR Solvents.")

If each signal in your NMR spectrum is flanked by two considerably smaller peaks equidistant from the signal, the extraneous signals are probably spinning sidebands. Increase the sample spinning rate, and scan over the same region. If the peaks change position but don't disappear, try to identify the cause and take corrective action. (See "Spinning Rate.")

If the peaks in your NMR spectrum are distorted or unusually broad, the sample may be spinning too fast (forming a vortex), too slowly (causing field inhomogeneity), or not at all. Check the spinning rate, and adjust it if necessary; you might also need to increase the sample size to prevent vortexing problems or decrease it to reduce inhomogeneity. (See "Spinning Rate.") If the peaks are still too broad, check to see if the NMR tube is straight and uniform; if it isn't, transfer the sample to a different NMR tube. (See "Sample Preparation.") If the sample might contain ferromagnetic impurities, filter it as you transfer it to the other NMR tube. (See "Sample Preparation.") If that doesn't help, the spectrum amplitude control may be set too high, or the magnetic field may be inhomogeneous; ask your instructor for help. (See "Signal Amplitude" and "Field Homogeneity.")

If some of the peaks in your spectrum extend to the top of the chart paper and flatten out there, your sample solution may be too concentrated. Dilute it by half, and try again. (See "Sample Preparation.") If the sample concentration is appropriate, the signal amplitude control may be set too high. See your instructor about having it readjusted. (See "Signal Amplitude.")

If the chemical shifts of all your peaks are off by the same amount, the reference peak was not positioned correctly. Use the sweep zero control to reposition the reference peak to zero for TMS, or to the appropriate value for a different reference compound. (See "Sweep.") If there is no reference peak, add TMS and then adjust the sweep zero control. (See "Sample Preparation.")

If you are running the NMR spectrum of a carboxylic acid, phenol, or enolic compound and can't find the signal for the OH proton, change the sweep range to include the region above 10 ppm. (See "Sweep.")

If the baseline of your NMR spectrum is not straight and horizontal, adjust the phasing control until it is. (See "Phasing.")

 ## Interpretation of ^{1}H NMR Spectra

A proton NMR spectrum provides numerical data in the form of chemical shifts, signal areas, signal multiplicities, and coupling constants. Working out the structure of a molecule from these numbers is a fascinating mental exercise comparable to the work of a cryptographer who reconstructs meaningful messages from coded symbols.

The *chemical shift* (δ) is the distance, measured in hertz or parts per million, from the center of a signal to some reference signal, usually that of TMS. The TMS signal occurs farther upfield (to the right) than nearly all

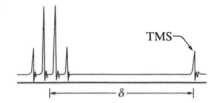

Figure G39 Chemical shift of a proton NMR signal

other proton signals, so the chemical shift of a signal is usually measured as its distance downfield (to the left) from that of TMS, as shown in Figure G39. Note that a signal may have more than one peak (four peaks, in this example).

The *signal area*, which is the sum of the areas under all of the peaks in a signal, is proportional to the number of protons giving rise to the signal. With a typical CW-NMR instrument, signal areas are determined by using an electronic integrator that traces a line across each proton signal after it is recorded. The area of the signal is proportional to the vertical rise of the integrator pen as it crosses the signal; that is, to the height of the "steps" drawn by the integrator pen, as shown in Figure G38. Integrated signal areas can be converted to proton numbers using the following relationship:

$$\text{number of protons responsible for signal} =$$
$$\text{total number of protons} \times \frac{\text{area under signal}}{\text{area under all signals}}$$

For example, suppose that a compound with the molecular formula $C_{10}H_{14}$ has four signals with relative areas of 42, 7, 14, and 35. The sum of the areas is 98, so the number of protons responsible for the first signal is

$$14 \times \frac{42}{98} = 6$$

By similar calculations, it can be shown that 1, 2, and 5 protons, respectively, are responsible for the other three signals. If the molecular formula of a compound is not known, relative proton numbers can be obtained by reducing the signal areas to the lowest ratio of integers.

The signal generated by a given set of protons may be split into several peaks as a result of *coupling* interactions with nearby proton sets (refer to your lecture textbook or see your instructor for an explanation of coupling). The *multiplicity* of a signal is simply the number of separate peaks it contains; its *coupling constant* is the distance between two adjacent peaks in the signal, measured in hertz (Hz). Figure G40 shows the signals of two sets of protons that are interacting with each other; the protons of set *a* have split the signal of the protons of set *b* into four peaks (a quartet), and the *b* protons have split the signal of the *a* protons into three peaks (a triplet). The coupling constant, which is equal for the two signals, is represented by J_{ab}. In the simplest case, the number of protons responsible for splitting the signal of a neighboring set of protons can be determined by subtracting 1 from the number of peaks in that signal. Thus, the three peaks in the *a* signal are produced by two neighboring *b* protons, and the four peaks in the *b* signal by three neighboring *a* protons. An interacting triplet–quartet grouping of this kind is good evidence for an ethyl (CH_3CH_2-) group.

Ideal triplets and quartets should be symmetrical, having relative peak area ratios of 1:2:1 and 1:3:3:1, respectively. As shown in Figure G40, however, the signals in an actual spectrum are often somewhat distorted, giving paired peaks of unequal height. Note that the two signals in the figure are not perfectly symmetrical but appear to "lean" toward each other, with the peaks on the side that face the other signal being higher than predicted. This and the fact that their coupling constants are equal provide additional evidence that the protons responsible for the two signals are, in fact, coupling with each other and not with some other proton sets in the molecule.

Stop and Think: What is the most likely structure for this compound if it contains a benzene ring and one alkyl side chain?

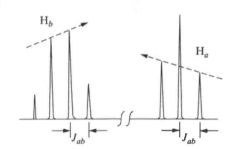

Figure G40 Signals of nearest neighbor protons

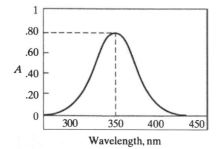

Figure G43 Electronic energy transition in 1,3-butadiene

electrons in aromatic and conjugated aliphatic systems. An example of such a transition is illustrated in Figure G43, in which a pi electron in the ground-state electron configuration of 1,3-butadiene jumps from its bonding molecular orbital to an unoccupied antibonding molecular orbital.

A UV–VIS spectrum is often quite featureless compared to an IR or NMR spectrum, and may consist of only one or two broad *absorption bands*. The broad-band structure is caused by rotational and vibrational transitions that accompany each electronic transition; each different combination of rotational and vibrational transitions has a different energy, so collectively they span a broad range of wavelengths. The height of an absorption band above the baseline of a UV–VIS spectrum is measured in units of *absorbance, A*. The position of an absorption band is given by its wavelength of maximum absorbance, λ_{max}, which is measured from the top of the band. For example, the absorption band illustrated in Figure G44 has an absorbance of 0.80 and a λ_{max} of 350 nm. Absorbance is related to *transmittance (T)*, the fraction of incident radiation transmitted through a sample, by the following equation:

$$A = \log(1/T) = -\log T \qquad (1)$$

Thus, the transmittance of a UV–VIS band is equal to 10^{-A}. For a band with $A = 0.80, T = 10^{-0.80} = 0.16$, meaning that about 16% of the light entering the sample passes through unchanged, and the remaining 84% is absorbed by the sample.

Figure G44 An ultraviolet absorption band

a. UV–VIS Spectra

 Sample Preparation

Routine UV–VIS spectra are nearly always obtained in solution. The solvent must be transparent (or nearly so) in the regions to be scanned. Water, 95% ethanol, methanol, dioxane, acetonitrile, and cyclohexane are suitable down to about 210–220 nm; many other solvents can be used at higher wavelengths. The preferred solvent is 95% ethanol, in part because it doesn't require additional purification; most other solvents must be purified or purchased as spectral-grade solvents. The solvent must not, of course, react with the solute. For example, alcohols should not be used as solvents for aldehydes.

If possible, the solution to be analyzed should produce a maximum absorbance of about 1 when the solute's strongest absorption band is scanned. Using Beer's law (see Equation **2**), we can show that the molar concentration of such a solution, if analyzed in a 1-cm sample cell, should be less than or equal to $1/\varepsilon_{max}$, where we define ε_{max} as the maximum molar absorptivity of the solute over the wavelength range to be scanned. For example, if the solute's strongest band has a molar absorptivity of 10,000 at its λ_{max} value, the solution concentration should be about 1×10^{-4} M. To prepare such dilute solutions accurately, it may be necessary to prepare a stock solution that is too concentrated by several powers of 10, and then measure an aliquot of this solution and dilute it. For example, to prepare a 1.0×10^{-4} M solution of cinnamic acid (mol wt = 148), you could measure 0.15 g (1.0 mmol) of the solid into a 100-mL volumetric flask, and fill it to the mark with solvent; then transfer a 1-mL aliquot of this 0.010 M solution into another 100-mL volumetric flask, and fill it to the mark with solvent. For microscale work, you could use 15 mg of the cinnamic acid and a 10-mL volumetric flask to make the stock solution, and dilute a 0.1-mL aliquot of this solution to 10 mL in another volumetric flask. For qualitative work, when knowing the exact concentration of the solution is not necessary, you can omit the dilution step and use a 10-μL syringe to measure a specified or calculated amount of a liquid sample into about 25 mL of the solvent. If the molar absorptivity of the solute is not known, it may be necessary to find the optimum concentration by trial and error, starting with a more concentrated solution and diluting it as needed to bring all of the absorption bands on scale.

 ## Sample Cells

The most commonly used *spectrophotometer cell* is a transparent rectangular container with a square cross-section, having a path length of 1.00 cm and a capacity of about 3 mL. Cells with capacities of about 1 mL and 0.5 mL are available for microscale work. Two sides of a typical cell are nontransparent (usually frosted), and the other two are transparent. Silica or quartz cells are used for the UV region; optical glass or plastic cells are suitable in the visible region. Cells must be scrupulously cleaned; they should never be touched on their transparent sides because even a fingerprint can yield a spectrum.

 ## Recording a Spectrum

The construction of UV–VIS spectrometers varies widely. Both single- and double-beam instruments are available, with and without recording capability. For a double-beam recording instrument, two identical spectrophotometer cells are filled about two-thirds full with (1) a solution of the compound being analyzed (the sample) and (2) the solvent used to prepare the solution. For a single-beam instrument, the same cell is used for both the sample and the pure solvent. A spectrophotometer cell filled with the sample or solvent is held by its nontransparent sides and inserted into the appropriate cell holder inside the instrument's sample compartment, oriented so that the light beam will pass through its transparent faces.

Before a spectrum is recorded, the user selects the wavelength region to be scanned and may also select a radiation source appropriate for that region. A tungsten lamp can be used between 300 and 800 nm, and a hydrogen lamp between 190 and 350 nm. The absorbance range of some instruments can be preset; a typical range is from zero to one or two absorbance units. Modern computerized instruments allow the operator to apply a baseline correction, so that the instrument automatically subtracts any absorption due to the solvent as the spectrum is scanned. Such instruments have a monitor to display the spectrum, and a printer or plotter to record it.

The fragment ions described previously and other common fragment ions are listed in Table G7. Structures have been determined for some (but not all) of these cations. For example, the $C_7H_7^+$ ion with mass number 91, which results from the cleavage of alkylbenzenes, has been formulated as either a benzyl cation or a tropylium ion; in most cases, it appears to have the latter structure. Before you can interpret a mass spectrum proficiently, using data like that in Tables G6 and G7, you need to learn about the characteristic fragmentation patterns and mechanisms for different classes of organic compounds. This kind of information and some general rules for interpretation of mass spectra are given in references on mass spectrometry listed in Category F of the Bibliography.

Table G7 Some common fragment ions

m/e	Possible formulas
15	CH_3^+
17	OH^+
18	H_2O^+, NH_4^+
26	$C_2H_2^+$
27	$C_2H_3^+$
28	CO^+, $C_2H_4^+$
29	CHO^+, $C_2H_5^+$
30	$CH_2NH_2^+$, NO^+
31	CH_2OH^+, CH_3O^+
35, 37	Cl^+
39	$C_3H_3^+$
41	$C_3H_5^+$
43	CH_3CO^+, $C_3H_7^+$
44	CO_2^+, $C_3H_8^+$
45	$CH_3OCH_2^+$, CO_2H^+
46	NO_2^+
49	CH_2Cl^+
51	$C_4H_3^+$
57	$C_4H_9^+$, $C_2H_5CO^+$
59	$COOCH_3^+$
65	$C_5H_5^+$
66	$C_5H_6^+$
71	$C_5H_{11}^+$, $C_3H_7CO^+$
76	$C_6H_4^+$
77	$C_6H_5^+$
78	$C_6H_6^+$
79, 81	Br^+
91	$C_7H_7^+$, $C_6H_5N^+$
93	$C_6H_5O^+$
94	$C_6H_6O^+$
105	$C_6H_5CO^+$

Appendixes and Bibliography

APPENDIX **IV**   Calculations for Organic Synthesis

In this book, the quantities of many reactants are given in units of chemical amount (amount of substance), moles or millimoles. You will have to convert such quantities to units of mass or volume before you can begin a synthetic experiment. In any experiment, it is the relationship between these *chemical* quantities that is significant, not the relationship between such *physical* quantities as mass and volume. Because there are no "mole meters" that measure molar amounts directly, we are forced to use balances and volumetric glassware for that purpose. That should not obscure the fact that the chemical units are fundamental; only by knowing the chemical amounts of reactants involved in a preparation, for example, can you recognize the stoichiometric relationships between them or predict the yield of the expected product.

It is helpful to regard a chemical calculation as a process by which a given quantity is "converted" to the required quantity. This can be accomplished by multiplying the given quantity by a series of ratios used as unit or dimensional *conversion factors*. Unit conversions are carried out by using conversion factors, such as 454 g/lb, that are written as ratios between two quantities whose quotient is unity (for example, 454 g = 1 lb, so 454 g/1 lb = 1). Dimensional conversions are carried out by using conversion factors that are ratios of quantities in different *dimensions,* such as mass, volume, and chemical amount. For example, the density of a substance can be regarded as a conversion factor linking the two dimensions of mass and volume, so it is used to convert the mass of a given quantity of the substance to units of volume, and vice versa. A conversion factor can be inverted when necessary. For example, the molar mass of butyl acetate, written as 116 g/1 mol, will convert moles of butyl acetate to grams; the inverse ratio, 1 mol/116 g, will convert grams of butyl acetate to moles. All calculations should be checked by making sure that the units involved cancel to yield the correct units in the answer. This does not ensure that your answer is correct, but if the units do *not* cancel, the answer is almost certainly wrong.

The following examples illustrate some fundamental types of calculations that you can expect to encounter in an organic chemistry lab course.

Chemical Amount and Mass.   The chemical amount (in moles or millimoles) of a substance is converted to its mass by multiplying by its molar mass. Remember that the molar mass of a substance is obtained by simply appending the units g/mol to its molecular weight, which is a dimensionless quantity. For example, the mass of 15.0 mmol of butyl acetate (mol wt = 116) is 1.74 g.

$$15.0 \text{ mmol} \times \frac{1 \text{ mol}}{1000 \text{ mmol}} \times \frac{116 \text{ g}}{1 \text{ mol}} = 1.74 \text{ g}$$

Note that the chemical amount in millimoles must be converted to moles before the conversion factor is applied; otherwise, the units will not cancel. Mass can be converted to chemical amount by inverting the conversion factor before multiplying.

Chemical Amount and Volume. The chemical amount (in moles or millimoles) of a pure liquid is converted to volume by multiplying by the liquid substance's molar mass and by the inverse of its density. For example, the volume of 2.50 mmol of acetic acid (mol wt = 60.1; d = 1.049 g/mL) is 0.143 mL.

$$2.50 \text{ mmol} \times \frac{1 \text{ mol}}{1000 \text{ mmol}} \times \frac{60.1 \text{ g}}{1 \text{ mol}} \times \frac{1 \text{ mL}}{1.049 \text{ g}} = 0.143 \text{ mL}$$

The volume of a solution needed to provide a specified chemical amount of solute is calculated by multiplying the number of moles required by the inverse of the solution's molar concentration. For example, the volume of 6.0 M HCl (which contains 6.0 mol of HCl per liter of solution) needed to provide 18 mmol of HCl is 3.0 mL.

$$18 \text{ mmol} \times \frac{1 \text{ mol}}{1000 \text{ mmol}} \times \frac{1 \text{ L}}{6.0 \text{ mol}} \times \frac{1000 \text{ mL}}{1 \text{ L}} = 3.0 \text{ mL}$$

Note that concentrations expressed in mol/L and mmol/mL have the same numerical value. Thus, a 6.0 M solution also has a concentration of 6.0 mmol/mL; using these units simplifies the previous calculation considerably:

$$18 \text{ mmol} \times \frac{1 \text{ mL}}{6.0 \text{ mmol}} = 3.0 \text{ mL}$$

Theoretical Yield. The maximum quantity of a product (usually expressed in mass units) that could be attained from a reaction is called the *theoretical yield* of the product. Theoretical yields can be calculated using *stoichiometric factors*—ratios derived from the coefficients (expressed in moles) of the products and reactants in a balanced equation for the reaction. For example, the stoichiometric factors relating the chemical amount of the organic product to the chemical amounts of the two reactants in the following reaction are (1 mol dibenzalacetone)/(1 mol acetone) and (1 mol dibenzalacetone)/(2 mol benzaldehyde).

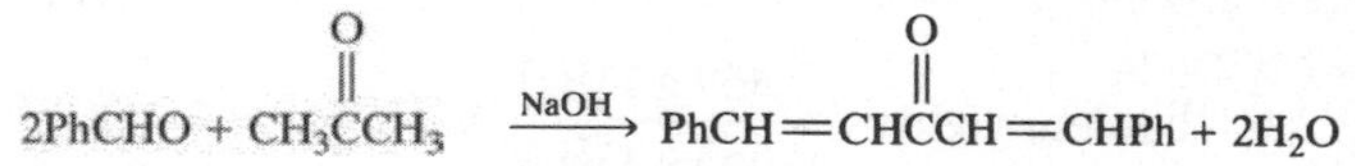

$$2PhCHO + CH_3\overset{\overset{\textstyle O}{\|}}{C}CH_3 \xrightarrow{\text{NaOH}} PhCH=CHC\overset{\overset{\textstyle O}{\|}}{C}CH=CHPh + 2H_2O$$

benzaldehyde (B)   acetone (A)   dibenzalacetone (DBA)

Suppose you were trying to prepare dibenzalacetone (mol wt = 234.3) starting with 0.500 g of benzaldehyde (mol wt = 106.1) and 0.150 g of acetone (mol wt = 58.1). (For convenience, we will abbreviate the names as dibenzalacetone = DBA, benzaldehyde = B, and acetone = A.) You can calculate the maximum chemical amount of product that could be formed from each reactant by converting the given quantity to moles, and then applying the appropriate stoichiometric factor:

$$0.500 \text{ g B} \times \frac{1 \text{ mol}}{106.1 \text{ g B}} \times \frac{1 \text{ mol DBA}}{2 \text{ mol B}} = 2.36 \times 10^{-3} \text{ mol DBA}$$

$$0.150 \text{ g A} \times \frac{1 \text{ mol A}}{58.1 \text{ g A}} \times \frac{1 \text{ mol DBA}}{1 \text{ mol A}} = 2.58 \times 10^{-3} \text{ mol DBA}$$

Because there is only enough benzaldehyde to produce 2.36×10^{-3} mol of dibenzalacetone, it is impossible to obtain more than that from the specified quantities of reactants. Once that much product has been formed, the reaction mixture will have run out of benzaldehyde, and the *excess* (leftover) acetone will have nothing to react with. Therefore, benzaldehyde is the *limiting reactant* upon which the yield calculations must be based. The theoretical yield of dibenzalacetone, in grams, is then

$$2.36 \times 10^{-3} \text{ mol DBA} \times \frac{234.3 \text{ g DBA}}{1 \text{ mol DBA}} = 0.553 \text{ g DBA}$$

Remember that the limiting reactant is always the one that would produce the least amount of product, which is not necessarily the one present in the lowest amount. In this example, benzaldehyde is the limiting reactant, even though the mass and chemical amount of benzaldehyde are much greater than the mass and chemical amount of acetone.

Percent Yield.   It is seldom, if ever, possible to attain the theoretical yield of product from an organic preparation. The reaction may not go to completion during the designated reaction period, leaving unreacted starting materials. There may be side reactions that reduce the yield of product, as in the reaction of benzaldehyde with acetone, where some benzalacetone ($PhCH = CHCOCH_3$) is formed as a by-product. In addition, there are invariably material losses when the product is separated from the reaction mixture and purified. The *percent yield* of a preparation compares the actual yield to the theoretical yield, as defined here:

$$\text{Percent yield} = \frac{\text{actual yield}}{\text{theoretical yield}} \times 100\%$$

For example, if you prepared 0.409 g of dibenzalacetone from 0.500 g of benzaldehyde and 0.150 g of acetone (theoretical yield = 0.553 g), the percent yield of your synthesis would be

$$\text{Percent yield} = \frac{0.409 \text{ g DBA}}{0.553 \text{ g DBA}} \times 100\% = 74.0\%$$

In many experiments, you will estimate the theoretical yield of a preparation based on the amounts of reactants given in the "Before You Begin" section. This will help you assess your performance by comparing your actual yield with an estimate of the "ideal" yield. But the percent yield that you *report* should be based on the amounts of reactants that you actually used in the synthesis, not on the amounts given (unless they are exactly the same).

Mass Percentage and Percent Recovery.   The mass percentage of a substance present in a particular mixture, such as the percentage of the compound cinnamaldehyde in a sample of cinnamon, is calculated by dividing the mass of the component by the mass of the mixture and multiplying by 100%.

$$\text{Mass percentage} = \frac{\text{mass of component of a mixture}}{\text{mass of mixture}} \times 100\%$$

For example, if 5.00 g of cinnamon contains 0.065 g of cinnamaldehyde, the mass percentage of cinnamaldehyde is 1.3%.

$$\text{Mass percentage} = \frac{0.065 \text{ g}}{5.00 \text{ g}} \times 100\% = 1.3\%$$

The percent recovery of a process that is used to isolate one or more components from a mixture is calculated similarly, but because the process is unlikely to isolate all of a component, it is not the same as the component's actual mass percentage.

$$\text{Percent recovery} = \frac{\text{mass of component recovered}}{\text{mass of mixture}} \times 100\%$$

For example, if you isolate 0.625 g of clove oil by steam-distilling 5.00 g of cloves, the percent recovery of clove oil is 12.5%.

$$\text{Percent recovery} = \frac{0.625 \text{ g}}{5.00 \text{ g}} \times 100\% = 12.5\%$$

Preparation of Solutions.   Suppose you need to prepare 75 mL of ~2.0 M sodium carbonate (Na_2CO_3) from solid sodium carbonate. First calculate the chemical amount of sodium carbonate (mol wt = 106.0) contained in 75 mL of 2.0 M sodium carbonate.

$$75 \text{ mL} \times \frac{1 \text{ L}}{1000 \text{ mL}} \times \frac{2.0 \text{ mol}}{1 \text{ L}} = 0.15 \text{ mol}$$

Now calculate the mass of that number of moles.

$$0.15 \text{ mol} \times 106 \text{ g}/1 \text{ mol} = 16 \text{ g}$$

You can, of course, combine these calculations.

$$75 \text{ mL} \times \frac{1 \text{ L}}{1000 \text{ mL}} \times \frac{2.0 \text{ mol}}{1 \text{ L}} \times \frac{106 \text{ g}}{1 \text{ mol}} = 16 \text{ g}$$

For most purposes, you could prepare the solution by dissolving 16 g of sodium carbonate in distilled water, transferring it to a 100-mL graduated cylinder, and adding more distilled water to the 75 mL mark. If the concentration must be more accurate, you could use a 100-mL volumetric flask to prepare 100 mL of 2.00 M solution, which will require 21.2 g of sodium carbonate (do that calculation yourself).

The volume of solvent used to dissolve the solute should be substantially less than the final volume of the solution.

Now suppose you need to prepare 9.0 mL of 3.0 M sulfuric acid by diluting concentrated sulfuric acid, which has a concentration of 18 mol/L. You need to know what volume of the concentrated acid must be diluted to yield the desired volume of 3.0 M sulfuric acid. The easiest way to do such a calculation is to use the dilution equation $M_1 \times V_1 = M_2 \times V_2$, where the terms on the left are the molar concentration and volume of the undiluted solution, and the terms on the right are the molar concentration and volume of the diluted solution. Because V_1 is unknown,

$$18 \, M \times V_1 = 3.0 \, M \times 9.0 \text{ mL}$$

solving for V_1 then yields

$$V_1 = \frac{3.0 \, M \times 9.0 \text{ mL}}{18 \, M} = 1.5 \text{ mL}$$

So, to prepare the 3.0 *M* sulfuric acid, you could *carefully* pour 1.5 mL of concentrated sulfuric acid into an amount of distilled water that is less than the final volume (5 mL, for example), wait for the solution to cool down (dilution of concentrated acids generates heat), and then transfer it to a 10-mL graduated cylinder and add more distilled water to the 9.0 mL mark. If it is important to control the concentration more accurately, you should calculate the volume of concentrated solution to three significant figures, and use volumetric glassware to prepare the diluted solution.

APPENDIX V   Planning an Experiment

Writing an Experimental Plan

Before starting any project—whether you are making a bookshelf, duck à l'orange, or isopentyl acetate—you must have a plan. An *experimental plan* should summarize what you expect to do in the laboratory and how you intend to go about it. You should state how the work is to be done in short phrases, without excessive detail. You can always refer to the "Directions" section of the experiment and the operation descriptions for the details, but as you become more proficient in the laboratory, you should find yourself relying less on the textbook and more on your experimental plan. A good plan should give you quick access to the essential information you will need while performing the experiment. Quantities of chemicals (including wash solvents, drying agents, etc.), reaction times, physical properties, hazard warnings, and other useful data should be included. You can list the supplies and equipment you will need for each operation (these are specified in most operation descriptions) so that you can have them cleaned and ready when you need them. You may also wish to sketch the apparatus you will be using so that you can assemble it quickly in the laboratory.

An experimental plan should help you organize your time efficiently by listing tasks in the approximate order in which you expect to accomplish them. For example, whenever a reflux period is specified in a procedure, you will have some free time to set up the apparatus for the next step, reorganize your work area, review an operation, start a minilab, take a melting point, record the spectrum of a previous product, or tie up other loose ends. Your plan should be flexible enough that you can alter it or deviate from it during the experiment, if there is good reason to do so. One simple and effective way of organizing your time is to use a laboratory checklist, such as the one shown in Experiment 4. You should refer to relevant sections of the experiment (especially "Understanding the Experiment" and the "Directions") as you prepare your checklist, as well as to the appropriate operation descriptions. Leave enough space between the items on your checklist so that you can add new ones, as necessary, during the experiment. As you complete each task in the laboratory, simply check it off the list and go on to the next one.

Creating a Flow Diagram

A flow diagram, such as the one in Figure 5.1 of Experiment 5, can help you organize your time by giving you a quick overview of the procedure, showing the purpose of each step. To create such a flow diagram, first list all of the substances that you know to be present in the reaction mixture before the reaction starts (reactants, solvents, catalysts), as shown in the following general flow diagram:

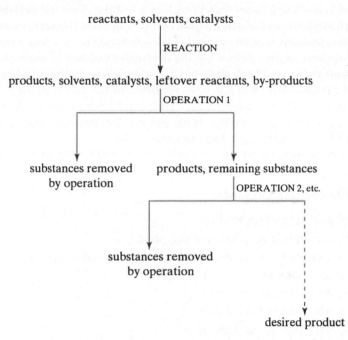

reactants, solvents, catalysts

REACTION

products, solvents, catalysts, leftover reactants, by-products

OPERATION 1

substances removed by operation   products, remaining substances

OPERATION 2, etc.

substances removed by operation

desired product

The reaction equation in the "Reactions and Properties" section tells you what substances will form as a result of the reaction. At the end of the reaction period, the reaction mixture will contain these products as well as the reaction solvent (if any), catalyst (if any), leftover reactants, and usually some by-products formed by various side reactions. The flow diagram should show how all of the unwanted substances in the reaction mixture are separated from the desired product. Each separation or purification operation is represented by a branch in the flow diagram, with the substance(s) being removed on one side, and the desired product—along with any remaining substances—on the other side. After the last operation, the product stands alone, with all of the impurities eliminated—on paper, at least!

Properties of Organic Compounds   APPENDIX **VI**

The tables in this appendix are to be used in conjunction with the procedures described in Part IV, "Qualitative Organic Analysis." Compounds that melt below ordinary ambient temperature (about 25°C) are listed in order of increasing boiling point (bp); those that (when pure) are generally solid at room temperature are listed in order of increasing melting point (mp). Both melting and boiling points are specified for some borderline cases; if either value is out of sequence, it is shown in italics.

Derivative preparations are described in Part IV, in the section entitled "Preparation of Derivatives," and are referred to by number in the headings of the appropriate columns. Melting points in parentheses are for derivatives that exist in more than one crystalline form or for which significantly different melting points have been reported in the literature. Sometimes the recrystallization solvent will determine the form in which a derivative crystallizes, so a significant deviation from a listed melting point shouldn't be considered conclusive proof that a product is not the expected derivative. If a given compound can form more than one product (for instance, mononitro and dinitro derivatives of an aromatic hydrocarbon), the reaction conditions for the preparation may determine the derivative isolated (a mixture of derivatives may also result). A dash (—) in a derivative column indicates either that the derivative has not been reported in the literature or that it is not suitable for identification (it may be a liquid, for example). See references from Category G in the Bibliography for physical constants and derivative melting points not listed in these tables.

Most compounds are listed by their systematic (IUPAC) names, except when those names would be too lengthy.

Abbreviations Used in Tables

d = decomposes on melting

s = sublimes at or below melting point

m = monosubstituted derivative (such as a mononitrated aromatic hydrocarbon)

di = disubstituted derivative

t = trisubstituted derivative

tet = tetrasubstituted derivative

List of tables

No.	Compound class	Page
1	alcohols	924
2	aldehydes	925
3	ketones	926
4	amides	927
5	primary and secondary amines	927
6	tertiary amines	928
7	carboxylic acids	929
8	esters	930
9	alkyl halides	931
10	aryl halides	932
11	aromatic hydrocarbons	932
12	phenols	933

Table 1 Alcohols

Compound	bp	mp	3,5-Dinitro-benzoate, D-1	4-Nitro-benzoate, D-1	α-Naphthyl-urethane, D-2	Phenyl-urethane, D-2
methanol	65		108	96	124	47
ethanol	78		93	57	79	52
2-propanol	82		123	110	106	88
2-methyl-2-propanol*	83	26	142	—	—	136
2-propen-1-ol	97		49	28	108	70
1-propanol	97		74	35	105	57
2-butanol	99		76	26	97	65
2-methyl-2-butanol	102		116	85	72	42

continued

Table 1 Alcohols *continued*

Compound	bp	mp	3,5-Dinitro-benzoate, D-1	4-Nitro-benzoate, D-1	α-Naphthyl-urethane, D-2	Phenyl-urethane, D-2
2-methyl-1-propanol	108		87	69	104	86
3-pentanol	116		101	17	95	48
1-butanol	118		64	36	71	61
2-pentanol	120		62	24	74	—
3-methyl-3-pentanol	123		94 (62)	69	104	43
3-methyl-1-butanol	132		61	21	68	57
4-methyl-2-pentanol	132		65	26	88	143
1-pentanol	138		46	11	68	46
cyclopentanol	141		115	62	118	132
2-ethyl-l-butanol	148		51	—	60	—
1-hexanol	157		58	5	59	42
cyclohexanol*	161	*25*	113	50	129	82
furfuryl alcohol	172		80	76	130	45
1-heptanol	177		47	10	62	60
2-octanol	179		32	28	63	114
1-octanol	195		61	12	67	74
1-phenylethanol	202		95	43	106	92
benzyl alcohol	205		113	85	134	77
2-phenylethanol	219		108	62	119	78
1-decanol	231		57	30	73	60
3-phenylpropanol	236		45	47	—	92
1-dodecanol*	259	24	60	45 (42)	80	74
1-tetradecanol		39	67	51	82	74
(−)-menthol		44	153	62	119	111
1-hexadecanol		49	66	58	82	73
1-octadecanol		59	77	64	89	79
diphenylmethanol		68	141	132	136	139
cholesterol		148	—	185	176	168
(+)-borneol		208	154	137 (153)	132 (127)	138

*May be solid at or just below room temperature.
Note: All temperatures are in °C. Italics designate melting or boiling points that are out of sequence.

Table 2 Aldehydes

Compound	bp	mp	2,4-Dinitrophenyl-hydrazone, D-3	Semicarbazone, D-4	Oxime, D-5
ethanal	21		168 (157)	162	47
propanal	48		148 (155)	154	40
propenal	52		165	171	—
2-methylpropanal	64		187 (183)	125 (119)	—
butanal	75		123	106	—
3-methylbutanal	92		123	107	48
pentanal	103		106 (98)	—	52
2-butenal	104		190	199	119
2-ethylbutanal	117		95 (30)	99	—
hexanal	130		104	106	51
heptanal	153		106	109	57
2-furaldehyde	162		212 (230)	202	91
2-ethylhexanal	163		114 (120)	254d	—
octanal	171		106	101	60

continued

Table 2 Aldehydes *continued*

Compound	bp	mp	2,4-Dinitrophenyl-hydrazone, D-3	Semicarbazone, D-4	Oxime, D-5
benzaldehyde	179		239	222	35
4-methylbenzaldehyde	204		234	234 (215)	80
3,7-dimethyl-6-octenal	207		77	84 (91)	—
2-chlorobenzaldehyde	213		213 (209)	229 (146)	76 (101)
4-methoxybenzaldehyde	248		253d	210	133
phenylethanal	*195*	33	121 (110)	153 (156)	99
2-methoxybenzaldehyde		38	254	215	92
4-chlorobenzaldehyde		48	265	230	110 (146)
3-nitrobenzaldehyde		58	290	246	120
4-nitrobenzaldehyde		106	320	221 (211)	133 (182)

Note: All temperatures are in °C. Italics designate melting or boiling points that are out of sequence.

Table 3 Ketones

Compound	bp	mp	2,4-Dinitrophenyl-hydrazone, D-3	Semicarbazone, D-4	Oxime, D-5
acetone	56		126	187	59
2-butanone	80		118	146	—
3-methyl-2-butanone	94		124	113	—
2-pentanone	102		143	112 (106)	58
3-pentanone	102		156	138	69
3,3-dimethyl-2-butanone	106		125	157	75 (79)
4-methyl-2-pentanone	117		95 (81)	132	58
2,4-dimethyl-3-pentanone	124		95 (88)	160	34
2-hexanone	128		110	125	49
4-methyl-3-penten-2-one	130		205	164 (133)	48
cyclopentanone	131		146	210 (203)	56
4-heptanone	144		75	132	—
2-heptanone	151		89	123	—
cyclohexanone	156		162	166	91
2,6-dimethyl-4-heptanone	168		92	122	210
2-octanone	173		58	124	—
cycloheptanone	181		148	163	23
2,5-hexanedione	194		257 (di)	185 (m); 224 (di)	137 (di)
acetophenone	202	*20*	238	198 (203)	60
2-methylacetophenone	214		159	205	61
propiophenone	218	*21*	191	182 (174)	54
3-methylacetophenone	220		207	203	57
2-undecanone	228		63	122	44
4-phenyl-2-butanone	235		127	142	87
3-methoxyacetophenone	240		—	196	—
2-methoxyacetophenone	245		—	183	83 (96)
4-methylacetophenone	*226*	28	258d	205	88
4-methoxyacetophenone		38	228	198	87
4-phenyl-3-buten-2-one		42	227 (223)	187	117
benzophenone		48	238	167	144
2-acetonaphthone		54	262d	235	145
3-nitroacetophenone		80	228	257	132
9-fluorenone		83	283	234	195
(−)-camphor		179	177	237	118

Note: All temperatures are in °C. Italics designate melting or boiling points that are out of sequence.

Table 4 Amides

Compound	bp	mp	Carboxylic acid, D-6	N-Xanthylamide, D-7
formamide	195d		—	184
propanamide		81	—	211
ethanamide		82	17	240
heptanamide		96	—	155
nonanamide		99	12	148
hexanamide		100	—	160
hexadecanamide		106	63	142
pentanamide		106	—	167
octadecanamide		109	69	141
butanamide		115	—	187
chloroacetamide		120	61 (53)	209
4-methylpentanamide		121	—	160
succinimide		126	185	247
2-methylpropanamide		129	—	211
benzamide		130	122	223
3-methylbutanamide		136	—	183
o-toluamide		143	104 (108)	200
furamide		143	133	210
phenylacetamide		156	77	195
p-toluamide		159	180	225
4-nitrobenzamide		201	240	233
phthalimide		238	210d	177

Note: All temperatures are in °C.

Table 5 Primary and secondary amines

Compound	bp	mp	Benzamide, D-8	p-Toluene-sulfonamide, D-9	Phenylthio-urea, D-10	Picrate, D-12
t-butylamine	44		134	—	120	198
propylamine	48		84	52	63	135
diethylamine	56		42	60	34	155
sec-butylamine	63		76	55	101	140
2-methylpropylamine	69		57	78	82	150
butylamine	77		42	—	65	151
diisopropylamine	84		—	—	—	140
pyrrolidine	89		—	123	—	112 (164)
3-methylbutylamine	95		—	65	102	138
pentylamine	104		—	—	69	139
piperidine	106		48	96	101	152
dipropylamine	109		—	—	69	75
morpholine	128		75	147	136	146
pyrrole	131		—	—	143	69d
hexylamine	132		40	—	77	126
cyclohexylamine	134		149	—	148	—
diisobutylamine	139		—	—	113	121
N-methylcyclohexylamine	147		86	—	—	170
dibutylamine	159		—	—	86	59
N-ethylbenzylamine	181		—	95	—	118
aniline	184		163	103	154	198 (180)

continued

Table 8 Esters

Compound	bp	mp	Carboxylic acid, D-16	Alcohol or phenol, D-16	N-Benzyl-amide, D-17	3,5-Dinitro-benzoate, D-18
ethyl formate	54		8	—	60	93
methyl acetate	57		17	—	61	108
ethyl acetate	77		17	—	61	93
methyl propanoate	80		—	—	43	108
methyl acrylate	80		13	—	237	108
isopropyl acetate	91		17	—	61	123
tert-butyl acetate	98		17	26	61	142
ethyl propanoate	99		—	—	43	93
methyl 2,2-dimethylpropanoate	101		35	—	—	108
propyl acetate	102		17	—	61	74
methyl butanoate	102		—	—	38	108
ethyl 2-methylpropanoate	111		—	—	87	93
sec-butyl acetate	112		17	—	61	76
methyl 3-methylbutanoate	117		—	—	54	108
isobutyl acetate	117		17	—	61	87
ethyl butanoate	122		—	—	38	93
butyl acetate	126		17	—	61	64
methyl pentanoate	128		—	—	43	108
ethyl 3-methylbutanoate	135		—	—	54	93
3-methylbutyl acetate	142		17	—	61	61
ethyl chloroacetate	145		63	—	—	93
pentyl acetate	149		17	—	61	46
ethyl hexanoate	168		—	—	53	93
hexyl acetate	172		17	—	61	58
cyclohexyl acetate	175		17	25	61	113
dimethyl malonate	182		135	—	142	108
diethyl oxalate	185		101*	—	223	93
heptyl acetate	192		17	—	61	47
phenyl acetate	197		17	42	61	146
methyl benzoate	199		122	—	105	108
diethyl malonate	199		135	—	142	93
o-tolyl acetate	208		17	31	61	135
m-tolyl acetate	212		17	12	61	165
ethyl benzoate	213		122	—	105	93
p-tolyl acetate	213		17	36	61	189
methyl *o*-toluate	215		104	—	—	108
benzyl acetate	217		17	—	61	113
diethyl succinate	218		188	—	206	93
isopropyl benzoate	218		122	—	105	123
methyl phenylacetate	220		77s	—	122	108
diethyl maleate	223		137	—	150	93
ethyl phenylacetate	228		77s	—	122	93
propyl benzoate	230		122	—	105	74
diethyl adipate	245		152	—	189	93
butyl benzoate	250		122	—	105	64
ethyl cinnamate	271		133	—	226	93
dimethyl phthalate	284		210d	—	179	108
(+)-bornyl acetate	*226*	27	17	208	61	154

continued

Table 8 Esters *continued*

Compound	bp	mp	Carboxylic acid, D-16	Alcohol or phenol, D-16	N-Benzyl-amide, D-17	3,5-Dinitro-benzoate, D-18
methyl p-toluate		33	180s	—	133	108
methyl cinnamate		36	133	—	226	108
benzyl cinnamate		39	133	—	226	113
1-naphthyl acetate		49	17	94	61	217
ethyl p-nitrobenzoate		56	240	—	—	93
phenyl benzoate		69	122	42	105	146
2-naphthyl acetate		71	17	123	61	210
p-tolyl benzoate		71	122	36	105	189
methyl m-nitrobenzoate		78	140	—	101	108
methyl p-nitrobenzoate		96	240	—	142	108

Note: All temperatures are in °C. Additional derivatives of the acid and alcohol portions of most esters can be found in Tables 1 and 7. Italics designate melting or boiling points that are out of sequence.
*Dihydrate; the anhydrous acid melts at 190°C.

Table 9 Alkyl halides

Compound	bp	Density, d^{20}, C-10	S-Alkylthiuronium picrate, D-19
bromoethane	38	1.461	188
2-bromopropane	60	1.314	196
1-chloro-2-methylpropane	69	0.879	167 (174)
3-bromopropene	71	1.398	155
1-bromopropane	71	1.354	177
iodoethane	72	1.936	188
1-chlorobutane	78	0.884	177
2-iodopropane	89	1.703	196
1-bromo-2-methylpropane	93	1.264	167 (174)
1-chloro-3-methylbutane	100	0.875	173
1-bromobutane	101	1.274	177
1-iodopropane	102	1.749	177
3-iodopropene	102	1.848	155
1-chloropentane	108	0.882	154
1-bromo-3-methylbutane	119	1.207	173 (179)
2-iodobutane	119	1.595	166
1-iodo-2-methylpropane	120	1.606	167 (174)
1-bromopentane	129	1.218	154
1-iodobutane	131	1.617	177
1-chlorohexane	134	0.876	157
1-iodo-3-methylbutane	148	1.503	173
1-iodopentane	155	1.516	154
1-bromohexane	155	1.173	157
1-iodohexane	181	1.439	157
1-bromooctane	201	1.112	134
1-iodooctane	225	1.330	134

Note: All temperatures are in °C; density is in g/mL, at 20°C.

Table 10 Aryl halides

Compound	bp	mp	Density, d^{20}, C-10	Nitro derivative, D-20	Carboxylic acid, D-21
chlorobenzene	132		1.106	52	—
bromobenzene	156		1.495	51 (70)	—
2-chlorotoluene	159		1.083	63	140
3-chlorotoluene	162		1.072	91	158
4-chlorotoluene	162		1.071	38 (m)	242
1,3-dichlorobenzene	173		1.288	103	—
1,2-dichlorobenzene	181		1.306	110	—
2-bromotoluene	182		1.423	82	150
3-bromotoluene	184		1.410	103	155
iodobenzene	188		1.831	171 (m)	—
2,6-dichlorotoluene	199		1.269	50 (m)	139
2,4-dichlorotoluene	200		1.249	104	164
3-iodotoluene	204		1.698	108	187
2-iodotoluene	211		1.698	103 (m)	162
1-chloronaphthalene	259		1.191	180	—
4-bromotoluene	*184*	28	—	—	251
4-iodotoluene		35	—	—	270
1,4-dichlorobenzene		53	—	106, 54 (m)	—
2-chloronaphthalene		56	—	175	—
1,4-dibromobenzene		89	—	84	—

Note: All temperatures are in °C; density is in g/mL, at 20°C. Nitro derivatives signified by (m) are mononitro compounds; all others are dinitro derivatives. Italics designate melting or boiling points that are out of sequence.

Table 11 Aromatic hydrocarbons

Compound	bp	mp	Nitro derivative, D-20	Carboxylic acid, D-21	Picrate, D-12
benzene	80		89 (di)	—	84u
toluene	111		70 (di)	122	88u
ethylbenzene	136		37 (t)	122	96u
p-xylene	138		139 (t)	300s	90u
m-xylene	139		183 (t)	330s	91u
o-xylene	144		118 (di)	210d	88u
isopropylbenzene	152		109 (t)	122	—
propylbenzene	159		—	122	103u
1,3,5-trimethylbenzene	165		86 (di) 235 (t)	350 (t)	97u
t-butylbenzene	169		62 (di)	122	—
4-isopropyltoluene	177		54 (di)	300s	—
1,3-diethylbenzene	181		62 (t)	330s	—
1,2,3,4-tetrahydronaphthalene	206		96 (di)	210d	—
diphenylmethane	262	26	172 (tet)	—	—
1,2-diphenylethane		53	180 (di) 169 (tet)	—	—
naphthalene		80	61 (m)	—	149
triphenylmethane		92	206 (t)	—	—
acenaphthene		96	101 (m)	—	161
fluorene		114	199 (di) 156 (m)	—	87 (77)
anthracene		216	—	—	138u

Note: All temperatures are in °C. Picrates designated "u" are unstable and cannot easily be purified by recrystallization.

Table 12 Phenols

Compound	bp	mp	Aryloxyacetic acid, D-22	Bromo derivative, D-23	α-Naphthyl-urethane, D-24
2-chlorophenol	176		145	49 (m) 76 (di)	120
3-methylphenol	202		—	84 (t)	128
2-methylphenol	*192*	31	152	56 (di)	142
4-methylphenol	*232*	36	135	49 (di) 108 (tet)	146
phenol	*182*	42	99	95 (t)	133
4-chlorophenol		43	156	33 (m) 90 (di)	166
2-nitrophenol		45	158	117 (di)	113
4-ethylphenol		47	97	—	128
5-methyl-2-isopropylphenol		50	149	55 (m)	160
3,4-dimethylphenol		63	163	171 (t)	142
4-bromophenol		64	157	95 (t)	169
2,5-dimethylphenol		75	118	178 (t)	173
1-naphthol		94	194	105 (di)	152
3-nitrophenol		97	156	91 (di)	167
4-*t*-butylphenol		100	86	50 (m)	110
1,2-dihydroxybenzene		105	—	193 (tet)	175
1,3-dihydroxybenzene		110	195	112 (di)	206
4-nitrophenol		114	187	142 (di)	150
2-naphthol		123	154	84 (m)	157
1,2,3-trihydroxybenzene		133	198	158 (di)	—
1,4-dihydroxybenzene		172	250	186 (di)	—

Note: All temperatures are in °C. Italics designate melting or boiling points that are out of sequence.

The Chemical Literature

APPENDIX VII

The literature of chemistry consists of *primary, secondary,* and *tertiary* sources. Most primary sources in chemistry contain descriptions of original research carried out by professional chemists. They include scientific periodicals (such as the *Journal of Organic Chemistry*), patents, dissertations, technical reports, and government bulletins. Secondary sources contain material from the primary literature that has been systematically organized, condensed, or restated to make it more accessible and understandable to users. Secondary sources include most monographs, textbooks, dictionaries, encyclopedias, reference works, review publications, and abstracting journals that deal with chemistry. Tertiary sources are intended to aid users of the primary and secondary sources or to provide facts about chemists and their work. Tertiary sources include guides to the chemical literature, directories of scientists and scientific organizations, bibliographies, trade catalogs, and publications devoted to the financial and professional aspects of chemistry. Some sources may combine several different functions; for example, *Chemical & Engineering News* prints articles about chemical research as well as financial and professional information, and thus serves as both a secondary and a tertiary source.

Although a few secondary sources critically evaluate primary material and correct errors before printing it, primary sources are generally used when it is important to obtain the most accurate and detailed information available on a topic. Errors can always occur when the material reappears in a secondary source, and important information may be left out. Because primary sources aren't organized in any systematic way, it is generally necessary to refer to other sources to determine where the desired information can be found. The Bibliography following this appendix lists a number of secondary and tertiary sources that can be used to obtain information directly, to gain access to the primary literature, or both. For example, *Beilstein's Handbook of Organic Chemistry* (hereafter referred to as *Beilstein*) gives detailed, reliable information about organic compounds and also provides citations to the literature in which the information was first reported. References to the Bibliography will be given in the form (C7), where the letter indicates a category (such as "Laboratory Safety"), and the number indicates a specific work in that category.

Using *Chemical Abstracts* and *Beilstein*

Most of the reference works cited in the Bibliography are limited in scope; they make no attempt to cover the entire field of chemistry or to list all of the known organic compounds. The two major works that do attempt that kind of coverage are *Beilstein* (A3) and *Chemical Abstracts* (J3). *Beilstein* summarizes all of the important information published about specific compounds, but it is many years behind the current literature in most areas. The earlier volumes of *Beilstein* are available only in German, so at least a rudimentary knowledge of that language is necessary to make good use of this resource. *Chemical Abstracts* (CA) prints *abstracts* (brief summaries) of scientific papers, patents, and other printed material related to chemistry shortly after their publication.

Before using *Chemical Abstracts* for the first time, read the introduction that appears in Issue 1 of each volume (two volumes are published each year), which describes the layout of the abstracts. Each abstract of a scientific paper (or other article) contains an abstract number, the title and author of the paper, a citation that tells where the original paper can be located, and a concise summary of the important information in the paper. The contents of *CA* can be searched by computer (as described in the "On-Line Searches" section) or by consulting the indexes. Although each weekly issue of *CA* has its own indexes, the semiannual and collective indexes are far more useful for literature searches. A Collective Index is published every 5 years; prior to 1957, these indexes came out every 10 years. In 1972, the Subject Index was divided into two parts: the Chemical Substances Index and the General Subject Index. Author, formula, and patent indexes are also published, along with ancillary materials such as the Ring Systems Handbook (A4), Registry Handbook, Index Guide, and Service Source Index, which are updated periodically.

The first thing you must do before searching *Chemical Abstracts* for information about a particular compound or subject is to find the *CA index name* of the compound or the *CA index heading* for the subject. In some cases, it may be possible to derive (or guess) the index name, but that is not always easy because *CA* follows its own rules of nomenclature, which often differ from IUPAC rules. The Index Guide, which now appears with each Collective Index and at intervals in between, gives cross-references from alternative names of substances to the *CA* index name. Thus, the entry under "aniline" lists the index name benzeneamine, followed by the *CA registry number* [62-53-3]. The Index Guide doesn't list every compound indexed or give every synonym for the compounds it does list, so you may have to try different approaches to find what you are looking for. If you can't locate a specific compound, try looking up a possible parent (unsubstituted) compound under its trivial name; the index name of this parent compound should begin with a root name under which you will find your compound listed in the Chemical Substances Index (or the Subject Index, prior to 1972). For example, suppose that you are searching for the following compound:

The unsubstituted compound (PhCH=CHCOPh) is known by such names as chalcone and benzalacetophenone. Looking up "chalcone" in a recent Index Guide provides the *CA* index name "2-propen-1-one, 1,3-diphenyl," so you will find the substituted compound listed—under the same root name—as "2-propen-1-one, 3-(4-methoxy)phenyl-1-phenyl." Keep in mind that the index name of a compound may change from time to time. This compound was listed under "chalcone, 4-methoxy" during the eighth Collective Index period (1967–1971) and before. Between the eighth and ninth Collective Index periods, some major changes were made in the *CA* nomenclature rules, which now require rigorously systematic names for most chemical substances.

If you have trouble finding the *CA* index name for a compound using the Index Guide, you might look for it in another source, such as *The Merck Index* (A11) or the *Dictionary of Organic Compounds* (A12). If you can locate the registry number for a compound, you can easily find its index name in the Registry Handbook. If you have a fairly good idea what the index name for a compound might be, you may be able to locate it in the formula indexes.

Once you locate the index name in use during a particular index period, you can locate abstracts listed under that name in the Chemical Substances Index or Subject Index for that period. Abstract citations in indexes from 1967 on are given in the form **80**:12175e, where the first number is the *CA* volume number and the second is the abstract number. In an index from prior to 1967, an abstract citation such as **51**:4321[b] refers to the volume and column number (there are two columns on each page) in which the abstract appears; the superscript (either a letter from "a" to "i" or a number from 1 to 9) indicates the location of the abstract in that column.

The information you are looking for may appear in the abstract itself, or you may have to read the original article cited in the abstract. Citations for such articles now appear in the form *Tetrahedron Lett.* **1996**, 37(37), 6767–6770 (Eng.), where the abbreviated name of the publication appears first, followed by the date, volume and issue number, page numbers, and language in which the paper is written. (Earlier citations were given with the volume number first, followed by the pages and year.) The full name of the publication will be found in the *Chemical Abstracts Service Source Index* (*CASSI*, A5), which also provides a brief publication history of each source and a list of the libraries that carry it.

The letter "e" in this citation is a check letter. If you looked up abstract number 12715 by mistake, you would find that its check letter is "b."

which includes abstracts from *CA* prior to 1967; the *REGISTRY* File, a list of virtually all currently known chemicals with their *CA* registry numbers; *CJACS,* which gives the complete texts of articles published in selected American Chemical Society journals since 1982; *CASREACT,* a database of recent organic reactions; *CHEMSOURCES,* a database of information on chemical products and their suppliers; and *CHEMLIST,* a listing of regulated and other hazardous substances. STN databases are available by subscription, and can be accessed with any computer that is connected to a telecommunications network. They are often accessible through university libraries. A simplified search option called STN*Easy* provides access to a variety of STN databases through the internet and features a graphical interface that doesn't require special training to use. Basic and advanced searches are available on STN*Easy,* and on-line help is provided when needed. For a basic search, the user simply enters a category that determines the databases to be searched, types in the words to be searched, and selects a search strategy. Search strategies include "any of these terms," which retrieves references that contain any or all of the words listed, and "all of these words," which only retrieves references that contain all of them.

Access to *Beilstein* is available through the BEILSTEIN on-line database (provided by STN International), DIALOG, and other vendors. The database is intended to cover not only the contents of the printed work but also information from Beilstein file cards and primary literature up to the current date. For detailed information about on-line searching of *Beilstein* or *CA,* see reference K3 or K6 in the Bibliography.

Using the Bibliography

A number of books, articles, and other literature sources in organic chemistry are listed in the following Bibliography under 12 general categories:

A. Reference Works
B. Organic Reactions and Syntheses
C. Laboratory Safety
D. General Laboratory Techniques
E. Chromatography
F. Spectrometry and Structure Analysis
G. Qualitative Organic Analysis
H. Reaction Mechanisms and Advanced Topics
J. Reports of Chemical Research
K. Guides to the Chemical Literature
L. Sources on Selected Topics
M. Software for Organic Chemistry

Each source is referred to here by the category letter and its number within the category.

Category A: Reference Works

Whereas *Beilstein* attempts to provide all of the important information about the millions of organic compounds mentioned in the chemical literature, the reference books that follow provide selected information about a much smaller number of compounds, usually numbering in the tens of thousands. The *CRC Handbook of Chemistry and Physics* (A15), *Lange's Handbook of Chemistry* (A6), and *Dean's Handbook of Organic Chemistry* (A7) tabulate physical properties and other data for many common organic compounds and contain a large amount of useful information about chemistry. *The Merck Index* (A11) is an excellent source of information on approximately 10,000 organic and inorganic compounds. It describes their uses and hazardous properties, provides detailed physical and structural data, and gives literature references for the isolation and synthesis of many compounds. The *CRC Handbook of Data on Organic Compounds (HODOC)* (A9) contains data and references to published spectra for more than 27,000 organic compounds. The *Aldrich Catalog* (A1) lists the many chemicals manufactured by the Aldrich Chemical Company and gives their physical properties, hazard warnings, procedures for safe disposal, references to published Aldrich spectra, and references to listings in *The Merck Index, Beilstein,* and *Fieser* (B7). The *Dictionary of Organic Compounds (DOC)* (A12) is an important multivolume set, updated by annual supplements, that gives structures, physical constants, hazard descriptions, sources, uses, derivatives, and bibliographic references for more than 145,000 organic compounds. It is also available on CD-ROM. Figure 1 shows the level of information provided by three of these reference works.

Before you use such a reference work to find information about organic compounds, always read the introduction or explanatory material at the beginning of the work or preceding the table you intend to use. The introductory section of a reference work will usually (1) describe the content and organization of the material, (2) list symbols and abbreviations, and (3) describe the system of nomenclature used. Different sources often use very different naming systems. For example, *The Merck Index* emphasizes therapeutic uses of compounds, so it lists aspirin under that name; but in *Lange's Handbook* you will find aspirin listed as "acetylsalicylic acid," and in the *CRC Handbook of Chemistry and Physics* it appears as "2-(acetyloxy)benzoic acid." In earlier editions of the *CRC Handbook,* the names of many compounds were entered under the name of the parent compound; thus, 2,4-dinitrobenzene was listed as "benzene, 2,4-dinitro." More recent editions list the names as they are normally written out. Often, the index of a reference work provides the quickest and most reliable access to a given entry. When using *The Merck Index* or the *Dictionary of Organic Compounds,* you should first consult the name index to locate the entry for a given compound. If you can't find the compound in the name index, you may be able to locate it in a formula index. In most formula indexes, carbon and hydrogen are listed first, followed by the other elements in alphabetical order.

Other useful reference works in organic chemistry include the *Ring Systems Handbook* (A4), which (with its supplements) records all known organic ring systems and provides information allowing users to locate compounds that have a particular ring system; and *CASSI* (A5), which provides bibliographic information for the journals and other sources indexed by *Chemical Abstracts* and lists the libraries holding each source. The *Beilstein Dictionary* (A2) is an invaluable aid to understanding the parts of

and *Sax's Dangerous Properties of Industrial Materials* (C5) provide detailed health and safety data for many common chemicals. *Bretherick's Handbook of Reactive Chemical Hazards* (C8) describes the properties of chemicals that are hazardous by virtue of their instability or their tendency to react with other chemicals. The ninth edition of *The Merck Index* (see A11) contains a section on first aid for poisoning and chemical burns; however, this section is not included in the more recent editions.

Category D: General Laboratory Techniques

Although this textbook covers the techniques you are most likely to use in your organic chemistry lab course, sources from this category and the following two categories may provide more detailed practical and theoretical information about specific lab techniques, information about more advanced techniques, or a different approach to the methods described here. *The Organic Chem Lab Survival Manual* (D11) describes many of the lab techniques used by organic chemistry students and tells you what things *not* to do, such as plugging a heating mantle directly into a wall socket. *Guide for the Perplexed Organic Experimentalist* (D3) deals with the practical aspects of laboratory work for anyone intending to do research in organic chemistry. Weissberger's *Technique of Organic Chemistry* (D7) and *Techniques of Chemistry* (D8) are multivolume sets that cover a wide variety of experimental methods. Information on classical laboratory techniques, such as distillation and recrystallization, can be found in Volume I of reference D7, which is subtitled *Physical Methods of Organic Chemistry*. The first four volumes of *Houben-Weyl* (D5) describe many laboratory methods for organic chemistry, in German. Microscale techniques based on Mayo–Pike- and Williamson-type glassware, respectively, are described in *Microscale Techniques for the Organic Laboratory* (D4) and *Macroscale and Microscale Organic Experiments* (D9). The *Encyclopedia of Separation Technology* (D6) and *Encyclopedia of Separation Science* (D10) provide comprehensive, up-to-date descriptions of separation techniques, including modern microscale techniques. *Purification of Laboratory Chemicals* (D1) provides methods for the purification of more than 4000 common chemicals. *Natural Products* (D2) describes laboratory techniques and gives specific procedures for the isolation and structure determination of natural products.

Category E: Chromatography

During your organic chemistry lab course, you will probably use a variety of chromatographic methods for the separation and analysis of organic compounds. These methods include thin-layer chromatography (TLC), paper chromatography (PC), gas chromatography (GC), and high-performance liquid chromatography (HPLC). *Chromatography Today* (E6) and *Principles and Practice of Chromatography* (E7) are good general sources of information on the theory and practice of all types of chromatography. *Gas Chromatography* (E1) and *High Performance Liquid Chromatography* (E3) are "open learning" texts designed for self-study. The remaining works provide up-to-date coverage of GC, HPLC, and TLC techniques and applications. *Principles of Instrumental Analysis* (F21) in the next section has chapters on instrumental chromatographic methods.

Category F: Spectrometry and Structure Analysis

During your organic chemistry lab course, you will probably need to record and interpret various kinds of spectra of organic compounds, such as infrared (IR) spectra, nuclear magnetic resonance (NMR) spectra, ultraviolet–visible (UV–VIS) spectra, and mass spectra (MS). *Principles of Instrumental Analysis* (F21) is a good source of information about the principles and applications of all important kinds of spectrometric methods, as well as other instrumental methods of analysis. An article in the *Journal of Chemical Education* (F9) covers the basics of IR and NMR spectral interpretation. The works by Silverstein (F20), Feinstein (F5), Kemp (F10), Pavia (F14), Whittaker (F24), and Yadav (F25) are good one-volume introductions to the interpretation of spectra of organic compounds. More comprehensive coverage of specific spectrometric methods is provided for infrared spectrometry by references F4 and F22; for nuclear magnetic resonance spectrometry by F1, F2, F6, and F13; for mass spectrometry by F3, F7, F8, F11, F12, and F23; and for ultraviolet–visible spectrometry by F15. The *Sadtler Standard Spectra* (F19) series consists of a large number of IR, NMR, and UV–VIS spectra in ring binders; although they aren't arranged systematically, individual spectra can be located using the index volumes. Spectra in the Aldrich collections (F16–F18) are arranged by functional class and in order of increasing molecular complexity within a functional class, making it possible to observe the effect of various structural features on the spectra.

Category G: Qualitative Organic Analysis

During your organic chemistry lab course, you may be required to identify one or more unknown organic compounds using either "wet-chemistry" methods (involving chemical tests and derivative preparations) or spectrometric methods, or both. *Organic Structure Determination* (G4), *The Systematic Identification of Organic Compounds* (G6), and *Spectral and Chemical Characterization of Organic Compounds* (G2) cover the traditional wet-chemistry methods but include chapters on spectrometric methods as well. *Qualitative Organic Analysis* (G3) emphasizes spectral methods of identification, and *Organic Structure Analysis* (G1) focuses on the use of multiple spectrometric methods to identify a molecule's major structural elements. The *CRC Handbook of Tables for Organic Compound Identification* (G5) lists the properties and derivative melting points for many organic compounds in the most important functional classes.

Category H: Reaction Mechanisms and Advanced Topics

Although reaction mechanisms are more often explored in an organic chemistry lecture course than in the laboratory course, you may be expected to understand and write mechanisms for some of the reactions you perform in the lab. *Electron Flow in Organic Chemistry* (H10) teaches an intuitive approach to organic chemistry by breaking down reaction mechanisms into elementary electron-flow pathways. *A Guidebook to Mechanism in Organic Chemistry* (H12) by Sykes is an excellent survey of reaction mechanisms suitable for advanced students; his *Primer* (H13) is a more basic introduction to mechanisms based on a simplified classification scheme. Other how-to books include *The Art of Writing Reasonable Reaction Mechanisms* (H4), *Writing Reaction Mechanisms in Organic Chemistry* (H7), and *Reaction Mechanisms at a Glance* (H8). *Name Reactions* (H5) provides detailed mechanisms for reactions known familiarly by the names of their discoverers. *Mechanism and Theory in Organic Chemistry* (H6) and *Perspectives on Structure and Mechanism in Organic Chemistry* (H3) are advanced textbooks that present the theoretical aspects of organic chemistry and provide up-to-date information about important reaction mechanisms. *Advanced Organic Chemistry* (H1) and *March's Advanced Organic Chemistry* (H11) provide good coverage of the mechanisms and synthetic applications of a large number of organic reactions, giving numerous references to the primary literature. *Determination of Organic Reaction Mechanisms* (H2) describes experimental techniques for studying reaction mechanisms, and *Organic Reaction Mechanisms* (H9) is an annual survey of recent developments in the field.

Category J: Reports of Chemical Research

Most professional chemists do *chemical research*—experimental or theoretical work designed to discover new facts about the various forms of matter, develop new techniques that can be used to study matter, or provide new insights about the fundamental nature of matter. Papers describing the results of their research are reported in such a large number of professional journals and other publications that it is impossible for anyone to investigate them all. For that reason, scientists consult various reports of chemical research to locate the papers that deal with their own research interests. *Chemical Abstracts* (J3), previously described in detail, is the most comprehensive single source of information about research in chemistry. The *Science Citation Index* (J7) is an index of literature citations to papers, patents, and books published in the past. For example, if you find an interesting paper by Linus Pauling in a chemistry journal, you can look up the paper in the *Science Citation Index* to find later articles that were based, in part, on Pauling's original paper. In this way, you can sometimes trace the development of an idea or a method from its origin to the present day. A similar index for chemistry, the *Chemistry Citation Index,* is available on CD-ROM. *Chemical Titles* (J4) and *Current Contents* (J5) reproduce the current tables of contents of the most important chemistry journals to inform chemists quickly of recent research in their fields. *Index Chemicus* (J6), a weekly guide to new organic compounds and their chemistry, is available in print and on a searchable database. The other works in this category (J1, J2) provide annual summaries and reviews of research in organic chemistry.

Category K: Guides to the Chemical Literature

If you need specific information to complete a lab report or write a research paper, you have to know where to look for it. *Information Sources in Chemistry* (K1) and *How to Find Chemical Information* (K4) are general guides to the chemical literature that list and describe a large number of information sources. *Library Handbook for Organic Chemists* (K5) is an up-to-date guide to the use of library information resources. *The Beilstein System* (K2) and *The Beilstein Online Database* (K3) tell how to search and use *Beilstein's* print and on-line versions, respectively. *From CA to CAS Online* (K6) serves the same function for *Chemical Abstracts*. The three articles by Somerville (K7) describe the contents and uses of some major works on organic reactions and syntheses. A brief but useful guide to information sources for organic chemistry can be found in Appendix A of *March's Advanced Organic Chemistry* (H11).

Category L: Sources on Selected Topics

This category includes a number of books and articles that can be used as resources for library research papers. Others can simply be read for enjoyment and enlightenment, on topics ranging from coffee and perfumes to the O. J. Simpson trial. Most are about topics related to the experiments or minilabs, such as reference L20 on sweetness (see Experiments 20 and 53), L61 on perfumes (see Experiment 13), and L65 on gas hydrates (see Experiment 16). Some works are listed here because they don't fit into any of the other categories. For example, L16 and L46 are guides for writing scientific papers and laboratory notebooks, L41 gives suggestions about presenting papers and posters, and L22 tells you how to name organic compounds.

Category M: Software for Organic Chemistry

A number of software titles are designed to be used in preparation for or during an organic chemistry laboratory. *Identification of Organic Compounds* (M8) and *MacSQUALOR* (M9) allow the user to identify simulated unknowns for qualitative organic analysis. *Introduction to Spectroscopy* (M4) helps the user analyze and interpret spectral data. *IR Simulator* (M10) and *NMR Simulator* (M11) generate simulated IR and NMR spectra from information entered by the user. *MassSpec* (M5) helps the user identify the structural fragments that correspond to peaks on a mass spectrum. *SynTree* (M7) helps the user work out retrosynthetic pathways leading from a selected target compound back to a readily available starting material. *ChemDraw* (M2) allows the user to generate a variety of chemical structures. *Name It* (M6) provides practice in naming organic compounds and drawing structures from their names. *Beaker* (M1) predicts properties and generates spectra of organic molecules, as well as providing some structure-drawing tools. *Chem3D* (M3) and *Spartan Student Edition* (M12) are used for molecular modeling and computational chemistry applications.

Bibliography

A. Reference Works

1. *Aldrich Catalog Handbook of Fine Chemicals.* Milwaukee, WI: Aldrich Chemical Co., 2005–06 (and other years).
2. *Beilstein Dictionary: German–English: For the Users of the Beilstein Handbook of Organic Chemistry.* Ft. Worth, TX: W. B. Saunders, 1992.
3. *Beilstein's Handbook of Organic Chemistry.* New York: Springer-Verlag, 1918 to date.
4. *Chemical Abstracts Ring Systems Handbook.* Washington, DC: American Chemical Society, 1993 with cumulative supplements.
5. *Chemical Abstracts Service Source Index (CASSI).* Washington, DC: American Chemical Society, 1907–2004 with quarterly supplements.
6. Dean, J. A., ed., *Lange's Handbook of Chemistry,* 16th ed. New York: McGraw-Hill, 2004.
7. Gokel, G. W., *Dean's Handbook of Organic Chemistry.* New York: McGraw-Hill, 2004.
8. *Kirk–Othmer Encyclopedia of Chemical Technology,* 5th ed. New York: Wiley, 2004–.
9. Lide, D. R., and Milne, G. W. A., eds., *CRC Handbook of Data on Organic Compounds,* 3rd ed. Boca Raton, FL: CRC Press, 1994.
10. Mundy, B. P., and Ellerd, M. G., *Organic Chemistry: An Alphabetical Guide.* New York: Wiley, 1996.
11. O'Neil, M. J., et al., eds., *The Merck Index: An Encyclopedia of Chemicals, Drugs, and Biologicals,* 14th ed. Whitehouse Station, NJ: Merck & Co., 2006.
12. Rhodes, P. H., ed., *Dictionary of Organic Compounds,* 6th ed. London: Chapman & Hall, 1995.
13. Rhodes, P. H., *The Organic Chemist's Desk Reference: A Companion Volume to the Dictionary of Organic Compounds,* 6th ed. London: Chapman & Hall, 1995.
14. Shugar, G. J., and Dean, J. A., *The Chemist's Ready Reference Handbook.* New York: McGraw-Hill, 1990.
15. Weast, R. C., ed., *CRC Handbook of Chemistry and Physics,* new editions annually. Boca Raton, FL: CRC Press, 2007 (and other years).

B. Organic Reactions and Syntheses

1. Atkinson, R. S., *Stereoselective Synthesis.* New York: Wiley, 1995.
2. Becker, H., et al., *Organicum: Practical Handbook of Organic Chemistry,* trans. by B. J. Hazzard. Reading, MA: Addison-Wesley, 1973.
3. Carruthers, W., *Cycloaddition Reactions in Organic Synthesis.* New York: Pergamon Press, 1990.
4. Carruthers, W., *Modern Methods of Organic Synthesis,* 4th ed. Cambridge, UK: Cambridge University Press, 2004.
5. Coffey, S., and Ansell, M. F., eds., *Rodd's Chemistry of Carbon Compounds,* 2nd ed. and supplements, New York: Elsevier, 1964–.

6. Corey, E. J., and Cheng, X.-M., *The Logic of Chemical Synthesis.* New York: Wiley, 1995.
7. Fieser, L. F., et al., *Fiesers' Reagents for Organic Synthesis.* New York: Wiley, 1967–.
8. Fringuelli, F., and Taticchi, A., *The Diels–Alder Reaction: Selected Practical Methods.* New York: Wiley, 2002.
9. Fuhrhop, J.-H., and Li, G., *Organic Synthesis: Concepts and Methods,* 3rd ed. New York: Wiley, 2003.
10. Greene, T. W., and Wuts, P. G. M., *Protective Groups in Organic Synthesis,* 3rd ed. New York: Wiley, 1999.
11. Harrison, I. T., and Harrison, S., *Compendium of Organic Synthetic Methods.* New York: Wiley, 1971–.
12. House, H. O., *Modern Synthetic Reactions,* 2nd ed. Menlo Park, CA: Benjamin, 1972.
13. Larock, R. C., *Comprehensive Organic Transformations: A Guide to Functional Group Preparations,* 2nd ed. New York: Wiley, 1999.
14. Laue, T., and Plagens, A., *Named Organic Reactions.* New York: Wiley, 2000.
15. Loupy, A., *Microwaves in Organic Synthesis.* New York: Wiley, 2003.
16. Millam, M. J., *Reaction Guide for Organic Chemistry.* Lexington, MA: D.C. Heath, 1989.
17. Nicolaou, K. C., et al., "The Art and Science of Organic and Natural Product Synthesis." *J. Chem. Educ.* **1998,** 75, 1225.
18. Norman, R. O. C., and Coxon, J. M., *Principles of Organic Synthesis,* 3rd ed. Cheltenham, UK: Stanley Thornes, 1993.
19. *Organic Reactions.* New York: Wiley, 1942–.
20. *Organic Syntheses,* 2nd ed, *Collective Volumes.* New York: Wiley, 2004 (and previous years).
21. Paquette, L. A., ed., *Encyclopedia of Reagents for Organic Synthesis.* New York: Wiley, 1995.
22. Patai, S., ed., *Chemistry of Functional Groups.* New York: Wiley, 1964–.
23. Pearson, A. J., *Handbook of Reagents for Organic Synthesis.* New York: Wiley, 1999.
24. Pelter, A., Smith, K., and Brown, H. C., *Borane Reagents.* London: Academic Press, 1988.
25. Proctor, R. G., *Asymmetric Synthesis.* New York: Oxford University Press, 1996.
26. Riddick, J. A., and Bunger, W. M., *Organic Solvents: Physical Properties and Methods of Purification,* 4th ed. New York: Wiley, 1986.
27. Sandler, S. R., and Karo, W., *Organic Functional Group Preparations,* 2nd ed. Orlando, FL: Academic Press, 1983, 1986, 1989.
28. Sandler, S. R., and Karo, W., *Polymer Syntheses,* 2nd ed. Orlando, FL: Academic Press, 1997.
29. Sandler, S. R., and Karo, W., *Sourcebook of Advanced Organic Laboratory Preparations.* San Diego, CA: Academic Press, 1992.

30. Stuart, W., *Organic Synthesis: The Disconnection Approach*. New York: Wiley, 1982.

31. Tatchell, A. R., et al., *Vogel's Textbook of Practical Organic Chemistry*, 5th ed. New York: Wiley, 1989.

32. Theilheimer, W. (1948–81), Finch, A. F. (1982–), eds., *Theilheimer's Synthetic Methods of Organic Chemistry*. Basel: Karger, 1946–.

33. Trost, B. M., and Fleming, I., eds., *Comprehensive Organic Synthesis: Selectivity, Strategy & Efficiency in Modern Organic Chemistry*. Elmsford, NY: Pergamon Press, 1991.

34. Wagner, R. B., and Zook, H. D., *Synthetic Organic Chemistry*. New York: Wiley, 1953.

35. Zweifel, G., and Nantz, M., *Modern Organic Synthesis: An Introduction*. New York: Freeman, 2006.

C. Laboratory Safety

1. Furr, A. K., ed., *CRC Handbook of Laboratory Safety*, 5th ed. Boca Raton, FL: CRC Press, 2000.

2. Gorman, C. E., ed., *Working Safely with Chemicals in the Laboratory*, 2nd ed. Schenectady, NY: Genium, 1995.

3. Lefèvre, M. J., *First Aid Manual for Chemical Accidents*, 2nd ed. New York: Van Nostrand Reinhold, 1989.

4. Lenga, R. E., ed., *The Sigma–Aldrich Library of Regulatory and Safety Data*. Milwaukee, WI: Sigma–Aldrich, 1993.

5. Lewis, R. J., Sr., *Sax's Dangerous Properties of Industrial Materials*, 10th ed. New York: Wiley, 2000.

6. Luxon, S. G., ed., *Hazards in the Chemical Laboratory*, 5th ed. Cambridge, UK: Royal Society of Chemistry, 1992.

7. National Research Council, *Prudent Practices in the Laboratory: Handling and Disposal of Chemicals*. Washington, DC: National Academies Press, 1995.

8. Urben, P. G., ed., *Bretherick's Handbook of Reactive Chemical Hazards*, 7th ed. Burlington, MA: Academic Press, 2006.

D. General Laboratory Techniques

1. Armarego, W. L. F., and Chai, C., *Purification of Laboratory Chemicals*, 5th ed. New York: Elsevier, 2003.

2. Ikan, R., *Natural Products: A Laboratory Guide*, 2nd ed. San Diego, CA: Academic Press, 1991.

3. Loewenthal, H. J. E., *Guide for the Perplexed Organic Experimentalist*, 2nd ed. New York: Wiley, 1992.

4. Mayo, D. W., et al., *Microscale Techniques for the Organic Laboratory*, 2nd ed. New York: Wiley, 2000.

5. *Methoden der Organischen Chemie, Houben-Weyl*, 4th ed. Stuttgart: Georg Thieme, 1952–.

6. Ruthven, D., *Encyclopedia of Separation Technology*. New York: Wiley, 1997.

7. Weissberger, A., ed., *Technique of Organic Chemistry*, 3rd ed. New York: Wiley, 1959–.

8. Weissberger, A., ed., *Techniques of Chemistry*. New York: Wiley, 1971–.

9. Williamson, K. L., *Macroscale and Microscale Organic Experiments*, 5th ed. Boston, MA: Houghton Mifflin, 2007.

10. Wilson, I. D., et al., eds., *Encyclopedia of Separation Science*. Orlando, FL: Academic Press, 2000.

11. Zubrick, J. W., *The Organic Chem Lab Survival Manual: A Student's Guide to Techniques*, 6th ed. New York: Wiley, 2004.

E. Chromatography

1. Fowlis, I. A., *Gas Chromatography*, 2nd ed. New York: Wiley, 1995.

2. Grob, R. L., and Barry, E. F., eds., *Modern Practice of Gas Chromatography*, 4th ed. New York: Wiley, 2004.

3. Lindsay, S., *High Performance Liquid Chromatography*, 2nd ed. New York: Wiley, 1992.

4. McNair, H. M., and Miller, J. M., *Basic Gas Chromatography*. New York: Wiley, 1998.

5. Meyer, V. R., *Practical High-Performance Liquid Chromatography*, 3rd ed. Chichester, UK: Wiley, 1999.

6. Poole, C. F., and Poole, S. K., *Chromatography Today*. New York: Elsevier, 1991.

7. Ravindranath, B., *Principles and Practice of Chromatography*. New York: Halsted, 1989.

8. Schomburg, G., *Gas Chromatography: A Practical Course*. New York: VCH, 1990.

9. Sherma, J., and Fried, B., *Thin-Layer Chromatography: Techniques and Applications*, 3rd ed. New York: Marcel Dekker, 1996.

10. Touchstone, J. C., *Practice of Thin Layer Chromatography*, 3rd ed. New York: Wiley, 1992.

F. Spectrometry and Structure Analysis

1. Akitt, J. W., and Mann, B. E., *NMR and Chemistry: An Introduction to Modern NMR Spectroscopy*, 4th ed. Cheltenham, UK: Stanley Thornes, 2000.

2. Bovey, F. A., *Nuclear Magnetic Resonance Spectroscopy*, 2nd ed. San Diego, CA: Academic Press, 1988.

3. Chapman, J. R., *Practical Organic Mass Spectrometry: A Guide for Chemical and Biochemical Analysis*, 2nd ed. New York: Wiley, 1995.

4. Colthup, N. B., Daly, L. H., and Wiberley, S. E., *Introduction to Infrared and Raman Spectroscopy*, 3rd ed. Orlando, FL: Academic Press, 1990.

5. Feinstein, K., *Guide to Spectroscopic Identification of Organic Compounds*. Boca Raton, FL: CRC Press, 1995.

6. Günther, H., *NMR Spectroscopy: Basic Principles, Concepts, and Applications in Chemistry*, 2nd ed. New York: Wiley, 1995.

7. Herbert, C. G., and Johnstone, R. A. W., *Mass Spectrometry Basics*. Boca Raton, FL: CRC Press, 2002.

8. Hoffmann, Edmond de, *Mass Spectrometry: Principles and Applications*. New York: Wiley, 1996.

9. Ingham, A. M., and Henson, R. C., "Interpreting Infrared and Nuclear Magnetic Resonance Spectra of Simple

Index

A

Abbe refractometer, 822, 823–824
abrasions, first aid for, 18
absolutes, 133
absorbance, 892
absorption bands, 892
abstracts, 934
accelerant, 118–119
accelerator planes, 900
accord, 133–134
acetaminophen, 48–55, 57, 519
  in analgesic drugs, 147–149
  structure of, 49, 148
acetanilide, 49, 51
  in liquid-liquid extraction, 682–683
  physical properties of, 57
  safety note, 59
  structure of, 49, 59
acetate esters, 520
  preparation of, 520–521
acetic acid, 73, 75, 76, 273
  physical properties of, 75
  safety note, 75
acetic anhydride, 273, 304
  physical properties of, 274
  safety note, 279
acetone, 407
  as alternative to methylene chloride, 34
  for cleaning glassware, 621
  flammability of, 15
  lycopene extraction using, 103
  physical properties and derivative melting points of, 121
  safety note, 105
acetophenone, 324
  IR spectrum of, 447
  physical properties of, 447
acetophenone phenylhydrazone, physical properties of, 447
acetylacetone, 406
acetyl chloride, 520
  safety note, 520
acetyl chloride test, 579, 581
acetylsalicylate, 51
acetylsalicylic acid, 304
Achilles, 111
Achillea millefolium, 111
acid anhydrides, reactions of, 389–394
acid-base ionization/dissociation constant, 387
acid-base reactions, 40–47
acid-base strengths, of organic compounds, 556–558
acid chlorides, 395–405
  safety note, 607
acids
  conjugate, 557
  equivalent weight of, 391
  pK_a values of, 382
Acta Universitatis Lundensis, 260

activity, of adsorbent, 709
acyl azides, 425
acyl compounds, 132–138
acylium ion, 325
adamantane, 174–181
  Beilstein entries on, 937
1-adamantyl carbocation, 175
addition funnel, 661
addition of reactants, 661–664
addition polymerization, 232–240
addition reactions
  alkene, 37
  bromine, 37
  experiment using, 86–92
  stereochemistry of, 509
addition under reflux, 663
adducts, 288
  endo, 289, 546
  exo, 289, 546
  melting points of maleic anhydride, 291
  preparation of, 292–293
  stereochemistry of, 293
adipic acid
  green synthesis of, 216–222
  melting point of, 217
  physical properties of, 219
  safety note, 220
  synthesis of, 34
adsorbents, 708
  in column chromatography, 709
  for thin-layer chromatography, 721
Advil, 147
Agent Orange, 253
AHAs. *See* α-hydroxy acids
AH,B theory, 460–461
air
  evaporation under dry, 696–698, 699–700
  excluding from reaction mixtures, 666–668
air condenser, 650, 651, 910
air-dried filtrate, 678
alanine, 461
alarm pheromone, 75
alcohols
  chemical tests for, 580
  classification tests for, 342–343
  coniferyl, 339
  derivatives of, 343, 600–601
    3,5-dinitrobenzoates, 343, 600
    α-naphthylurethanes, 343, 600–601
    p-nitrobenzoates, 343, 600
    phenylurethanes, 343, 600–601
  functional-class tests for, 579
  IR bands, 868–869
  nucleophilic substitution rates of, 541–542
  oxidation of by potassium permanganate, 543–544

preparation of, 199–207, 241–249, 260–268, 269–280
  primary, 253, 297, 591
  properties of, 924–925
  reactions of, 188–198, 250–259, 340–346
  secondary, 86–92, 253, 591
  tertiary, 253, 591
Alconox, 621
aldehydes
  for aldol condensation reactions, 554
  chemical tests for, 580
  classification tests for, 342
  derivatives of, 343, 601–602
    2,4-dinitrophenylhydrazones, 343, 601–602
    oximes, 343, 602
    semicarbazones, 343, 602
  functional-class tests for, 579
  IR bands, 869–870
  properties of, 925–926
  reactions of, 340–346
Alder, Kurt, 287
alditols, preparation of, 459–467, 464–465
aldohexose, 565
aldol condensation, 363
aldol condensation products, preparation of, 554–555
aldopentose, 565
Aliquat 336, 219
alkaline hydrolysis test, 579, 581–582
alkane clathrate, separation of, 152–159
alkanes
  IR bands, 866
  physical properties of, 93–99
alkene addition reaction, 37
alkenes
  addition to, 199–207
  IR bands, 866–867
  preparation and properties of gaseous, 534–535
  preparation of, 188–198
  reactions of, 160–165, 208–215, 216–222, 232–240, 354–360
  safety note, 196
alkenylbenzenes, reactions of, 333–339
alkylation, 94
  of bidentate nucleophile, 509–510
alkyl bromides, safety note, 531
alkyl halides
  derivatives of, 611–612
    S-alkylthiuronium picrates, 611–612
  preparation of, 208–215, 223–231, 250–259
  properties of, 931
  reactions of, 174–181
  reactivities of in nucleophilic substitution reactions, 531–532

S-alkylthiuronium picrates, of alkyl halides, 611–612
All Creatures Great and Small, 536
allicin, 111, 356–357
alliin, 356
D-allitol, 462
Allomyces javanicus, 349
D-allose, 462
S-allylcysteine, 111
allyl isothiocynate, 357
allyltoluidine, 416
α-cleavage, 549
α-hydroxy acids (AHAs), 487
Alpiny, 57
alumina
  as drying agent, 746
  eluotropic series for, 710
alumina activity grades, 709
aluminum block, 911
aluminum chloride
  physical properties of, 328
  safety note, 329
aluminum chloride and chloroform test, 583
Amanita caesarea, 478
Amanita muscaria, 127
Amanita phalloides, 478
Amanita porphyria, 443
α-amanitin, 478–479
amantadine, 174
amatoxins, 478
ambident nucleophile, 182–187
ambroxan, 134
American Chemical Society, 913
"American Flag Red" dye, 415–423
amides, 136
  alkaline hydrolysis test for, 581–582
  of carboxylic acids, 607–608
  derivatives of, 602–604
    hydrolysis products, 603
    N-xanthylamides, 603–604
  functional-class tests for, 579
  IR bands, 874
  preparation of, 395–405
  properties of, 927
  reactions of, 424–433
amines. *See also* aromatic amines; primary amines; secondary amines; tertiary amines
  biological, 435–437
  characterization of, 603
  chemical tests for, 580
  classification of, 437–438, 589, 593
  functional-class tests for, 579
  identification of unknown, 434–441
  IR bands, 873–874
  IR spectra of, 438
  reactions of, 415–423, 434–441

955

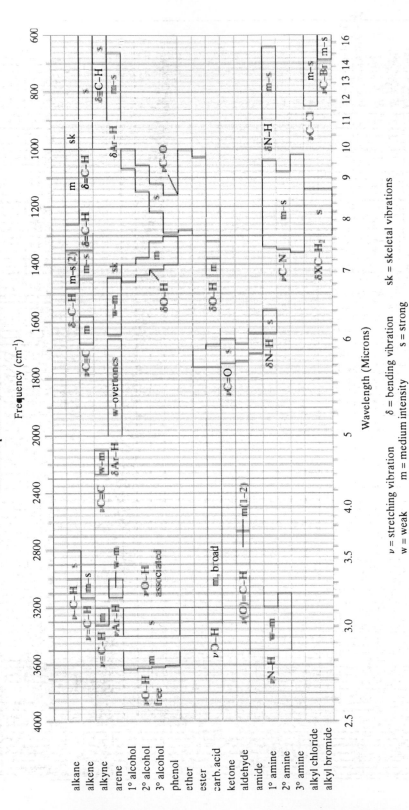

Infrared Spectrum-Structure Correlation Chart

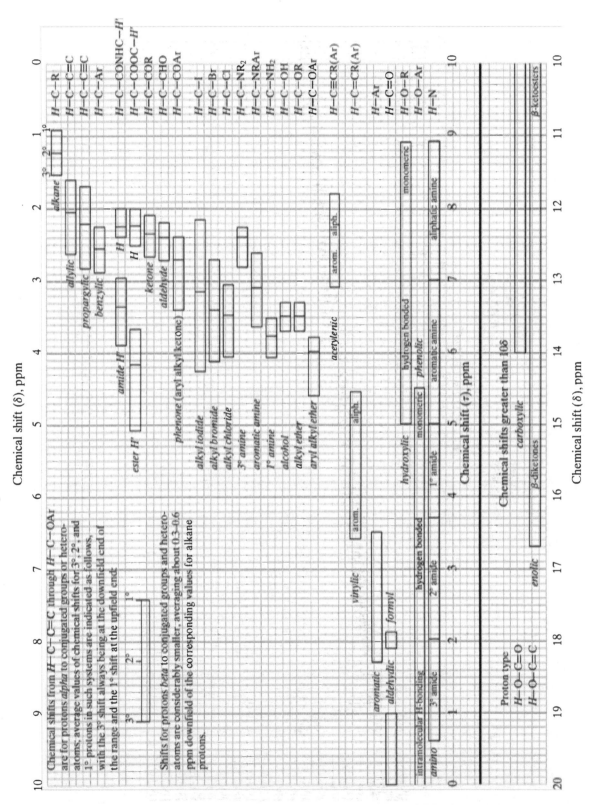

NMR Spectrum-Structure Correlation Chart

Chemical shift (δ), ppm

Chemical shift (τ), ppm

Chemical shift (δ), ppm